Hydrodynamics
of
Gas-Solids
Fluidization

Gulf Publishing Company
Book Division
Houston, London, Paris, Tokyo

Hydrodynamics
of
Gas-Solids Fluidization

Nicholas P. Cheremisinoff
Paul N. Cheremisinoff

7226-1924

CHEMISTRY

ACKNOWLEDGMENTS

We express a special thanks to Drs. C. S. Teo and L. S. Leung of the University of Queensland for contributing Chapter 11, "Vertical Flow of Particulate Solids in Standpipes and Risers," and to Dr. M. B. Ajinkya of Exxon Research and Engineering Co. for contributing Chapter 13, "Gas Premixing Techniques." Heartfelt gratitude is also extended to our many friends in industry who devoted time, effort, and materials to this volume. Although too numerous to name here, their respective organizations are cited throughout the text. Finally, we extend our gratitude to Gulf Publishing Company.

Hydrodynamics of Gas-Solids Fluidization

Library of Congress Cataloging in Publication Data

Cheremisinoff, Nicholas P.
   Hydrodynamics of gas-solids fluidization.
   Includes bibliographical reference and index.
   1. Fluidization. I. Cheremisinoff, Paul N. II. Title.
TP156.F65C45 1984   620.2'842   83-18555
ISBN 0-87201-352-9

Contents

Preface vii

1. Properties and Characteristics of Loose Solids 1

   Introduction. Physical Properties of Loose Solids. Angles of Repose, Internal Friction, and Slide. Forces of Adhesion and Solids Flowability. Particle Size Classification. Aerodynamic Properties of Single Particles. Nomenclature. References.

2. Flow Properties and Handling of Granular and Powdered Solids 43

   Introduction. Flow Properties Measurements. Solids Flows from Vessels. Granular Solids Flows Through Inclined Tubes and Channels. Design of Mass Flow Systems. Explosion Properties of Powders. Mechanical Considerations in Storage Vessels. Nomenclature. References.

3. Rheological Behavior of Fluidized Solids 91

   Introduction. Transport of Powdered and Fluidized Solids. Method of Similarity Theory. Hydrodynamic Analogies to Liquid Flows. Application of Friction Factor Correlations to Solids. Rheological Measurements. Nomenclature. References.

4. Hydrodynamics of Fluidization 137

   Introduction. Flow Through Fixed Beds. Onset of Fluidization and General Characteristics. Minimum Fluidization Velocity. Minimum Bubbling Velocity. Bed Expansion. Hydrodynamics of Bubbles. Nomenclature. References.

5. Hydrodynamics of Entrainment 207

   Introduction. Mechanisms and Observations of Entrainment. Entrainment Correlations and Modeling. Nomenclature. References.

6. Commercial Fluid-Bed Processes 235

   Introduction. Reactors in the Petroleum Industry. Drying and Processing Operations. References.

7. **Coal Gasification** 271

Introduction. Overview of Reactor Types. Major Gasification Processes. Kinetics of Coal Gasification. Nomenclature. References.

8. **Coal Liquefaction** 311

Introduction. Hydrodynamics of Three-Phase Fluidization. Major Liquefaction Processes. Nomenclature. References.

9. **Principles of Fluid-Bed Reactor Modeling** 345

Introduction. General Concepts and Definitions. Diffusion into Porous Particles. Combustion of Particles. Fluid-Bed Flow Modeling. Principles of Reactor Design. Nomenclature. References.

10. **Experimental Methods** 401

Introduction. Measurement of Bubble Phenomena. Measurement Techniques for Particle Behavior. Measurement of Performance Parameters. Nomenclature. References.

11. **Vertical Flow of Particulate Solids in Standpipes and Risers** 471
C.S. Teo and L. S. Leung, University of Queensland, Australia

Introduction. General Theories for the Upflow and Downflow of Solids. Quantitative Demarcation Between Flow Regimes. Drift-Flux Model and Kwauk's Model for Generalized Two-Phase Flow. Equations Pertaining to Each Flow Regime. Vertical Downflow of Solids in Standpipes. Vertical Pneumatic Conveying in Riser Flow. Nomenclature. References.

12. **Considerations in Pneumatic Transport** 543

Introduction. Regimes of Flow. Choking and Pressure Drop. Commercial Techniques for Pneumatic Conveying. Nomenclature. References.

13. **Gas Premixing Techniques** 571
Milind B. Ajinkya, Exxon Research and Engineering Co., U.S.A.

Introduction. Pipeline Mixing. Jet Mixing. Industrial Mixers. Summary. Nomenclature. References.

14. **Particulate Capture—Dry Methods** 593

Introduction. Gravitational Separation. Electrostatic Precipitation. Cyclone Separators. Fabric Filter Dust Collectors. Nomenclature. References.

15. **Particulate Capture in Venturi Scrubbers** 645

Introduction. Description of Operation. Droplet Dynamics. Comparison of Scrubber Models. Operating Variables and Performance. Heat and Mass Transfer Considerations. Additional Comments. Nomenclature. References.

Appendix A: Source Listing and Abstracts of the Fluidized-Bed Literature 685

Appendix B: Notation and Unit Conversion Factors 805

Appendix C: List of Cyclone Suppliers/Manufacturers 853

Index 855

PREFACE

Gas-solid fluidization is a subject having wide engineering applications overlapping different industries. Fluidized-solids technology has grown almost exponentially over the past several decades with commercial applications in the production of vinyl chloride, phthalic anhydride, melamine, polyethylene, polypropylene, and fluidized catalytic cracking of petroleum. Fluidization is essentially a low-energy method of contacting granular solids with process fluids, and as such, could be used in the production of clean, inexpensive energy from coal resources. In the development of the synthetic fuels industry, fluidized reactor systems are being considered for coal gasification, coal liquefaction, and shale pyrolysis. Other present-day applications include combustion, nuclear fuel preparation, and operations in drying, coating, and similar physical methods of manufacturing.

Despite the large-scale applications of this technology, fluidization remains a comparatively less-developed area of chemical engineering. Scale-up to commercial systems is often a formidable task, requiring costly pilot-plant testing in successively larger units or operations. The design literature in general is poorly organized and in some cases contradictory, particularly where heat and mass exchanges and/or chemical reactions are involved. Part of this dilemma lies in the inadequate understanding of the hydrodynamic phenomena in systems involving gas-solids flows. Understanding the complex interaction between particles, and particles and fluid is critical not only to the design of reactor systems but to their peripheral operations, which include solids transfer lines, risers, product/recycle separation schemes, feedstock and catalyst feeding systems, etc.

It is the intent of this book to relate hydrodynamic concepts of gas-solid flows to design practices in fluidization engineering. Many of the early chapters deal with the properties and characteristics of fluid-particle transport and contacting. These fundamental discussions are applied in subsequent chapters to industrial problems.

Finally, this volume contains two contributed chapters prepared by experts. We wish to acknowledge each of these contributors. Without the efforts of these individuals, this volume would not have been possible.

Nicholas P. Cheremisinoff
Paul N. Cheremisinoff

1

Properties and Characteristics of Loose Solids

CONTENTS

INTRODUCTION, 2

PHYSICAL PROPERTIES OF LOOSE MATERIALS, 2

ANGLES OF REPOSE, INTERNAL FRICTION, AND SLIDE, 5

FORCES OF ADHESION AND SOLIDS FLOWABILITY, 8

   Adhesion, 8
   Agglutination, 11
   Mechanical Properties, 11

PARTICLE SIZE CLASSIFICATION, 14

   Size and Distribution Laws, 14
   Particle Size Measurement Techniques, 19

AERODYNAMIC PROPERTIES OF SINGLE PARTICLES, 26

   Drag Forces and Particle Settling, 26
   Particle Trajectories in Flowing Gas Streams, 35

NOMENCLATURE, 40

REFERENCES, 42

INTRODUCTION

Many granular and powdered forms of solids are produced in manufacturing processes as either final products or intermediate constituents for producing marketable items. These materials are almost never uniform in size and are often highly irregular in shape-characteristics which largely establish their hydrodynamic behavior in both bulk form and in two-phase systems. These materials are produced by crushing, grinding, precipitation, attrition, spraying, or other particulate-forming processes, and only under very carefully controlled conditions do they appear in relatively uniform sizes and shapes. The quantitative correlation of bulk particulate behavior, both alone and in fluid-solid systems is difficult because of the large number of parameters that relate to particle size and size distribution, particle shape, particle surface characteristics, and discrete particle physical properties. The conventional characterization of granular and powdered materials is in terms of an appropriately defined mean size. Regardless of the measurement method employed to define a size distribution, data can be redefined in terms of an appropriate characteristic dimension or size, which most often is an equivalent spherical particle diameter. This has the distinct advantage of allowing granular solid properties to be related through standard hydrodynamic correlations when dealing with two-phase flow systems.

This first chapter introduces some basic definitions and physical and aerodynamic properties of discrete solids. Subsequent chapters apply these concepts to describing the two-phase phenomenon and in extending analogies to engineering calculations.

PHYSICAL PROPERTIES OF LOOSE MATERIALS

Loose solid matter is composed of an assemblage of large numbers of individual particulates. The physical properties and forces of attraction which exist between individual particles have important effects on their flow behavior when subjected to fluidization by gas or liquid media. With many materials, forces of attraction exist between particles, in which case the material is described as being cohesive. Ideal loose solids have no forces of attraction between them. The properties of loose materials in contrast to fluids and composite solids are characterized by several parameters that must be measured or known prior to the design of any fluid-solids contacting system.

The first of these important properties is the density of the material, of which there are several specific terms, namely, bulk, particle and skeletal densities.

The *bulk density* of solids is the overall density of the loose material including the interparticle distance of separation. It is defined as the overall mass of the material per unit volume. A material's bulk density is sensitive to the particle size, the mean particle density, moisture content, and the interparticle separation (i.e., degree of solids packing). It is measured simply by pouring a weighed sample of particles through a funnel into a graduated cylinder, and from this the volume occupied determines the loose bulk density. By gently vibrating the container walls, the distance between particles decreases and hence, the volume decreases. The material thus becomes denser with time and its bulk density achieves some limiting value, ϱ_{max}, known as the *tapped* or *packed bulk density*.

The ratio of $\varrho_{max}/\varrho_{min}$ can be as high as 1.52 depending on the material. Consequently, when bulk densities are reported it is important to note whether the value was determined under loose or tapped conditions, along with the mean particle size. Most literature values report an average bulk density that is representative of the material most often handled. Loose solids may be broadly characterized according to their bulk densities:

Light material	$\varrho_b < 600$ kg/m^3
Average	$600 < \varrho_b < 2,000$ kg/m^3
Extra heavy	$\varrho_b > 2,000$ kg/m^3

The loose bulk density (kg/m^3) can be computed as:

$$\varrho_b = \frac{G_1 - G}{V} \qquad (1\text{-}1)$$

where G_1, G = weights of filled and empty cylinders
V = internal volume of cylinder

Bulk density is related to particle density through the interparticle void fraction ϵ in the sample.

$$\varrho_b = \varrho_p(1 - \epsilon) \qquad (1\text{-}2)$$

The value of ϵ varies between the limits of 0 and unity; however, many particles of interest in fluidization have a loosely poured voidage of approximately 0.4 to 0.45.

Particle density, ϱ_p, is the density of a particle including the pores or voids within the individual solids. It is defined as the weight of the particle divided by the volume occupied by the entire particle. Some textbooks refer to particle density as the material's *apparent density*.

The *skeletal density*, ϱ_s, also called the *true density*, is defined as the density of a single particle excluding the pores. That is, it is the density of the *skeleton* of the particle if the particle is porous. For nonporous materials, skeletal and particle densities are equivalent. For porous particles, skeletal densities are higher than the particle density.

Measurements of the skeletal density are made by liquid or gas pycnometers. When liquids are used, the pycnometer has a fixed and known volume. A specified weight of solids is immersed in a liquid of known density, which wets the solids and penetrates into the pores of the particles. The volume of liquid displaced by the solids is then determined by difference and the skeletal density of the weighed solids computed from the measured displaced volume. The most common liquid used in pycnometer work is water. For materials whose specific gravities are less than water (e.g., coal and coke particles), Varsol is used.

Gas pycnometers provide more accurate measurements of the skeletal density due to better penetration of the particle pores by the gas. They are, however, less frequently employed because of cost and elaborate procedures required during measurements.

The particle and skeletal densities are related through the following equation:

$$\varrho_p = \frac{1 + \varrho_f \xi}{\dfrac{1}{\varrho_s} + \xi} \qquad\qquad (1\text{-}3)$$

where ϱ_p = particle density
ϱ_s = skeletal density
ϱ_f = density of fluid contained in pores of solid
ξ = pore volume per unit of mass of solids

When the particle pores are saturated with gas, $\xi\varrho_f$ is negligible, and Equation 1-3 reduces to:

$$\frac{1}{\varrho_p} = \frac{1}{\varrho_s} + \xi \qquad\qquad (1\text{-}4)$$

Direct measurement of particle density can be made by immersing the material in a non-wetting fluid, such as mercury, which does not penetrate into the pores. The technique resembles that of the liquid pycnometer with the exception that the volume of fluid displaced is that for the entire particle and not just the skeleton.

Another property of importance is the *pore volume*. It can be measured indirectly from the adsorption and/or desorption isotherms of equilibrium quantities of gas absorbed or desorbed over a range of relative pressures. Pore volume can also be measured by mercury intrusion techniques, whereby a hydrostatic pressure is used to force mercury into the pores to generate a plot of penetration volume versus pressure. Since the size of the pore openings is related to the pressure, mercury intrusion techniques provide information on the pore size distribution and the total pore volume.

Moisture can significantly affect loose materials, particularly their flowability. Low temperatures, particle bridging, and caking can alter interparticle void fractions and cause dramatic changes in bulk density. Moisture becomes bound to solids because of mechanical, physicochemical, and chemical mechanisms. Moisture retained between particles and on their surfaces is strictly a mechanical mechanism. Physicochemical binding results when moisture penetrates inside particle pores because of diffusion and adsorption onto pore walls. Chemically bound moisture appears as hydrated or crystalline structures. The terms *moisture* or *moisture content* is used to denote the degree of liquid retained on and in solids.

Moisture is defined as the ratio of the fluid's weight retained by solids to the weight of wet material:

$$W = \frac{G_w - G_d}{G_w} \tag{1-5}$$

where G_w and G_d are the weights of wet and absolute dry material, respectively. Moisture content, W_c, is the ratio of the moisture weight to the weight of absolute dry material:

$$W_c = \frac{G_w - G_d}{G_d} \tag{1-6}$$

Values of W and W_c can be expressed as either fractions or percents. The presence of moisture tends to increase the relationship between moisture content and the density of loose or lump materials as follows:

$$\varrho_m = \varrho(1 + W_c) \tag{1-7}$$

And for dusty and powdered materials:

$$\varrho_m = \varrho \frac{1 + W_c}{(1 + \frac{W_c}{3} \varrho_f/\varrho_p)} \tag{1-8}$$

where ϱ_m, ϱ = densities of wet and dry loose materials, respectively
ϱ_p = particle density
ϱ_f = density of liquid filling the solid particle pores

In addition to the physical properties just described there are those properties which affect the flowability of the material. Specifically, these properties are the material's angle of repose, angle of internal friction, and the angle of slide.

ANGLES OF REPOSE, INTERNAL FRICTION, AND SLIDE

The *angle of repose* is defined as the angle between a line of repose of loose material and a horizontal plane. Its value depends on the magnitude of friction and adhesion between particles and determines the mobility of loose solids, which is a critical parameter in designing conical discharge and feeding nozzles and in establishing vessel geometries. In all cases the slopes of such nozzles should exceed the angle of repose.

The angle of repose is the measured angle between a horizontal plane and the top of a pile of solids. The *poured angle* of repose is obtained when a pile of solids is formed, whereas the *drained angle* results when solids are drained from a bin. Figure 1-1 distinguishes between the two terms signifying the angle of repose. For monosized particles or particles with a relatively narrow size distribution, the drained and poured angles are approximately the same. If, however, the solids have a wide size distribution, the drained angle is higher than the poured angle.

In bin design, the drained angle is more important. However, the differences between the angles are rarely important, and since the poured angle is easier to measure, it is most frequently reported in the literature. In general, the lower the angle of repose is, the more free flowing is the material, and hence, the shallower the bin angle required. Materials can be roughly categorized according to their angles of repose as follows:

- For very free-flowing granules: $25° < \beta < 30°$
- For free-flowing granules: $30° < \beta < 38°$
- For fair to passable flow of powders: $38° < \beta < 45°$
- For cohesive powders: $45° < \beta < 55°$
- For very cohesive powders: $55° < \beta < 70°$

The angle of repose is sensitive to the conditions of the supporting surface—the smoother the surface, the smaller the angle. The angle may also be reduced by vibrating the supporting surface. When handling slow moving materials having large angles of repose, well-designed bunkers and hoppers are provided with highly polished internal surfaces and low amplitude vibrators.

The angle is also sensitive to moisture. Specifically, moisture tends to increase the angle of repose. The variation of β with moisture content is likely due to the surface layer of moisture that surrounds each particle and surface tension effects which bind aggregates of solids together.

The *angle of internal friction, α,* is defined as the equilibrium angle between flowing particles and bulk or stationary solids in a bin. Figure 1-2 illustrates the definition. The angle of internal friction is invariably greater than the angle of repose.

The *angle of slide* is defined as the angle from the horizontal of an inclined surface on which an amount of material will slide downward due to the influence of

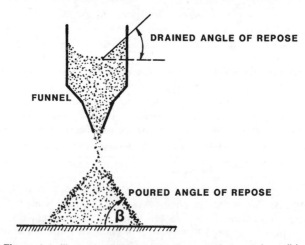

Figure 1-1. Illustration of the angle of repose for granular solids.

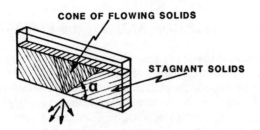

Figure 1-2. Illustration of the angle of internal friction.

Table 1-1
Physico-Mechanical Properties of Loose Materials

Loose Material	Bulk Density (g/cm³)	Angle of Repose (degrees)	Friction Coefficient	
			Inside	Outside on Steel
Sulfur	0.67	40	0.8	0.625
Magnesite-caustic	1.02	31	0.575	0.5
Magnesium oxide	0.47	36	0.49	0.37
Phosphate powder	1.52	29	0.52	0.48
Calcium chloride	0.68	35	0.63	0.58
Napthalene (crushed)	0.57	37	0.725	0.6
Anhydrous sodium carbonate	0.585	41	0.875	0.675
Sodium chloride (fine)	0.93	38	0.725	0.625
Carbamide (powdered)	0.54	42	0.825	0.56
Superphosphate (granulated)	1.1	31	0.64	0.46
(powdered)	0.8	36	0.71	0.7
Nitrophoska (granulated)	1.1	38	0.55	0.4
Salicylic acid (powdered)	0.46	44	0.95	0.78
Talc	0.85	40	—	—
Cement	1.15	30	0.5	0.45
Chalk	1.1	42	0.81	0.76
Sand (fine)	1.51	33	1.0	0.58
Graphite	0.45	40	—	—
Coal (fine)	0.95	36	0.67	0.47
Earth (dry)	1.2	30	0.9	0.57
Wheat	0.77	29	0.35	0.28
Peas	0.743	26	0.4	0.42

gravity. The angle is important in the design of chutes and hoppers as well as pneumatic conveying systems. It provides a measure of the relative adhesiveness of a dry material to a dissimilar surface. The angle depends on the type of solids, the physical and surface properties (e.g., roughness, cleanliness, dryness), the surface configuration (e.g., degree of curvature), the manner in which the solids are placed on the surface, and the rate of change of the slope of the surface during measurements. Table 1-1 provides typical values of loose solids as measured without vibration of the horizontal support surface.

FORCES OF ADHESION AND SOLIDS FLOWABILITY

The ability of solids to flow freely under the influence of gravity is called *fluidity* and is characterized by flow through an orifice. It is a function of the granulometric composition of the solids, the particle geometry and size distribution, the coefficient of internal friction, moisture content, and other parameters. A material's fluidity is important to the design of bins, bunkers, and a variety of feeding and mixing devices. Specific to these systems is its influence on requirement times for filling and discharge. Fluidity can be characterized in terms of a coefficient:

$$K_f = \tau' r^{2.58/G} \tag{1-9}$$

where K_f = fluidity coefficient
$\quad \tau'$ = loose solids' discharge time through funnel (s)
$\quad r$ = orifice radius (mm)
$\quad G$ = total sample weight (gms)

The coefficient varies over a wide range depending on the material properties, with typical values being $1.2 \sim 6.4$ for metal powders and $3 \sim 4$ for quartz sand. In general, the larger K_f is, the more tightly packed are the solids.

The limiting outflow velocity through orifices in the bottoms of bins may be estimated from the following expression:

$$V_o = K_e F^{n'} \tag{1-10}$$

where $\quad F$ = cross-sectional area of orifice
$\quad K_e, n'$ = experimentally determined coefficients

For granular materials the following formula is recommended:

$$V_o = (2.546 - 0.162 \bar{d}_p) F^{0.25} \tag{1-11}$$

where $\bar{d}_p$ is the mean particle diameter (mm) and F and V_o are in units of m^2 and m/s, respectively.

Equations 1-9 to 1-11 are empirical relations that describe solids flow behavior, but do not relate specific solid properties other than perhaps particle size. How properties affect solids flowability depends on the specific forces of attraction between particles. This can be described by the phenomena of adhesion and agglutination, as well as the mechanical properties of loose solids.

Adhesion

Adhesion is the phenomenon observed when particles stick to solid surfaces. Obviously, this is undesirable and must be accounted for in the design of bins, chutes, pneumatic conveying systems, and gas-solid contacting devices. Adhesion is caused by molecular, capillary, electrical, and coulombic forces. Often, these forces interact, and it is difficult to distinguish which force is primarily responsible. There are however, exceptions where one force dominates.

The *molecular forces of adhesion* are determined by van der Waals' forces of interaction between particle molecules and the supporting surface. These forces are evident even before there is direct contact between the particles and surface, and they depend on the properties and size of the pair of contacting bodies, the roughness of the supporting surface, and the area of contact. Molecular adhesion forces may be reduced by polishing the supporting surface and by decreasing the solid's particle size.

Capillary forces of adhesion are due to the condensation of water vapor into the pores of loose solids during the presence of a wet film. A liquid memiscus develops between the particles and the supporting surface, resulting in the formation of surface forces. These forces press the solids onto the vessel surface. Capillary forces may be reduced by hydrophobing the surface (i.e., by making it moisture resistant through the addition of a liquid surface-active agent in the loose material).

Electrical forces of adhesion only manifest during direct contact between particles and the supporting surface. During mixing, particles rub against each other, as well as against the vessel walls and any internals. This action gives rise to electrical charges, causing a potential difference and resulting in particles sticking to each other. The greater the contact potential difference, the greater are the electrical adhesion forces. The contact potential difference depends on the amount of charge on the particles' surfaces and the supporting surface. When particles come into contact with a semi-conductor (e.g., metal paint, plastics) a contact potential difference develops that is much greater than that observed during contact with a conductor (metals). For this reason, particles will more readily adhere to painted surfaces than to pure metals.

Coulomb's forces of adhesion arise when charged particles approach the supporting surface. When this happens, on the opposite side of the surface, charges are generated that are equal to the particle charges but are of opposite sign. Such a case leads to mirror-image coulombic forces. These forces are only manifested by the presence of a gap between particles and the supporting surface. When a particle touches the supporting surface, the charges escape, resulting in a decrease of Coulomb's forces. The higher the wall's conductivity, the less pronounced are Coulomb's forces and consequently, the smaller the forces of adhesion. Surface wetness also promotes the process.

Each type of adhesion force has a different effect depending on particle size. In terms of particle radius, these relationships are as follows: Coulomb's forces are proportional to $1/r_p^2$; electrical forces, to $r_p^{0.666}$; molecular forces to r_p; capillary forces, $r_p(1 - r_p^{x-1})$, for exponent $x > 1$.

Because of the radically different natures of the adhesion component forces, a universal method for minimizing them is not possible. For example, while the hydrophobization of the support surface decreases capillary forces, it tends to increase electrical and coulombic forces; whereas increasing wetness decreases electrical and Coulomb's forces but increases capillary forces.

A force, F_t, must be applied to a particle in order to "tear" it away from the supporting surface. If this "tearing-off" force is perpendicular to the supporting surface, it simply overcomes the adhesion forces (F_{ad}) which can be referred to as sticking static forces. If F_t is applied in a direction tangent to the supporting surface, it is spent in overcoming the frictional static forces of adhesion. Finally, if external force F_t is directed at some angle to the surface, it is spent in overcoming both friction and adhesion forces. Consequently, the adhesion forces may be evaluated by the force required to tear particles away from the surface. The tear-off force can be applied indirectly through several approaches. Common methods include sloping the supporting surface area, and applying a centrifugal field or vibration. In the first approach, force F_t is determined by the slope when the particle begins to move:

$$F_t = V(\varrho_1 - \varrho_2)g \sin \theta \tag{1-12}$$

where V = volume of the moving particle
ϱ_1, ϱ_2 = densities of particles and surrounding medium, respectively
g = acceleration due to gravity
θ = angle of supporting surface from the horizontal

In the centrifugal method, the supporting surface rotates along with the particles.

$$F_t = V(\varrho_1 - \varrho_2)(\vec{j} + \vec{g}) \tag{1-13}$$

where $\vec{j}$ and $\vec{g}$ are vectors of centrifugal and gravitational acceleration, respectively. In the vibration method the supporting surface is vibrated:

$$F_t = V(\varrho_1 - \varrho_2)(\vec{a} + \vec{g}) \tag{1-14}$$

where $\vec{a}$ is the acceleration vector of fluctuating motion.

Adhesion is characterized by the dimensionless *adhesion* number, ν_F, defined as the ratio of the weight of those particles left on the surface after applying force F_t to their initial weight (%) on the surface.

$$\nu_F = \frac{G}{G_o} 100 \tag{1-15}$$

The adhesion number depends on F_t, and therefore, this force is sometimes used in evaluating the adhesion properties of solids. In some cases, adhesion is evaluated in terms of the "tear-off" force per unit contact area of surface. If the tear-off force is directed tangentially to the surface, adhesion may be characterized indirectly by the coefficient of internal friction f_1.

$$F_t = f_1 F_N \tag{1-16}$$

where F_N is the force applied normal to the particle layer.

Agglutination

Numerous types of fine-granular and powdered materials experience an increase in their bulk densities with time due to particle agglutination. A material undergoes thickening due to particle redistribution. Low amplitude vibrations cause fine particles to penetrate between the voids and interstices of large particles. This increases surface contact area between particles, resulting in an increase in adhesion.

Agglutination increases with increasing air humidity (since capillary adhesion forces become important). Some materials, such as powdered fertilizers tend to undergo agglutination, forming dense masses. The rate of agglutination can be determined from the measured resistance of a column of material under a specified applied loading.

Materials subject to this applied load-per-unit surface area of the sample column (δ_d) may be divided into the following categories of agglutination: light ($\delta_d < 0.1$ MN/cm^2); significant ($0.1 < \delta_d < 0.2$ MN/cm^2); mean ($0.2 < \delta_d < 1$ MN/cm^2); strong ($\delta_d > 1$ MN/cm^2). Materials in the light agglutination category include powdered superphosphates, sulphates, nitrophoska; those in the significant category include carbamide, diamophos, granular ammonium nitrate; and those in the strong to medium category include powdered ammonium nitrate, potassium chloride, bicarbonate, and common salt.

Decreasing the adhesion between particles reduces the rate of agglutination. Methods of achieving this include humidity control, increasing particle sizes by granulation, decreasing the contact area between particles by preparing them in special forms, such as powdering particles with talc, clay, etc., or by introducing hydrophobic substances to the solids.

Mechanical Properties

A layer of solid particles is subjected to compression, σ, and shear stresses, τ_f, from the mass of successive solids layers. These stresses do not exist in all directions at the same time. It is possible to locate inside the stressed loose material, three perpendicular planes where no shear stresses prevail (see Figure 1-3). These planes are referred to as "main planes," and the normal stresses acting on them are called "main stresses."

From the so-called flat problem of stress condition, the relationship between main normal stresses and shear stresses can be obtained. Consider a rectangular prism within a bulk sample of loose material, as shown in Figure 1-4. The sides ab and bc coincide with the planes of the main stresses σ_1 and σ_2, and the prism's height is equal to unity. From a force balance, we obtain:

$$\tau_f = \frac{\sigma_1 - \sigma_2}{2} \sin 2\alpha_1 \qquad (1\text{-}17)$$

This relationship is graphically illustrated by Moore's stress circle analysis, shown in Figure 1-5. To obtain the stress circle in $\sigma - \tau_f$ coordinates, the stresses (σ_1 and

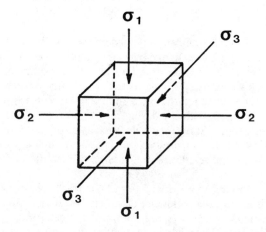

Figure 1-3. Illustration of the main stresses in loose materials.

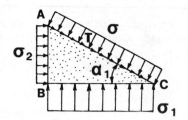

Figure 1-4. Illustration of the forces acting on the prism in a bulk sample of loose material.

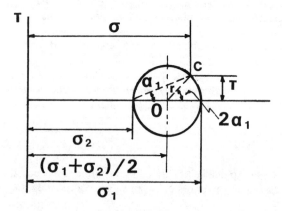

Figure 1-5. Graphical representation of shear and normal stresses by Moore's circle.

σ_2) are plotted on the abscissa. On the $\sigma_1 - \sigma_2$, a circle of the same diameter is drawn. For any point C in the first quadrant of the circle:

$$\sigma = \frac{\sigma_1 + \sigma_2}{2} + r \cos 2\alpha_1$$

$$\tau = r \sin 2\alpha_1 \tag{1-18}$$

where r is the radius of Moore's circle.

Consider an elementary plane in the bulk material which does not coincide with the main planes. If the applied shear stress is gradually increased to some value $\tau_{f\text{-lim}}$ for a constant normal stress σ, the solids in this plane will shift. The stress $\tau_{f\text{-lim}}$ is referred to as the limiting stress of fluidity of the material.[1]

Each value of σ has a corresponding $\tau_{f\text{-lim}}$ value. For ideal loose materials with no adhesive properties, σ and $\tau_{f\text{-lim}}$ are zero. For loose materials that bind even at $\sigma = 0$, a limiting shear stress exists. This limiting value is referred to as the initial limiting shear stress, τ_o. Friction arises when particle layers shift. Hence, for ideal loose materials,

$$\tau_{f\text{-lim}} = \sigma_i f_1 \tag{1-19}$$

and for binded loose materials,

$$\tau_{\lim} = \tau_o + \sigma_i f_1 \tag{1-20}$$

where f_1 is the coefficient of internal friction.

For a series of $\tau_{f\text{-lim}}$-σ values, a locus of limiting shear stresses exists. This locus of values is a line that is tangent to all Moore circles traced from the values σ_1 and σ_2 corresponding to $\tau_{f\text{-lim}}$. The graph of limiting shear-stresses versus normal stresses is shown in Figure 1-6. All points that lie below the line of limiting stresses characterize the stationary stress of the material. Loose materials (except liquids) are subjected to stress when motionless. This is the reason a pile of loose material does not disperse over a horizontal supporting surface.

The graphical relationship of $\tau_{\lim} = f(\sigma)$ is important in evaluating mechanical properties. The origin (point O in Figure 1-6) is selected so that the value of the vertical stress σ_1 is equal to $h_o \varrho_b$ at the horizontal stress $\sigma_2 = 0$. The parameter h_o is the limiting height of a vertical column of loose material without a supporting wall, and ϱ_b is the bulk weight of the material.

The value of h_o must be experimentally determined for each material. At point O, vertical and horizontal stresses are the main stresses; their corresponding Moore circle has a radius of $r = h_o \varrho_b/2$. As shown by Figure 1-6 for binding loose materials, two different shear stress relations exist; namely curved section OA which can be described by a Moore circle of radius r, and the straight-line AB, where $\tau = \tau_o + \sigma \tan\psi$. The limiting shear-normal-stresses plot for ideal loose materials has no nonlinear relation (i.e., line AB would extrapolate to the origin).

The specific elements of the graph in Figure 1-6 characterize the mechanical properties of loose materials. For example, $\tan\psi$ is equal to the *coefficient of internal friction*.

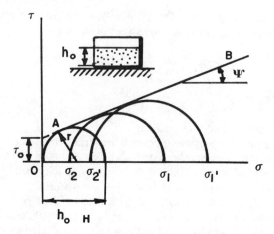

Figure 1-6. Graph of limiting shear stresses versus normal stresses.

The ratio of limiting shear stresses $\tau_{\text{f-lim}}$ to the corresponding normal stress σ is a shear resistance coefficient f_σ. For section AB,

$$f_\sigma = f_1 + \tau_0/\sigma \tag{1-21}$$

where τ_0 is the *initial resistance to shear* which may be approximately determined from:

$$\tau_0 = \frac{h_0 \varrho_b}{4} \tag{1-22}$$

If $\sigma > > \tau_0$ the values of $f_\sigma \approx f_1$. Over the limits of line AB, the coefficient of internal friction is constant.

For ideal loose materials the angle of repose is equal to the angle of internal friction but for binding materials, the angle of repose is always larger.

PARTICLE SIZE CLASSIFICATION

Size and Distribution Laws

The term *particle size* requires careful definition unless used in a very general sense. The word "diameter" was originally defined in terms of spheres, but it is also descriptive of particles of irregular shapes. Diameters of irregular particles may be defined in terms of the geometry of the individual particulates. These diameters are usually referred to as statistical diameters since large numbers of particles must be measured and averaged to provide a representative size. Numerous definitions for particle size have been used by various investigators. Cadle[2] and McCrore and Delly[3] provide detailed discussions of the various definitions along with guidelines for their application.

One relatively straightforward definition for particle diameter is based on its linear dimensions and is characterized as a mean arithmetic value:

$$d_i = \frac{\ell bh}{3} \qquad (1\text{-}23)$$

Another appropriate definition is to express the size as a mean geometric value:

$$d_i = (\ell bh)^{0.333} \qquad (1\text{-}24)$$

where ℓ, b, h are particle length, width, and height, respectively.

The value of d_i discretely varies between certain limits, d_{min} to d_{max}, where the ratio of d_{max}/d_{min} may be greater than 1,000 depending on the solid material. The granulometric composition of loose solid particles may be characterized by a distribution of discrete random values of d_i, where its series of measured values is $d_1, d_2, d_3 \ldots d_n$ having corresponding probabilities $p_1, p_2, p_3 \ldots p_n$ or frequencies $n_1, n_2, n_3 \ldots n_n$. For a wide particle size distribution (i.e., d_{max}/d_{min} is large), determination of the entire series of d_i is difficult. Consequently, the series is approximated by discrete classes (or fractions) of d_i. The class includes the group of d_i values between specified limits of $d_{\ell i}$ and d_{ni}, which are representative of the mean value of the class in the new series:

$$\bar{d}_i = \frac{d_{hi} + d_{\ell i}}{2} \qquad \text{(where i = 1 ... K)} \qquad (1\text{-}25)$$

The number of classes in this K series should be no less than 5 and no greater than 20. If the number of classes is too small, the characteristics of the granular composition cannot be properly represented. If the number of classes exceeds 20, the danger of including nonrepresentative subsets arises simply because of the large number of particles included. In the latter case, the particle size distribution becomes distorted by random deviations.

The value of the fraction (class) is normally expressed as the percent of the total amount of sample to be analyzed, either with respect to the total mass or volume. Thus, the mean arithmetic value of the particle diameter is:

$$\bar{d} = \bar{d}_1 \frac{G_1}{G} + \bar{d}_2 \frac{G_2}{G} + \ldots + \bar{d}_n \frac{G_k}{G} = \sum_{i=1}^{K} \bar{d}_i \frac{G_i}{G} = \sum_{i=1}^{K} \bar{d}_i \frac{c_i}{100} \qquad (1\text{-}26)$$

where $\bar{d}_1, \bar{d}_2 \ldots \bar{d}_n$ = mean values of particle diameter of first, second, and K classes

$G_1, G_2, \ldots G_K$ = particle weights

G = sample weight (total weight of all particles in all classes)

d_i = mean value of diameter of particles in i^{th} class

c_i = percentage by weight of ith class particles in sample

K = number of classes (fractions)

The dispersity of loose material is often represented by particle size distribution plots as shown in Figure 1-7. Mean values of d_i for each size class are shown plotted on the abscissa while corresponding percent sample compositions or the cumulative percentage of classes $\bar{d}_1$ and $\bar{d}_2$ are plotted on the ordinate. In the former, the particle differential distribution curve by sizes $f(d_i)$ is obtained, whereas in the second case, the integral curve $(F(\bar{d}_i)$ is obtained. The relative amount of each fraction on the differential curve is determined by the area of a rectangle whose base is equal to the interval of the values of conditional diameters and whose height is the corresponding weight fraction (or percentage) of the mean particle diameter of the class.

The integral curve provides the weight fraction directly over the size range from d_{min} to d_i. Numerically, it is equal to the area limited by the curve $F(\bar{d}_i)$ (where the ordinates are d_{min} and d_i and the abscissa interval is $\Delta d = d_i - d_{min}$).

Depending on the particle size, loose materials may be classified as lumps ($d_{max} > 10$ mm), coarse-grained ($d_{max} = 2$ to 10 mm); fine-grained ($d_{max} = 0.5$ to 2 mm), powders ($d_{max} = 0.05$ to 0.5 mm) and pulverized material ($d_{max} < 0.05$ mm). It should be noted that the mean particle diameter is in a sense an arbitrary definition which to some extent depends on the discretion of the investigator. Absolute consistency must, however, be employed when characterizing particle samples. Table 1-2 lists some commonly used definitions of mean sizes.

Particle size distributions can be conveniently expressed as a cumulative distribution, i.e., in terms of particle size versus weight, volume, or number fraction of particles smaller or larger than the stated particle size. Graphically, cumulative particle size distributions can be represented on log-normal probability, normal probability, and Rosin-Rammler plots.

In a *log-normal probability distribution,* the logarithm of the particle sizes is normally distributed. A cumulative log-normal distribution will result in a straight line on "log-probability" coordinates. The standard deviation for this distribution is defined as:

$$\sigma_s = \frac{50\% \text{ particle size}}{15.9\% \text{ particle size}} \tag{1-27}$$

The greater is the value of σ_s, the wider the particle size distribution.

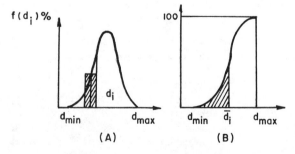

Figure 1-7. Particle size distribution plots: (A) differential; (B) integral.

Table 1-2
Common Definitions of Mean Diameters

Name	Common Symbol	Definition
Arithmetic mean	$\bar{d}_{10}$	$\dfrac{1}{n} \Sigma d_i f_i$
Geometric mean	$\bar{d}_g$	$(d_1^{f_1} d_2^{f_2} d_3^{f_3} \ldots d_n^{f_n})1/n$
Harmonic mean	$\bar{d}_{ha}$	$\left[\dfrac{1}{n} \Sigma \dfrac{f_i}{d_i} \right]^{-1}$
Mean surface diameter	$\bar{d}_{20}$	$\left(\dfrac{\Sigma f_i d_i^2}{n} \right)^{0.5}$
Mean weight diameter	$\bar{d}_{30}$	$\left(\dfrac{\Sigma f_i d_i^3}{n} \right)^{0.333}$
Linear mean diameter	$\bar{d}_{21}$	$\dfrac{\Sigma f_i d_i^2}{\Sigma f_i d_i}$
Surface mean diameter	$\bar{d}_{32}$	$\dfrac{\Sigma f_i d_i^3}{\Sigma f_i d_i^2}$
Weight mean diameter	$\bar{d}_{43}$	$\dfrac{\Sigma f_i d_i^4}{\Sigma f_i d_i^3}$

A *normal probability* or Gaussian distribution is essentially a standard definition in mathematics, in which a plot of frequency versus particle size results in a symmetrical bell-shaped curve (see Figure 1-8). The equation of the ordinate in Figure 1-8 is:

$$Y = \frac{1}{(2\pi)^{0.5}\sigma_s} \exp\left[-\frac{1}{2}\left(\frac{\alpha' - \bar{\alpha}'}{\sigma_s} \right)^2 \right]$$ (1-28A)

and

$$X = \frac{\alpha' - \bar{\alpha}'}{\sigma_s}$$ (1-28B)

where $\bar{\alpha}'$ is the average size or parameter obtained by dividing the sum of the individual values by the frequency:

$$\bar{\alpha}' = \frac{\Sigma\alpha'}{n}$$ (1-29)

and the deviation from the mean is defined as the value minus the average value:

$$\alpha'' = \alpha' - \bar{\alpha}'$$ (1-30)

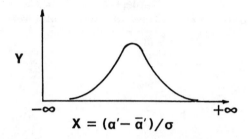

Figure 1-8. The standard Gaussian distribution curve.

The standard deviation is then equal to the square root of the sum of the deviations squared divided by the frequency

$$\sigma_s = \left(\frac{\Sigma(\alpha'')^2}{n}\right)^{0.5}$$ (1-31)

When plotted on probability coordinates, a cumulative normal distribution gives a straight line. The mean particle size is the 50% point on the probability scale.

A *Rosin-Rammler distribution* is used to characterize solids that have been processed by crushing and grinding operations. The expression for the distribution is given in terms of the percent solids R, larger than a stated particle size d.

$$R = 100 \exp\left(-\frac{d}{\bar{d}}\tilde{h}\right)$$ (1-32)

where $\bar{d}$ = size constant (referred to as the Rosin-Rammler mean)
$\tilde{h}$ = size distribution constant

A cumulative plot of log (100/R) versus log d will result in a straight line having a slope of $\tilde{h}$ for particle size distributions obeying the Rosin-Rammler relation. The Rosin-Rammler mean, $\bar{d}$, is defined as the particle size corresponding to R = 36.8%.

In later chapters, particle size will be described in terms of the Sauter mean; i.e., the volume surface mean particle size.

$$\bar{d}_{vs} = \frac{1}{\Sigma W_i/d_i}$$ (1-33)

where W_i = weight fraction of the i particle size range
d_i = average particle diameter in the i particle size range

Table 1-3
Typical Sphericity Factors for Various Materials as Compiled by Shirai[8]

Material	Sphericity (ϕ_s)
Sand	0.534–0.861
Silica	0.554–0.628
Pulverized coal	0.696
Bituminous coal	0.625
Celite cylinders	0.861
Iron catalyst	0.578

Another useful characteristic size is a median diameter, denoted as d_{50}. This is the diameter at which 50% of some property, such as weight, number, surface area, etc., of the distribution, is due to particles smaller than d_{50}. It can be directly obtained from the 50% point on a cumulative plot of the size distribution. The most frequently used median diameters are the weight median size (i.e., 50% point on a wt % versus size cumulative plot), and the number median diameter. For normal distributions, the mean and median sizes are the same.

Particle shape influences the flow characteristics of loose solids and consequently, affects their aerodynamic properties when exposed to flowing fluids. There are a variety of measures reported in the literature[4-6] of nonsphericity of particles. In this text we adopt the definition given by Kunii and Levenspiel,[7] whereby particle sphericity, ϕ_s, is:

$$\phi_s = \frac{F_s}{F_p} \tag{1-34}$$

where F_s and F_p are the surface areas of a sphere and the particle having identical volumes, respectively. Equation 1-34 defines sphericity over the range of $0 < \phi_s < 1$, with the value of unity corresponding to a sphere. Typical literature values are cited in Table 1-3.

Particle Size Measurement Techniques

Particle size measurement is almost a subjective task. There is essentially no standardized method of particle size measurement applicable over the entire range of sizes likely to be encountered. There are several techniques, each having limitations with respect to size range. Furthermore, due to differences in these techniques, reproducibility of size or even size distribution for a given sample is rarely achieved between the different methods. One must therefore, select one or more techniques applicable over the entire range of interest and evaluate particle sizes in a strict, consistent manner. The selection of a specific measuring technique depends on the properties of the solids being measured and the definition of the characteristic mean size that is to be applied to a given problem.

The principal techniques employed in measuring particle sizes are sieving, the impaction method, centrifugation, elutriation, sedimentation, electrical conductivity, light scattering and blockage, and image analysis.

Sieving is the simplest and most common sizing method employed. The technique involves depositing solids on top of a series of screens, each screen having smaller openings than the one above. By vibrating the screens, particles fall through them until a screen having openings too small for the particle to pass through is reached. Particles that pass through all the screens are collected in a solid pan located under the last screen. In the United States, standard screens of either the Tyler Series or the U.S. sieve series are interchangeable. Table 1-4 lists the U.S. Tyler, Canadian, British, French and German standards. Since the U.S. sieve series is recognized by the International Standards Organization (I.S.O.), it should be employed most often when using this method.

Sieving has several disadvantages, primarily related to obtaining reproducibility in sizing particles. First, agglomeration of the solids on the screens or attrition during shaking can lead to erroneous size distributions. Secondly, the cut-off size for standard sieves is approximately 45 μm; consequently, the fines associated with the distribution cannot be properly classified by this method. Sonic sifters enable a lower cut-off size to be achieved and have the added advantage of requiring a minimum sample size of only 3 to 5 gms. However, difficulties in reproducibility are sometimes encountered unless standard procedures are followed closely.

Some materials tend to agglomerate during dry sieving. If the solids are insoluble, a wet sieving technique can be employed, whereby solids are washed through the sieves with a high pressure, low volume water jet. Since the material must be dried before weighing, an additional potential source of measuring inaccuracy is introduced to the analysis.

The *impaction technique* employs cascade impactors, which are devices in which a stream of suspended solids is forced to follow a series of curved flow paths. Larger particulates will tend to deviate from their flow paths due to inertia effects, thus impacting on a surface and becoming captured. The smaller particles will remain in the flowing stream. The smaller particulates may also be captured when the stream velocity is increased. In this case the inertia of the smaller particles becomes sufficient to allow them to impact on a capturing surface. Impactors contain up to seven impaction stages on which the particles of decreasing size are captured. In general, cascade impactors are small devices which can be directly inserted into a duct or pipe to obtain *in situ* size distribution measurements. Cascade impactors are usually equipped with a total filter that is capable of capturing particles less than 0.3 μm in size. It can also be preceded by a miniature cyclone to capture particles larger than 20 μm.

Table 1-4
Comparison of International Sieve Size Standards

U.S.A.[1]		Tyler[2]	Canadian[3]		British[4]		French[5]		German[6]
*Standard	Alternate	Mean Designation	Standard	Alternate	Nominal Aperture	Nominal Mean No.	Aperture (mm)	No.	Aperture (mm)
125 mm	5"		125 mm	5"					
106 mm	4.24"		106 mm	4.24"					
100 mm	4"		100 mm	4"					
90 mm	3½"		90 mm	3½"					
75 mm	3"		75 mm	3"					
63 mm	2½"		63 mm	2½"					
53 mm	2.12"		53 mm	2.12"					
50 mm	2"		50 mm	2"					
45 mm	1¾"		45 mm	1¾"					
37.5 mm	1½"		37.5 mm	1½"					
31.5 mm	1¼"	1.05"	31.5 mm	1¼"					
26.5 mm	1.06"		26.5 mm	1.06"					
25.0 mm	1"		25.0 mm	1"					25.0 mm
22.4 mm	⅞"	0.883"	22.4 mm	⅞"					
19.0 mm	¾"	0.742"	19.0 mm	¾"					20.0 mm
16.0 mm	⅝"	0.624"	16.0 mm	⅝"					18.0 mm
13.2 mm	0.530"	0.525"	13.2 mm	0.530"					16.0 mm
12.5 mm	½"		12.5 mm	½"					12.5 mm
11.2 mm	7/16"	0.441"	11.2 mm	7/16"					
9.5 mm	⅜"	0.371"	9.5 mm	⅜"					10.0 mm
8.0 mm	5/16"	2½	8.0 mm	5/16"					8.0 mm
6.7 mm	0.265"	3	6.7 mm	0.265"					
6.3 mm	¼"		6.3 mm	¼"					6.3 mm

Table 1-4 (continued)
Comparison of International Sieve Size Standards

U.S.A.[1] *Standard	U.S.A.[1] Alternate	Tyler[2] Mean Designation	Canadian[3] Standard	Canadian[3] Alternate	British[4] Nominal Aperture	British[4] Nominal Mean No.	French[5] Aperture (mm)	French[5] No.	German[6] Aperture (mm)
5.6 mm	No. 3½	3½	5.6 mm	No. 3½			5.000	38	5.0 mm
4.75 mm	4	4	4.75 mm	4					
4.00 mm	5	5	4.00 mm	5			4.000	37	4.0 mm
3.35 mm	6	6	3.35 mm	6	3.35 mm	5	3.150	36	3.15 mm
2.80 mm	7	7	2.80 mm	7	2.80 mm	6	2.500	35	2.5 mm
2.36 mm	8	8	2.36 mm	8	2.40 mm	7	2.000	34	2.0 mm
2.00 mm	10	9	2.00 mm	10	2.00 mm	8	1.600	33	1.6 mm
1.70 mm	12	10	1.70 mm	12	1.68 mm	10			
1.40 mm	14	12	1.40 mm	14	1.40 mm	12	1.250	32	1.25 mm
1.18 mm	16	14	1.18 mm	16	1.20 mm	14	1.000	31	1.0 mm
1.00 mm	18	16	1.00 mm	18	1.00 mm	16			
850 μm	20	20	850 μm	20	850 μm	18			
710 μm	25	24	710 μm	25	710 μm	22	0.800	30	800 μm
600 μm	30	28	600 μm	30	600 μm	25	0.630	29	630 μm
500 μm	35	32	500 μm	35	500 μm	30	0.500	28	500 μm
425 μm	40	35	425 μm	40	420 μm	36	0.400	27	400 μm
355 μm	45	42	355 μm	45	355 μm	44	0.315	36	315 μm
300 μm	50	48	300 μm	50	300 μm	52			

Table 1-4 (continued)
Comparison of International Sieve Size Standards

U.S.A.[1]		Tyler[2]	Canadian[3]		British[4]		French[5]		German[6]
*Standard	Alternate	Mean Designation	Standard	Alternate	Nominal Aperture	Nominal Mean No.	Aperture (mm)	No.	Aperture (mm)
250 μm	60	60	250 μm	60	250 μm	60	0.250	25	250 μm
212 μm	70	65	212 μm	70	210 μm	72	0.200	24	200 μm
180 μm	80	80	180 μm	80	180 μm	85	0.160	23	160 μm
150 μm	100	100	150 μm	100	150 μm	100	0.125	22	125 μm
125 μm	120	115	125 μm	120	125 μm	120			
106 μm	140	150	106 μm	140	105 μm	150			
90 μm	170	170	90 μm	170	90 μm	170	0.100	21	100 μm
									90 μm
75 μm	200	200	75 μm	200	75 μm	200	0.080	20	80 μm
63 μm	230	250	63 μm	230	63 μm	240	0.063	19	71 μm
									63 μm
									56 μm
53 μm	270	270	53 μm	270	53 μm	300	0.050	18	50 μm
45 μm	325	325	45 μm	325	45 μm	350	0.040	17	45 μm
38 μm	400	400	38 μm	400					40 μm

[1] U.S.A. Sieve Series—ASTM Specification E-11-70
[2] Tyler Standard Screen Scale Sieve Series.
[3] Canadian Standard Sieve Series 8-GP-1d.
[4] British Standards Institution, London BS-410-62.
[5] French Standard Specifications, AFNOR X-11-501.
[6] German Standard Specification DIN 4188.

* These sieves correspond to those recommended by ISO (International Standards Organization) as an International Standard and this designation should be used when reporting sieve analysis intended for international publication.

The principle behind impaction methods is illustrated in Figure 1-9. As shown, inertial impaction involves the collection of moving particles by impingement onto a target surface. The particle's inertia is defined as its change in motion and is equal to the product of the force that is attempting to create a change in the direction of motion and the time through which it acts, i.e.,

$$\text{Inertia} = \int d(mu) \tag{1-35}$$

The generalized target efficiency equation for any single-stage impaction capture is:

$$\eta = \exp - \left[\frac{0.018}{D_c} \psi'^{0.5+R'} - 0.6R'^2 \right] \tag{1-36}$$

where η = effective target efficiency
D_c = a characteristic dimension for collector surface
R' = ratio of particle diameter to characteristic collector size (d_p/D_c)

Parameter ψ' is a dimensionless group called the impaction parameter, defined as:

$$\psi' = \left\{ \frac{C\rho_p v_r d_p^2}{18\mu D_c} \right\}^{0.5} \tag{1-37}$$

where v_r = relative velocity of the particle with respect to the target
C = slip velocity correction factor for particles less than 1 μm in size

$$C = 1 + \frac{3.45 \times 10^{-4}T}{d_p} \tag{1-38}$$

where T = absolute temperature (°R)
d_p = particle size (μm)

Equation 1-37 is applicable for Reynolds numbers in the range of 0.04 $\sim$ 1.4.

When cascade impactors are used as a stack sampling device, sampling must be done under isokinetic conditions (i.e., same flow rate into sampler as in the flow field). It should be noted that impactors tend to measure agglomerated solids as the agglomerates, which can be a disadvantage depending on the application. Accurate information on particle densities is required in order to properly compute the size distribution.

Centrifugation classification is a method used to evaluate the particle size distributions of powders. Centrifugal forces have the effect of accelerating particle settling rates, causing particulates to deposit at various locations in the classifier, depending on the settling velocity of the particle. Centrifugal classifiers measure aerodynamic sizes and are often employed for powders having aerodynamic sizes

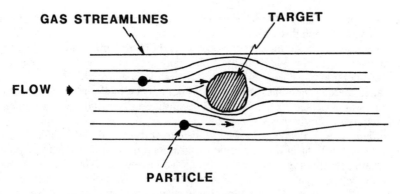

Figure 1-9. Illustration of the particle impaction method.

between 2 and 50 μm. Measured size distributions are sensitive to particle agglomeration, electrostatic forces, and various surface properties.

Elutriation devices are employed for size analyses of dry particulates. Here, the particles are introduced into an upward-flowing gas stream. Those particulates having settling velocities less than the fluid velocity are carried upward or elutriated by the fluid. By varying the fluid velocity, a particle size distribution can be obtained. Such devices provide an aerodynamic size measurement and are mostly employed for particles with sizes ranging from 5 to 200 μm.

Sedimentation techniques allow particles to settle at a velocity determined by their effective size and density. Particle sizes measured are effective sedimentation or settling diameters, which are the same as those obtained in elutriation devices. Typical size ranges measured by such devices are approximately $1 \sim 500$ μm in liquids, and $2 \sim 200$ μm in gas sedimentation systems.

Electrical conductivity techniques are based on the difference in conductivity between solids and the suspending fluid. One such commercial device is the Coulter Counter (manufactured by Coulter Electronics). The measurement principle involves suspending particles in an electrolyte, which is then forced through a small aperture through which an electric current flows. Particles will displace the electrolyte in the aperture, resulting in the production of a current pulse. The amplitude of the pulse is proportional to the particle volume, and the pulse frequency provides a measure of concentration. A series of electronic channels is used to count the pulses of a given amplitude, which in turn are used to evaluate the particle size distribution. A monosized standard particle is employed for calibration to establish the exact size of the channels to be used for each aperture. This device typically covers a range of $1 \sim 250$ μm, but measurements as low as 0.5 μm are possible under specially controlled conditions.

Light scattering and blockage techniques operate using the following principle. Dispersed particulates are passed through a laser beam and the light scattered by the flowing particles is detected by a photomultiplier. Particle size ranges detectable by this technique can range as low as 0.3 μm to as high as 3,000 μm when used as an *in situ* measuring device. The principal advantage of an on-line system is that it is a nonintrusive probe; that is, the laser beams are focused on the moving gas stream through transparent windows.

These systems can be complicated to operate and often require multiple measurements to extend over the widest particle size range. Laboratory models generally require redispersion of solids. This means that on-line systems will tend to measure particle agglomerates whereas the laboratory unit may de-agglomerate the particles and count them as primary particles. In addition, these systems usually detect only a projected area as in the case of microscopy.

Image analysis is a technique that has evolved over the past decade which couples a computer with a light or an electronic miscroscope to provide measurements of particle shape, morphology, texture, color, as well as particle size. The computer replaces the tedious task of particle sizing and characterization performed by the microscope. An image analyzer automatically scans a projected image of the particles or a microscopic photograph of an array of particles. From this information the computer calculates particle size distributions, shape factors, length-to-diameter ratios, or whatever parameter of interest that is programmed into the analysis. These systems can differentiate between particles of different shapes and can selectively count only those particles with a specified shape. This is a tremendous advantage since material that is foreign to the solids sample (e.g., filter fibers from the sample device) can be discounted. The range of particle sizes measured by this technique is comparable to that of the microscope itself. Thus, if an electronic microscope is employed, the range can extend down to 0.001 μm. The principal disadvantage with this method is that it only evaluates the projected areas of particles, which could be a maximum value if the particles are not isotropic.

AERODYNAMIC PROPERTIES OF SINGLE PARTICLES

Drag Forces and Particle Settling

The motion of solid particles in flowing fluid streams (gas or liquid) is a complex hydrodynamic phenomenon due to the interaction between particles, the formation of particulate aggregates, and the break-up or attrition of solids into finer dispersions. Although far from the true phenomenon, the study of single particle behavior in flows is instructive, as it provides a fundamental understanding of the forces responsible for particle motion.

When a viscous fluid flows around a wholly submerged body certain resistances to the fluid motion arise in the form of drag. To overcome these resistances, energy is expended. The developed *drag force* and consequently the energy required to overcome it depend largely on the flow regime and geometry of the solid body. *Laminar flow* conditions prevail when the fluid medium flows at low velocities over small bodies or when the fluid has a relatively high viscosity. If the submerged body is a sphere, then the fluid streamlines of flow will appear as in Figure 1-10. In laminar flow, a well-defined boundary layer forms around the body (Figure 1-10A), and the fluid streamlines retain their identities. The loss of energy in this

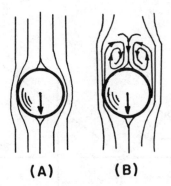

(A)   **(B)**

Figure 1-10. Illustration of flow around a solid particle: (A) laminar flow; (B) turbulent flow.

situation is due primarily to frictional drag. If the fluid's average velocity is increased sufficiently, the influence of inertia forces becomes more pronounced and the flow becomes turbulent. In this situation, *inertia forces* cause the fluid to adhere to the particle surface, forming only a very thin *boundary layer,* and generating a turbulent wake, as shown in Figure 1-10B. The pressure in the wake is significantly lower than that at the *stagnation point* on the leeward side of the particle. Hence, a net force, referred to as the *pressure drag,* acts in a direction opposite to that of the fluid's motion. Above a certain value of the Reynolds number, the role of pressure drag becomes significant and the *friction drag* can be ignored.

The dynamics of motion of a solid spherical body immersed in a fluid can be examined independent of the nature of the forces responsible for its displacement. A moving particle immersed in a fluid (gas or liquid) experiences forces caused by the action of the fluid. These forces are the same whether the particle is moving through the fluid or whether the fluid is moving over the particle's surface. Consequently, in the foregoing discussion consider the fluid to be in motion with respect to a stationary spherical body. The fluid shock acting against the sphere's surface produces an additional pressure, P. This pressure is responsible for the drag force, R, acting in the direction of fluid motion.

Figure 1-11 shows an infinitesimal element of the sphere's surface, dF, having a slope, α, normal to the direction of flow. The pressure resulting from the shock of the fluid against the element produces a force, $d\tau$, in the normal direction of flow. This force is equal to the product of the surface area and the additional pressure, PdF_0. The component acting in the direction of flow, dR, is equal to $d\tau \cos \alpha$. Hence, the force, R, acting over the entire surface of the sphere is:

$$R = \int PdF_0 \cos \alpha = \int PdF = PF \qquad (1-39)$$

where dF is the projection of dF_0 on the plane normal to the flow. The term F refers to a characteristic area of the particle, either the surface area or the maximum cross-sectional area perpendicular to the direction of flow.

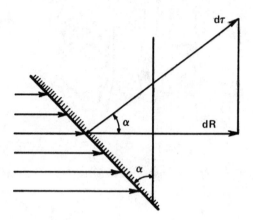

Figure 1–11. Illustration of an infinitesimal element of a sphere's surface inclined at angle α to the direction of flow.

Pressure, P (= R/F), depends on several factors, namely, the diameter of the particle, d; the fluid velocity, u; fluid density, ϱ; and fluid viscosity, μ:

$$P = f(d, u, \varrho, \mu) \tag{1-40}$$

Applying the theory of similarity, the parameters in Equation 1-40 can be transformed into the following dimensionless groups:

$$Eu = \Phi(Re) \tag{1-41}$$

where the *Euler number* is defined as $P/u^2\varrho$, and the Reynolds number is expressed in terms of the diameter of the sphere ($Re = ud\varrho/\mu$).

Substituting for density the ratio of specific gravity to the *gravitational acceleration*, an expression similar to the *Darcy-Weisbach equation* is obtained:

$$\frac{R}{F} = C_D \frac{u^2}{2g} \gamma \tag{1-42}$$

C_D is the *drag coefficient*, which is a dimensionless function of the Reynolds number.

The relationship between C_D and Re for flow around a smooth sphere is shown in Figure 1-12. The experimental curve may be approximated by three separate linear correlations, each of which covers a definite Reynolds number range, as noted by the dashed lines on the plot.

The regressed expressions corresponding to these lines and the range of the Reynolds numbers over which each applies are as follows:

For the *laminar regime* (referred to as the *Stokes' law range*):

$$C_D = \frac{24}{Re}; \text{ for Re} < 2 \tag{1-43}$$

For the intermediate (or *transition*) range:

$$C_D = \frac{18.5}{Re^{0.6}}; \text{ for } 2 < Re < 500 \tag{1-44}$$

And for the turbulent regime (or *Newton's law range*):

$$C_D = 0.44; \text{ for } 500 < Re < 200,000 \tag{1-45}$$

Thus, Equations 1-43 through 1-45 provide functional expressions for the drag coefficient over the entire practical range of Reynolds numbers which may then be used in Equation 1-42 to evaluate the drag force over a spherical particle. The literature contains an overabundance of data and information on drag coefficients for single particles of relatively simple geometries. See for examples, Brodkey,[9] Hinze,[10] Heiss and Coull,[11] and others.[12-15]

We may now direct our attention to a very practical problem of interest—that of particle free-fall behavior in an infinite expanse of stagnant fluid. If a particle of mass m and weight mg, initially at rest for time $t_1 = 0$, is allowed to fall under the action of gravity force, at some later time, t_2, the particle will accelerate to a defi-

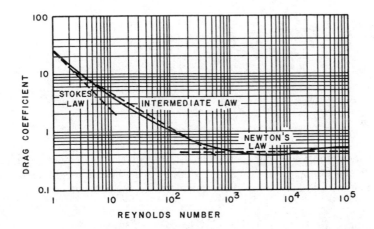

Figure 1-12. Drag coefficients for spheres.

nite value. During its downward flight the particle is subjected to the resistance of the surrounding fluid medium. This resistance increases as the particle velocity increases up to the point in time when accelerating and resisting forces are equivalent. From this point on, the particle continues to fall at a constant maximum velocity, known as the terminal velocity, u_s.

The resultant force causing the particle to fall is derived from the difference between the downward force of its own weight and the upward buoyancy force of the surrounding medium. The buoyant force is proportional to the mass of fluid displaced by the particle; that is, as the particle falls through a surrounding medium it displaces a volume of fluid equivalent to its own weight, and hence:

$$u = \frac{\pi d^3}{6} g(\varrho_p - \varrho) \tag{1-46}$$

where d = particle diameter
ϱ_p = density of the solid particle
ϱ = density of the fluid

And from Equation 1-42, the *resistance force* exerted by the fluid on a spherical particle is:

$$R = C_D \frac{\pi d^2}{4} \frac{\varrho u^2}{2} \tag{1-47}$$

The terminal *settling velocity* of the particle is reached when *accelerating* and *resisting forces* become equal:

$$\frac{\pi d^3 g}{6} (\varrho_p - \varrho) = C_D \frac{\pi d^2}{4} \frac{\varrho u^2 s}{2} \tag{1-48A}$$

Hence,

$$u_s = \left(\frac{4gd(\varrho_p - \varrho)}{3 C_D \varrho}\right)^{0.5} \tag{1-48B}$$

where the appropriate drag coefficient, C_D, can be evaluated from Equations 1-43 to 1-45. For example, for the settling velocity in the laminar regime, C_D is defined by Equation 1-43 and hence, the terminal settling velocity is:

$$u_s = \frac{d^2 g(\varrho_p - \varrho)}{18\mu} \tag{1-49}$$

where μ is the viscosity of the surrounding fluid.

The maximum particle size whose velocity follows Stokes' law can be established by substituting $\mu Re/d\varrho$ for the settling velocity in the above expression and noting Re is equal to 2. Hence, the limiting value for the laminar settling regime is:

$$d_{max} = \left(\frac{36\mu^2}{\varrho g(\varrho_p - \varrho)}\right)^{0.333} \simeq 1.56\left(\frac{\mu^2}{\varrho(\varrho_p - \varrho)}\right)^{0.333} \tag{1-50}$$

At very low Reynolds numbers, when particles tend to approach sizes comparable to the mean free path of the fluid molecules, the medium can no longer be considered as continuous. In this case, the particles fall between the fluid particles at a faster rate than predicted by the above aerodynamic analysis using standard drag coefficients. A multiplying correction factor to Stokes' law introduced by Cunningham[16] takes into account such fall between the molecules.

For Reynolds numbers close to and below 10^{-4}, the Stokes settling velocity expression Equation 1-49 takes the form:

$$u_s = C_{sc}\frac{gd_p^2(\varrho_p - \varrho)}{18\mu} \tag{1-51}$$

where C_{sc} is the Stokes-Cunningham correction factor defined as:

$$C_{sc} = \left(\frac{2A\Lambda}{d_p} + 1\right) \tag{1-52}$$

where Λ is the mean free path of the fluid molecules and A is a numerical constant given as follows:

$$A = A_o + Be^{-Dd_p/2\Lambda} \tag{1-53}$$

The experimental constants A_o, B, and D have been evaluated to be approximately 1.25, 0.42, and 1.10, respectively. An approximate value of 1.25 may be used for A for most calculations. Zenz et al.[17] note that the Stokes-Cunningham correction is less than 1% for particles larger than 16 μm falling freely in air at standard conditions.

In the intermediate Reynolds number range ($2 < Re < 500$), the settling velocity expression is similarly derived by substituting Equation 1-44 for C_D into Equation 1-48:

$$u_s \simeq 0.78\frac{d_p^{0.43}(\varrho_p - \varrho)^{0.715}}{\varrho^{0.285}\mu^{0.43}} \tag{1-54}$$

And, similarly, for the Newton's law range,

$$u_s \simeq 5.46\left(\frac{d_p(\varrho_p - \varrho)}{\varrho}\right)^{0.5} \tag{1-55}$$

Design formulas for the terminal settling velocity can be obtained by expressing u_s in terms of the Reynolds number in Equation 1-48 and raising both sides of the expression to the square power:[18]

$$\frac{Re^2\mu^2}{d_p^2\varrho^2} = \frac{4gd_p(\varrho_p - \varrho)}{3C_D\varrho} \tag{1-56}$$

Hence,

$$Re^2C_D = \frac{4}{3}\frac{d_p^3\varrho^2 g}{\mu^2}\left(\frac{\varrho_p - \varrho}{\varrho}\right) \tag{1-57}$$

The RHS of this expression is recognized as the dimensionless *Archimedes number:*

$$Ar = \frac{d_p^3\varrho^2 g}{\mu^2}\left(\frac{\varrho_p - \varrho}{\varrho}\right) \tag{1-58}$$

Note that the settling velocity does not appear in the Archimedes group. Instead, Ar is defined only in terms of the particle and fluid properties, whence:

$$C_D Re^2 = \frac{4}{3}Ar \tag{1-59}$$

Appropriate values of the critical *Archimedes number* can be computed by substituting for the critical (boundary) values of the Reynolds number corresponding to the transition from one range of settling to the other.

For the Stokes' law range ($Re < 2$), on substituting Equation 1-43 for C_D into Equation 1-59, we obtain:

$$\frac{24}{Re}Re^2 = \frac{4}{3}Ar$$

Hence,

$$Re = \frac{Ar}{18} \tag{1-60}$$

The upper limiting or critical value of the Archimedes number for this range, i.e., at $Re = 2$, is:

$$Ar_{crit1} = 18 \times 2 = 36$$

Consequently, the existence of the *laminar settling regime* corresponds to the condition $Ar < 36$. For the *intermediate range*, where $2 < Re < 500$, C_D is replaced by Equation 1-44 in Equation 1-59 to provide:

$$Re^{1.4} = \frac{4}{3}\frac{Ar}{18.5}$$

or

$$Re = 0.152 \, Ar^{0.715} \tag{1-61}$$

And for the critical value $Re = 500$, the limiting value of Ar for the intermediate range is:

$$500 = 0.152 \, Ar_{crit2}^{0.715}$$

or

$$Ar_{crit2} = 83,000$$

Thus, the intermediate settling range corresponds to a change of the Ar number in the range $36 < Ar < 83,000$. For Newton's law range, where $Ar > 83,000$, the relationship between Re and Ar may be found by substituting $C_D = 0.44$ into Equation 1-59:

$$Re = 1.74(Ar)^{0.5} \tag{1-62}$$

Evaluation of the Archimedes number establishes the settling range for particles. The Reynolds number then can be evaluated using one of the above equations (1-60, 1-61, 1-62), whence the *settling velocity* can be determined:

$$u_s = \frac{\mu Re}{d_p \varrho} \tag{1-63}$$

An interpolation formula valid for all three *settling regimes* also can be used:

$$Re = \frac{Ar}{18 + 0.575 \, (Ar)^{0.5}} \tag{1-64}$$

For low values of Ar, the second term in the denominator may be neglected, and Equation 1-64 reduces to Equation 1-60; at high Ar values the first term in the denominator can be neglected and the expression simplifies to Equation 1-62, which corresponds to the Newton's law range.

The criteria for settling can be presented in a convenient graphical form through some simple alterations of the settling formulas. Starting with Equation 1-57 which may be expressed in terms of the surrounding fluid kinematic viscosity and substituting in for the definition of the Reynolds number ($Re = ud/\nu$):

$$\frac{gd_p^3}{\nu^2}\left(\frac{\varrho_p - \varrho}{\varrho}\right) = \frac{3}{4}C_D\frac{u^2d_p^2}{\nu^2} \tag{1-65}$$

The LHS of this expression is recognized as the dimensionless Galileo number,

$$Ga = \frac{gd_p^3}{\nu^2} \tag{1-66}$$

That is:

$$Ar = Ga\frac{(\varrho_p - \varrho)}{\varrho} \tag{1-67A}$$

$$= \frac{3}{4}C_DRe^2 \tag{1-67B}$$

The Archimedes number contains parameters characterizing the properties of the gas-solid system and the criterion for defining the regime of settling. To evaluate the size of a particle having settling velocity u_s under free-fall conditions, both sides of Equation 1-67B can be multiplied through by the dimensionless complex Re/Ar:

$$\frac{Re^3}{Ar} = \frac{4}{3}\frac{Re}{C_D} \tag{1-68}$$

Denoting the dimensionless complex Re^3/Ar by K:

$$K = \frac{Re^3}{Ar} = \frac{4}{3}\frac{Re}{C_D}$$

$$= \frac{u_s^3}{g\nu}\frac{\varrho}{(\varrho_p - \varrho)} \tag{1-69}$$

$$= \frac{u_s^3\gamma^2}{\mu(\gamma_p - \gamma)g^2}$$

The dimensionless complex K along with the Reynolds number is shown plotted against the Archimedes number in Figure 1-13. The K-Re relationship is given for spheres, rounded particles, and angular-shape, elongated and platelike particles, showing a significant effect of shape on the drag. Values for the shape factor used in preparing the different curves in Figure 1-13 are 0.77 for particles of rounded shape, 0.66 for angular-shape particles, and 0.43 for platelike particles.

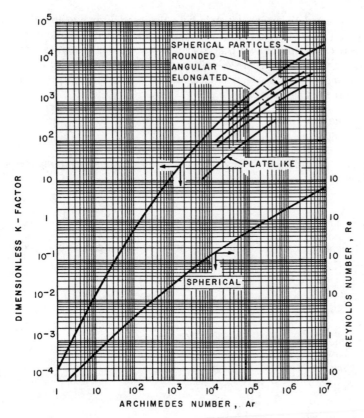

Figure 1-13. Plots of dimensionless K-factor and Reynolds number versus Archimedes number.

Particle Trajectories in Flowing Gas Streams

In dilute particle-gas flows it is of great interest to approximate the trajectories of particles. Such analyses are useful not only from an instructive point of view in understanding the hydrodynamics of particle flows, but in evaluating different methods of injection and/or the effect of equipment internals. The calculation of particle trajectories in infinite media are treated by a number of investigators (see, for example, Lapple and Shepherd,[19] and Zenz and Weil[20]). In the following discussions an analysis of one-dimensional particle motion in the absence of the gravitational field is presented. Although this is a limiting situation, predictions from such an analysis apply to very small particles, where gravity force may be neglected. At any rate, such an analysis does provide a good first approximation and theoretical starting point for the more practical considerations of choking and saltation limits.

Consider a particle injected with an initial velocity u_o normal to an upward-flowing gas stream of velocity c_o. With the injection point denoting the origin of the system, the particle will follow a trajectory with its resultant velocity at any point in time being the vector sum of the velocity components u_x and u_y (see Figure 1-14).

The component u_x has a negative acceleration, $-du_x/dt$, due to resistance. The resistance force acting on a particle of mass, m, is:

$$R = -m\frac{du_x}{dt} \tag{1-70}$$

The resistance according to Stokes' law is $R = 3\pi\mu du_x$, and assuming the particle to be spherical:

$$18\frac{\mu g}{d_p^2 \gamma_p} u_x = -\frac{du_x}{dt} \tag{1-71}$$

An analytical expression for the x-velocity component can be obtained by integrating this expression over the limits:

$$t = \left(\frac{d^2\gamma_p}{18\mu g}\right) \ln\frac{u_o}{u_x} \tag{1-72}$$

And, denoting

$$K' = \frac{18\mu g}{d_p^2\gamma_p} \tag{1-73}$$

the relationship between x and t is:

$$u_x = u_o e^{-K't} \tag{1-74}$$

Hence, the distance traveled by the particle in the x— direction is:

$$x = \int_0^t u_x dt = \int_0^t u_o e^{-K't}dt = \frac{u_o}{K'}(1 - e^{-K't}) \tag{1-75}$$

or

$$x = \frac{u_o - u_x}{K'} \tag{1-76}$$

Note that as $t \to \infty$, $u_x \to 0$ and therefore, the particle decelerates over the x-distance until the limiting value of $x_{t=\infty} = u_o/K'$ is reached. Thus for a group of particles to be distributed over the entire cross-section of the flowstream, they must be injected with an initial velocity u_o that exceeds a certain minimum value.

At the point of injection, the u_y component relative to the system boundary or equipment wall is zero. Since the velocity of the gas is c_o, the velocity of the parti-

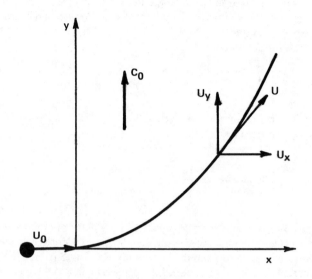

Figure 1-14. Particle injection into an upward-moving gas stream.

cle should be considered relative to that of the gas. Because of drag resistance, the particle's velocity in the y-direction will decrease gradually, and at a certain moment when the particle reaches velocity u_y (relative to the wall in the y-direction), the particle velocity relative to the gas will be $u_y - c_o$. Hence, an expression for the relative particle velocity, analogous to Equation 1-71 is:

$$K'(u_y - c_o) = - \frac{d(u_y - c_o)}{dt} \tag{1-77}$$

As c_o is constant relative to the wall, the integration of this equation provides an expression for the y-velocity component:

$$u_y = c_o(1 - e^{-K't}) \tag{1-78}$$

A second integration with respect to time over the intervals of 0 to t provides the path of the particle in the y-direction:

$$y = c_o\left[t - \frac{1}{K'}(1 - e^{-K't})\right] \tag{1-79}$$

Equation 1-79 can be used to compute the distance traveled by the particle in the direction of gas flow over time (or to compute the time needed for a particle to travel distance y in the direction of the flow). The resultant velocity of the particle is the vector sum of its components:

$$u = (u_x^2 + u_y^2)^{0.5} \tag{1-80}$$

Substituting the expression for time t (Equation 1-72) into Equation 1-79 provides an expression for particle trajectory:

$$y = \frac{c_o}{K'} \left[\ln \left(\frac{u_o}{u_o - xK'} \right) - \frac{xK'}{u_o} \right] \tag{1-81}$$

As is often the case, particles may be injected into a piece of equipment, such as a furnace or a lift line, at some angle other than 90°. Consider when the particle is injected downward at angle β from the horizontal. Sell[21] and Albrecht[22] derived the equation of motion in the $x-$ direction, i.e., perpendicular to the gas flow, for this case:

$$x = \frac{u_o \cos \beta}{K'} (1 - e^{-K't}) \tag{1-82}$$

When $t \to \infty$,

$$x_\infty = \frac{u_o \cos \beta}{K'} \tag{1-83}$$

The path along the y-direction is:

$$y = \frac{c_o}{K'} [K't - (1 - e^{-K't})] + \frac{u_o \sin \beta}{K'} (1 - e^{-K't}) \tag{1-84}$$

Eliminating $1 - e^{-K't}$ from Equation 1-84, we obtain through Equation 1-83 an expression describing the particle trajectory. The particle velocity components can be obtained by differentiating Equations 1-83 and 1-84 with respect to time.

An example of the trajectories for different-size particles is shown plotted in Figure 1-15. Note that the time required for each size particle to reach its steady-state flow condition varies significantly. Figure 1-16 shows a short computer program solving Equations 1-82 and 1-84 along with the conditions for this example. The program is suitable for quick computations on a hand calculator.

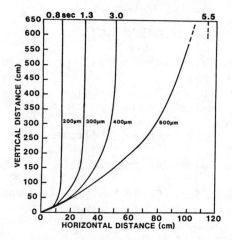

Figure 1-15. Examples of trajectories of particles injected into the upward flowing gas at a 20° angle from the horizontal.

```
5 ! PROGRAM NAME 'TRJCTRY'--IT
     CALCULATES PARTICLE TRAJEC
     TORIES
10 ! INPUT:GAS VISCOSITY-M(P).,
     PAR.DENS.-R(G/CC),GAS VEL.-C(
     CM/S)
12 ! INPUT:INIT. PART. VEL.-U0(
     CM/S),ANGLE-B(deg),PAR. DIA.
     -D(I)(CM)
20 READ M,R,C,U0,B
40 DIM D(50),T(50),X(50),Y(50)
60 D(1)=.01
80 T(1)=0
100 FOR I=1 TO 5
120 K=18*M/(R*D(I)^2)
135 D1=D(I)*10000
140 PRINT "DP(MICRONS)=",D1
150 PRINT "    X(CM)    Y(CM)
     TIME(SEC)"
160 FOR J=1 TO 15
180 A1=U0/K
200 B1=1-EXP(-K*T(J))
220 X(J)=A1*B1*COS(B)
240 Y(J)=A1*(K*T(J)-B1+B1*SIN(B)
     )
260 PRINT USING 290 ; X(J),Y(J),
     T(J)
270 T(J+1)=T(J)+.1
280 NEXT J
290 IMAGE D.DDE,2X,DD.DDE,2X,DD.
     DD
300 D(I+1)=D(I)+.005
305 PRINT
310 PRINT
320 NEXT I
340 END
360 DATA .00021   961,914,305,20
```

* Conditions for Predicted Trajectories in Figure 1-15.

Char particles injected into air at 200°F.

μ = 0.021 cp, C_o = 914 cm/s, ϱ_p = 0.961 g/cm^3, u_o = 305 cm/s, β = 20°

Figure 1-16. Computer program for evaluating particle trajectories in the absence of a gravitational field.

NOMENCLATURE

A, A_o	coefficients for Stokes-Cunningham correction factor
Ar	Archimedes number
$\bar{a}$	accelerating vector of fluctuating motion
B	coefficient for Stokes-Cunningham correction factor
b	particle width
C	slip velocity correction factor, see Equation 1-38
C_D	drag coefficient
C_{sc}	Stokes-Cunningham correction factor
c_o	gas velocity
D	coefficient for Stokes-Cunningham correction factor
D_C	diameter or characteristic dimension of equipment
$\bar{d}_p$	mean particle diameter
d_{50}	particle diameter of 50 wt % sample
d_{vs}	volume surface diameter
Eu	Euler number
F	cross-sectional area
F_{ad}	adhesion force
F_N	normal force
F_p, F_s	actual particle and sphere surface areas, respectively
F_t	force
f	coefficient of internal friction
f_1	coefficient of friction
f_σ	shear resistance coefficient
G	weight of material
Ga	Galileo number
g	gravitational acceleration
$\bar{g}$	gravitational acceleration vector
h	particle height
h_o	limiting height of vertical column of solids without retaining walls
h	size distribution constant in Rosin-Rammler distribution
$\vec{j}$	centrifugal acceleration vector
K	dimensionless complex group, see Equation 1-69
K'	group defined by Equation 1-73
K_e	experimental coefficient in Equation 1-10
K_f	fluidity coefficient
ℓ	particle length
m	particle mass
n	size or frequency of sample
n'	experimental coefficient in Equation 1-10
P	pressure
R	drag force or percent solids larger than stated particle size
R'	ratio of particle diameter to collector size
Re	Reynolds number

r	radius
r_p	particle radius
T	absolute temperature
t	time
u	velocity
u_s	terminal settling velocity
u_x, u_y	x- and y-velocity components
V	volume
V_o	solids flow velocity through an orifice
W_c	fractional moisture content with respect to bone-dry material
W	fractional moisture content
X	abscissa for Gaussian distribution, see Equation 1-28B
x	exponent or coordinate axis
Y	ordinate definition of Gaussian distribution, (see Equation 1-28A)

Greek Symbols

α	angle of internal friction or general angle
α'	dummy variable signifying parameter or diameter
α_1	angle defined in Figure 1-4.
β	angle of repose or general angle
δ_d	applied load per unit surface area
γ	specific gravity
ϵ	void fraction
η	efficiency
θ	angle of supporting surface from horizontal
Λ	mean free path of fluid molecules
μ	viscosity
ν	fluid kinematic viscosity
ν_F	dimensionless adhesion number, refer to Equation 1-15
ξ	pore volume per unit mass of solids
ϱ	density
σ	compression force
σ_s	size distribution standard deviation
τ_f	stress
τ'	loose solids discharge time through funnel
υ_r	particle relative velocity
ϕ_s	sphericity or particle shape factor
ψ	angle defined in Figure 1-6.
ψ'	dimensionless impaction number, see Equation 1-37

REFERENCES

1. Pool, K. P., B. F. Tailor, and G. P. Wall, *Trans. Inst. Chem. Eng.*, 42: 7, 8, 305 (1964).

2. Cadle, R. D., *Particle Size,* Reinhold Pub. Co., New York (1965).

3. McCrone, W. C., and J. G. Delly, *The Particle Atlas,* Vol. I-IV, Ann Arbor Science Pub., Ann Arbor, MI (1973).

4. Leva, M., et al., *Chem. Eng. Progr.,* 44: 511, 619, 707 (1948).

5. Uchida, S., and S. Fugita, *J. Chem. Soc.* (Japan) (Ind. Eng. Section), 37: 1,578, 1,583, 1,589, 1,707 (1934).

6. Shirai, T., Ph.D. Thesis, Tokyo Institute of Technology (1954).

7. Kunii, D., and O. Levenspiel, *Fluidization Engineering,* Robert E. Krieger Publishing Co., Huntington, NY (1977).

8. Shirai, T., *Fluidized Beds,* Kagaku-gijutsu-sha, Kanazawa (1958).

9. Brodkey, R. S., *The Phenomena of Fluid Motions,* Addison-Wesley Publishing Co., Reading, MA (1967).

10. Hinze, J. O., *Turbulence,* McGraw-Hill Book Co., New York (1959).

11. Heiss, J. F., and J. Coull, *Chem. Eng. Prog.,* 48: 497 (1952).

12. Pettyjohn, E. S., and S. Christiansen, *Chem. Eng. Prog.,* 44: 175 (1948).

13. Hughes, R. R., and E. R. Gilliland, *Chem. Eng. Prog.,* 48: 497 (1952).

14. Cheremisinoff, N. P., *Fluid Flow: Pumps, Pipes and Channels,* Ann Arbor Science Publishers, Ann Arbor, MI (1981).

15. Azbel, D., and N. P. Cheremisinoff, *Fluid Mechanics and Unit Operations,* Ann Arbor Science Pub., Ann Arbor, MI (1983).

16. Cunningham, E., *Proc. Roy. Soc.* (London), 83: 357 (1910).

17. Zenz, F. A., and D. F. Othmer, *Fluidization and Fluid-Particle Systems,* Reinhold Publishing Corp, New York (1960).

18. Lyachshenko, P. V., *Gravitatsionye Metody Obogachshenis,* Grostopisdat, Moscow (1940).

19a. Lapple, C. E., and C. B. Shepherd, *Ind. Eng. Chem.,* 32: 605 (1940).

19b. J. H. Perry (Ed.), *Chemical Engineer's Handbook,* 2nd Ed., McGraw-Hill Book Co., Inc., New York, (1941), p. 1,853.

20. Zenz, F. A., and N. A. Weil, *AIChE Journal,* 4: 472 (1958).

21. Sell, W., *Forsch. Geb. Ing. Wes.,* Germany (1931), p. 347

22. Albrecht, F., *Phys. Zeit,* 32: 48 (1931).

2

Flow Properties and Handling of Granular and Powdered Solids

CONTENTS

INTRODUCTION, 44

FLOW PROPERTIES MEASUREMENTS, 45

SOLIDS FLOWS FROM VESSELS, 48

Description of Flow Regimes, 48
Solids Discharge Rates, 52

GRANULAR SOLIDS FLOWS THROUGH INCLINED TUBES AND CHANNELS, 62

DESIGN OF MASS FLOW SYSTEMS, 67

Jenike Method for Mass Flow Vessels, 67
Design Guidelines for Volumetric Feeding, 69

EXPLOSION PROPERTIES OF POWDERS, 77

MECHANICAL CONSIDERATIONS IN STORAGE VESSELS, 80

NOMENCLATURE, 85

REFERENCES, 86

INTRODUCTION

The flow of granulated solids is of interest to a wide range of process operations; typical examples include moving-bed heat exchangers, shaft-type ore-roasting furnaces, a variety of solids feeders, storage and surge vessels that discharge solids to subsequent operating stages, reactor systems employing packed- and moving-bed concepts. In fluidized-bed operations, the gravity-assisted flows of unaerated solids is of importance in a variety of ancillary equipment such as standpipes, cyclone diplegs, and catalyst preparation operations that include mechanical mixing and feeding.

In Chapter 1, a brief introduction to the elements of force analysis in solids was given. Here, these introductory discussions are extended to analyzing the effects of inertia, interstitial fluid, and packing nonuniformity on granulated solids flows assisted by gravity action. Emphasis in this chapter is placed on design criteria for establishing mass flow systems and thus avoiding flow abnormalities, which disrupt operations or adversely affect the kinetics where reactions are involved.

Before proceeding to the chapter material, a review of some commonly accepted terminology is given:

Slope angle—The downward angle of slope measured in degrees from horizontal.

Archability—The tendency of a cohesive powdered or granular solid to form an arch or bridge in the hopper or silo.

Rathole—The result of material collecting on the wall of the storage container, leaving a hollow core in the center of the storage container.

Compressibility—A value arrived at by taking the difference between the aerated bulk density and the packed bulk density and dividing this difference by the packed bulk density.

Working bulk density—A value equal to the packed bulk density, minus the loose bulk density, times the compressibility plus the loose bulk density.

Angle of repose—The angle between the horizontal and the slope of a heap of material dropped from a specified elevation. For our purposes, it can be defined as the constant angle to the horizontal, assumed by a cone-like pile of material.

Angle of fall—The angle of repose resulting from a jarring effect.

Angle of difference—The value arrived at by noting the difference between the angle of repose and the angle of fall.

Dispersibility—The direct measure of the ability of a material to flood or be fluidized.

Cohesion and uniformity—Cohesion and the uniformity coefficient are alternate flow properties used in the flow evaluation. Cohesion is used with powders and very fine particles, or with materials on which an effective cohesion force can be measured. The uniformity coefficient is used for granular and powdered granular materials in which an effective surface cohesion cannot be measured.

Surface area—The surface area of a given particle.

Hygroscopicity—The tendency of a solid to pick up moisture on its surface from the ambient atmosphere; to "cake up."

FLOW PROPERTIES MEASUREMENTS

Solid matter differs from liquids and gases in that it can sustain shear stresses. The subjects of statics and dynamics of solids addresses analyses of such stresses, which obviously depend on the orientation of the plane on which they act.

Atkinson et al.[1] and Bridgwater and Scott[2] note that screening analyses of solids stresses and motion can be made by ignoring the role of interparticle distances of separation. Furthermore, fluid effects due to buoyancy and/or pressure gradients associated with fluid motion can be distinguished from the effects due to the forces between individual particles and can thus be analyzed independently.

When a sample of granular material is subjected to strain under a constant normal stress, the shear stress-strain relationship will appear as in Figure 2-1. It is found that the shear stress first increases and then decreases to an asymptotic value as

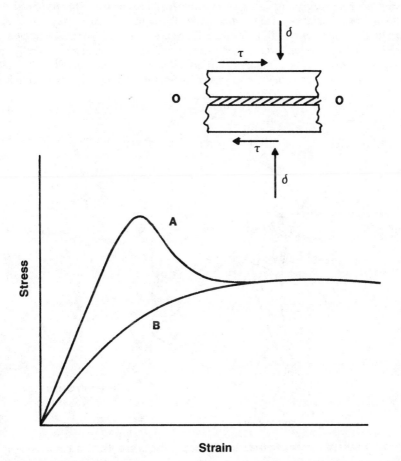

Strain

Figure 2-1. Illustration of typical shear stress (τ) / strain (σ) relations for granulated solids.

traced by curve A. When the shear stress is removed and subsequently reimposed, τ rises to its limiting value, however, the peak in the shear stress will essentially vanish as shown by curve B. Solids described as being "loosely packed" have characteristic $\tau - \sigma$ curves that follow curve B. On reaching a constant, τ, the solids develop a structure in the region of high strain, known as the *failure zone* or slip zone (0-0 in Figure 2-1). This region permits indefinite slip without the solid sample experiencing a change in volume. The specific volume of solids in regions of high strain is of prime concern in evaluating and measuring flow properties.

Figure 2-1 demonstrates that solids deform in an elastic manner when subjected to small applied shear stresses, and at some limiting value, unlimited strain takes place. Afterwards, the shear stress assumes a steady value, which may be lower than that required for the initial failure. As noted in Chapter 1, for a given specific volume, the locus of σ and τ values for initial failure is referred to as the yield locus.

A more advanced description of particulate solid behavior prior to failure is in terms of the Hvorslev failure surface and the Roscoe surface. The graphical description of these surfaces, used to characterize the failure of sands, clays, and various particulate materials is illustrated in Figure 2-2. The surfaces are shown in terms of a plot of normal stress, shear stress, and specific volume, whereby the location of the critical state line is identified. With many materials, solids will be overconsolidated (curve A in the τ vs. σ plot of Figure 2-1) and will suffer an initial

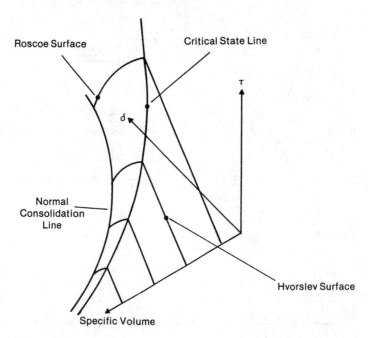

Figure 2-2. Illustration of the Hvorslev and Roscoe surfaces and the location of the critical state line.

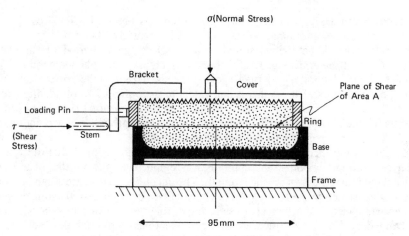

Figure 2-3. Illustration of the Jenike shear cell tester.

failure by intersection of the stress profile with the Hvorslev surface. The critical state line denotes the location of the ultimate stress and voidage state. If the internal cohesive forces of the material are sufficient to sustain tension, the Hvorslev surface will cut the plane when $\sigma = 0$ with $\tau > 0$. An introduction to critical state concepts is given by Bridgwater and Scott,[2] and detailed discussions can be found in References 1 and 3-6.

The flow properties of solids can be measured by a variety of flow property tests, such as rotational cells and annular shear cells. The measuring device most commonly used to evaluate flows from bunkers and vessels is the Jenike shear apparatus.[7] The instrument obtains the yield locus (which corresponds to a given initial value of the solids specific volume) by means of several measurements of the normal and shear stresses acting on a given plane at the time of failure. Figure 2-3 gives a cross-section view of the Jenike shear cell which consists of a split ring. The shearing imposed by the cell is translational. When a known normal force is applied, the solid material is free to expand vertically. A transducer is used to measure the applied shear force while the upper ring is removed relative to the lower at a constant speed. Schwedes[8] notes that since the shear zone is lens-shaped and does not occupy the entire cell volume, reliable measurements of the strain are not always possible.

The material in the shear zone is first brought to a reproducible voidage before evaluating a point on the yield locus. To do this, the solids sample is sheared under a specified normal stress until a constant shear stress is measured, in which case the solids can be assumed to be in a critical state. Stresses are evaluated from the measured forces by dividing them by the cell's cross-sectional area.

Once at the critical state, shearing action is stopped, a lower normal stress applied and shearing commenced until the applied shear stress either reaches a steady value or passes through a maximum. The maximum shear stress and its corresponding normal stress provide one point on the yield locus characterizing the initial critical state. From a series of successive measurements obtained using fresh, solid samples each time, additional points on the yield locus are obtained.

When powdered material is stored in a vessel for some period of time, the strength of that material is generally found to increase. This phenomenon can be simulated in the laboratory by first bringing the shear zone to the critical state and then applying a normal stress that is equivalent to the principal consolidating stress during shearing.[2] This stress level is maintained for a specified processing time, after which the sample is sheared under a lower stress to provide a new point on the yield locus, corresponding to that consolidation time.

A typical yield locus is shown in Figure 1-6. It should be noted that the Jenike shear cell can only evaluate the compressive region, even though the locus itself may extend into regions of tensile strength. The unconfined yield stress can be evaluated by constructing the Mohr's circle which passes through $\alpha = 0$ and is tangent to the yield locus. The principal stress acting during the critical state consolidation is obtained by drawing a critical Mohr's circle that passes through the coordinates of the point representing the initial consolidation procedure in the cell. Jenike[7] and Schwedes[8] provide detailed discussions of this analysis.

Recall also from Chapter 1 that the angle of internal friction can also be determined from the yield locus. The envelope of critical Mohr's circles for various initial critical states is usually a straight line and the slope of this is the tangent of the effective angle of internal friction.

By evaluating several yield loci, the unconfined yield stress can be determined as a function of the principal consolidating stress. This forms the basis for characterizing the cohesive properties of granular solids.

To properly design vessels to accommodate solids mass flow, information on the angle of internal friction between solids and vessel walls is needed. Such data can be obtained by substituting a plate of the same material as the vessel wall for the lower half of the Jenike cell. Measurements can then be made for several σ, τ values.

SOLIDS FLOWS FROM VESSELS

Description of Flow Regimes

Vessels are an integral component in any particulate handling operation, where either the solids are deposited for storage for some prespecified period of time, or the bin itself serves as part of a feeding system. As solids feeding systems, bins and hoppers should be designed for mass-flow conditions.

If the operation objective is that of controlled volumetric feeding of solids, the vessel or bin must be designed so as to promote a natural flow of the bulk material to be handled. Often in large-capacity bins, hoppers and various surge vessels employed with other equipment requiring uniform quality and/or quality of feed, the particulate material tends to segregate, causing abnormalities in the flow. In addition to uniform feeding, some processes require uniform downflow rates and/or uniform solids size distribution across the vessel's cross-section. Examples of this latter case include moving-bed cracking and adsorption systems and pebble heaters. If these characteristics are not attained, maldistributions of process fluids passing through a bed of solids and undesirable temperature gradients can result. There may be further process requirements such as an approximately uniform residence time distribution if the solids degrade with time or are undergoing reactions. In addition, the vessel must have sufficient strength to withstand the forces acting on it without the need for costly overdesign.

The basic design features of common surge vessels and storage bunkers are shown in Figure 2-4A. The vessel shown consists of an upper, parallel-sided column—the bin—and a lower convergent part—the hopper. In many designs the vessel will have a plane or an axis of symmetry and a single outlet located at the bottom of the hopper.

During the filling of bins, the solids form a cone-shaped pile as illustrated in Figure 2-4B. The apex of this cone is observed directly below the feed point and the surface of the solids forms in accordance with the material's poured angle of repose. If the solids have a wide size distribution, one observes during pouring that the smaller particles tend to remain directly below the feed point, whereas the coarser material rolls down the slope towards the base of the cone. The size of the pile will eventually be limited by the walls of the bin, and the contents of the filled bin will be very much segregated. Specifically, the center portion or core of the vessel will contain a very high percentage of the fine particulates, whereas a high concentration of the coarse particles will exist around the periphery.

Although the segregation of particles within the vessel itself may not be of importance, when the solids are discharged, the coarse and fine particles do not exit together. If the entire vessel contents are withdrawn through a single discharge orifice at the center of the hopper base, the mass of high fines concentration will flow first. Depending on the vessel geometry and actual dimensions of the filled portion of the bin, material will discharge in increasing order of coarseness or the flow will tend to fluctuate for a period of time until the vessel is nearly empty and the remaining flow will consist almost entirely of coarse particles. Figure 2-4C illustrates the nonuniformity of gravity flows for wide size-distribution solids. It should be emphasized that with this type of flow nonuniformity is strictly a result of the filling operation, and consequently any alteration in solids feeding schemes which prevents segregation will result in a more uniform mixture discharge.

The flow pattern illustrated in Figure 2-4A is characteristic of mass flow in which all of the solids are in motion and the velocity profile is approximately uniform. The flow pattern shown in Figure 2-4C is referred to as *funnel* or *core flow*. This condition is not only a result of the solids feeding arrangement but of improper vessel design as well. For example, if the vessel walls are not sufficiently smooth and steep, the solids will tend to flow in a narrow core above the outlet.

Variations in solids packing arrangements (i.e., voidage) can have a marked effect on the solids flow patterns. Uniform loading of solids into a vessel is somewhat of an art, and great deal of practical know-how resides in techniques of packing catalytic packed-bed reactors for example. Variation in the packing structure exists in vessels particularly near the wall, but this generally extends only about five particle diameters into the bulk solids. Potentially much more serious variations in specific volumes stem from the rate and speed of introduction of particles. If the load-

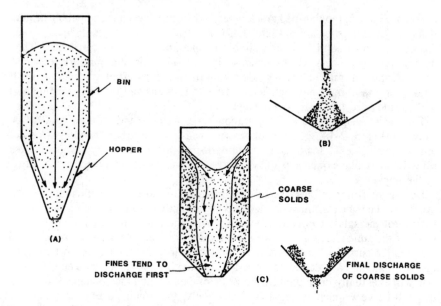

Figure 2-4. (A) Ideal mass flow from a vessel; (B) segregation of particles during filling; (C) uneven discharge of solids from a vessel.

ing rate is low, each particle can settle into a position of greatest stability on its own, but this is inhibited by particle interaction. The voidage can be influenced by loading and unloading if this occurs in a systematic manner, for example, in a vessel that is subject to pressure or temperature variations, where consolidation and increased stresses arise from fatigue or creep. These conditions can lead to particle attrition, the rupture of vessel walls, or internal failure within the solid material.

Variation in bed permeability to flow also can arise from particle segregation attributed to the development of slip zones. This leads to interparticle percolation, which involves the drainage of small particles through larger ones in regions of high strain.[9] Such a phenomenon is likely only to affect the microstructure in a vessel and will be of less importance than the phenomenon of free-surface segregation.

The consequences of the above conditions are illustrated in Figure 2-5. Figure 2-5A shows the effect of filling a vessel from a large free-fall height. In this case, smaller particles bounce to the vessel periphery. On the other hand, if the solids are deposited gently on the surface, small particles will percolate down through the layers of sliding particles and congregate in the center. During discharge, a mass flow hopper (Figure 2-5B) achieves a reasonably uniform downflow and the various fractions are discharged at the same rate, even though there will be radial inhomogeneity. With core flow (Figure 2-5C), however, the contents at the vessel center are discharged first. The discharging core is then replenished by surface layers cascading into the vessel center. Core-flow vessels thus have static regions that further promote segregation.

The various complications due to flow maldistributions attributed to variations in bed voidage are described by Craven[10] and Szekely et al.[11] As already noted, these can have marked effects on reactor yields, selectivities, and stabilities.

Other flow abnormalities encountered when vessels are improperly designed are shown in Figure 2-6. One situation is that no flow occurs upon opening of the discharge port. This condition can arise if the solids develop sufficient strength to resist the inertia forces that cause flow. Figure 2-6A shows the condition of solids arching (or bridging) in which the solids form a stable arch across the hopper. This situation can occur in either mass- or funnel-type flows. Arching can also be caused by the condition shown in Figure 2-6B known as mechanical interlocking. As a rule of thumb, interlocking can be avoided by sizing the outlet dimension to exceed ten times the maximum particle diameter.[10]

The third undesirable flow situation, shown in Figure 2-6C, is called *ratholing*. In this case, a stable empty channel is formed above the outlet. This situation is only observed in funnel flow vessels.

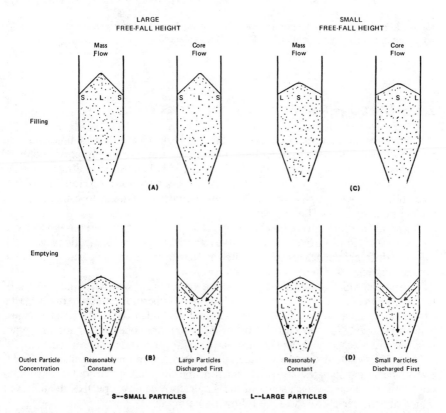

Figure 2-5. Illustration of the influence of vessel design and filling methods on particle residence time.

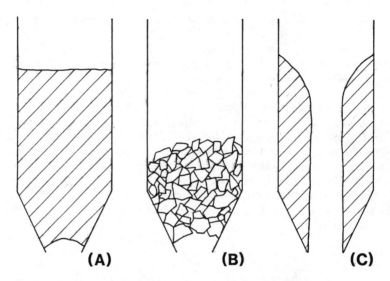

Figure 2-6. Illustration of flow abnormalities resulting from improperly designed vessels: (A) solids arching; (B) mechanical interlocking; (C) ratholing.

Solids Discharge Rates

There have been numerous studies on the rate of gravity-assisted solids discharge from cylindrical vessels, conical bins, pipes, etc. The literature reports scores of empirical correlations for granular- and powdered solids- discharge rates through various-size orifices and orifices of irregular geometry (see References 11–26). The following paragraphs summarize major studies pertaining to estimating discharge rates for mass flow vessels.

Zenz and Othmer[27] give a good review of the early literature pertaining mostly to catalyst downflows through pipes and vessels; however, no distinctions as to the effect of different particle properties such as size distribution and particle cohesiveness are given.

The rate at which solids discharge from a vessel is substantially independent of the head of the material in the vessel and its size. Futhermore, the rate of discharge of coarse granular solids appears only mildly dependent on material properties. This is not, however, the case for materials which are cohesive, or for fine powders, where a substantial dependence on physical properties is observed.

In the immediate discussions, attention is first focused on the discharge of relatively coarse particulates, to which much of the literature prior to 1960 provides correlations. Table 2-1 lists some of the major correlations reported, the terms of which are further clarified in the following paragraph.

Correlations for noncohesive, coarse particle flows were reported by Kelley,[12] Gregory,[13] Shirai,[14] Zenz,[16] and others (see Table 2-1). Kelley gave a correlation derived for bead- and pellet-catalyst flows through two-, three- and four-in. diameter orifices.

$$m_A = 0.156 \, D_o^{2.84} \tag{2-1}$$

where m_A = flow in lb/s
D_o = orifice diameter in in.

Gregory's correlation,[13] given in Table 2-1, is similar to Equation 2-1 and was developed for stick-slip downflow of powders in pipes. Gregory's studies recommended that the internal diameters of pipes exceed five to seven times the diameter of the largest particles. The study showed some dependency on particle size suggesting that the solids used were cohesive in nature. For example, he observed that materials of narrow size ranges flowed best, whereas wider size distribution solids exhibited an increasing tendency to stick to the conduit walls. In addition, fine materials less than $75\mu m$ in size were observed to have a high tendency to stick. Surface preparation and material were also seen to play a role; for example, mild steel pipe causes sticking more readily than stainless steel or glass.

Shirai[14] reported a correlation for the flow of sand, quartz, and active-earth powder:

$$m_A = \frac{0.00383 \, \varrho_b D_o^{2.5}}{(f)^{0.5}} \tag{2-2}$$

where   f = friction factor
ϱ_b = solids bulk density (lb/ft^3)

D_o is in units of inches and m_A is in lb/s.

Rausch[15] studied the flow characteristics through pipes and conical hoppers of a variety of materials that included soybeans, alumina spheres, steel ball bearings, lead shot, sand, iron powder, glass beads, and others. Rausch developed the generalized graphical correlation shown in Figure 2-7, which consists of a plot orifice diameter to particle size versus $m_A(\tan \beta)^{0.5}/C_w C_o \varrho_b (g)^{0.5} d_p$. The terms in this group are:

β = solids angle of repose in air
d_p = particle diameter
ϱ_b = solids bulk density
C_o = cone angle correction factor
C_w = wall effect correction factor

The correlation in Figure 2-7 is based on conditions in atmospheric air. For solids discharging into a medium other than air, the discharge rate obtained from the plot can be corrected using the following formula:

$$m_o = m_A \left(\frac{\tan \beta \, (1 - \varrho_o/\varrho_p)}{\tan \beta_o} \right)^{0.5} \tag{2-3}$$

Table 2-1
Correlations for Estimating Solids Discharge Rates Through Orifices

Correlation	Solids Studied	Particle Size (μ)	Orifice Diameter (in.)	Investigator
$m_A = 0.1416\, D_o^{2.96}\, H_s^{0.04}$	TCC catalytic-cracking catalyst	2,540	1–4	Newton et al.[11]
$m_A = 0.156\, D_o^{2.84}$	TCC catalytic-cracking catalyst	3,000	2–4	Kelley[12]
$m_A = 0.278\, D_o^{2.5}$	Catalyst, miscellaneous solids		1–50	Gregory[13]
$m_A = 0.00383\, \varrho_b\, D_o^{2.5}/(f)^{0.5}$	Sand, quartz, active-earth powder	100–600	0.09–0.355	Shirai[14]
$m_o = m_A\left[\dfrac{\tan\beta\,(1-\varrho_M/\varrho_P)}{\tan\beta}\right]^{0.5}$	Miscellaneous solids	127–15,000	1/16–2	Rausch[15]
$\dot{m}_A = \varrho_b(gh_w)^{0.5}/(\tan\alpha)^{0.5}$	Glass and plastic beads	540, 4,000	3/8, 2	Zenz et al.[16]
$m_A = k_1 D_o^{2.5}[f'(\tan\beta) + k_2(D_p/D_o)]$	Miscellaneous solids			Takahashi[17]
$m_A = k\varrho g^{0.5} D_o^{2.5}$	Sand and miscellaneous solids			Franklin et al.[18]

Table 2-1 (continued)
Correlations for Estimating Solids Discharge Rates Through Orifices

Correlation	Solids Studied	Particle Size (μ)	Orifice Diameter (in.)	Investigator
$m_A = \left[\dfrac{K+1}{2(2K-3)\sin\theta'}\right]\left(\dfrac{\pi}{4}\varrho g^{0.5} D_o^{2.5}\right)$	Miscellaneous solids			Savage,[19] Davidson et al.[20]
$m_A = \dfrac{1}{2(\tan\theta')^{0.5}}\left(1-\dfrac{ff}{ffa}\right)\left(\dfrac{\pi}{4}\varrho g^{0.5} D_o^{2.5}\right)$	Miscellaneous cohesive solids			Johanson[21]
$m_A = \dfrac{1}{2(\tan\theta')^{0.5}}\left(1-\dfrac{ff}{ffa}\right)^{0.5}[\varrho LB(gB)^{0.5}]$				

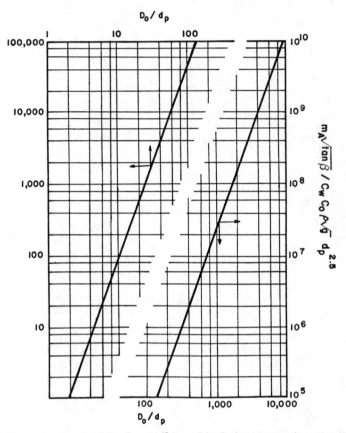

Figure 2-7. Correlation developed by Rausch[15] for solids discharge rates through orifices into the air.

where ϱ_p = particle density

ϱ_o, β_o = density of the surrounding medium and the solids angle of repose in the other medium, respectively

The wall effect correction factor, C_w, is used to adjust the bulk density. If the D_o/d_p ratio is large, the average density of particles discharging through the orifice is approximately equal to the density along the vessel axis. Zhavoronkov et al.[28] proposed the following correlation for C_w:

$$C_w = \frac{\varrho_o}{\varrho_b} = \left(\frac{n_r - 1}{n_r}\right)^2 + 0.5 \left[1 - \left(\frac{n_r - 2}{n_r}\right)^2\right]$$

$$= \frac{n_r^2 - 1}{n_r} \tag{2-4}$$

where n_r is the ratio of the orifice to particle diameter or the tube to particle diameter. Equation 2-4 is based on an infinite bed depth of spherical particles. Note that in a finite-bed depth a similar wall effect occurs at the bottom and top of the bed. The following correlation is noted by Zenz et al.[27] where the bed-height-to-bed-diameter ratio is unity:

$$C_w = \frac{\varrho_o}{\varrho_b} = \left[\frac{n_r - 1}{n_r}\right]^3 + 0.5\left[1 - \left(\frac{n_r - 2}{n_r}\right)^2\right] \qquad (2\text{-}5)$$

Equations 2-4 and 2-5 are based on the analysis of static beds of spheres and hence represent only limiting cases to the practical situation. In practice, the material passing through the orifice is in a state of motion. In addition, particle shape is known to have a dramatic wall effect.[29]

The cone angle correction factor, C_o, in Figure 2-7 is a correction for the flow rate from flat-bottomed bins to that from hoppers with inclined walls. It is a function of the angle, θ, between the inclined walls and the horizontal, and also of D_o/d_p. Figure 2-8 shows Rausch's[15] correction factor plotted against D_o/d_p with θ as a parameter. At high values of D_o/d_p, the material's angle of internal friction is more significant than the hopper slope θ.

Zenz[16] developed a correlation somewhat similar to that of Rausch for discharging into ambient air:

$$\dot{m}_A = \varrho_b (gh_w)^{0.5}/(\tan \alpha)^{0.5} \qquad (2\text{-}6)$$

where $\dot{m}_A$ = solids efflux rate (kg/s-m² of hole area)
  g = gravitational acceleration (m/s²)
  ϱ_b = solids bulk density (kg/m³)
  h_w = narrowest dimension of opening through which solids are flowing (m)
  α = bulk solids angle of internal friction.

Zenz[30] notes that in cases where the solids are large relative to the discharge opening, an area correction factor that consists of reducing the length and width or

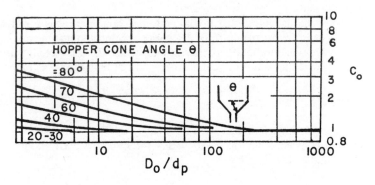

Figure 2-8. Cone angle correction factor given by Rausch.[15]

the diameter of the opening by 1.5 times the particle diameter must be applied. In a subsequent paper, Zenz et al.[31] generalized the correlation for discharge into any medium:

$$\dot{m}_A = \frac{(gh_w)^{0.5}}{(\tan \alpha)^{0.5}} \varrho_b \left(\frac{\varrho_b - \varrho_f}{\varrho_b} \right)^{0.5} \tag{2-7}$$

where ϱ_f is the density of the surrounding medium.

Takahashi[17] reports one of the earliest correlations in the following form:

$$m_A = k_1 D_o^{2.5}/(f'(\tan \beta) + k_2(d_p/D_o)) \tag{2-8}$$

where k_1, k_2 = constants dependent on the material
          $f'(\tan \beta)$ = empirical function of the angle of repose of the solids

Newton et al.[11] reported a correlation that is contrary to the majority of solids flow literature in which the head of the solids above the orifice, H_s, enters the expression:

$$m_A = 0.1416 D_o^{2.96} H_s^{0.04} \tag{2-9}$$

The units in this formula are in. for D_o, ft for H_s, and lb/s for m_A. The exponent on the head term is small and if H_s is neglected, the formula approaches that of Kelley[12] (Equation 2-1).

Most of the correlations described thus far are similar in form to that derived by Franklin and Johanson:[18]

$$m_A = k\varrho_b(g)^{0.5} D_o^{2.5} \tag{2-10}$$

where k is a constant obtained from regression analysis of the data. Correlations of this type were derived from dimensional analysis, assuming the independence of flowrate from head as previously noted.

Brown and Richards[4] found that in flat-bottomed bins there was a statistically empty annulus near the perimeter of the discharge opening and that the thickness of this annulus was related to both particle size and shape. Beverloo et al.[32] used this observation to correlate data for circular orifices in flat-bottomed bins in the form:

$$\dot{m}_A = 0.58 \varrho g^{0.5}(D_o - k'd_p)^{2.5} \tag{2-11}$$

where d_p = mean particle diameter
          k' = a constant found to be about 1.4 for spherical particles but slightly higher for sand

The units in this formula are SI.

Equation 2-11 can be restated in terms of the effective outlet cross-sectional area:

$$\dot{m}_A = 0.74 \, \varrho A_e (gD_e)^{0.5} \tag{2-12}$$

Note that subscript e refers to the fact that the statistically empty perimeter has been accounted for. This formula can be applied to outlets in flat-bottomed bins of any shape, taking D_e as the minor dimension. Brown et al.[4] notes, however, that the flowrate through elliptical and slot outlets is about 20% less than that through a circular outlet of equivalent area.

A slightly different correlation for flat-bottomed bins was developed by Harmens,[33] in which the influence of a hopper bottom is accounted for by a correction factor of $(\tan \alpha \tan \theta')^{-0.35}$, provided:

$$\theta < \frac{\pi}{2} - \alpha$$

where α is the effective angle of internal friction of the solids. Including the correction factor into Equation 2-12, the following formula is applicable to hopper bottoms:

$$\dot{m}_A = 0.74 \, (\tan \alpha \tan \theta')^{-0.35} \varrho A_e (gD_e)^{0.5} \tag{2-13}$$

Equation 2-13 can be applied with confidence to particles greater than 1 mm in size. The units in Equation 2-13 are SI.

Although the above correlations are in part derived from theoretical considerations, largely related through dimensional analysis, a more rigorous description of gravity-assisted flows is needed. Attempts have been made by various investigators (see Savage,[19] for example) to include inertia terms into models based on a force balance, from which the velocity of solids discharge can be solved for.

Consider the system shown in Figure 2-9, where solids are in uniform flow through a straight-walled converging channel. The wall friction is assumed to be negligible so that there is no variation in the θ direction. If a steep mass flow channel is assumed, then $\cos \theta' \approx 1$. For a conical channel, the equation of motion in polar coordinates for the r direction is:

$$-\frac{d\sigma_r}{dr} + 2\left(\frac{\sigma_\theta - \sigma_r}{r}\right) - \varrho g = \varrho u \frac{du}{dr} \tag{2-14}$$

where σ_r, σ_θ = stresses in the radial and tangential directions, respectively
$\quad\quad\quad u$ = velocity in r direction.

From continuity,

$$u = \frac{A^\circ}{r^2} \tag{2-15}$$

where A° is a constant.

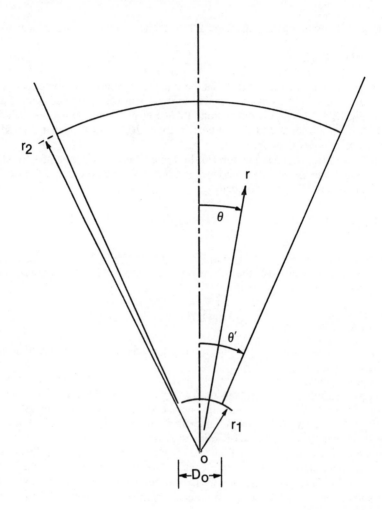

Figure 2-9. Coordinate system for flow in a converging channel as defined by Savage.[19]

Assuming the stress field in the hopper is passive, then,

$$\sigma_\theta = K\sigma_r \tag{2-16}$$

where $K = (1+\sin \alpha)/(1-\sin \alpha)$. Combining Equations 2-14 through 2-15 and integrating using the boundary conditions:

$$\sigma_r(r_1) = \sigma_r(r_2) = 0 \tag{2-17}$$

the following analytical expression for the velocity is obtained:

$$u_1 = -\left\{ \frac{(1 + K)gD_o}{2[2(K - 1) - 1]\sin\theta'}\left[\frac{1 - (r_1/r_2)^{2(K-1)-1}}{1 - (r_1/r_2)^{2(K+1)}}\right]\right\}^{0.5} \quad (2\text{-}18)$$

Equation 2-18 gives the solids velocity at the discharge opening. For a substantial head, i.e, $r_2 >> r_1$, this reduces to:

$$u_1 \doteq \left[\frac{(K + 1)gD_o}{2(2K - 3)\sin\theta'}\right]^{0.5} \quad (2\text{-}19)$$

Equation 2-19 shows the velocity to be independent of the head. Thus the mass flowrate, $\dot{m}$, is:

$$\dot{m} = \left[\frac{K + 1}{2(2K - 3)\sin\theta'}\right]^{0.5}\frac{\pi}{4}\varrho g^{0.5}D_o^{2.5} \quad (2\text{-}20)$$

Note that Equation 2-20 has the same general form of the expressions derived from dimensional analysis considerations. Note that the empty annulus concept could be introduced by replacing D_o by $(D_o - k' d)$. Savage[19] notes, however, that even with this correction the predictions of Equation 2-20 are about 50% in excess of observations. This is attributed to the neglect of wall friction and the approximation for cos θ'.

Davidson et al.[20] start from the same assumptions as Savage[19] and derive the same expression for the mass flow rate.

Williams[34] relaxed the restriction on flow being radial and imposed a finite wall friction in the model. This leads to a set of partial differential equations which must be solved numerically. Analytical solutions were however obtained along the center line and along a wall, and from these solutions upper and lower bounds on the mass flow rate were derived. The upper-bound solution reduces to Equation 2-20, if the restriction that cos $\theta' = 1$ is introduced. To account for a finite particle size, Williams introduced an effective particle diameter in which the observed flow rates of large particles from a range of hoppers fell between the upper and lower bounds that differed by only 20%.

All correlations presented thus far in this chapter apply strictly to coarse noncohesive solids. With cohesive materials, the discharge rate may be substantially less than predicted by the above formulas.

Johanson[21] derived a force balance on an arch of constant thickness at a mass flow hopper outlet. Cohesive forces were included in the analysis by assuming an unconfined yield stress, f_c, of the material to be the principal stress acting along the arch. Stress transmission from above was ignored in the analysis. Note that the value of f_c corresponds to the principal stress acting in the hopper at that point that can be estimated from the Jenike vessel design procedure.[7,10] Johanson assumed the acceleration of the arch at the outlet to be zero, and an expression for the discharge rate through a circular outlet was obtained as follows:

$$\dot{m} = \frac{1}{2 \tan^{0.5} \theta'} \left(1 - \frac{ff}{ff_a} \right)^{0.5} \frac{\pi}{4} \varrho g^{0.5} D_o^{2.5} \tag{2-21}$$

where ff is the hopper flow factor correction term, and ff_a is the ratio of the unconfined yield stress of the solids to the principal consolidating stress (f_c/σ_1), evaluated at the value of σ, acting at the hopper outlet. The estimation of these parameters is described later in this chapter.

As previously noted, the flow of fine particulates (i.e., particle sizes at and below 1 mm) appears to lie in a different regime, where the discharge rate tends to decrease with particle diameter. Bridgwater et al.[2] offers an explanation for this: In order to induce flow through an orifice, the particles must dilate. This dilation thus gives rise to a region of underpressure. In contrast, with large particles, the permeability is large and the magnitude of the underpressure is small. Since with small particles the permeability is small and the underpressure is significant, a considerable reduction in flow rate compared with coarse material is realized. Reductions on the order of 10% of the rate found for coarse materials are not uncommon. mon.

Prediction of this effect in terms of easily measurable powder flow properties is difficult, partly because the rate of voidage in the applied stresses is not well defined. Crewdson et al.[35] and Spink and Nedderman[36] have experimentally studied this phenomenon and give a theoretical analysis for axisymmetric and plane flow, respectively. The principal features of the observations were well reproduced, but quantitative agreement was only fair. Holland et al.[37] was able to predict the discharge rate in terms of the pressure gradient existing at the outlet, but in practice, this piece of information is not available.

Zenz and Othmer[27] note that by analogy to the drainage of viscous and nonviscous fluids, a reduction in the effective viscosity of a bed of solids will have the similar effect of increasing flow rate. The concept of an effective viscosity for granular solids is discussed in the next chapter. A reduction in the viscosity can be accomplished by pressurizing the vessel, either directly by means of a connection atop a closed vessel, or by the addition of aeration gas. Both methods result in higher flows with the latter technique resulting in a lubrication of the flow at the port (thus reducing the viscosity at this point).

GRANULAR SOLIDS FLOWS THROUGH INCLINED TUBES AND CHANNELS

Some introductory remarks on these practical flow situations are warranted, although more detailed design methodology is presented in Chapter 11. Information on the various factors affecting gravity flow of granular solids is essential in the design of feeding mechanisms of solids into reactors and other equipment. As noted in the previous section, several investigators[11,13-15] have reported gravity flow of solids through orifices and vertical pipes and correlated their data in the form of empirical formulations. In general, these equations are specific and contain no information on the influence of particle size, solids' angle of repose, and other physical properties.

Manchanda and Krishna[38] made an experimental study of solids flows in inclined tubes of conical funnels. The materials used in this study were close-cut fractions of spherical glass and plastic beads, and crushed sandstone and coal.

Similar observations of vertical flows were observed for the case of flows through inclined legs. That is, the effects of particle size, discharge openings, and particle density on the flow rate are similar. Figure 2-10 shows typical discharge-rate curves obtained by Manchanda et al. for both vertical and inclined tube flows. As shown, the flow rate is higher in the case of inclined tubes. They further observed that the flow rate tends to increase gradually from a 90° inclination up to

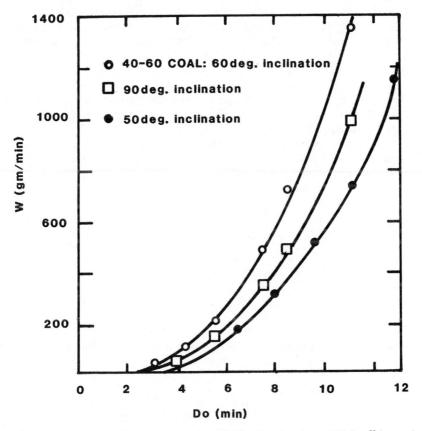

Figure 2-10. Sample discharge rate curves reported by Manchanda and Krishna[38] for vertical and inclined solids flow.

about 60°, and then decreases, dropping off to zero flow at an angle close to the materials' angle of repose. An empirical relation developed from the study for discharge rates is:

$$(m_A/\varrho_p)f' \;=\; 362 \left\{ \frac{\sin \beta - \sin \alpha}{1 - \sin \alpha} \, (D_o/d_p) \right\}^{0.545} \tag{2-22}$$

where f′ = tangent of poured angle of repose
   α = poured angle of repose
   β = angle of funnel inclination

More detailed studies of solids flows have been carried out by various workers to better define the hydrodynamics. Much of this interest has been for feed chutes, where information on the uniformity of solids feeding is of interest. Fundamental studies[39-41] have been aimed at examining the flow behavior at the solids-free surface and in defining a universal velocity profile for solids flows. Ishida and Shirai[42] studied open channel flows of solids, observing that the particle velocity was greatest at the free surface, decreased with depth, and was smallest at the channel floor. The velocity within granular layers of solids was measured using an optical fiber probe and the velocity distributions obtained and analyzed on the basis of the variational principle by comparing them with fluids. In this manner, a relationship between stress and rate of deformation for the solids flows was derived.

Figure 2-11 shows typical velocity profiles through flowing layers of glass beads reported by Ishida and Shirai:[42] The resemblance of these profiles to that observed for liquid flow is striking.

Ishida et al. note that the size of particles is much greater than that of fluid molecules but that a cluster of particles may be treated macroscopically as a continuum. This implies then that the equation of continuity and the stress equation of motion

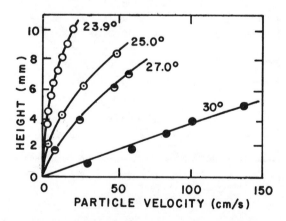

Figure 2-11. Typical velocity profiles for solids flowing down inclined channels as reported by Ishida et al.[42]

are applicable. These alone are not sufficient to describe the motion of solids under given boundary conditions. In addition, a relationship between stress and deformation is needed in order to describe the behavior of the particular matter. For a Newtonian fluid this relation exists through the consistency index (i.e., viscosity). Also, for a non-Newtonian fluid, several relations such as the Bingham model, the Ostwald-de Waale model, and the Reiner-Philipoff model describe the stress-deformation relation.

It therefore seems logical to define a relation for particle flow based on the experimental results by applying the variational principle.

The parabolic velocity distribution for a Newtonian fluid on an inclined flat plate can be obtained by finding the velocity distribution to minimize the following integral:

$$J = \int_0^H \left[\frac{\mu}{2}\left(\frac{dv_z}{dh}\right)^2 - \varrho g v_z \sin \alpha_i \right] dh \qquad (2\text{-}23)$$

The integrand consists of two energy terms: The first is the viscous dissipation $(1/2)(-\tau: \nabla v)$, and the second is the rate of work done by gravity on the volume element, ϱ (vg).

The velocity distribution to minimize the value of J can be found by Pontryagin's maximum principle[43] from which the following parabolic distribution is obtained.

$$v_z = \frac{\varrho g H^2 \sin \alpha_i}{2\mu}\left[1 - \left(\frac{y}{H}\right)^2 \right] \qquad (2\text{-}24)$$

Similarly, the velocity distribution for a Bingham fluid on an inclined flat plate can be obtained by evaluating the velocity distribution to minimize the following integral.

$$J = \int_0^H \left[\tau_B \frac{dv_z}{dh} + \frac{\mu_B}{2}\left(\frac{dv_z}{dh}\right)^2 - \varrho g v_z \sin \alpha_i \right] dh \qquad (2\text{-}25)$$

The following relation is obtained for the velocity distribution:

$$v_z = \frac{\varrho g (H - H_c)^2 \sin \alpha_i}{2\mu_B} \qquad \text{for } y < H_c \qquad (2\text{-}26\text{A})$$

$$v_z = \frac{\varrho g (H - H_c)^2 \sin \alpha_i}{2\mu_B}\left[1 - \left(\frac{y - H_c}{(H - H_c)}\right)^2 \right] \qquad \text{for } y \geq H_c \qquad (2\text{-}26\text{B})$$

where the critical thickness for a Bingham fluid is given by:

$$H_c = \tau_B/(\varrho g \sin \alpha_i) \qquad (2\text{-}27)$$

The shear stress τ_{yz} at arbitrary depth y is given by the following equation:

$$\tau_{yz} = \varrho g y \sin \alpha_i \qquad (2\text{-}28)$$

Combining Equations 2-28, 2-24, and 2-26B, the following relation between stress and rate of deformation was obtained by Ishida and coworkers:

$$\tau_{yz} = -\mu(dv_z/dy) \text{ (for a Newtonian fluid)} \tag{2-29}$$

$$\tau_{yz} = \tau_B - \mu_B(dv_z/dy) \text{ (for a Bingham fluid)} \tag{2-30}$$

The following approximate integral was proposed assuming a linear velocity distribution:

$$J = \int_0^H \left[k_\tau y \left(\frac{dv_z}{dh}\right) + \left(\frac{k_\mu y}{2}\right)\left(\frac{dv_z}{dh}\right)^2 - \varrho g v_z \sin \alpha_i \right] dh \tag{2-31}$$

$$k_\mu = \text{coefficient of apparent viscosity of particles (gm/cm}^2\text{-s)}$$

The following expression for the velocity distribution was then obtained (the complete derivation is given by Ishida et al.):

$$v_z = 0 \qquad\qquad (\text{for } \alpha_i < \alpha_{i_c}) \tag{2-32A}$$

$$v_z = \frac{\varrho g \sin \alpha_i - k_\tau}{k_\mu} (h) \text{ (for } \alpha_i \geq \alpha_{i_c}) \tag{2-32B}$$

where the critical angle of channel inclination α_{i_c} is given by:

$$\sin \alpha_{i_c} = k_\tau/(\varrho g) \tag{2-33}$$

Combining Equations 2-28 and 2-32B the following relation between stress and rate of deformation for the flow of particles on an inclined plate is obtained:

$$\tau_{yz} = k_\tau y - k_\mu y(dv_z/dy) \tag{2-34}$$

Note that Equations 2-31 and 2-34 closely resemble Equations 2-25 and 2-11 for a Bingham fluid; however, both yield stress, $k_\tau y$, and apparent viscosity, $k_\mu y$, for particles are proportional to height. This is due to the fact that buoyancy does not act in the layer of solid particles. Depth y, which is proportional to the normal stress σ, is important and gives a velocity distribution that is entirely different from that for a Bingham plastic.

For example, a Bingham fluid is capable of deformation even at a small inclination angle σ_i, when the thickness of the layer is greater than critical thickness H_c. Particles, in contrast, will remain stationary when α_i is less than the critical angle of inclination.

In practice, the critical angle of inclination approximately corresponds to the material's angle of repose. It should be noted that a plot of the velocity gradient (dv_z/dh) versus the channel slope will result in a linear relationship, the slope of which is $\varrho_b g/k\mu$. By using Equations 2-32B and 2-33 as a first-step approximation, the values of k_μ and k_τ can be evaluated for a particular solids material. These values may be considered as flow properties of each kind of particle system.

DESIGN OF MASS FLOW SYSTEMS

Jenike Method for Mass Flow Vessels

Jenike[7,10] provides a procedure for determining the proper dimensions of vessels to ensure mass flow. This method along with other analyses[44-46] are outlined by Bridgwater and Scott.[2] Jenike's method involves several steps: the determination of the solid material's flow properties by shear cell testing; evaluation of the equations for the stress and velocity fields in the vessel with attention given to the outlet region; analysis of possible obstructions to flow; and evaluation of the outlet dimension to avoid obstructions and of the wall slope required for mass flow of the solids to be handled.

The following assumptions are applied in the analysis:

1. The material is in failure everywhere—this helps to define a relationship between the stresses when the solids are in steady-state motion.
2. Density is a known function of the major principal stress—this provides equations to evaluate σ_x, σ_z, τ and ϱ.
3. Inertia terms are taken to be small and do not appear in the stress equations.
4. The velocity field is defined from continuity, and the assumption of the principle of isotropy is invoked (i.e., the directions of the principal stress and the principal rate of strain coincide). From this, two partial differential equations are obtained from which two unknown velocity components are solved for.

Jenike defines the flow factor, ff (same as appears in Johanson's[21] analysis—Equation 2-21), as the ratio of the local principal stress to the principal stress at the outlet region, $\sigma_1/\bar{\sigma}_1$. He showed that toward the apex of a converging channel, the stress field reduces to a simple form, referred to as the radial stress field. The stress in this field is proportional to the distance from the apex, r, and a geometrical parameter, s. Factor s is a function of the angular coordinate, θ, and the principal stress is defined by:

$$\sigma_1 = r\varrho g (1 + \sin \alpha)s(\theta) \tag{2-35}$$

The solutions of the radial stress field presented by Jenike are given in graphical form, whereby the allowable hopper wall angles to ensure mass flow are expressed in terms of the flow factor. Figure 2-12 shows flow factor (ff) contours for mass flow in conical hoppers (A) and in symmetrical plane flow hoppers (B) for an effective angle of internal friction of 50°. According to Jenike,[10] for plane flow, the discharge outlet should be a slot with an aspect ratio (i.e., length to width ratio) in excess of 3.

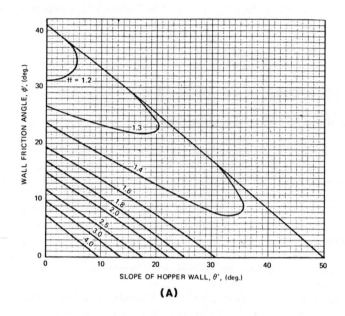

(A)

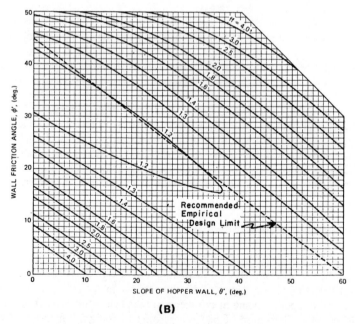

(B)

Figure 2-12. Flow factor (ff) contour maps for an effective angle of internal friction of 50° in:(A) conical hoppers; (B) symmetrical plane flow hoppers.[10]

Note that for the axisymmetric mass-flow case, the area in which the contours occur is more limited than in plane flow. In both situations, the limits on the wall friction angle, ϕ', and the slope of the hopper wall, θ', are those that allow convergence to the radial stress field in a channel where there is a slip at the walls. If combinations of ϕ' and θ' fall outside these limits, either funnel flow or no flow will occur.

Obstructions to flow are evaluated on the basis that an arch will fail if the principal stress acting on it, $\bar{\sigma}_1$, exceeds the unconfined yield strength of the solids, f_c. In the Jenike procedure, the evaluation of arching is made by plotting $\bar{\sigma}_1$ and f_c against the principal consolidating stress σ_1. This is expressed in the form of the flow function defined as:

$$FF = \sigma_1/f_c \tag{2-36}$$

Hence, both the flow factor and flow function are plotted using the same axis against the principal consolidating stress. The following criteria are given by Jenike to evaluate flow obstructions:

1. When $\bar{\sigma}_1 > f_c$ (i.e., the ff-σ_1 curve falls above the FF-σ_1 curve), the stress acting in the arch is sufficient to overcome its strength, and flow occurs.
2. When $\bar{\sigma}_1 < f_c$ (i.e., the ff-σ_1 curve falls below the FF-σ_1 curve), the stress acting in the arch is insufficient to overcome the strength, and the arch will be stable.
3. When $\bar{\sigma}_1 = f_c$ (i.e., at the intersection of the flow factor and the flow function), the arch is critical. In this case the stress acting in this critical arch is $\bar{\sigma}_{\text{crit 1}}$. This value establishes the critical outlet dimension.

The critical minimum outlet dimension is given by:

$$B_{\text{crit}} = \frac{H(\theta') - \sigma_{\text{crit1}}}{\varrho g} \tag{2-37}$$

where θ' is the inclination of the hopper wall to the vertical. Function $H(\theta')$ is given graphically by Jenike. For $\theta' = 0$, $H(\theta') = 1$ for plane flow, and for axisymmetric flow $H(\theta') = 2$. The function $H(\theta')$ is observed to increase slowly with θ'.

Equation 2-37 provides the diameter of a circular outlet for axisymmetric flow, or the width of a slot in plane flow. See Bridgwater and Scott[2] for further details on applying the procedure.

Design Guidelines for Volumetric Feeding

From the foregoing discussions it is concluded that a properly designed mass-flow bin is one where the walls of the hopper are steep and smooth enough to produce mass flow, and where the outlet is of sufficient size to prevent arching. It

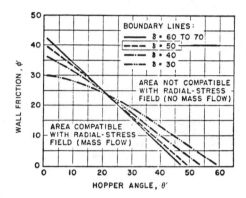

Figure 2-13. The limits for mass flow design for conical hoppers.

should be noted that the Jenike design procedure invokes several assumptions that obviously pose limitations on any design. It is therefore advisable to introduce some conservative overdesign to the system. For example, hopper walls should be at least 5° steeper than the borderline case for conical flow (Figure 2-13 shows the limits for mass-flow design for the case of conical hoppers).

Ensuring accurate discharging rates from bins and vessels not only requires an accurate sizing of the vessel, but also a well-designed feeder arrangement to the downstream end of the operation. Depending on the particular application and process requirements, feeding systems designed with mass-flow bins can discharge materials to within ± 1% accuracy. Some areas where a high degree of accuracy in discharge/feeding systems is required are in calcine and concentrate feeding,[47] mining and metallurgical applications,[48] and packaging in the food and pharmaceutical industries.[49]

Doeksen[47,50] provides several recommendations for coupling mass-flow bin and high-accuracy feeder arrangements. First, the feeder should fully activate the solids material at the outlet zone of the vessel to produce a flow that is both steady, and uniform in density. If the feeder is of the belt type, then a circular outlet as shown in Figure 2-14A is recommended. If a slotted outlet is used with a belt feeder, the outlet should be tapered (Figure 2-14B).

When handling dry, powdered materials, a vent box can be included in the feeder arrangement to eliminate minor flooding. Also, a vent pipe can alleviate air pressure buildup and permit air to flow freely in or out of the bulk material at the bin outlet. This is illustrated in Figure 2-14C.

With screw feeders circular outlets are acceptable, however, when employing a slotted outlet, a tapered screw feeder (i.e., one with increasing diameter and pitch) should be used. Doeksen[47] recommends extending the screw into the circular casing up to the feeder outlet and allowing for a one-ft spacing at the opposite end of the screw to avoid flooding conditions. A vent can also be installed in this type of feeding arrangement. Figure 2-15 shows standard feeding arrangements for dry powders.

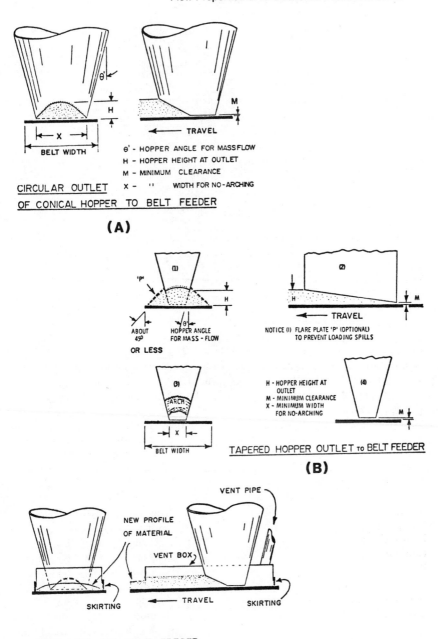

Figure 2-14. Recommended configurations for: (A) circular outlet of conical hopper to belt feeder; (B) tapered hopper outlet to belt feeder; (C) vent box on a belt feeder.

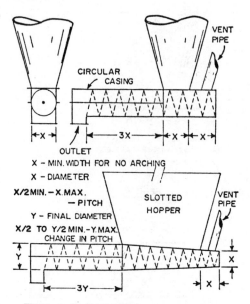

Figure 2-15. Screw feeder arrangements.

In some applications a prefeed device is required. An example of this application is when the specified feed rate requires a small feeder that is not compatible with the bin opening. A prefeed device would typically consist of a bin activator and paddle shaft, as shown in Figure 2-16. The prefeeder must be sized in excess of the critical arching dimension. When properly designed and the solids angle of repose accounted for, bin activators can be installed without connecting sleeves. Normally, minimal fugitive dust problems will occur with materials other than dry powders.

There are a wide range of materials that exhibit cohesive properties. The following are typical examples.

Potash	Hay (chopped)
Compacted garbage	Molasses (chopped)
Prepared foundry sand	Sorghum (chopped)
Limestone (powdered)	Copper ore (fine and coarse)
Rice hulls	Copper concentrate
Triple super phosphate	Wood chips
Gypsum (coarse) (dust)	Sawdust
Coffee	Wood bark
Coal	Crackling
Clay (200 mesh)	Nickel ore
Polyester floc	Sugar
Diatomaceous earth	Poultry feed (pellets)
PVC powder	Horse feed (pellets)
Calcite (moist)	Salt (granulated) (rock)

Soybean meal

Chlorinated trisodium phosphate

Cement

Meat meal

Bran

Cake flour

Alumina

Wheat middlings

Plastic chips

Lead concentrate

Filler cake (for animal feed)

Flue dust

Wheat flour

Iron ore

Oat flour

Refractory (powder)

Foam (ground)

Calcium carbonate

Ammonium hydroxide

Paper (shredded)

Some of the standard techniques used to induce mass flows in bins include vibration and aeration (i.e., air lance and continuous air flow pads). The latter approach can lead to the additional problem of transforming cohesive powders into floodable material. This can occur when the degree of aeration permeates every particle constituting the mass of solids, regardless of the particle size. This situation can lead to ratholing (Figure 2-6C) or uneven, spasmodic flows.[51] Also, when highly floodable type solids are allowed sufficient time to deaerate, particles tend to stick to each other, acquiring adhesive/cohesive characteristics.

A major problem in efficiently feeding powdered materials from hoppers is caused by the improper selection of a feeder based on volumetric throughput requirements without regard for the material flow properties. That is, a certain size

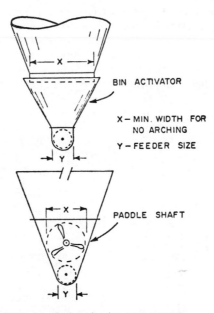

Figure 2-16. A typical prefeeder arrangement.

feeder may be adequate for the intended flow rates of the process, however, the solids may be cohesive and thus have a tendency to arch over the hopper-bottom opening. In this situation the feeder is useless. When flow-aid devices such as vibrators are used to break the arch, the material flow to the feeder may be erratic, and hence, a loss in feeding accuracy develops.

Another situation that may arise is that even if the hopper opening is of sufficient size to prevent arching, and gravity flow to the feeder is steady, the total cross-section of the material in the hopper-bottom must be "kept alive," i.e., discharged at the same time. If it is not, dead areas of material are likely to form above the feeder due to the inherent mass resistance in cohesive powders. Once this occurs, density stability in the lower hopper section becomes erratic thereby negating accurate feeding. That is, although volumetric accuracy may be maintained, accuracy by weight would vary erratically due to extreme density variations. In either case, it becomes evident that mismatches often exist between the bin and the feeder arrangement.

Conventional bin-dischargers which are designed for installation directly under the bin/hopper bottom utilize the principle of vibration throughout the entire cross-section of the hopper-bottom (and well up into the bin). Note however that the discharging flow pattern is near the periphery of the vibrating (gyrating) element and not throughout the entire cross-section of the hopper-bottom. Further, the majority of these devices do not have the capability to directly vary the flow rates. Variable speed "take-away" devices are normally used to satisfy the feeding requirement.[51]

Specially designed feeders that operate on the principle of controlled vibration have proven reasonably successful in achieving steady mass flows at good volumetric efficiencies. One design, called a "live-bottom" feeder[51] is illustrated in Figure 2-17. This design incorporates a feed-tray component which consists of narrow slots and sloping plates that resemble a louver. The louver-like arrangement is activated by a high-frequency, low-amplitude precision-tuned vibrator. When the vibrator is inactive, the solids in the bin/hopper arch over the narrow slots of the sloping plates and the flow stops. When activated, the arch is broken up by the vibrations and the material flows through the slots with controlled consistency. By

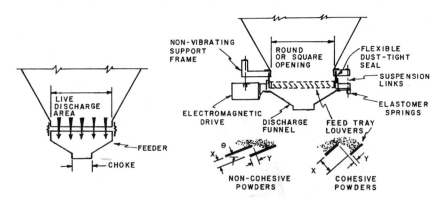

Figure 2-17. A live-bottom feeder for handling highly cohesive powders.

varying the amplitude of the feed-tray component, a controlled feed-rate change occurs. This arrangement serves a two-fold purpose; first as a bin-discharger and then as a volumetric feeder. These designs have been successfully used in a variety of feeding applications, including:

- Methyldopa preblend, a highly cohesive powder with floodable properties
- Powders for coating ingot molds
- Adipic acid from silos
- Powdered soup and cookie mixes to packaging lines
- Various cohesive batters for bag-filling operations
- Detergent powders

Another approach to the problem of inducing flow of cohesive materials is the pneumatic blasting technique. Unlike vibratory devices, pneumatic blasting does not move materials exclusively through the reduction of friction. Instead, a pneumatic blast of air or appropriate inert gas shocks the mass of cohesive material, fracturing it and causing it to flow freely. This technique can be used on bulk solids sticking to the walls of hoppers, silos, or chutes, or on solids building up under screens or even on flow problems in stockpile storage.

The reliability of pneumatic blasting depends on several factors including particle size, surface area, density, hygroscopicity, and the solid's flow properties. The degree of free air flow from the device directly affects the force output of the unit as well as the velocity of the air escaping. The objective in the design is to achieve the optimum degree of velocity and force with minimum air pressure, and in most cases minimum volume. That is, the ideal design will allow a given volume of air at a given pressure to be released in the least amount of time.

Figure 2-18 illustrates the principle of pneumatic blasting. Air enters the blaster via a quick exhaust valve. Air enters a chamber and compression causes a piston to move forward and seat, and air flows through an orifice in the center of the piston, filling a chamber. To discharge the blaster, the quick exhaust valve is activated, releasing air in the chamber, which allows pressure from the chamber to force the piston back into the air space. Air in a reservoir is expelled through the discharge tube.

The quick release valve is activated by any number of control systems, (manual pneumatic, manual electric, or timed electric), and each provides features for various applications. The latter two control systems use solenoid valves to actuate the blaster system. Timed-electric systems provide complete automation; the entire system can be actuated through a relay connection sensitive to an open gate, operating feeder, or conveyor. In this case, the "timed-electric" controls operate the blaster system only upon demand of material.

In very large vessels multiple units may be required at various levels. These units can be operated in sequence. For example, the bulk solids can first be evacuated from the bin section of the vessel (Figure 2-18B) and followed by an air blast in the upper portion (Figure 2-18C). This operating scheme is often necessary due to local variations in the solid's density and cohesive properties (i.e., they tend to increase with time).

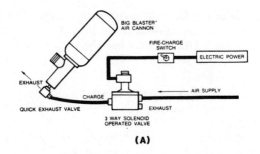

(A)

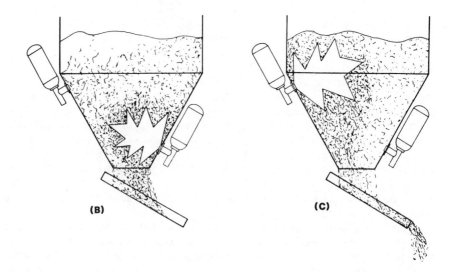

(B)   **(C)**

Figure 2-18. Illustration of the operating principle behind the pneumatic blasting technique.

An interesting approach to promoting the flow of very small particulates or powders is the addition of finely divided silicas to the solids. These are widely used in the pharmaceutical industry, for example, where flow agents promote the flow of powders through the processing stages of tableting. The mechanism by which silica flow agents promote the flow of powders is not well understood, although a number of investigators[52-56] have posed explanations. Experimental studies on the collapse of powder beds undergoing gentle vibration, with and without low concentrations of flow agent, suggest that the role of these additives is to increase interparticle friction and promote flow by preventing the collapse of a column of powder into more intimate particle-particle contacting. This results in a system having a higher transient rigidity. Cohesive powders have cohesive properties that result from the interaction of several physical mechanisms: high moisture levels; triboelectric charge effects that may initiate weak particle-particle bridging, which impedes flow; and others. Flow agents such as silica likely promote flow by absorbing excess moisture which causes liquid bridging and/or helps to dissipate triboelectric charges. In the latter case individual particles become coated with silica particles. The absorbed moisture on this monolayer of silica serves as a conducting medium on the surface of the fine particle.

There are a variety of flow agents commercially available, e.g., Cab-o-sil, a silica flow agent manufactured by the Cabot Corporation, and Aerosil by the Degussa Chemical Company. Magnesium sterate, a wax-type material, is also used as a flow-agent. Kay[57] notes, however, that this material affects the flow characteristics of fine powders in a different manner. Magnesium-stearate tends to cause particle agglomeration. Hence, the material acts as a dedusting agent and transforms the powder into a free-flowing set of large granules.

EXPLOSION PROPERTIES OF POWDERS

The combination of high concentrations of solids in air mixtures in bins, mixers, grinding operations, and pneumatic transport systems can give rise to dangerous dust fires and dust explosions. Knowledge of the conditions and criteria under which explosions might occur is a precondition for the selection of suitable prevention methods. There are basic explosion technical characteristic data for powders that need to be included in the design of handling, storage, and feeding systems. Standard procedures for obtaining such data and quantifying it in terms of particle size ranges involve igniting dust-laden air mixtures of different concentrations in standard test cells such as the Hartmann tube. In a controlled environment information on the type of dust, dust concentration, grain size distribution, vessel geometry, degree of turbulence, oxygen content, and pressure conditions leading to explosions can be quantified. Tests are normally run under a constant pressure rise up to some maximum value. This maximum value, at which an explosion will develop in a confined environment, is referred to as the rapidity of pressure rise, dP/dt. A

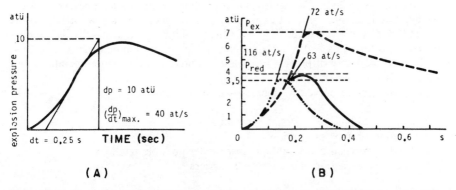

Figure 2-19. Illustration of (A) typical explosion-pressure/time-curves; (B) estimation of rapidity of pressure rise.

typical plot of explosion pressure versus time is shown in Figure 2-19. This temporal pressure rise provides a measure of the rate at which the reaction proceeds and is computed from the tangent line of maximum increase out of the quotient of the difference in pressure and difference in time.

Explosion characteristic sizes are sensitive to the grain composition, dust concentration, and the vessel's capacity. Consequently, several tests are normally required to assess explosion potential when handling a certain powder. Such tests provide an upper and lower explosion limit of stagnant explosive-dust concentrations, along with minimum values of the explosion pressure maximum.

The literature (Reference 58, for example), indicates that with the same powder, explosions proceed in vessels of different sizes with the same final pressure, but not at the same rate. Explosions will proceed more slowly in larger containers than in smaller vessels, which gives rise to the so-called cubic law of explosion pressure:

$$\left(\frac{dP}{dt}\right)_{max} V^{0.333} = K_{sT} \tag{2-38}$$

where V = vessel volume
$\quad\quad\quad K_{sT}$ = dust constant

Hence, the rate at which an explosion proceeds can be found for a specified vessel size using the value for the pressure rise (Figure 2-19B).

Industry has several procedures for testing explosion characteristics, most of which are used in conjunction with guidelines established by the Bureau of Mines. Most procedures involve various stages of testing that include a test for combustibility, an ignition test, a decomposition test, a falling weight test, and a test on dust explosion hazards.

Results of these different examinations are normally expressed by a subjective number-rating system (typically 1 to 6, where 1 characterizes the least dangerous and 6 the most dangerous step). On this basis, danger classes are identified for handling powdered materials.

Danger classes can be distinguished according to the processing operations, e.g., drying, grinding, storing, dust explosion. Each of these groups is further distinguished by degrees of danger (e.g., 0 indicates not inflammable—that is, no dust explosion; 3 indicates highly inflammable or high explosion danger).

There are a variety of preventive measures outlined for grinding operations and dilute-phase powder transport.

Common general preventive measures include:

• Avoiding dangerous material concentrations
• Avoiding sources of ignition
• Avoiding oxygen concentrations that render possible ignitions
• Special construction and protective barriers

If an explosion test indicates for example that the concentration range for an explosion of a certain powder is 70 to 100 gr/m³, the system should be so designed as to avoid those material concentrations. Often, however, because of the required fineness of materials in processing, this approach is acceptable in only a few cases. The avoiding of ignition sources is a critical safety measure, since it can be realized in a relatively simple way with most plant operations. This is done by building in safety breakers, protective sieve machines, magnets, or metal detectors in front of the operation.

Precondition for every combustion procedure and thus for every explosion, is a sufficient quantity of oxygen (i.e., air quantity). Thus, the possibility of a dust explosion can be minimized by lowering the oxygen concentration. The only exceptions are materials that split off oxygen by themselves or react with other gases. When selecting a suitable protective gas there will have to be taken into account the fact that this gas does not render possible any combustion-like reaction with the powder. Inert gases used most frequently are carbon dioxide and nitrogen as well as technically arising mixtures from both gases. Noble gases are acceptable also but generally are limited in application because of their high prices.

A major concern when planning for protective gas coating is knowing at what oxygen concentration there will be a complete inert status for a certain dust gas mixture. In general, it is sufficient to reduce the oxygen content to about 8% with exact values depending on the specific powder. Therefore, with most powders a complete extraction of oxygen is not necessary to avoid dust explosions. Further reductions of the oxygen concentration would only result in a reduction of the explosion pressure and also in a reduction of the rate of pressure rise, but this does not mean a completely inert status.

Equipment can be intentionally designed to operate and experience dust explosions, and the construction is prepared accordingly. In this respect, three designs of explosion-proof equipment are distinguished, namely, shock pressure-proof, pressure proof, and pressurized constructions. Selection and calculation of these constructions depend on the explosion technical characteristic data such as maximal explosion pressure and maximal rate of pressure rise.

In many cases the control of the maximal explosion pressure is too expensive because of corresponding constructive measures. This leaves the maximal explosion pressure of a certain dust-laden air mixture to be reduced to a still-controllable decreased pressure by means of pressure-releasing devices.

The pressure-releasing devices most often employed are safety discs and explosion flaps. Materials suitable for safety discs are plastic material foils, metal foils, paper, and pasteboard. The most important criterion of the bursting diaphragms is the minimum pressure of response i.e., the pressure at which the diaphragm bursts with slow pressure rise. It is also important that in case of an explosion the total surface of the release opening is released. Explosion flaps with weight- or spring-load have the advantage of closing automatically after an effective pressure release. Due to the revolving bearing, these flaps are subject to constant maintenance. Behind the two types of pressure-releasing devices there is required in most of the cases an escape line into the open air.

Shock pressure-proof containers must be dimensioned in such a manner as to withstand a dust explosion without bursting. Such vessels are designed to withstand constant deformations that necessitate a repair or replacement. The calculation of shock pressure-proof apparatuses is done, as far as possible, according to the calculation prescription for pressure tanks.[59] The elastic limit must be chosen for ferritic steels as admissible stress and for austenitic steels the % yield strength without safety factor must be chosen.

Pressure-proof construction is another viable approach. Vessels and equipment in this category do not provide for constant deformations. Apparatuses are designed to handle a certain fixed pressure decrease only within fixed time intervals on the basis of a specified internal test pressure.

Explosion-suppressing systems are preventive measures that attempt to alter process or storage conditions upon approaching an explosion condition. That is, the expansion of an explosion is limited, and the maximum possible explosion pressure of a certain dust-air mixture is reduced. The start of an explosion can be detected by a pressure sensor. Pressure sensors can, for example, operate a relay to signify the start of a preconditioning operation or quenching operation to alter oxygen concentrations in the vessel or operation.

MECHANICAL CONSIDERATIONS IN STORAGE VESSELS

In addition to the problems associated with potential dust explosions, vessels in which solids flow are subject to vibrations that must be accounted for in the structural design. High-frequency, low-amplitude vibrations usually pose only an annoyance to the operation; however, low-frequency, high-amplitude, irregular vibrations can damage the vessel, neighboring equipment, and connections. Vibrations are caused by two sources: the material flow itself and external sources such as feeders and conveying systems that transmit vibrations to the bin. Only remarks pertaining to the former are given in this section.

Vibrations in vessels are caused when a portion of the material expands as it flows, causing regions of low density or voids to form. This expansion region or void formation enlarges to a point where the surrounding unexpanded material becomes unstable and suddenly begins to flow or flows more rapidly than before. This action fills the void or compacts the loose material. The process then starts over as the material expands again.

There are two forms of instability that lead to vessel vibrations during solid flows. The first type of instability is related to changes in physical properties of the material such as differences in the kinematic and static coefficients of friction[60] of the material at the walls or on itself (slip stick). It is also attributed to an increase in cohesion with time, causing bridges and voids to form at the transition from the cylinder to the hopper in a storage bin;[61] or an increase in wall friction angles with time thus causing severe changes in the flow pattern.

The second type of instability is associated with the basic flow pattern limits of steady flow, such as limiting wall-friction conditions or the limited central flow channel of funnel flow bins.

In each case, unstable incipient-flow stress conditions in the non-flowing regions can arise.

Recall from earlier discussions that slip-stick flows refer to the jerky, erratic motion of certain types of solids. This is best observed when such solids are allowed to slide over a flat plate at a constant shear-strain rate. These solids exhibit a jerky motion in which the shear force rises and falls at a constant frequency between well-defined limits. Materials of this type may be quite compressible and exhibit a tendency to adhere to the plate or to different layers of the material itself. Also, relatively uniform-sized particles will show slip-stick flow when forced to move over rough or irregular surfaces. A similar flow phenomenon is observed during flows through storage vessels. As solids near the vessel walls are caught up, material furthest away continues to flow as a central core causing an expanded density region. Material at the vessel walls will suddenly be released and thus flow into the expanded region (Figure 2-4C). The resulting vibrations from such flows are usually low in amplitude and high in frequency and thus normally do not pose problems to the vessel structure.

Increased adhesion of solids to the walls or increased internal cohesion can result in the formation of large voids that subsequently collapse. This condition leads to severe shocks to the bin structure. Under the most drastic situation the top of a bin can be sucked in and severely deformed because of a sudden vacuum resulting from the failure of material into a large void. The solutions to these problems lie in changing the storage conditions or wall-friction conditions to prevent the time variations. Typical examples of precautionary measures include lowering the storage temperature; heating the walls to prevent moisture migration to the walls; periodically recycling the material to limit its stagnation time.

In a funnel-flow bin, solids tend to flow at a constant velocity through a narrow core. If the material has sufficient cohesion and the diameter of the steady flow channel is smaller than the critical rathole diameter, a stable rathole develops. If the flow channel exceeds the critical rathole diameter, then the pressures from the flowing central core decrease as the flow continues. If they decrease sufficiently or the cohesion is small enough, an incipient failure region arises near the central flow channel. This secondary region collapses suddenly as the stress level reaches incipient failure conditions. With slightly cohesive solids, a critical flow channel diameter exists for which the secondary failure will be limited to the upper part of the bin. As the flow channel increases or if the material is less cohesive, the secondary failure may occur at the bin walls and involve almost the entire mass of solids. The frequency at which such failures occur is a function of the feed rate. The amplitude of over-pressures imposed on the bin structure will depend on the density variation occurring in the central channel (before and after the secondary failure), the size of the central channel, and the amount of material involved in the secondary failure. In general, free-flowing solids with an ability to change bulk densities with rearrangement of particles tend to give significant pulsing problems in funnel-flow type bins.

Critical vessel-wall friction conditions refer to the fact that the walls of the hopper are not sufficiently steep and smooth to accommodate mass flow. They are, however, steep and smooth enough for material at the walls to become unstable under certain flow conditions. As noted earlier, flows of this type are characterized by a central steady-flow region surrounded by an unsteady region bounded by the vessel walls. Such conditions may occur in an expanded-flow bin or in a funnel-flow bin, especially if the walls are close to a mass-flow condition.

Jenike[62] has shown that when a vessel is initially filled, pressures within the hopper section are quite large and the solids can be described as being over-consolidated. When a central flow channel exists, solids expand and the pressures within the flow channel decrease, resulting in less restraining force on the region of material between the flow channel and the hopper wall. The head of material in a cylinder may become sufficient to cause this region of material to become unstable and to slip at the wall, resulting in a vibration. During the conditions of slip, the solids within the central flow channel compact and the pressures within the flow channel increase thereby stopping the slip from occurring and switching the flow back to the central channel.

Carson and Johanson[63] have analyzed this critical friction problem for the case of stable ratholing through application of the following assumptions:

1. The stresses acting on the central core flow channel are taken to be average values.

2. The central core flow channel is assumed to have a diameter, d, above which the channel opens at some angle, θ_i, which is less than the hopper slope. Note that θ_i is a function of the solids effective angle of internal friction. This assumption leads to the following stress and shear expressions:

$$\sigma_i = \frac{\varrho_b \overline{D}}{4 \sin \alpha} \tag{2-39}$$

$$\tau_i = \sigma_i \sin \alpha \tag{2-40}$$

where ϱ_b = bulk density of the solids
$\overline{D}$ = average diameter of central flowing core
α = the effective angle of internal friction

The additional stresses for the system geometry defined by Carson et al. are:

$$\sigma_v = \varrho_b h \tag{2-41A}$$

$$\sigma_\alpha = \sigma_i (1 + \sin \alpha) \tag{2-41B}$$

where the model's geometry is shown in Figure 2-20.

Equilibrium equations were written in the horizontal and vertical directions and solved for τ_c and σ_c. For flow to occur at the walls:

$$\tan \phi' = \tau_c / \sigma_c \tag{2-42}$$

where ϕ' is the angle of wall friction developed between solids and the vessel wall material. The results of this analysis are expressed in terms of a series of plots of wall friction angle versus hopper slope angles with h/D as a parameter. The vertical distance between a given solution line and the mass flow limit represents a range of ψ' values over which the vibrations can occur. A typical solution reported by Carson and Johanson is shown in Figure 2-21.

Their analysis was extended further to estimate instabilities when funnel flows extend to the cylinder walls. This condition can arise in a flat-bottom bin. Figure 2-22 shows the results of the analysis for the limiting conditions of d/D = 0.1 as a function of the effective angle of internal friction. For tall bins, the limiting effective h/D value ranges between 1 and 2. In this case, the unsteady cone angle θ_c is not sensitive to level changes in the vessel. If the level drops to approximately one vessel diameter above the discharge point, the secondary flow channel acquires a steeper angle denoted by curve A in Figure 2-22. Curve B denotes the condition for a steady flow channel. The model predictions indicate that for a very low head, the transition from steady flow to the secondary flow situation can occur for $\alpha > 31°$.

The analysis is somewhat limited in that it ignores the effects of cohesion. With cohesive solids, secondary flow is likely not to occur, or if it does, it will do so at a smaller θ_c for a given head. Consequently, the magnitude of the vibrations associated with this type of flow would be expected to be considerably less.

Analyses such as these are invaluable when sizing and designing bins. It is important to account for potential vibrations in the structural design of vessels. In terms of general guidelines, the Carson and Johanson model indicates that flow instabilities and subsequent vibrations are likely to occur with free-flowing solids characterized by low α values. With free-flowing materials in funnel-flow bins, vibrations can occur at any outlet size but are likely to be more severe with smaller outlets. In the case of cohesive materials, vibrations are likely to occur on a cyclic basis. Note, however, that massive collapses are possible, which can lead to intermittent over-pressures.

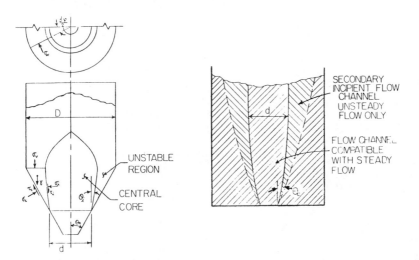

Figure 2-20. System geometry defined by the Carson and Johanson[63] rathole flow analysis.

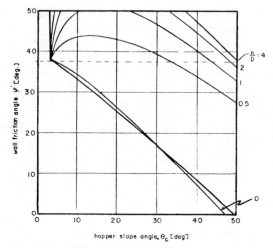

Figure 2-21. Typical solution reported by Carson and Johanson[63] for the case of α = 50° and $d/\bar{D}$ = 0.4.

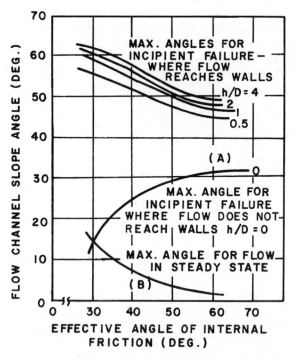

Figure 2-22. The limiting relation between θ_c, α, and h/D for d/D = 0.1 at the velocity characteristics of flow.[63]

Vessel vibrations induced by material flows can be minimized and in some cases, eliminated by designing for mass flow. The slopes of hoppers should therefore be relatively steep to assure flow throughput without material clinging to its sides.

Conical-shaped tanks instead of square or rectangular ones avoid valley angles where the material can build up to a degree that would eventually lead to a completely plugged vessel. Also, construction materials and inside "finish" must be taken into consideration to prevent hang-ups due to the inherent sliding friction between the material and the wall it slides on.

An important factor also to be considered in bin design is the potential for chemical reactions of the material. Should the material be hygroscopic in nature and allowed to sit in the vessel for prolonged periods of time, the end result would be a solidified mass. Materials of this nature should be stored in reasonably-sized bins and with the caution of not allowing the material to turn to an unmovable mass, or have its flow characteristics radically altered.

NOMENCLATURE

A	cross-sectional area
A^*	constant in Equation 2-15
B	minor dimension of outlet
C_o	cone angle correction factor
C_w	wall-effect correction factor
D_e	effective diameter of outlet
D_o	orifice diameter
d_p	particle diameter
FF	flow function of solids, σ_1/f_c
f	friction factor
f'	tangent of poured angle of repose
ff	flow factor of hopper, $\sigma_1/\bar{\sigma}_1$
g	gravitational acceleration
H	solids layer height
H_s	solids head in vessel
h	height above apex of hopper or height in general
h_w	dimension of noncircular discharge opening
J	integrand of Equation 2-23
K	ratio of horizontal to vertical normal stresses
K_{st}	dust constant
k	empirical flow constant in Equation 2-10
k_1, k_2	flow constants in Equation 2-8
k'	constant in Equation 2-11
k_τ	coefficient of yield stress
k_μ	coefficient of apparent viscosity
L	length of slot

m_A, $\dot{m}_A$ mass flow rate in English and SI units, respectively

    n_r ratio of orifice to particle diameter, or ratio of tube to particle diameter

    P fluid pressure

    p local fluid pressure

    r radial coordinate

    r_1 radial position of outlet

    r_2 radial position of top surface

    S perimeter

    s geometric parameter

    t time

    u radial velocity component

    V vessel volume

    v solids layer velocity over z coordinate

    y coordinate

Greek Symbols

    α_{ic} critical angle of slide

    α poured angle of repose or inclination of slip plane to horizontal

    β angle between major principal stress and normal to hopper wall, or angle of repose

    β_o solids angle of repose in medium other than air

    θ hopper cone angle

    θ' inclination of hopper wall to vertical

    μ fluid viscosity

    ϱ_b solids bulk density

    ϱ_f fluid density

    ϱ_o density of surrounding fluid medium

    $\bar{\sigma}_1$ major principal stress acting in an arch

    $\bar{\sigma}_{crit1}$ major principal stress acting in critical arch; i.e., one that is just stable

    σ_r, σ_θ stresses in radial and tangential directions, respectively

    τ shear stress

    ϕ' wall friction angle

REFERENCES

1. Atkinson, J. H., and P. L. Bransby, "The Mechanics of Soils," *An Introduction to Critical State Soil Mechanics,* McGraw-Hill Book Co., NY (1978).

2. Bridgwater, J., and A. M. Scott, "Flow of Solids in Bunkers," in *Handbook of Fluids in Motion,* N. P. Cheremisinoff and R. Gupta (Eds.), Ann Arbor Science Pub., Ann Arbor, MI (1983), Ch. 31, pp. 807–846.

3. Scott, R. F., *Principles of Soil Mechanics* Addison-Wesley Publishing Co., Inc., Reading, MA (1963).

4. Brown, R. L., and J. C. Richards, *Principles of Powder Mechanics*, Pergamon Press, Inc., Elmsford, NY (1966).

5. Williams, J. C., and A. H. Birks, "The Comparison of the Failure Measurements of Powders with Theory," *Powder Technology*, 1:199–206 (1967).

6. Hertjes, P. M., G. K. Khoe, and D. Kuster, "A Condition Diagram for Some Noncohesive Round Glass Particles," *Powder Technology*, 21:63–71 (1978).

7. Jenike, A. W., "Gravity Flow of Bulk Solids," *Utah Eng. Expt. Station Bull.*, 108 (1961).

8. Schwedes, J., "Measurement of Powder Properties for Hopper Design," *J. Eng. Ind. Trans., ASME Ser. B.* 95:55–59 (1973).

9. Bridgwater, J., M. H. Cooke, and A. M. Scott, *Trans. Inst. Chem. Eng.*, 56:157–167 (1978).

10. Craven, P., *Brit. Chem. Eng. Symp. Ser.* 65:(S4/Q1) 1–14 (1980).

11. Szekely, J., J. W. Evans, and H. Y. Sohn, *Gas-Solid Reactions*, New York Academy of Science Press. Inc. (1976).

12. Kelley, A. E., *Petrol. Eng.*, 16:136 (1945).

13. Gregory, S. A., *J. Appl. Chem.*, 2: (suppl. issue 1): S1 (1952).

14. Shirai, T., *Chem. Eng. Japan*, 16: 86 (1952).

15. Rausch, J. M., Ph.D. Thesis, Princeton Univ. (1948).

16. Zenz, F. A., *Hydrocarbon Process.*, 54(5): 125–128 (1975).

17. Takahashi, K., *Bull. Inst. Phys. Chem. Research* (Tokyo), 12: 984 (1933).

18. Franklin, F. C., and L. N. Johanson, *Chem. Eng. Sci.* 4:119–129 (1956).

19. Savage, S. B., *Brit. J. Appl. Phys.* 16:1,885–1,888 (1965).

20. Davidson, J. F., and R. M. Nedderman, *Trans. Inst. Chem. Eng.* 51: 29–35 (1973).

21. Johanson, J. R., *J. Appl. Mech. Trans., ASME Ser. E.* 86:459–506 (1964).

22. Delaplaine, J., Ph.D. Thesis, University of Delaware (1953).

23. Deming, W. E. and A. L. Mehring, *Ind. Eng. Chem.*, 21: 661 (1929).

24. Herrmann, A., *Berghau*, (18): 75 (1953).

25. Kuwai, G., *Chem. Eng. Japan*, 17: 453 (1953).

26. Shanahan, C. E., and J. Schwarz, M.S. Thesis, Mass. Inst. Tech. (June 1954).

27. Zenz, F. A., and D. F. Othmer, *Fluidization and Fluid-Particle Systems*, Reinhold Pub. Corp., New York (1960).

28. Zhavoronkov, N. M., *Zhur. Fiz. Khim.*, 23: 342 (1949).

29. Shaffer, M. R., M.S. Thesis, Lafayette, IN, Purdue University (1953).

30. Zenz, F. A., *Hydrocarbon Process. Pet. Refiner.*, 41(2): 159–168 (1962).

31. Zenz, F. A., and F. E. Zenz, *Ind. Eng. Chem. Fund.*, 18 (4): 345–348, (1979).

32. Beverloo, W. A., H. A. Leninger, and J. van de Velde, *Chem. Eng. Sci.*, 15: 260–269 (1961).

33. Harmens, A., *Chem. Eng. Sci.*, 18: 297–306 (1963).

34. Williams, J. C., *Chem. Eng. Sci.*, 32: 247–255 (1977).

35. Crewdson, B. J., A. L. Ormond, and R. M. Nedderman, "Air-Impeded Discharge of Fine Particles from a Hopper," *Powder Technology*, 16:197–207 (1977).

36. Spink, C. D., and R. M. Nedderman, "Gravity Discharge Rate of Fine Particles from a Hopper," *Powder Technology*, 21: 245–261 (1978).

37. Holland, J. et al., "Fluid Drag Effects in the Discharge of Particles from Hoppers," *Trans. Inst. Chem. Eng.*, 47:154–159 (1969).

38. Manchanda, K. D., and N. G. Krishna, "Gravity Flow of Granular Solids Through Vertical and Inclined Tubes," in *Fluidization and Related Processes*, Symp. at the Indian Institute of Technology, Kharagpur (Jan. 6–7, 1964).

39. Ohyama, Y., *Riken Iho*, 19: 1,052 (1940).

40. Ono, E., *Ohyo Butsuri*, 36: 347 (1967).

41. Utsumi, R., and K. Ueda, *Zairgo*, 20: 773 (1971).

42. Ishida, M., and T. Shirai, *Journ. of Chem. Eng. of Japan*, 12 (1): 46–50 (1979).

43. Pontryagin, L. S., et al., *The Mathematical Theory of Optimal Processes*, Interscience Publishers, Inc., (1962).

44. Walker, D. M., *Chem. Eng. Sci.*, 21: 975–997 (1967).

45. Arnold, P. C., and A. G. McLean, "An Analytical Solution for the Stress Function at the Wall of a Converging Channel," *Powder Technology*, 13:255–260 (1976).

46. Arnold, P. C., and A. G. McLean, "Improved Analytical Flow Factors for Mass Flow Hoppers," *Powder Technology*, 15:279–281 (1976).

47. Doeksen, G., "Design of Mass Flow Systems," in *Proceedings of the First International Conference on Particle Technology*, IIT Research Inst., Chicago, IL (1973), pp 17–27.

48. Oszter, Z. F., "Comments on Specific Feeder Applications," *Canadian Mining and Metallurgical Bulletin*, (March 1966), pp. 363–377.

49. Ruf, W., "Fully Automatic Approach to Bagging Non-Fat Dry Milk and Similar Powders," in *Proceedings of International and Scientific Conf. Mngmt. Inc.*, (May 10–12, 1977), pp. 139–144.

50. Doeksen, G., *CIM Transactions*, 73: 257–266 (1970).

51. Kurylcheck, A. L., "The Application, Function and Performance of the Siletta Live-Bottom Dual-Purpose Feeder," in *Proceedings of Int'l. Powder &*

Bulk Solids Handling & Processing Conf., Rosemont, IL, Industry & Scient. Conf. Mngmt. Inc. (May 10–12, 1977).

52. Nash, J. H., G. G. Leiter and A. P. Johnson, "Effects of Antiagglomerant Agents on Physical Properties of Finely Divided Solids," *I. & E.C. Product Research and Development,* 4 (2): 140–145 (June 1965).

53. Peleg, M., C. H. Mannheim, N. Passy, "Flow Properties of Some Food Powders," *Journal of Food Science,* 38: 959–964 (1973).

54. Peleg, M., C. H. Mannheim, "Effect of Conditioners on the Flow Properties of Powdered Sucrose," *Powder Technology,* 45–50 (1973).

55. Reid, A. J., "The Effect of Flowagents on the Mechanical Properties of Powder Beds," M.Sc. Thesis, Laurentian University, Ontario, Canada (1978).

56. Kaye, B. H., R. Davies, and R. Kahrun, "An Exploration of the Use of the Instron Tester to Monitor the Structure of Powder Beds Containing Silica Flowagents," paper presented at Eighth Fineparticle Society Conference, Chicago, IL (August 18–19, 1976).

57. Kaye, B. H., "Silica Flowagents and the Movement of Powder," in *Proceedings of Int'l Powder & Bulk Solids Handling & Processing Conf.*, Rosemont, IL, Ind. & Sci. Conf. Mngmt. Inc. (May 10–12, 1977).

58. Ritter, K., "Betriebliche Massnahmen zur Verhuetung von Staubbraenden und Staubexplosionen," *Staub-Reinhalt,* Nr. 3, Maerz, Luft 31 (1971).

59. Azbel, D. and N. P. Cheremisinoff, *Chemical and Process Equipment Design: Vessel Design and Selection,* Ann Arbor Science Pub., Ann Arbor, MI (1983).

60. Wei, M. L., and J. R. Johanson, "Elimination of Vibrations in an Ore Unloading Bin," *ASME, J. Engineering Industry,* 96, Ser. B. (No. 3): 761–766 (Aug. 1974).

61. Jenike, A. W., "Load Assumptions and Distributions in Silo Design," unpublished paper presented at Norwegian Society of Chartered Engineers, Conf. on Construction of Concrete Silos, (Feb. 28–Mar. 2 1977).

62. Jenike, A. W., J. R. Johanson, and J. W. Carson, "Bin Loads–Part 2: Concepts," *ASME J., Engineering Industry,* 95, Ser. B (1): 1–5 (Feb. 1973).

63. Carson, J. W., and J. R. Johanson, "Vibrations Caused by Solids Flows in Storage Bins," in *Proceedings of Int'l Powder & Bulk Solids Handling & Processing Conf.*, Illinois, Ind. & Sci. Conf. Mngmt. Inc. (May 10–12, 1977).

3

Rheological Behavior of Fluidized Solids

CONTENTS

INTRODUCTION, 91

TRANSPORT OF POWDERED AND FLUIDIZED SOLIDS, 92

METHOD OF SIMILARITY THEORY, 100

HYDRODYNAMIC ANALOGIES TO LIQUID FLOWS, 110

APPLICATION OF FRICTION FACTOR CORRELATIONS TO SOLIDS FLOWS, 122

RHEOLOGICAL MEASUREMENTS, 127

NOMENCLATURE, 132

REFERENCES, 134

INTRODUCTION

When a bed of fine solids or powders is aerated or gently fluidized, the two-phase mixture takes on flow properties that are analogous to liquid behavior. This phenomenon is most prevalent at the uppermost bed interface where wave-like structures are observable and objects whose specific weights are less than that of the emulsion phase will float on the surface. Such observations are made in both non-bubbling or aerated solids (i.e., below minimum bubbling conditions) and in gently bubbling fluid beds.

The resemblance to liquid behavior suggests flow characteristics of fluidized solids are analogous to those of viscous liquids. That is, the flowability of aerated bulk materials might therefore be described by conventional single-phase pipe-flow correlations as related through a proper rheological description of the two-phase system. This is of practical design interest since in many fluidized-bed operations, the transfer of solids between two fluidized vessels is an indispensable process. Solids may be transferred in one of three flow regimes: pneumatic conveying, fluidized bed and moving bed. The rheological state of fluidized and semi-fluidized materials has greatest implications with the last type.

TRANSPORT OF POWDERED AND FLUIDIZED SOLIDS

One of the oldest techniques employed for the transport of fine-grained bulk material is the air slide. The operating principle involves the transfer of bulk material by vertical aeration into a condition resembling that of a liquid. This state of fluidization is achieved when the pressure of the air stream equals the pressure exerted by the bulk material on the channel base. When the channel is tilted two to six degrees from the horizontal, the bulk material will then flow gravity assisted in the desired direction as illustrated in Figure 3-1.

The range of application of air-gravity conveying of bulk materials is great, and includes most free-flowing particulates and granular bulk solids of particle sizes ranging from a few microns to several millimeters. Although it is often possible to convey slightly cohesive powders, difficulties arise with very fine materials because of interparticle forces that cause the degree of cohesiveness to become excessive. At the upper end of the size range, especially with high-density materials, air-gravity conveying tends to become uneconomical since the quantity of air required

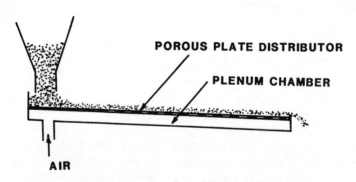

Figure 3-1. Illustration of a conventional fluidized-bed conveyor.

to maintain the flow can be large. The following is a list of typical examples of solid materials that can be handled by air-gravity conveying techniques.

Alumina	P.V.C. resin
Animal feedstuffs	Potash
Barytes	Pulverized coal
Bauxite	Pulverized fuel ash
Catalysts	Powdered ores
Cement	Rockdust
Fertilizers	Sand
Flour	Soap powder
Gypsum	Soda ash
Kiln dust	Talc

The principle of fluidization of a bed of solid particles or granules (described further in Chapter 4), is generally well known, and stages of the process may be summarized conveniently by a typical plot of the pressure drop across the bed against the superficial velocity of the fluidizing agent as shown in Figure 3-2.

As the superficial velocity, defined as the volume flow rate of fluid per unit cross-sectional area of the fluidizing vessel when empty, is gradually increased, the pressure drop across the bed increases, more or less linearly (shown by line A-B). At point B the pressure drop has become equal to the downward gravity force per unit cross-sectional area of the bed of particles, but a further slight increase (to point C) may be observed as the particles become "unlocked," and then redistribute themselves into the loosest possible packing arrangement (point D).

At still higher superficial gas velocities, ideally, no change in the pressure drop across the bed occurs as it remains fully supported, simply expanding to permit the upward passage of the larger quanity of fluid (D → E, in Figure 3-2). This behavior is normally seen in liquid fluidized beds, but where the fluidizing agent is a gas, the uniformly distributed upward flow usually degenerates into bubbles, gas "channels," or slug flows causing substantial fluctuation of the pressure drop across the bed.

The point at which the bed initially fluidizes (i.e., at the loosest possible packing arrangement) is referred to as "incipient fluidization," and the "minimum fluidizing velocity," U_{mf}, can be determined experimentally by plotting Δp against U as the superficial velocity is slowly decreased (E → D → F). For a given particulate solid the value of U_{mf} is likely to be independent of the depth of the bed as shown in Figure 3-2B. However, in deep beds there may be some variation in the measured value of U_{mf} as a result of the top layers of the bed tending to become fluidized first, while the remainder of the bed acts as an extended distributor.

Further increases in the gas superficial velocity result in a progressive expansion of the particulate bed accompanied, especially in the case of gas fluidization, by increasingly vigorous bubbling. As the superficial velocity approaches the terminal velocity of free fall (U_t) of the finer particles in the bed, these particles will tend to become entrained in the upward flowing gas. Further increases of velocity will lead eventually to a state in which the entire bed may be conveyed upwards away from the distributor.

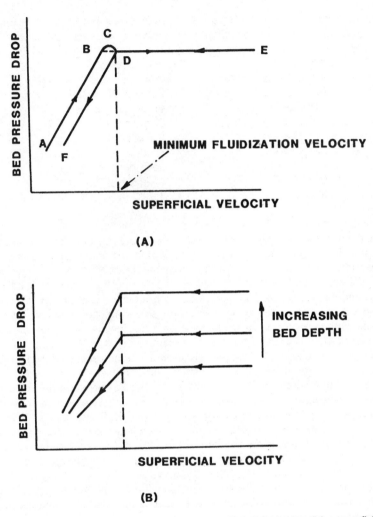

Figure 3-2. The relationship between the pressure drop across the bed and the superficial velocity of the fluidizing gas (illustration of the principle of fluidization): (A) the effect of rearrangement of particulates into the loosest possible (unfluidized) packing; (B) the effect of increasing the mass of material in the bed.

Geldart[1] has classified materials according to their fluidizing properties: materials within Group B generally fluidize well, as do those in Group A, but in the latter case there is likely to be greater expansion of the bed with increasing superficial air velocity and a relatively slow settling of the bed when the fluidizing air is shut off; Group D materials can be fluidized satisfactorily, but the larger particle size and/or high density means that much larger quantities of air are required; more cohesive powders are included in Group C. The division between Groups A and C is not distinct, but generally Group C includes very fine powders in which the interparticle forces are high, making satisfactory fluidization difficult to achieve.

Various methods of predicting the minimum fluidizing velocity and the terminal velocity of particles from a knowledge of particle properties such as size, density, and shape are discussed in the literature. Woodcock[2] recommends a convenient expression for U_{mf}, which gives a prediction that is sufficiently reliable for most applications involving particles in the size range 50 to 500 μm:

$$U_{mf} = 420 \varrho_p d_v^2 \qquad\qquad (3\text{-}1)$$

where U_{mf} is in m/s, with the particle density ϱ_p in kg/m^3, and the mean particle diameter d_v in m.

The use of a chart to show the variation of U_{mf} with ϱ_p and d_v provides a convenient means of prediction. Furthermore, the variation of the terminal velocity U_t, with ϱ_p and d_v can be shown on the same chart to give an indication of the superficial velocity at which elutriation of fines from the surface of the bed could begin to occur (see References 3-5, for examples). Figure 3-3 shows one such chart recommended by Woodcock and Mason[6] based on fluidization with ambient air, prepared from mathematical models relating U_{mf} and U_t with the size, density, and shape of the particles, as described in Reference 2. A feature of this chart is the indication of zones of behavior, based on Geldart's classification.

With this rather brief introduction to gas fluidization, it is easily understood that a fluidized powder will flow along a channel, in the manner of a liquid, provided that there is an input of energy to the powder sufficient to maintain the flow. Various methods of satisfying this energy requirement may be devised, the most obvious (and economical) being to use the potential energy of the bulk solid itself by allowing it to flow along a downward-inclined channel under the influence of gravity alone. However, this approach is limited to very free-flowing, fine granular materials.

Many solids may be fluidized at very low air velocities and pressures, and since desirable mass-flow rates are relatively high, a specific power consumption of 1 W-s/kg-m is typical for air-slide operations. This is significantly lower than the power requirements of other methods of pneumatic transport.[7,8]

A distinct advantage of air slides over mechanical conveying equipment is the simplicity in design. The basic design consists of a bipartite U-shaped channel with an inserted porous plate distributor as the base.

Isler[9] proposed the modified air slide shown in Figure 3-4. In this design the propulsion of the fluidized solids is effected by a pressure that diminishes along the length of the channel. The staggering of the pressure is accomplished by partitions in the air-supplying and air-conveying channel. The pressure build-up above the fluidized material pushes the solids into the next compartment and so forth. Stegmaier[8] reports a specific power consumption of about 2 W-s/kg-m for this design. A major drawback with this approach is that long-distance conveying is not practical since the pressure drop causes the air to expand and the dense-phase flow reverts to dilute-phase flow.

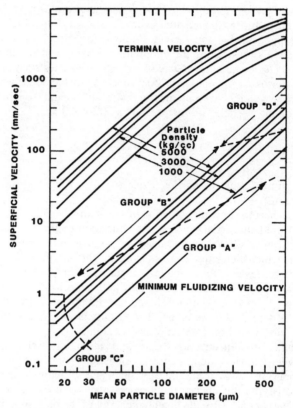

Figure 3-3. Minimum fluidizing and terminal velocities for particles fluidized by air at normal ambient conditions as recommended by Woodcock.[2,6]

Isler's proposed design is actually that of an uphill conveyor as shown in Figure 3-4B. The test channel employed in his original work was 6 m long and 250 mm wide, in which cement was satisfactorily conveyed on an upward slope of up to 12°. This pressurized design does have drawbacks; for example, the overall length is restricted, an air-lock feeder is required, and the air-control valves to the plenum compartments require careful adjustment.

A variety of other configurations have been proposed by different investigators[10,11] and Stegmaier[8] lists some of the designs from the German patents. Several configurations for horizontal transport chutes are shown in Figure 3-5. Figure 3-5A shows the "jetstream" chute proposed by Futer.[10] The base in this design consists of a perforated plate with orifices that direct the gas flow parallel to the channel floor in the direction of transport. This arrangement tends not to fluidize the solids but rather causes the material to slide on a blanket of air. The power requirements for such a design are relatively high.

Figure 3-5B shows a saw-toothed-base chute configuration. The rising portion of the conveyor base serves the purpose of fluidizing the solids. A variation of this is shown in Figure 3-5C, where the downward-sloping sections cause the material to slide off through the force of gravity. The rising sections of the base serve to lift material by air jets. The rising and sloping sections may be aerated separately.

Various investigators (for example, References 12, 13) review the main features of the various types of conveying systems used for the transport of bulk particulate solids. Clearly the air-assisted gravity conveyor has established its place among recognized methods of conveying. Probably the most important single factor in favor of air-gravity conveyors is their remarkably low energy consumption. It is not easy to make direct comparisons between the performance of various types of pneumatic and mechanical conveyors since so much depends upon the type of mate-

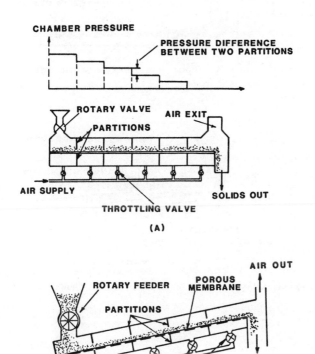

Figure 3-4. Pneumatic chute proposed by Isler:[9] (A) horizontal flow system; (B) upwardly-inclined solids flow system.

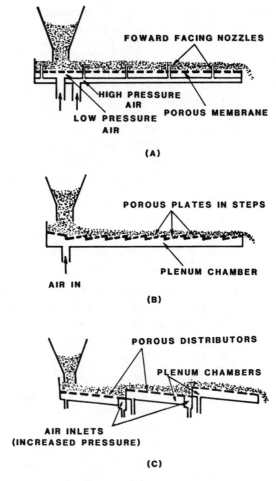

Figure 3-5. Various configurations for horizontal pneumatic chutes reported in the literature.

rial being conveyed, the distance, changes of elevation during conveying, etc. However, a few examples drawn from the published literature should serve to illustrate the kind of savings that can be made by using air-gravity conveyors in situations where other conditions are appropriate. This is shown in Figure 3-6.

Additional discussions on air-assisted gravity flows are given in References 14–18.

In addition to the operation of bulk materials conveying, fluidized-bed processes where solids are transferred as moving beds are of interest. Such processes are employed in the production of olefins from heavy oil and the gasification of organic slurries and in solid-waste handling.[19,20] Various designs and potential applications for fluidized-bed processes involving moving beds have been proposed by Kunii et al.,[19] Bailie,[21] and Engler et al.[22]

Despite the applications, understanding of the flow phenomenon in both systems is poor and design methodology for the most part is empirical. The transport of fluidized solids along horizontal and inclined channels has been investigated by Singh et al.,[23] Keunecke,[24] Muskett et al.,[25] and others.[6,26]

Chari[27] investigated the horizontal transport of four types of relatively incompressible solids: i.e., a batch of solid particles that show only a small increase in the bulk density of tapping. Trees;[28] Chen, Walawender, and Fan;[29,30] and Kunii[19] studied moving-bed flows in inclined pipes. The inclined pipes in these studies connected two fluidized beds to form a circulation system. The principal conclusion from these studies is that the friction in the pipes establishes the solids circulation rate. Chen et al.[31] also examined the influence of various operating parameters on the rate of solids transport. The parameters of study included the fluidizing gas velocity, the initial (packed-bed) height of solids, the location of the transfer line inlet, the presence of internals, and the distributor configuration. Results were interpreted quantitatively on the basis of the difference between the bulk density in the transfer line and that in the fluidized bed.

In the following discussions two generalized approaches to describing these types of flows are reviewed. The first involves an empirical approach to describing horizontal and near-horizontal fluidized-bed transport and the latter is a theoretical analysis. Scale-up methodology for such systems is also described.

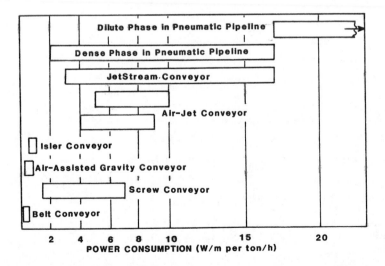

Figure 3-6. The approximate ranges of powder consumption of pneumatic conveying systems with two mechanical systems for comparison.

METHOD OF SIMILARITY THEORY

In Chapter 1 the principles of the similarity theory were alluded to in the derivation of the settling law expressions for single particles. The use of the similarity theory provides an approach to correlating important process parameters in the form of unified equations.

Although somewhat out of place in this chapter, some of the fundamental principles of the similarity theory and dimensional analysis are presented in the immediate discussions. This background information is first needed to describe the derivation of moving fluidized beds given at the end of this section, but secondly, it is needed for later discussions on experimental methods.

There are three basic methods of deriving dimensionless groups and relating them through a governing equation of the process or phenomenon. They are best illustrated by the flow system described in Chapter 1—that of steady-accelerated particle motion. Consider the governing expression for this system as follows:

$$w = w_0 + at \tag{3-2}$$

where w = velocity at time t (m/s)
$\quad\quad\;\; w_0$ = velocity at time t = 0 (m/s)
$\quad\quad\;\;\; a$ = acceleration (m/s^2)
$\quad\quad\;\;\; t$ = time from starting motion (s)

The first method involves variable transformation through the use of *scale factors*, from which we can write expressions describing two phenomena:

$$w_1 = w_{01} + a_1 t_1 \tag{3-3A}$$

$$w_2 = w_{02} + a_2 t_2 \tag{3-3B}$$

And for similarity of two phenomena we have:

$$\frac{w_1}{w_2} = C'_w, \; w_1 = C'_w w_2; \; \frac{w_{01}}{w_{02}} = C'_w, \; w_{01} = C'_w w_{02};$$

$$\frac{a_1}{a_2} = C_a, \; a_1 = C_a a_2; \; \frac{t_1}{t_2} = C_t, \; t_1 = C_t t_2$$

Substituting the new notations of w_1, w_{01}, a_1, and t_1 into the expression for the first phenomenon

$$C_w w_2 = C'_w w_{02} + C_a C_t a_2 t_2 \tag{3-4}$$

Equations 3-3A and 3-4 can coexist only under the condition of the reduction of multiples formed from factors. This is equivalent to the condition of equality in pairs:

$$C_w = C_w'$$

$$C_w = C_a C_t$$

The last condition gives two characteristic parameters that are indicators of similarity:

$$\tilde{j}' = \frac{C_w}{C_w'} = 1$$

$$\tilde{j}' = \frac{C_a C_t}{C_w'} = 1$$

In the expression for $\tilde{j}'$, C_w is related to different process velocities but it cannot be reduced.

Substituting the scale factors by the ratios of values, gives:

$$\tilde{j}' = \frac{\dfrac{w_1}{w_2}}{\dfrac{w_{01}}{w_{02}}} = 1$$

$$\frac{w_1}{w_{01}} = \frac{w_2}{w_{02}} = \text{idem}$$

Thus, the first dimensionless number is a dimensionless velocity (or in this case a relative velocity):

$$K_1 \equiv \frac{w}{w_0} \tag{3-5}$$

In the same manner the expression $\tilde{j}''$ yields the second dimensionless group:

$$\tilde{j}'' = \frac{\dfrac{a_1}{a_2}\left(\dfrac{t_1}{t_2}\right)}{\dfrac{w_{01}}{w_{02}}} = 1$$

$$\frac{a_1 t_1}{w_{01}} = \frac{a_2 t_2}{w_{02}} = \text{idem}$$

The second dimensionless number defines time similarity and is known as the criterion of *kinematic Homochronity:*

$$K_2 \equiv \frac{at}{w_0} \tag{3-6}$$

A constant-scale value, w_0, is assumed in both expressions for the dimensionless numbers. According to the terms of the initial equation, the governing relationship is:

$$\frac{w}{w_0} = f\left(\frac{at}{w_0}\right)$$

or $K_1 = f(K_2)$ \hfill (3-7)

In the second method of similarity transformation the form of this function is known.

The second method consists of dividing all terms of the homogeneous equation by one of its terms serving as a scale. In the above example the expression is divided by w_0:

$$\frac{w}{w_0} = 1 + \frac{at}{w_0}$$

Hence,

$$K_1 = \frac{w}{w_0}$$

$$K_2 = \frac{at}{w_0}$$

The form of the function thus becomes evident as:

$$K_1 = 1 + K_2 \tag{3-8}$$

The unified expression is not always as obvious as this example. More often it is a complicated function, and although simple expressions are not always attainable, the second method will at least clarify the combination of physical parameters of importance through derivation of the dimensionless numbers.

The third method consists of transforming parameters to new independent units of measurement of the physical parameters. Assume that the following explicit relationship is known a priori:

$$w = f(w_0, a, t)$$

The base units of measure are m and s, and the dependent units of measure are m/s (for velocity) and m/s² (for acceleration). Transforming to new independent units of measure, which are less by the L/T ratio, w, a, and t will be changed to:

$$w\frac{L}{T} = f\left(w_0\frac{L}{T}, a\frac{L}{T^2}, tT\right) \tag{3-9}$$

The phenomenon is independent of the units chosen for measuring specific process characteristics. Therefore, the basic equation retains its structure at different values of the coefficients L and T. The numerical values of these coefficients are so chosen to provide expressions that are simple and convenient in application. For example, L and T may be defined in terms of:

$$w_0\frac{L}{T} = 1$$

$$a = \frac{L}{T^2} = 1$$

$$tT = 1$$

Then,

$$T = \frac{1}{t}$$

$$\frac{L}{T} = \frac{1}{w_0}$$

$$\frac{L}{T^2} = \frac{1}{a}$$

$$\frac{1}{w_0} = \frac{T}{a} = \frac{1}{at}$$

$$a\frac{L}{T^2} = a\left(\frac{1}{w_0}\right)\frac{1}{T} = \frac{at}{w_0}$$

Using these definitions in Equation 3-9 gives the result obtained from the first method of transformation:

$$\frac{w}{w_0} = f\left(1, \frac{at}{w_0}, 1\right)$$

or

$$\frac{w}{w_0} = f\left(\frac{at}{w_0}\right)$$

or

$$K_1 = f(K_2)$$

The three methods illustrated are applicable provided that the equation governing the physical process is known. It is more often the situation, however, that only a qualitative description of a process is known. That is, the quantitative relationships among the different physical parameters and their forms are unknown. Then the theory of similarity helps to determine the hypothetical form and prioritizes the most important dimensionless groups. Carefully planned experiments may then be performed to validate the hypothesis. The method used to predict the form of a dimensionless number without knowledge of the basic equation is called dimensional analysis, and its application is conjugated with the *Buckingham π theorem.*

Dimensional analysis can be illustrated by starting with $w = f(w_0, a, t)$, and denoting the dimensions of the various parameters symbolically:

$$w(m/s) = LT^{-1}$$

$$w_0(m/s) = LT^{-1}$$

$$a(m/s^2) = LT^{-2}$$

$$t(s) = T$$

The dimensional equation describing the process may be assumed to have the form of a power function:

$$w = Cw_0^x a^y t^z \tag{3-10}$$

where C is the constant of the equation determined from experiments, and x,y,z are powers to be determined. Expressing the equation of dimensions in accordance with the assigned symbols:

$$LT^{-1} = C(LT^{-1})^x(LT^{-2})^yT^z$$

or

$$LT^{-1} = CL^{x+y}T^{-x-2y+z} \tag{3-11}$$

The powers of the symbols on both sides of the expression must be equal:

$$1 = x + y$$

$$-1 = x - 2y + z$$

Thus, there are two equations with three unknowns, which may be solved by inspection. Assume $z = +1$; then $x = 0$ and $y = 1$. Consequently,

$$w = Cw_0^0at + Cat$$

The dimensionless number $K_1 = w/w_0$ and w_0 result from the examination. Only one dimensionless number may be derived from the remaining physical values $-K_2 \equiv at/w$, with a variable scale w, which is undesirable in this case. Therefore, considering the second variant in Equation 3-10:

$$\frac{w}{w_0} = Ca^xt^y \tag{3-12}$$

For this equation, the formula containing dimensions is:

$$L^0T^0 = C(LT^{-2})^xT^y$$

And comparing the powers we obtain

$$0 = x;$$

$$0 = -2x + y;$$

$$y = 0$$

These conditions are possible at zero dimension of the (RHS) of the equation, which is obtained by dividing through by w_0:

$$\left(\frac{LT^{-2}T}{LT^{-1}}\right) = (LT)^0$$

Therefore,

$$\frac{w}{w_0} = C\left(\frac{at}{w_0}\right) \text{ or } K_1 = f(K_2)$$

The specific form of this function can now be determined from experiments.

The application of dimensional analysis involves the logical selection of values which results positively only if the initial set of all factors governing the process is selected properly. However, it is not always possible for a process to be analyzed thoroughly without experiments. Therefore, the possibility of overlooking a dimensionless group exists, especially from the numbers having the same name, such as $K_1 \equiv w/w_0$ (*simplex number*, differing from a *complex number* such as $K_2 \equiv at/w_0$ formed from different values). Therefore, *dimensional analysis* may be used in simple cases of generalization where there is not a large number of variables.

The Buckingham π theorem states that any dimensionally homogeneous equation connecting N physical values, the dimensions of which are expressed by n fundamental units, can be reduced to a functional relationship between π dimensionless numbers:

$$\pi = N - n \tag{3-13}$$

The number of dimensionless groups (called *simplexes*) containing π numbers is equal to the number of pairs of the same values in the basic equation. Equation 3-13 states the rule for determining the number of dimensionless groups characteristic of the process. For the above

$$N = 4(w, w_0, a, t)$$

$$n = 2(m, s)$$

Consequently, the total number of $\pi = N - n = 2$ (where $K_1 = w/w_0$; $K_2 \equiv at/w_0$. Among them, one dimensionless number is a simplex $K_1 \equiv w/w_0$ because the basic equation contains one pair of the same values w and w_0.

Thus, using the first theorem of similarity and its associated methods we obtain a definite amount of dimensionless groups, i.e., generalized process characteristics, for any basic physical equation. Among these could be simplex dimensionless numbers (so called *parametric dimensionless numbers* of a geometric or physical nature, which are relative sizes of a system reflecting similarity) and complexes (called numbers, such as the *Reynolds number, Froude number, Euler number,* etc.). Any combination of the laws of similarity (dimensionless numbers) is also a criterion of similarity. The numbers may be divided, multiplied, and/or raised to powers by each other to obtain new dimensionless groups. The transition from dimensional characteristics of a process to generalized characteristics decreases considerably the amount of variables. Further simplification may be achieved by combining dimensionless groups.

We may now direct our attention to the case of a horizontally moving fluidized bed in which one of the parameters of interest to the designer is the rate of solids throughput. The rate of flow of a bed depends on the two-phase state of the system, the hydrodynamic conditions, the geometry of the vessel, and the physical properties of both the solid material and the fluidizing medium. Figure 3-7 illustrates the system configuration.

One approach to describing this system is through a gross correlation of the hydrodynamics, where a functional relationship for the velocity of the horizontal solids flow can be expressed as follows:[32]

$$\nu_h = f(R_H, \nu_f, \varrho_s, G', \epsilon) \qquad (3\text{-}14)$$

where ν_h = velocity of horizontal flow of fluidized bed
R_H = hydraulic radius of bed material
ν_f = kinematic viscosity of fluidizing gas
ϱ_s = bulk density of solid material
ϵ = voidage of fluidized state

The mass throughput can be defined in terms of an equipment-loading parameter, which includes a characteristic dimension of the equipment. Thus G' is the mass flow rate of the solids phase per unit width of the distributor.

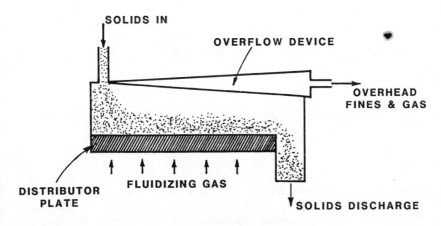

Figure 3-7. Horizontal-moving fluidized bed.

Equation 3-14 can be reduced to a dimensionless form by application of the principles of dimensional analysis previously described. Selecting the following terms as the base dimensions:

$$R_H(m), \; \nu_f(m^2/s), \; \varrho_s(kg/m^3)$$

then from the Buckingham π theorem:

$$\pi = f(1, 1, 1, \pi_1, \epsilon) \tag{3-15}$$

or

$$\frac{\nu_h}{R_H \nu_f \varrho_s} = f\left(1, 1, 1, \frac{G}{R_H{}^a \nu_f{}^b \varrho_s{}^c}, \epsilon\right) \tag{3-16}$$

By evaluating the dimensions of the numerators and denominators, the exponents are derived and the following dimensionless groups identified:
Solids-phase Reynolds number:

$$Re_{bed} = \frac{\nu_h R_H}{\nu_f} \tag{3-17}$$

Dimensionless solids loading rate:

$$K_n = \frac{G'}{\nu_f \varrho_s} \tag{3-18}$$

And hence, the functional relationship describing the horizontal motion of a fluidized bed is:

$$Re_{bed} = f(K_n, \epsilon) \tag{3-19A}$$

It is likely that this expression will take the form:

$$Re_{bed} = A' K_n{}^s \epsilon^q \tag{3-19B}$$

Verteshev et al.[32] evaluated the empirical coefficient A' and the empirical exponents s and q for various solids fluidized by water. The author also evaluated the correlation using air as the fluidizing medium in a two-dimensional horizontal moving fluid bed. The results obtained are shown in Figure 3-8 where the empirical coefficients and exponents were obtained by the method of least squares and found to be respectively: $A' = 2.5$, $s = 1$, $q = 1.2$.

In the correlation, the process parameters are defined as follows:

The hydraulic radius of the moving bed:

$$R_H = \frac{Hb}{2H + b} \qquad (3\text{-}20)$$

where H and b are the average height of the fluidized solids, and the distributor width, respectively.

The mass flow rate of the solids:

$$m = M/\tau_T \qquad (3\text{-}21)$$

The velocity of horizontal solids flow:

$$\nu_h = \frac{L_m}{M_1} \qquad (3\text{-}22)$$

where L is the length of the distributor.

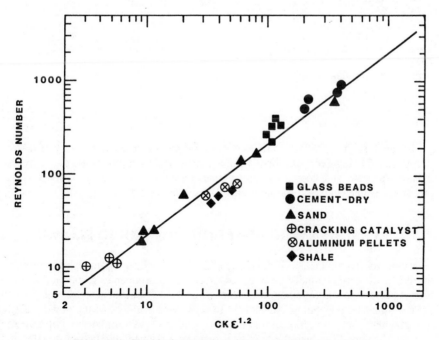

Figure 3-8. Empirical correlation of horizontal fluidized solids flow.

The void fraction of the fluid bed:

$$\epsilon = 1 - \frac{M_1}{bL\varrho_s H} \tag{3-23}$$

From these definitions we obtain an expression for the solid phase flow rate:

$$G' = \nu_h \varrho_s (1 - \epsilon) H \tag{3-24}$$

And solving for the average bed height:

$$H = \frac{b}{2} \left(\frac{1}{2.5\epsilon^{1.2}(1 - \epsilon)} - 1 \right) \tag{3-25}$$

And the velocity of horizontal motion of the fluidized solids is:

$$\nu_h = \left(\frac{5.1Q}{b^2} \right) \frac{\epsilon^{1.2}}{1 - 2.5\epsilon^{1.2}(1 - \epsilon)} \tag{3-26}$$

where Q is the volumetric flow rate of the solids ($= G'b/\varrho_s$).
Finally, the average bulk solids flow holdup in the vessel is:

For a cylindrical vessel:

$$\tau_b = \frac{\pi R_H^2 L}{\nu_f b} (1 - \epsilon) \frac{1}{K_n} \tag{3-27}$$

For a rectangular vessel:

$$\tau_b = \frac{(1 - \epsilon)}{K_n} \frac{HL}{\nu_f} \tag{3-28}$$

This analysis has produced practical expressions for describing the system flow in Figure 3-7. However, the correlation is a gross over-simplification of the hydrodynamic process and does not provide fundamental understanding. A more rigorous analysis can be based on analogies to the flow of liquids.

HYDRODYNAMIC ANALOGIES TO LIQUID FLOWS

Dry powdered material will normally slide down inclined channels provided that the slopes of these channels are in excess of about 35° (depending upon a combination of properties that together define the "flowability" of the material, and also on the roughness of the channel surfaces). To achieve flowability of the powder along the channel when the slope is much less, it is necessary either to improve the "flowability" or to reduce the frictional resistance between the bed of powder and the walls and bottom of the channel or vessel.

Supplying air to the powdered material in the channel through a porous bottom will assist the flow of various bulk particulate solids. Depending on the material, transport can take place with a downward slope of less than one degree. However, it is not clear whether this results predominantly from the air filtering through the solid particles and reducing the contact forces between them (thus causing partial fluidization) or from the formation of air layers between the bed of particles and the channel surfaces, allowing slip to take place with consequent sharp reduction of the boundary shear stresses. With fine free-flowing solids, which can easily be fluidized, the former effect is the more significant, and these materials can be conveyed satisfactorily at extremely shallow slopes. Very cohesive "sticky" materials are, generally, unsuitable for conveying in channels in this manner. However, powders that are slightly cohesive can often be transported in air-assisted gravity conveyors provided that the minimum slope of the conveying channel is greater; perhaps around 6° to 10°. Observation of such a material suggests that the particles are not fluidized, but move virtually as a solid mass sliding along the channel, and in fact the two-phase system appears homogeneous.

Table 3-1 lists various sources of experimental data on air-assisted gravity flow in inclined channels. The literature reveals only a very limited amount of information on the relationships between the solids flow rate, the slope of the channel, the superficial air velocity, and the depth of the flowing bed. In most cases information on the variation of the bed depth has not been given explicitly, and attempts should be made to deduce this, where possible, from graphical or tabulated data involving the solids mass flow rate, the breadth of the channel, and the bulk density of the suspension. This approach does of course depend upon reliable values of bulk density, and as explained later, this quantity is not always easy to determine for the flowing bed.

Several investigators[2,6,23,25,26] have attempted to describe fluidized-solids flows in horizontal and near-horizontal channels through hydrodynamic models. In these studies the two-phase system is described as being homogeneous. A generalized approach to this type of model is described in the following paragraphs.

Consider an infinitesimal slice of the homogeneous flowing material moving down an inclined channel with the coordinates defined as in Figure 3-9. Assuming the flow to be at steady-state for a specified set of conditions, the overall mechanical energy balance may be written as:

$$\Delta\left(\frac{U_m^2}{2\beta}\right) + \Delta(gy) + \int_1^2 v_f dP + \sum_1^2 F + W_f = 0 \tag{3-29}$$

where
U_m = mean velocity of homogeneous material in channel
F = work done by flow in overcoming resistance of channel
W_f = work done by flowing material
$\int v_f dP$ = an equation of state
β = a correction factor in the kinetic energy term.

For laminar flow, β has a value of 0.5. If the velocity profile is flat over the vessel cross-section, as in fully turbulent flow, β is equal to unity.

Table 3-1
Range of Various Investigators of Fluidized Solids Flows Down Inclined Channels[6]

Porous Gas Distributor	Conveying Channel Breadth (mm)	Length (m)	Material	Particle Mean Diameter (μm)	Particle Density (kg/m³)	Slope of Channel (degrees)	Solids Mass Flowrate (kg/s)	Investigator
Canvas ("thick" and "thin")	50	0.85	Sand	~200	2,700	0-15	0-0.4	Mori, Y., et al. (1955)[33]
	50	0.85	Bauxite	95	3,200	0-15	0-0.8	
	50	0.85	Alumina	35	3,900	0-15	0-0.1	
Sintered metal plate	150	2	Sand	200	2,640	1-6	0.8-4	Siemes, W.; Hellmer, L. (1962)[34]
Ceramic plates	50-100	6	"Thomas phosphate"	64	3,330	0.3-2.3	2.7-19.2	Keuneke, K., (1965)[24]
	50-100	6	Cement	15	3,000	0.9-3.2	1.4-7.4	
	75-150	6	Gypsum	12	2,500	3.4-4.0	1.0-5.0	
	50-100	6	Potash	129	2,000	0.6-2.9	1.4-10.9	
	75-100	6	"Balancer meal"	80*	1,427	2.6-4.0	1.1-4.2	
Woven cotton fabric	37-67	2.6	Sand	~180	2,650+	1.6-10.6	0-3	Harris, W. F., (1965)[35]

Table 3-1 (continued)
Range of Various Investigators of Fluidized Solids Flows Down Inclined Channels[6]

Porous Gas Distributor	Conveying Channel Breadth (mm)	Conveying Channel Length (m)	Material	Particle Mean Diameter (μm)	Particle Density (kg/m^3)	Slope of Channel (degrees)	Solids Mass Flowrate (kg/s)	Investigator
Porous plastic	84	0.18	Sand	266	2,640	0–10	0–0.6	Qassim, R. Y. (1970)[36]
Sintered plastic ("Vyon D")	75	2.4	Sand	150	2,650[+]	0–8	0–1.5	Muskett, W. J., et al. (1973)[25]
Sintered plastic ("Vyon F")	150	3	Sand	177	2,700	0–9	0–7.3	McGuigan, S. J. (1974)[37]
	150	3	Sand	177	2,700	0–9	0–7.3	McGuigan, S. J., Pugh, R. R. (1976)[38]
Ceramic filter	42	0.12	Glass beads	~210	2,520	0–15	0.03–0.16	Shinohara, K., et al. (1974)[39]
Sintered plastic ("Vyon D")	100	6	P.V.C. "Corvic"	~140	1,400	0–11	1.5–3	Woodcock, C. R., Mason, J. S. (1976, 1979)[2,6]

* Mixture of coarse particles (groats and chaff) and very fine particles (meal).
+ Approximate value (no value given in reference).

If the two-phase flow is considered as an incompressible fluid, then the terms $\int \upsilon dP$ and W_f vanish.

The following assumptions are applied in the model development for the case of steady-uniform fluidized solids flow:

1. The analogy of flow through a pipe applies.
2. The model is one-dimensional, i.e., an average velocity is assumed across the channel height.
3. The fluidized state of the solids can be related to an effective viscosity which can be predicted from a standard rheological model.

For the coordinate system defined in Figure 3-9, Equation 3-29 can be expressed in the differential form as:

$$\frac{U_m}{\beta} \frac{dU_m}{d\ell} + g\left(\sin \alpha + \frac{dH}{d\ell}\right) + \frac{dF}{d\ell} = 0 \tag{3-30}$$

where $dF/d\ell$ represents the frictional pressure losses and from assumption (1), may be approximated by the Darcy equation.

From continuity and rearranging terms, the following expression is derived for the fluidized-bed height profile for laminar flow conditions:

$$\frac{dH}{d\ell} = -\frac{\dfrac{32\mu_e U_m}{\varrho g D_H^{\,2}} + \sin \alpha}{1 - \dfrac{U_m^{\,2}}{\beta g H}} \tag{3-31}$$

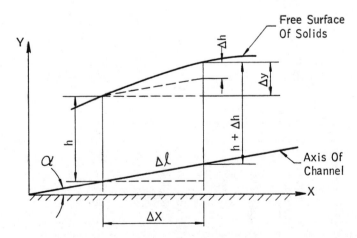

Figure 3-9. Coordinate system for fluidized solids flowing down an inclined channel.

The mean solids velocity is defined by:

$$U_m = \frac{Q}{\varrho bH} \qquad (3\text{-}32)$$

and the hydraulic diameter is defined in the usual manner ($D_H = 4bH/(b + 2H)$).

The effective viscosity of the two-phase flow is dependent on the solids mass throughput, G, the angle of channel tilt, α, the fluidizing gas velocity, U_f (and hence, the bed voidage ϵ), and the solids and gas physical properties.

Experiments with a paddle viscometer[40] have demonstrated that most fluidized solids have properties resembling non-Newtonian fluids, with the effect of an increasing fluidizing gas rate resulting in pseudoplasticity.

For a power law fluid,

$$\mu_e = K \left| \frac{dU_m}{dh} \right|^{n-1} \qquad (3\text{-}33)$$

where K = fluid's consistency index
       n = flow behavior index

Thus Equation 3-31 can be written as:

$$\frac{dH}{d\ell} = - \frac{\dfrac{2K}{\varrho gC} \left(\dfrac{3n + 1}{n} \right)^n U_m^n + \sin \alpha}{1 - \dfrac{U_m^2}{\beta gH}} \qquad (3\text{-}34)$$

where $\beta = \dfrac{(2n + 1)(5n + 3)}{3(3n + 1)^2}$

$$C = (D_H/2)^{n+1}$$

Equation 3-34 can also be used to estimate the rheological parameters K and n from the measured profile gradient $dH/d\ell$, by rewriting the expression as:

$$\Delta = \left[1 - \frac{U_m^2}{\beta gH} \right] \frac{dH}{d\ell} + \sin \alpha + \frac{2K}{\varrho gC} \left[\frac{3n + 1}{n} \right]^n U_m^n = 0 \qquad (3\text{-}35)$$

where Δ represents the deviation of the computation from zero. Hence, by standard parameter estimation techniques, values of K and n are evaluated (if the actual values of K and n are guessed, Δ will go to zero; if K and n values are poorly guessed, Δ will differ significantly from zero). For the model to be of use from a design standpoint, the rheological parameters should be independent of solids throughput, channel inclination, and channel dimensions.

Singh et al.[23] proposed the following design procedure of a tilted fluidized bed with such a model. It is assumed that the designer has the following information before the start of the calculations:

1. The channel length.
2. The mass flow rate of the fluidized solids.
3. The flow properties of the fluidized solids (i.e., K and n).

Such a model can be used to predict the channel width, b; the height of the free surface at the feed end, H_0; and the angle of inclination, α.

To use Singh et al's.[23] model it is assumed that the flow at the discharge end is free so that changes in the potential energy due to variation in the height of the free surface is available for the transport of material. Hence, from an energy balance over the channel length:

$$H_0 - \int_0^{\ell_0} \frac{dH}{d\ell} \, d\ell = 0 \tag{3-36}$$

To start the calculations, possible values for b and α are chosen and an initial value for H_0 assumed so that Equation 3-34 can be numerically integrated. If the assumed H_0 value is large, then Equation 3-36 will not be satisified, and the profile must be numerically integrated again (Equation 3-34) for a new H_0 value. The computations must be repeated until Equation 3-36 is satisfied to within an acceptable level of deviation, say $\pm$ 1% for example. Once convergence is achieved, the estimated height of the fluidized bed can be evaluated as being acceptable or not for the intended application. If it is not, the previous process is repeated by selecting new values for α and/or b. A preferred design is one which favors a minimum width b, since the fluidizing gas flow requirements are directly proportional to the channel width.

An even simpler procedure in using the model is to estimate the height of bed at the end of the channel. It has been demonstrated by Zenz[41,42] that the efflux of freely flowing bulk solids from a bin bearing a round hole or slot in its bottom and situated in dry ambient air can be represented by the following dimensionally consistent relationship:

$$W_s = \varrho_b (gh_w)^{0.5}/(\tan \alpha_i)^{0.5} \tag{3-37}$$

where W_s = solids efflux rate (kg/s-m^2)
 g = acceleration field (m/s^2)
 ϱ_b = solids bulk density (kg/m^3)
 α_i = bulk solids angle of internal friction (deg.)

Equation 3-37 can be rearranged to a form that is analogous to that of the Francis equation describing flow over a weir:

$$h_0 = \left(\frac{W_s^2}{\varrho_s(\varrho_s - \varrho)} \tan \alpha_i \right)^{0.333} \tag{3-38}$$

where h_0 is the height of the solids flowing over the discharge end of the channel. This is a reasonable description since any crossflow or horizontal moving fluid bed should certainly be equipped with some type of flow control at its discharge.

Note that the angle α_i represents the inclination of the shear plane between the flowing and the stationary solids measured from the horizontal. For water flowing over a weir the angle appears as in Figure 3-10. It represents the shallowest direction vector of the particles flowing toward the hole and must be evaluated from experiments for any given material. It is a characteristic of each material to the same extent as the angle of repose. The few reported measurements of angle α_i suggest it is approximately 70° for many materials.[41]

Thus, the hydrodynamic model may be applied in the following way. By specifying the solids mass throughput (and efflux rate from a chosen distributor width), and using data on the solid bulk density and angle of internal friction, Equation 3-38 is used to estimate the free surface height at the end of the channel, and Equation 3-34 numerically integrated to the inlet of the channel for the free surface profile. Hence, there is no trial and error procedure as required by Equation 3-36.

Singh et al.[23] tested the model based on the trial and error procedure for silica sand in an air slide channel that was 9.15 m in length and had a V-shaped bottom specifically designed to minimize the quantity of sand retained below the distributor. Table 3-2 summarizes the size distribution of the sand used along with the range of experimental conditions. The flow parameters for the fluidized-sand runs reported by Singh and co-workers are cited in Table 3-3. The parameter K_s is a slip factor proposed by Botterill and Bessant[5] that is a function of the distributor and theoretically varies between the limits of zero and unity. It denotes the degree of slippage at the distributor and is applied in the definition of the hydraulic diameter:

$$D_H = \frac{4bH}{K_s b + 2H} \tag{3-39}$$

When $K_s = 0$, complete slippage occurs.

Singh's comparisons between predicted and measured profiles for bed tilts up to about 3° from the horizontal were remarkably good.

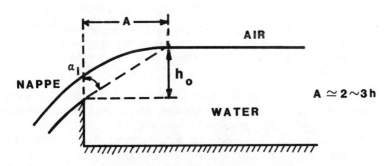

Figure 3-10. Weir flow of water in ambient air.

Table 3-2
Sand Particle Size Distribution and Range of Experimental
Conditions of Singh et al.[23]

Sieve Size (mm)[2]	Size Analysis of Silica Sand (% passing, by wt)
0.4	99.6
0.3	96.1
0.25	62.0
0.212	21.9
0.180	5.7
0.150	0.1

Sand: washed free of soluble salt before purchase.
Minimum fluidization velocity measured in a 150 mm
  cylindrical bed = 39 mm/s (ca. 20 °C, 102 kPa).
Density of sand = 2630 kg/m³.
Density of fluidized sand at 2.5 U_0 = 1375 kg/m³.
Angle of inclination of the channel α = 0°, -1°, -2°, -3°.
Sand flow rate = 5-100 t/h.
Diameter of the orifices in the distributor pipe = 2.8 mm, 4 mm.
Fluidizing gas velocity = 50-110 mm/s.

Table 3-3
Flow Parameters Evaluated by Singh et al.[23] for Fluidized Sand Flow
Down an Inclined Channel

α (degrees)	Sand Flow Rate (t/h)	$k_s = 0$		$k_s = 1$	
		k	n	k	n
0	10.1-33.6	20*	0.45	10.1	0.2
		(20-25)	(0.35-0.5)**	(7-14)	(0.15-0.4)
-1	10.2-61.2	30.3	0.22	27	0.1
		(27-34)	(0.18-0.27)	(27-37)	(0.06-0.12
-2	5.9-56.9	40.5	0.14	30.3	0.08
		(37-44)	(0.1-0.18)	(27-37)	(0.06-0.12)
-3	4.8-49.3	44	0.2	33.7	0.09
		(40-54)	(0.11-0.23)	(30-40)	0.07-0.12)

* Values of k and n for which the overall minimum variance was observed.
** () gives the range of values of m and n such that within this range the value of the mini-
mum variance would not exceed 110% of the overall minimum variance.

The authors also tested the model, using Equation 3-38 to obtain an estimate of
the free surface profile at the channel discharge. The channel was plexiglass and
was 7.62-cm wide by 65 cm long with a 2.54-cm tall weir at the channel exit. The
bed could be tilted up to an angle of 6° from the horizontal. The following list summarizes the range of conditions for channel flow experiments using composite solids. (The composite solids consisted of 70% stainless steel with 30% aluminum
coating.)

(The composite solids consisted of 70% stainless steel with 30% aluminum coating.)

50 wt % particle size	~ 275 μm
Solids throughput	~ 80–220 g/s
Channel bed tilt	~ 0°–6°
Fluidizing gas velocities	~ 0.12–0.30 m/s
Aspect ratio (average solids height to channel width)	~ 0.3–1.5

Figure 3-11 shows comparisons between predicted free surface height profiles and measured over the length of the channel.

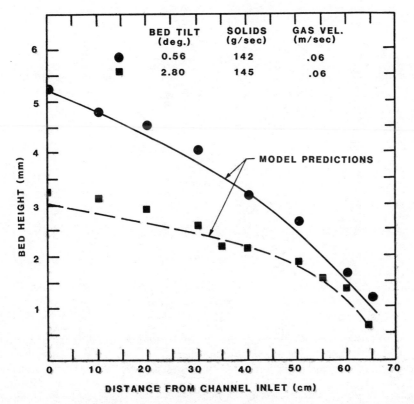

Figure 3-11. Measured and predicted fluidized solids height profiles as a function of bed tilt angle.

In using Equation 3-31 to compute the solids height profile, an average solids velocity through the channel was estimated by $U_m = G_s/\varrho A_H$ (where $A_H = 1/4\pi D_H^2$). This estimate was not found to agree with the measured average solids velocity, however, it did provide a good estimate of the measured solids free surface velocity. Figure 3-12 shows that good agreement between the estimated average solids velocity, U_m, and measured solids free surface velocity was obtained for thick beds.

The velocity profile over the solids depth may be obtained from an expression describing the velocity profile of a power law fluid.

$$U = U_{mpL}\left(\frac{3n+1}{n+1}\right)\left[1 - \left(1 - \frac{H}{H_{fs}}\right)^{(n+1)/n}\right] \qquad (3\text{-}40)$$

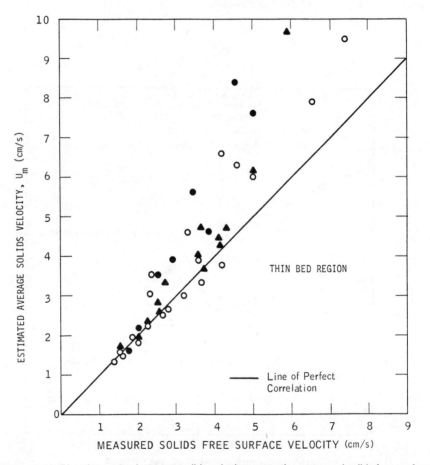

Figure 3-12. Plot of measured average solids velocity versus the measured solids free surface velocity.

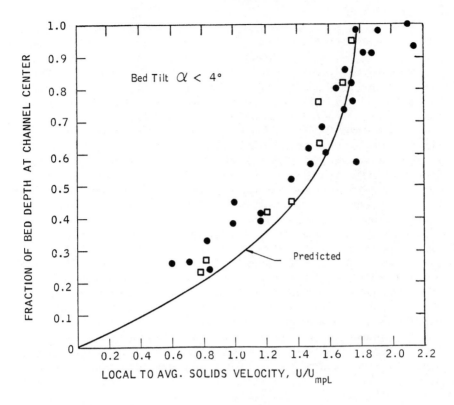

Figure 3-13. Comparison of measured to predicted velocity profiles.

where H_{fs} = height of free surface computed from Equation 3-31
 U = local velocity
 U_{mpL} = average velocity for a power law fluid.

At the bed surface H = H_{fs} and U = U_{fs}, and making the following approximation U_{fs} = U_m, the average velocity U_{mpL} is given by:

$$U_{mpL} = U_{fs}\left(\frac{3n+1}{n+1}\right)^{-1}   U_m\left(\frac{3n+1}{n+1}\right)^{-1} \qquad (3\text{-}41)$$

From the computed U_{mpL}, Equation 3-40 was used to construct the velocity profile for any set of operating conditions. Figure 3-13 shows that Equations 3-40 and 3-41 give good predictions of the average solids velocity and velocity profiles.

We may conclude from these model validations that aerated solids flows are indeed describable by standard analogies of pipe or channel flows with a definite rheological behavior. After all, a fluid's viscosity is fundamentally a measure of its resilience or deformability. The more viscous the material, the less is its ability to deform and therefore flow. The smaller and farther apart the fluid molecules, then the lower is its viscosity; also the smaller the solid particles are and the greater the solid's void fraction, with or without aeration, the less viscous is the material.

The limiting case of solids conveying would occur when all solids in the channel maintained their bulk density and moved along much like a plastic material extruded through a die. For powdered materials to undergo extrusion flow they must possess the property of *bulk deformability,* a term which is analogous to viscosity in liquid flows. Powders which fall into the category of extrusion-type flow materials display continuous yield or bulk viscosity characteristics. Rowe et al.[43] describe a simple procedure for evaluating these characteristics based on the falling sphere viscometer. In the method, a 250 ml cylinder is filled with the powdered material of interest and a 1 cm diameter steel ball is released from immediately above the solid's surface. If the sphere falls to the bottom, as if it were in a liquid, then the solid material is capable of extrusion flow.

Some powdered materials that do not pass this simple drop weight test, can be rendered deformable by doping the powder with colloidal silica. Zenz[44] notes that an equal volume of silica added to FCC catalyst (this translates to a 4% by weight addition) results in a deformability that is comparable to that of powdered coal. In the drop weight test described by Zenz, the silica was observed to be dispersed as small agglomerates within a matrix of the catalyst particles when studied under magnification. This suggests that the role of colloidal silica seeding is that of interspersed deformable or "soft" particles analogous to small gas bubbles trapped in a fluidized bed of solids. Hence, the rheological properties of solids mixtures appear more complex than can be described by a simplified one-dimensional flow model.

APPLICATION OF FRICTION FACTOR CORRELATIONS TO SOLIDS FLOWS

The transport of solids in a fluid-bed circuit can be classified into two general types, namely, transport within a fluidized bed itself, and transport between fluidized beds through transfer lines. Both are examined in detail in subsequent chapters. The internal circulation observed in a fluid bed is usually very rapid and can be modeled based on the bubbling phenomenon[45-47] or the slugging phenomenon.[48] External circulation (i.e., solids transport between vessels) experiences a variety of different flow regimes. Emphasis in this section is on the latter, again, for the very specific case of bulk solids flows.

Moving-bed solids flows in inclined lines are of importance in transfer lines for the circulation of solids between reactors. One of the best examples is that of solids transfer between fluidized beds in the fluid catalytic cracking (FCC) process. This is a reactor-regenerator process in which catalyst particles are circulated between the reactor and the regenerator. The successful circulation of solids is of prime importance in the design and operation of this process. The principle of solids circulation used in the FCC process is also applied to other reactor systems in the petroleum industry. Examples include fluid hydroforming for reforming naptha vapor,[49] fluid coking for the treatment of heavy oil,[50] and sand cracking for the thermal cracking of various petroleum feedstocks.[51] Examples outside of the petroleum industry include the drying of air by circulation of silica gel beads between two multistage fluid beds[52] and solid waste gasification in which hot solids and char are circulated between two fluid-bed units.[53]

Chen et al.[29] have shown that moving-bed solids flows can be described by a macroscopic momentum balance for heterogeneous flow systems using a properly defined friction factor. Since their model readily lends itself as a design procedure, the analysis is summarized in the following paragraphs.

Chen et al. defined their model system as shown in Figure 3-14, and starting with the equation given by Standart,[54] described the rate of change of the momentum of the system:

$$\frac{d}{dt}\int_{v} P\overline{v}dV = -\oint_{A_e} [P\overline{v}(\overline{v} - \overline{v}_e) + P\overline{U} + \overline{\overline{\tau}}]d\overline{A} + \Sigma \int_{v} P_i\overline{F}_i dV \qquad (3\text{-}42)$$

Equation 3-42 can be applied to flow in the transfer line. The balance can be modified by applying the assumptions that

1. The only external force is gravitational.
2. The flow is a steady-state, two-phase (gas-solids), one-dimensional, countercurrent flow with no mass transfer through the pipe wall.

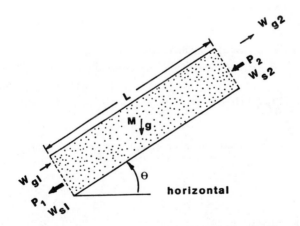

Figure 3-14. System defined by Chen et al.[17] for describing moving-bed flows down inclined pipes.

3. The pipe is straight and has a constant cross-sectional area.
4. The inertial terms can be neglected.
5. The bulk solids density in the system is approximately constant.

From this Chen et al.[31] reduced the expression to:

$$\varrho_b AL \sin \theta - A(P_1 - P_2) - F_{wr} = 0. \tag{3-43}$$

P_1-P_2 is the pressure drop over the length of the transfer line. Other variables in the equation can be easily measured, except the friction loss term, F_{wr}, which can be estimated from either a friction-factor correlation or a flow-curve expression.

The wall friction can be attributed to both gas and solids, however, that from gas is negligible. A friction factor for the flow of fluid in a pipe analogous to the Fanning friction factor can be written for the solids flow:

$$f_b = \frac{\dfrac{D_t F_{wr}}{4AL}}{\dfrac{1}{2}\varrho_b \nu_s^2} = \frac{\dfrac{D_t}{4}\left(\varrho_b g \sin \theta - \dfrac{P_1 - P_2}{L}\right)}{\dfrac{1}{2}\varrho_b \nu_s^2} \tag{3-44}$$

where ν_s is the average solids velocity defined by

$$\nu_s = \frac{W_s}{\varrho bA} \tag{3-45}$$

The friction factor is a function of the design and operating parameters and can be expressed as:

$$f_b = a_0 D_t^{a_1} - d_p^{a_2} U_g^{a_3} \nu_s^{a_4} \tag{3-46}$$

where a_1 through a_4 are experimentally determined exponents.

From the work of Metzner and Reed,[55] the wall shear stress is defined as:

$$\tau = \frac{D_t F_{wr}}{4AL} = \frac{D_t}{4}\left(\varrho_b g \sin \theta - \frac{P_1 - P_2}{L}\right) \tag{3-47}$$

Borrowing a definition from single-phase laminar flow, the average shear rate is:

$$\dot\gamma = \frac{8\nu_s}{D_t} \tag{3-48}$$

where ν_s = average solids velocity

   D_t = line diameter.

And defining the rheology of the two-phase flow in terms of a power law fluid:

$$n = \frac{d\ln\tau}{d\ln\dot{\gamma}} \qquad (3\text{-}49A)$$

$$K = \tau/\dot{\gamma}^n \qquad (3\text{-}49B)$$

where   n = flow behavior index, characterizing the degree of non-Newtonian behavior of a time-independent fluid
K = fluid's consistency index

The generalized Reynolds number for a time-independent non-Newtonian fluid (see Skelland[56]) is:

$$Re_{MR} = \frac{D_t^n \nu_s^{2-n} \varrho_b}{m} \qquad (3\text{-}50)$$

where

$$m = k\left(8^{n-1}\right) \qquad (3\text{-}51)$$

Thus, when the flow is in the laminar region, where $Re_{MR} < 2,100$, the following relationship applies:

$$f_b = \frac{16}{Re_{MR}} \qquad (3\text{-}52)$$

Chen et al.[29] studied sand flows for a range of experimental conditions, which included varying the superficial fluidizing gas velocity, the height of the bottom of the transfer line relative to the distributor plate, the height of the overflow outlet relative to the distributor, the effective length of the transfer line, the pressure in the freeboard, and the transfer line diameter.

The data obtained were reconciled in terms of the friction factor correlation (Equation 3-46) and the flow curves. The exponents in Equation 3-46 evaluated from parameter estimation techniques resulted in:

$$f_b = 1.314 \times 10^5 D_T^{0.7} \overline{d}_p^{1.655} U_g^{-0.663} \nu_s^{-1.553} \qquad (3\text{-}53)$$

Application of Equation 3-53 must be made with caution since overpredictions as high as 100% and underpredictions as great as -50% of the friction factor were reported.[29]

A sampling of the flow curves (i.e., plot of wall shear stress vs. $\dot{\gamma}$) reported by Chen et al. is shown in Figure 3-15. The parameter for each curve is the slip velocity defined as:

$$U_{s\ell} = U_g + \epsilon_g \nu_s \qquad\qquad (3\text{-}54)$$

where U_g = superficial gas velocity in transfer line
  ϵ_g = volume fraction of gas phase
  ν_s = solids velocity

Further analysis by Chen et al. revealed that the consistency index K decreases as the slip velocity increases, indicating that the solids become less viscous and acquire more fluid-like flow behavior. Furthermore, a critical velocity, u_o, was observed below which the flow behavior index, n, was found to be negligibly small. That is, at slip velocities below u_o, solids transport is plug flow, and above u_o, a velocity profile develops. This interpretation appears correct since aerated solids flows in transparent inclined pipes show that when the gas leakage rate is high, small gas bubbles flow along the top layer of the transfer line, and solids in different planes flow at different velocities.

Figure 3-16 shows Chen et al.'s plot of the friction factor, f_b, versus the generalized Reynolds number for different distributors tested. The data are shown to agree well for $Re_{MR} < 2,100$, meaning that the particles move in the line without significant variation in their radial positions.

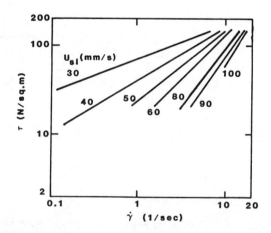

Figure 3-15. Sampling of typical flow curves obtained by Chen et al.:[29] data obtained for one type of distributor with D_t = 0.0508 m, d_p = 0.00051 m.

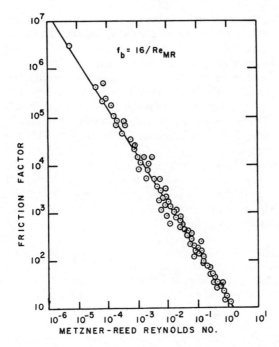

Figure 3-16. The friction factor/modified Reynolds number curve for laminar flow.[29]

RHEOLOGICAL MEASUREMENTS

For liquids and gases, viscosity is measured indirectly through the promotion of a specific flow and then measuring the resistances or pressure losses in this flow. The same principle has been applied to fluidized solids by various investigators (see Matheson et al.,[57] Furukawa et al.,[58] Kramers,[59] and Grace[60] for examples). The reported ranges of rheological properties of fluidized materials do, however, vary significantly, not only because of solids properties and size distributions but due to different measurement techniques employed.

Siemes et al.[61] report that rheological measurements of fluidized layers can be properly made only when the imposed flow conditions have no significant effect on the fluidized state. That is, the boundary conditions of the flow in the fluidized solids layer must be the same as in a liquid or gas. Also, the parameters of the flow region must be large as compared with the size of the solid particles and the average distance between them.

Matheson et al.[57] reported the first experiments on measuring fluidized solids viscosity using a Stormer viscometer consisting of a flat blade paddle agitator immersed in the fluidized material. They reported a viscosity value obtained at a paddle speed of 200 rpm by comparing a liquid of known viscosity. The principal observation from this study was that the fluidized material was measured to be significantly less viscous as the rate of gas flow was increased. Furthermore, for a constant gas rate, viscosity was found to decrease with decreasing particle size.

The addition of large size particles was found to have little effect on the viscosity up to relatively large amounts. However, the addition of even trace amounts of fine particulates produced a significant lowering of the viscosity. Furukawa and Ohmae[58] also reported viscosity data obtained using a flat blade paddle agitator and at 113 rpm; they obtained qualitatively similar results. Kramers[59] used a rotating dumbbell in viscosity measurements while Peters and Schmidt[62] determined the viscosity of a fluidized layer using the falling sphere method with the application of Stokes law. Trawinski[63] also used the falling sphere technique in the study of layers of bulk material fluidized by liquids. In this study both theoretical and analytical descriptions of the fluidized state were given by applying the hole of the liquid state. According to Trawinski,[63] the effective viscosity of a fluid with a laminar flow of the medium is given by:

$$\mu_s = \mu_g + C(1 - \epsilon_{wp}) \frac{\varrho_p(\varrho_p - \varrho_g)g}{\mu_g} d_p^3 \frac{\frac{w}{W_{WP}} 1/\epsilon_{wp} - K\left(\frac{w}{W_{WP}}\right)^{0.5}}{K\left(\frac{w}{W_{WP}}\right)^{0.5} - 1} \quad (3\text{-}55)$$

where μ_s, μ_g = effective viscosity of fluidized bed and gas viscosity, respectively

ϵ_{wp} = relative intergrain volume at fluidization

K = expansion coefficient

w = actual superficial gas velocity

W_{wp} = gas velocity at minimum fluidization

C = dimensionless coefficient evaluated to be 2 for water-fluidized layers and 64 for gas-fluidized layers

Siemes[64] and Siemes and Hellmer[61] were among the first to recommend laminar flow viscometers based on the Hagen-Poiseuille method using the dimensions of the pipe and flow rate. The method was essentially described earlier, where the present case of pipe flow is replaced by channel flow. The principal assumptions in applying this technique are that the flow process will have no marked effect on the state of the fluidized layer, and the quasi-liquid fluidized layer flows in inclined channels like a viscous liquid.

An interesting approach to viscosity measurements that avoids the issue of unnaturally disturbing the fluidized state is that of Grace,[60] Murray,[65] Ormiston[66] and others,[67] in which viscosity was inferred from the behavior of bubbles in the fluidized bed.

Murray[65] estimated the apparent viscosity of a fluidized bed from an estimation of the viscous drag coefficient for rising bubbles. Rowe and Partridge[68] noted problems with this approach and showed the resulting equation, μ_A, turns out to be a function of bubble size. Ormiston[66] estimated values μ_A between 12 and 45 poise based on the rising velocity of bubble slugs in fluidized beds and on velocity profiles in slugging beds. Stewart[67] based estimates of μ_A on the difference between predicted and observed pressure measurements as a bubble passed a probe.

Grace[60] proposed an indirect method of estimating bed viscosities based on the shape of bubbles in fluidized beds. The method is briefly described in the following section.

Davies and Taylor[69] and Mendelson[70] describe gas bubbles rising through a liquid column to be spherical, ellipsoidal, or spherical-cap in shape (the latter configuration is shown in Figure 3-17). In low viscosity liquids, the included angle, θ, is approximately $100°$, but in higher viscosity fluids, spherical-cap bubbles are more rounded and higher values of θ are observed.[60]

Included angle θ for gas-liquid systems is found to be a function of the Reynolds number:

$$Re_M = D_b U_B \varrho / \mu \qquad (3\text{-}56)$$

where D_b = equivalent bubble diameter ($D_b = (6V_B/\pi)^{0.333}$; where V_B = bubble volume)
U_B = bubble rise velocity
ϱ = liquid density.

For spherical-capped bubbles the following criteria apply:

$$\left.\begin{array}{l} We > 20 \\ E\ddot{o} > 40 \\ D/b > 10 \text{ for } \theta < 180° \\ D/a > 10 \text{ for } \theta > 180° \end{array}\right\} \qquad (3\text{-}57)$$

where D is the column diameter, and b and a are the basal radius of a spherical-cap bubble and the radius of curvature of the leading edge of a spherical-cap bubble, respectively.

The Weber and Eötvos numbers are defined as:

$$We = D_b U_B^2 / \sigma \qquad (3\text{-}58A)$$

$$E\ddot{o} = D_b^2 g \varrho / \sigma \qquad (3\text{-}58B)$$

In fluidized beds, the first two conditions of Equation 3-57 are inevitably satisfied because of the absence of surface tension forces. Experiments using photographic and x-ray techniques have shown also that bubbles in fluid beds resemble spherical-capped, although there is some controversy over this as is discussed in Chapter 4.

Based on these observations, Grace[60] proposed quantitative estimates of the apparent viscosity of a fluidized bed based on measured and/or estimated values of the rise velocities of bubbles. Values for μ_a can be estimated as follows: using the included angle, a Reynolds number is computed from the following empirical formula:[60]

$$Re_M = 23e^{-0.004\theta}, \qquad (200° < \theta < 260°) \qquad (3\text{-}59)$$

Then from estimates of the equivalent bubble diameter, D_b, μ_a is computed:

$$\mu_a = \frac{D_b U_b \varrho_p (1 - \epsilon_{mf})}{Re} \qquad (3\text{-}60)$$

Grace[60] estimated viscosities for different fluidized materials (Ballotini, Silver Sand, Synclyst Catalyst, and Magnesite) using this method to range from 4 to 13 poise. Measurements were found to agree with those obtained using a rotating cylindrical viscometer.[71] Grace[60] unfortunately does not report the range of fluidizing gas velocities over which estimates of μ_a were made.

Table 3-4 and Figure 3-18 summarize the range over which various investigators measured apparent fluid-bed viscosities. The importance of the apparent viscosities in fluidized bed is two-fold. First, it is important for a fundamental understanding of the flow phenomenon. Secondly, apparent shear viscosities arise in fluidized beds from particle shearing stresses, and it is important to be able to estimate the order of magnitude of these stresses when assessing the stability of uniformly fluidized systems with respect to perturbations. Further work is needed in this area to better define accurate measurement techniques.

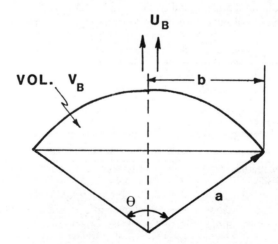

Figure 3-17. Illustration of a spherical-cap bubble.

Table 3-4
Summary of Viscosity Measurements by Various Investigators

Material	Mean Particle Size (μm)	U/U_{mf}	Fluidizing Medium	Range of Apparent Bed Viscosity (poise)	Investigator
Glass powder	277	0.9~2.5	Water	5~13	Furukawa and Ohmae (1958)
	384	0.8~14	Water	7~125	
Smooth glass and polystyrol beads	200–350		Air	1~5	Schugerl (1961)
Sharp-edged quartz and silicone carbide	200–350		Air	5~10	
Silver sand	500		Air	25<	Stewart (1968)
Magnesite	240		Air	15<	
Ballotini	60–550		Air	4~12	Rowe and Partridge (1965) as deduced by Grace
Silver sand	72–500		Air	5~14	
Synclyst catalyst	52		Air	4	
Magnesite	240		Air	9	
Quartz sand	100–300		Air	1.5~4	Seimes and Hellmer (1962)

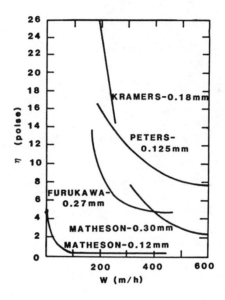

Figure 3-18. Fluidized-bed viscosities reported by various investigators.

NOMENCLATURE

A′   coefficient in Equation 3-19B
A   cross-sectional area of flow
a   radius of curvature of leading edge of bubble or acceleration
b   basal radius of spherical-cap bubble or channel width
C   group defined in Equation 3-35
C_a, C_w dimensionless normalized parameter
D_b bubble diameter
d_p particle diameter
D_t tube diameter
d_v volume surface diameter
Eö   Eötvos number
F   frictional losses
f_b friction factor
G   mass flow rate
G′   solids loading, i.e., mass flow rate per unit width of channel
g   gravitational acceleration
H   height
H_o solids height at channel discharge
ĵ   similarity indicator

K   fluid consistency index
K_2 dimensionless kinematic Homochronity number (see Equation 3-6)
K_n dimensionless solids loading rate (see Equation 3-18)
K_s slip factor
L,ℓ length
M   total solids mass charged to bed
m   solids mass flow rate
N   number of variables in Buckingham π theorem
n   number base units in Buckingham π theorem or flow behavior index
P   pressure
Q   solids volumetric flowrate
Re   Reynolds number
Re_{MR} modified Metzner-Reed Reynolds number (see Equation 3-50)
R_H hydraulic radius
T   time
t   time in seconds
U_g superficial gas velocity
U_m mean solids velocity
U_{mf} minimum fluidization velocity
V_b bubble volume
We   Weber number
W_f work
W_s solids efflux rate
w, w_o velocity
y   coordinate

Greek Symbols

α channel angle of tilt from horizontal
α_i solids angle of internal friction
β kinetic energy correction term
$\dot{\gamma}$ average shear rate
ϵ voidage
ϵ_{mf} voidage at minimum fluidization
θ bubble included angle
μ viscosity
μ_e effective viscosity of fluidized solids
ν_f kinematic viscosity
ν_h horizontal velocity of moving fluid bed
ν_s average solids velocity
ϱ density
ϱ_p particle density
ϱ_s solids bulk density
τ wall shear stress
τ_T residence time

REFERENCES

1. Geldart, D., *Powder Technology,* 7: 285–292 (1973).
2. Woodcock, C. R., "Economical Transport of Bulk Particulate Solids in Air-Assisted Gravity Conveyors and an Approach to Their Design," Int. Conf. on Pneumatic Conveying, Cafe Royal, London (January 1979).
3. Leva, M., *Fluidization,* McGraw-Hill, NY (1959).
4. Kunii, D., O. Levenspiel, *Fluidization Engineering,* John Wiley & Sons, NY (1969).
5. Botterill, J. S. M., and D. J. Bessant, Symposium Rheology of Particulate Systems, Harrogate Inst. Complex, U.K. (March 27, 1973).
6. Woodcock, C. R., and J. S. Mason, *Pneumotransport 4,* 4th Int. Conf. on Pneumatic Transport of Solids in Pipes, (June 26–28, 1978).
7. Weber, M. et al., *Krausskopf Verlag Mainz,* Berlin (1974).
8. Stegmaier, W., *Bulk Solids Technology,* 2(1): 47–55 (1978).
9. Isler, W., *Zement-Kalk-Grips* 13 (10): 482–486 (1960).
10. Futer, E., *Mech. Eng.,* 7: 21–23 (April 1969).
11. Schauki, N., *deutsch hebe- and fordertechnik,* 19, 1, S. 49–53 (1973).
12. "New Techniques in Pneumatic Conveying," *Chemie-Ing.-Tech.,* 36 (5): 555–556 (1964) (in German).
13. Vitunac, E. A., "Considerations in the Selection of a Pneumatic Conveying System," *Mining Eng.,* 83–87 (May 1968).
14. Nordberg, B., "Air Activated Gravity Conveyors," *Rock Products,* 52: 115–124, (August 1949).
15. Avery, W., "Meet the Airslide," *Pit and Quarry,* 41 (2): 62–67 (1949).
16. Butler, P., "No-Moving Parts Conveyor Shifts Dry Powdered Solids," *Process Eng.* (August 1974).
17. Leitzel, R. E., and W. M. Morrisey, "Air-Float Conveyors," in *Bulk Materials Handling,"* Vol. 1, M. C. Hawk (Ed.), Univ. Pittsburgh, Sch. Mech. Eng., (1971) pp. 307–325.
18. Bushell, E., Maskell, R. C., "Fluidized Handling of Alumina Powder," *Mech. Handling,* 47 (3): 126–131 (1960).
19. Kunii, D., et al., *Int. Chem. Eng.,* 14: 588–593 (1974).
20. Kunii, D., M. Hasegawa, and J. Fukuda, *Proceedings of Pachec '77,* (1977), pp. 176–182.
21. Bailie, R. C., "Production of High Energy Fuel Gas from Municipal Wastes," U.S. Patent #3,853,498 (1974).
22. Engler, C. R., W. P. Walawender, and L. T. Fan, "Transfer of Solids between Parallel Fluidized Beds," *AIChE Symposium Series* 74 (176): 75–81 (1978).
23. Singh, B., T. G. Callcott, and G. R. Rigby, *Trans. Inst. Chem. Eng.* (London), 55: 1, 68 (1977).

24. Keunecke, K., *VDI Forschungsh,* 509, 34 (1965).

25. Muskett, W. J., and J. S. Mason, *Pneumotransport 2,* organized by BHRA, (5–7 Sept. 1973), Paper F1.

26. Ishida, M., H. Hatano, and T. Shirai, *Powder Technology,* Vol. 27, (1980).

27. Chari, S. S., *AIChE Symposium Series,* 67 (116): 77–84 (1971).

28. Trees, J., *Trans. Inst. Chem. Eng.,* 40: 286–296 (1962).

29. Chen, T. Y., W. P. Walawender, and L. T. Fan, *AIChE,* 26: 1, 31–36 (Jan. 1980).

30. Chen, T. Y., W. P. Walawender, and L. T. Fan, in *Handbook of Fluids In Motion,* N. P. Cheremisinoff and R. Gupta (Eds.), Ann Arbor Science Pub., Ann Arbor, MI (1983), Ch. 27, pp. 691–714.

31. Chen, T. Y., W. P. Walawender, and L. T. Fan, *Powder Technology,* 22: 89–96 (1979).

32. Verteshev, M. S., A. D. Arkachenov, and O. K. Kamalov, *Intl. Chem. Eng.,* 9 (3): 505–507 (July 1969).

33. Mori, Y. et al., "Transportation of Solid Material by an Air Slide Conveyor" *Kagaku Kogaku* (Japan), 19: 16–22 (1955) (in Japanese).

34. Siemes, W., and L. Hellmer, "Measurement of Fluidized Bed Viscosity in a Pneumatic Duct," *Chem. Eng. Science,* 17: 555–571 (1962) (in German).

35. Harris, W. F., "Pneumatic Conveying—Special Problems of Density," *Mech. Handling,* 52 (11): 521–527 (Nov. 1965).

36. Qassim, R. Y., "On the Flow of Fluidized Suspensions," Ph.D Thesis, University of London, UK, (1970).

37. McGuigan, S. J., "Flow Behaviour of Shallow Fluidized Beds," Ph.D. Thesis, Univ. of Aston, UK, (1974).

38. McGuigan, S. J., R. R. Pugh, "The Flow of Fluidized Solids in an Open Channel," *Proc. Pneumotransport 3,* BHRA Conf., Paper E2, Bath, UK, (April 1976).

39. Shinohar, K., K. Saito, and T. Tanaka, "Flow Properties of Particles on Air-Slide," *Micromeritics,* 19: 64–72 (1974) (in Japanese).

40. Matheson, G. L., W. A. Herbst, and P. H. Holt, *Ind. Eng. Chem.,* 4: 1,099 (1949).

41. Zenz, F. A., and F. E. Zenz, *Ind. Eng. Chem. Fund.,* 18 (4): 345–348 (1979).

42. Zenz, F. A., *Hydrocarbon Process,* 54 (5): 125–128 (1975).

43. Rowe, P. N., and F. A. Zenz, *Fluidization Technology,* Vol. II, D. L. Keairns (Ed.) McGraw Hill Book Co., NY (1975) p. 151.

44. Zenz, F. A., "Rheology of Particulate Solids" in *Handbook of Fluids In Motion,* N. P. Cheremisinoff and R. Gupta (Eds.), Ann Arbor Science Pub., Ann Arbor, MI (1983), Ch. 23, pp. 623–634.

45. Kunii, D., K. Yoshida, and O. Levenspiedl, "Axial Movement of Solids in Bubbling Fluidized Beds," in *Fluidization,* Proc. Tripartite Chemical Engineering Conf., Montreal (1968), pp. 79–84.

46. Woollard, I. N. M., and O. E. Potter, *AIChE*, 14: 388–391 (1968).

47. Rowe, P. N., *Chem. Eng. Sci.*, 28: 979–980 (1973).

48. Potter, O. E., and W. Thiel, "Solids Mixing in Slugging Fluidized Beds," in Fluidization Technology, Vol. II, D. L. Keairns, (Ed.), Hemisphere Publishing Corp., Washington, DC, (1976), pp. 185–192.

49. Kraft, W. W., W. Ulrich, and W. O'Connor, "The Significance of Details in Fluid Catalytic Cracking Units: Engineering Design, Instrumentation and Operation," in *Fluidization*, D. F. Othmer (Ed.), Van Nostrand Reinhold Co., NY (1956).

50. Krebs, R. W., "Fluid Coking," in *Fluidization*, D. F. Othmer (Ed.), Van Nostrand Reinhold Co., NY (1956).

51. Schmalfeld, P., *Hydrocarbon Proc. Pet. Ref.*, 42 (7): 145–148 (1963).

52. Cox, M., *Trans. Inst. Chem. Eng.*, 36: 29–42 (1958).

53. Hasegawa, M., J. Fukuka, and D. Kunii, "Research and Development of Circulation System Between Fluidized Beds for Application of Gas-Solid Reactions," *Proc. 2nd Pachec '77*, (1977), pp. 176–182.

54. Standart, G., *Chem. Eng. Sci.*, 19: 227–236 (1964).

55. Metzner, A. B., and J. C. Reed, *AIChE*, 1: 434–440 (1955).

56. Skelland, A. H. P., *Non-Newtonian Flow and Heat Transfer*, John Wiley & Sons, NY (1967).

57. Matheson, G., W. Herbst, and P. Holt, *Industr, Engrg. Chem.*, 41: 1,099 (1949).

58. Furukawa, J., and T. S. Ohmae, *Industr. Engrg., Chem.*, 50: 821 (1958).

59. Kramers, H. *Chem. Eng. Sci.*, 1: 35 (1952).

60. Grace, J. R., *Can. Journ. Chem. Eng.*, 48: 30–33 (Feb. 1970).

61. Siemes, W., and L. Hellmer, *Chem. Eng. Sci.*, 17: 555–571 (1962).

62. Peters, K., and A. Schmidt, *Oesterr. Chemikerztg.*, 54: 253 (1953).

63. Trawinski, H., *Chem. Ing. Techn.*, 25: 229 (1953).

64. Siemes, W., *Chem. Ing. Techn.*, 24: 82 (1959).

65. Murray, J. D., *Rheol. Acta* 6: 27 (1967).

66. Ormiston, R. M., "Slug Flow in Fluidized Beds," Ph.D. Thesis, Cambridge Univ., (1966).

67. Stewart, P. S. B., *Trans. Inst. Chem. Eng.*, London, 46: 80 (1968).

68. Rowe, P. N., and B. A. Partridge, *J. Fluid Mech.*, 23: 583 (1965).

69. Davies, R. M., and Sir G. I. Taylor, *Proc. Roy. Soc.*, A200: 375 (1950).

70. Mendelson, H. D., *AIChE J.*, 13: 250 (1967).

71. Schugerl, K., M. Merz, and F. Fetting, *Chem. Eng. Sci.*, 15: 39 (1961).

4

Hydrodynamics of Fluidization

CONTENTS

INTRODUCTION, 138

FLOW THROUGH FIXED BEDS, 138

ONSET OF FLUIDIZATION AND GENERAL CHARACTERISTICS, 144

MINIMUM FLUIDIZATION VELOCITY, 149

MINIMUM BUBBLING VELOCITY, 158

BED EXPANSION, 161

    Empirical Correlations, 161
    Energy Balance Method, 165

HYDRODYNAMICS OF BUBBLES, 177

    Jet Penetration, 177
    Bubble Characteristics, 183
    Two-Phase Theory for Bubble Flow, 196
    Channeling and Slugging, 198

NOMENCLATURE, 200

REFERENCES, 202

INTRODUCTION

The growth of fluidized-bed technology has been almost exponential in the chemical, petroleum, and allied industries since its advent during World War II. At that time, the petroleum industry implemented the first fluidized-bed cat crackers to produce large quantities of aviation fuel. Included among today's applications of this technology are cracking and reforming of hydrocarbons, coal carbonization and gasification, ore roasting, Fischer-Tropsch synthesis, aviline production, pthalic anhydride production, polyethylene manufacturing, calcining, coking, aluminum production, granulation, vinyl chloride production, melamine production, incineration, coatings preparations, nuclear fuel preparation, and many other well-established operations.

Despite industry's wide usage, the design of fluidized-bed systems is rudimentary. Often the scale-up to large commercial applications involves a costly stepwise process of building and testing various sizes of pilot-scale operations. Even with such conservative approaches, final designs do not always fulfill expectations. The reason for this shortcoming is that the flow behavior of a fluidized bed of solids is very complex and highly sensitive to scale and specific operating conditions. Coupled with this is the fact that although the hydrodynamics of these systems have been widely studied, as testified by the scores of papers in the literature, unified equations or models that adequately describe the physics of particle interactions and bubble phenomena have not been developed. Therefore, there is a critical need for a more fundamental understanding of the hydrodynamic behavior. Without this information, proper design to include heat and mass exchanges and chemical reactions cannot be achieved.

Fluidization as a method of contacting granular solids and fluids can be a multiphase system. That is, in addition to the gas-solid and liquid-solid two-phase systems, three-phase fluidization is of great commercial importance, as in the case of coal liquefaction. Although some attention is given to three-phase fluidization, the emphasis in this and subsequent chapters is on the two-phase, gas-solid flow system.

FLOW THROUGH FIXED BEDS

Consider a column that is filled with loose solids up to a certain level. If a fluid is passed upward through the bed of solids at a relatively low velocity, then the liquid or gas will merely percolate through the void spaces between particles. The solid particles in this case will remain undisturbed, and the system is referred to as a *fixed bed.*

The pressure drop across a fixed bed of solids is a function of the average fluid velocity through the bed ($\bar{v}$), the fluid's viscosity (μ_f) and density (ϱ_f), a characteristic dimension representative of the interparticle distance of separation through which the fluid flows (d_e), and the level of the bed (ℓ).

$$\Delta P = f(\mu_f, \varrho_f, \bar{v}, d_e, \ell) \tag{4-1}$$

From dimensional analysis, the pressure drop per unit height of solids is:

$$\frac{\Delta P}{\ell} = C\mu_f^{2-n}\bar{v}^n d_e^{n-3}\varrho_f^{n-1} \tag{4-2}$$

where C is an experimental coefficient.

If the solids are randomly packed in the column, then the characteristic dimension most appropriate to describing the average flow area is an equivalent diameter:

$$d_e = 4 \times \frac{\text{mean cross-sectional area of flow channels through bed}}{\text{mean wetted perimeter of flow channels}} \tag{4-3}$$

Multiplying this definition by ℓ/ℓ, yields:

$$d_e = \frac{\text{(total bed volume)}}{\text{(total bed surface)}} = \frac{\epsilon}{S} \tag{4-4}$$

where S = surface of solids per unit bed volume
ϵ = average void fraction

The average interstitial fluid velocity will depend on the volumetric throughput and the cross-section of flow channels:

$$\bar{v} = \frac{Q}{S\epsilon} = \frac{U}{\epsilon} \tag{4-5}$$

where U is the superficial velocity through the column. Equation 4-5 is obvious from the fact that the fractional free area in any plane passed through the bed must be the same as the average fractional free volume of the entire bed.

For spherical particles, the equivalent diameter and true surface per unit bed volume are, respectively:

$$d_e = \epsilon d_p/6(1 - \epsilon) \tag{4-6}$$

$$S = 6(1 - \epsilon)/d_p \tag{4-7}$$

where d_p is the mean diameter of the spherical particles in the bed

Substituting Equations 4-6 and 4-7 into Equation 4-2 gives the following expression for pressure drop per unit depth of a fixed bed of spherical particles:

$$\frac{\Delta P}{\ell} = C\mu_f^{2-n}d_p^{n-3}\varrho_f^{n-1}U^n \frac{(1 - \epsilon)^{3-n}}{\epsilon^3} \tag{4-8}$$

The frictional pressure loss through a network of pores can be described by Darcy's equation:

$$\frac{\Delta P}{\ell} = \frac{2f\varrho_f U^2}{gd_p} \tag{4-9}$$

where f is a friction factor that is a function of the Reynolds number and the fraction of bed occupied by the fluid.

Combining Equations 4-8 and 4-9, an expression for the friction factor is obtained:

$$f = C\mu_f^{2-n}U^{n-2}\varrho_f^{n-2}d_p^{n-2} \frac{(1 - \epsilon)^{3-n}}{\epsilon^3} \tag{4-10A}$$

or

$$f = C\frac{(1 - \epsilon)^{3-n}}{\epsilon^3} / Re^{2-n} \tag{4-10B}$$

where $Re = d_p U\varrho_f/\mu_f$

At low Reynolds number values, the pressure drop does not depend on the density $(n = 1)$, from which

$$f \propto (1 - \epsilon)^2/\epsilon^3 Re \tag{4-11}$$

And at high Re values, the viscosity term no longer dominates $(n = 2)$, from which

$$f \propto (1 - \epsilon)/\epsilon^3 \tag{4-12}$$

The theoretical expression (Equation 4-10) is observed experimentally at low Reynolds number values; however, at high Re values the large sensitivity of f to ϵ suggested by the expression is not observed in practice.

Among the classical studies of flow through fixed beds is that of Carman[1,2] and Kozeny.[3] For flow through a packing arrangement of spheres, Carman evaluated coefficient C and exponent n to be 90 and 1, respectively, for low values of Re. For other packing-element geometries (e.g., rings, saddles, wire crimps):

$$d_p = 6V_p/S_p \tag{4-13}$$

where V_p and S_p are the particle's volume and surface, respectively, from which frictional pressure losses are derived:[2]

$$\frac{\Delta P}{\ell} = \frac{180(1 - \epsilon)^3 \mu_f U}{g\epsilon^3 d_p^2}$$

$$= \frac{5(1 - \epsilon)^2 \mu_f U}{g\epsilon^3 (V_p/S_p)^2} \tag{4-14}$$

Equation 4-14 is known as the Carman-Kozeny equation (derived by Kozeny and tested by Carman over a range of voidages extending from 0.26 to 0.89). The principal assumption in the derivation of Equation 4-14 is that the granular bed can be approximated by a group of parallel, similar channels, such that their total surface and total internal volume are equal to the bed's particle surface and the bed's void volume, respectively. The general expression for streamline flow through a channel of uniform cross-section is:

$$\frac{\Delta P}{\ell_c} = \frac{k\mu_f U}{gR_H^2} \tag{4-15}$$

where ℓ_c = channel length
R_H = hydraulic radius of channel
k = coefficient which reflects specific geometry of channel

Noting the following:

$$U = (U/\epsilon)(\ell_c/\ell)$$

$$R_H = \epsilon/S = \epsilon(V_p/S_p)/(1 - \epsilon)$$

$$\ell_c = \ell(\ell_c/\ell)$$

from which is derived:

$$\frac{\Delta P}{\ell} = \frac{k(\ell_c/\ell)^2(1 - \epsilon)^2 \mu_f U}{g\epsilon^3 (V_p/S_p)^2} \tag{4-16}$$

where the group $k(\ell_c/\ell)^2$ has been experimentally evaluated to be 5.0, with $k \simeq 2.5$, according to Carman.[1] This value of k corresponds to a narrow rectangular channel. Equation 4-14 affords the means of estimating the specific surface of irregular packings from pressure drop measurements:

$$S_p/V_p = \left(\frac{g\Delta P\epsilon^3}{5(1 - \epsilon)^2 \mu_f U\ell}\right)^{0.5} \tag{4-17}$$

Estimates of the particle surface by this method should be viewed as minimum, since Equation 4-17 does not take into account blocked pore passages nor does it include the faces of closely packed disks or plates.

Numerous other investigators[4-19] have attempted to develop universal correlations for the pressure losses across a fixed bed. Table 4-1 lists some of the more successful correlations. Perhaps the most widely referenced correlation is that of Ergun:[18,19]

$$\frac{\Delta P}{\ell}g_c = 150\frac{(1 - \epsilon_m)^2}{\epsilon_m^3}\frac{\mu_f U}{(\phi_s \bar{d}_p)^2} + 1.75\frac{1 - \epsilon_m}{\epsilon_m^3}\frac{\varrho_f U^2}{\phi_s \bar{d}_p^2} \tag{4-18}$$

where ϕ_s is the particle shape factor, and $\bar{d}_p$ and ϵ_m denote mean values; that is:

$$\bar{d}_p = \frac{1}{\Sigma(x/d_p)_i} \tag{4-19}$$

where x_i is the fraction of material in size interval i.

Two terms contribute to the pressure loss in Equation 4-18, namely viscous and kinetic energies. At low values of the Reynolds number, the viscous term dominates:

$$\frac{\Delta P}{\ell}g_c = 150\frac{(1 - \epsilon_m)^2}{\epsilon_m^3}\frac{\mu_f U}{(\phi_s \bar{d}_p)^2}, \qquad (Re_p < 20) \tag{4-20}$$

And at high Re values the kinetic energy loss is important:

$$\frac{\Delta P}{\ell}g_c = 1.75\frac{(1 - \epsilon_m)}{\epsilon_m^3}\frac{\varrho_f U^2}{\phi_s \bar{d}_p}, \qquad (Re_p > 1,000) \tag{4-21}$$

where the particle Reynolds number is defined in the usual manner:

$$Re_p = \frac{\bar{d}_p \varrho_f U}{\mu} \tag{4-22}$$

For the transition flow regime both equations apply.

Table 4-1
Various Correlations for Pressure Drop and Friction Factors in Fixed Beds

Correlation	Range and Application	Comments	Investigator
$f_m = \dfrac{g d_p \Delta P \epsilon^3}{2\ell \varrho_f U^2 (1-\epsilon)^{3-n} \lambda^{3-n}}$ $\lambda = \text{shape factor} = 5.205\, S_p/V_p^{0.666}$	$10 < Re < 1{,}000$	Shape factor defined as particle surface to sphere surface having same volume	Leva[6]
$\Delta P/\ell = \dfrac{2\tilde{f}\varrho_f U^2 S}{g\epsilon^{1.7}}$ $= \dfrac{2\tilde{f}\varrho_f U^2(1-\epsilon)}{g\epsilon^{1.7}(V_p/S_p)}$	$100 < Re < 4{,}000$	Friction factor $\tilde{f}$ defined by Blake[16]	Oman and Watson[4]
$\Delta P/\ell = \dfrac{2\tilde{f}\varrho_f U^3 S}{g\epsilon^3}$ $= \dfrac{2\tilde{f}\varrho_f U^2(1-\epsilon)}{g\epsilon^3(V_p/S_p)}$ $\tilde{f} = f\epsilon^3/6(1-\epsilon)$	Applicable to spheres only	$\tilde{Re} = Re/6(1-\epsilon)$, for spheres	Blake[16]
Graphical correlation of f vs. Re	$0.1 < Re < 2{,}000$; $0.35 < \epsilon < 0.45$	Should not be applied to voidages widely different from those over which correlation was developed	Bakhmeteff and Feodoroff[17]

ONSET OF FLUIDIZATION AND GENERAL
CHARACTERISTICS

If the fluid velocity introduced through the bottom of the previously mentioned packed column of loose solids is gradually increased, the following sequence of events occurs. Figure 4-1A shows the case just described, where the fluid percolates through the fixed bed, and the pressure drop and Reynolds numbers are related. That is, ΔP_d will result and its magnitude will be established by the fluid's superficial velocity, U_d, and the properties of the solids (i.e., shape, density, orientation, etc.). As the fluid rate increases, so does the ΔP, but eventually the particles begin to be lifted by the gas, and the bed expands. During this expansion the solids rearrange their positions to present as little resistance to the flow as possible. This is denoted by Figures 4-1B and 4-1C for successive increments in fluid velocity. In Figure 4-1C, the loosest packing arrangement of solids that are in physical contact with each other is finally achieved.

If the fluid velocity is increased beyond this point, particles begin to move about freely with frequent collisions. The motion of particles in this state resembles that observed in the hindered settling of particles in a slurry medium. Figure 4-1C is referred to as the condition for the onset of fluidization or the minimum fluidization condition, and the superficial velocity through the column responsible for this state is called the *minimum fluidization velocity*. At slightly higher gas velocities, all the particles in the bed are in motion. Increases in the fluid Reynolds number result from incremental increases in ΔP as the bed of solids continues to expand and particles move in more rapid, independent motion. Eventually, at very high superficial

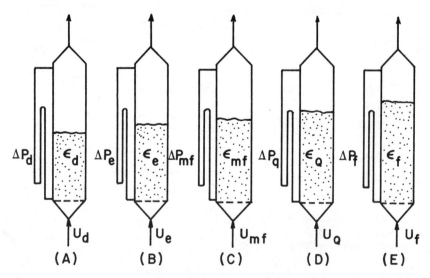

Figure 4-1. Illustration of the sequence of events leading to a dense-phase fluidized bed.

velocities, particles will be entrained by the upward flowing fluid, and the system will appear as dilute phase transport (Figure 4-1E).

The onset of fluidization is observed when the drag force exerted by the upward moving fluid stream matches the weight of the particles in the bed. Hence, from a force balance:

$$\Delta PF_b = W = (F_b \ell_{mf})(1 - \epsilon_{mf})(\varrho_s - \varrho_f) \tag{4-23}$$

where F_b = cross-sectional area of the bed of solids
ℓ_{mf} = expanded bed height at minimum fluidization
ϵ_{mf} = bed voidage at minimum fluidization conditions

Rearranging, the pressure drop occurring at minimum fluidization is:

$$\frac{\Delta P}{\ell_{mf}} = (1 - \epsilon_{mf})(\varrho_s - \varrho_g) \tag{4-24}$$

At the onset of fluidization, the voidage (referred to as the *minimum gas voidage*) is somewhat higher than in a packed bed. It essentially corresponds to the loosest state of a packed layer of solids having a small weight. As such, a value for ϵ_{mf} can be estimated from random packing data. The minimum gas voidage can, however, be readily measured by subjecting a small column of a known quantity of solids to a rising gas stream which initiates incipient particle motion. By recording the expansion of the bed and from knowledge of the buoyant weight of the bed (W), the column's cross-section (F), and solids and gas densities, we obtain:

$$\epsilon_{mf} = 1 - \frac{W}{\ell_{mf}F(\varrho_s - \varrho_g)} \tag{4-25}$$

Values for ϵ_{mf} reported for different solids fluidized by air at ambient conditions are given in Figure 4-2.

A good indication of fluidization behavior of granular material may be obtained from the pressure-drop flow relationships of the expanded bed. Figure 4-3 ideally illustrates the fluidization characteristics of a material. Branch ϵ_e' to ϵ_e on the plot pertains to the *fixed-bed pressure drop* of the bed at a voidage ϵ_e. At ϵ_e, expansion occurs and continues along the horizontal line. Particle motion sets in when the voidage has slightly surpassed a value ϵ_{mf} (i.e., the *minimum fluidization*). Fixed-bed conditions are reestablished as the flow rate is lowered again. This occurs at the pressure drop that is exactly equal to the value that may be calculated from the buoyant weight of the bed, designated as $\Delta\varrho_w$.

The range over which gas velocities span in transforming a bed of solids from *incipient fluidization* to the dilute phase state is shown in Figure 4-4. Note that for $d_p = 0.002$ in., for instance, the velocity range is nearly one hundredfold. As particle diameter increases, the range narrows considerably. However, even for $d_p = 0.012$ in. it is still about fortyfold. On the average, the ratio of the *terminal velocity,* U_t, to the minimum fluidization velocity is about 70 for many industrial applications.

Two main types of fluidization have been observed experimentally. In cases in which the fluid and solid densities are not too different and particle sizes are small, and the gas velocity is low, the bed fluidizes evenly, with each particle moving individually through a relatively uniform *mean free path.* The dense phase in this case acquires flow characteristics analogous to liquids. This is referred to as *particulate fluidization.*

When fluid and solid densities differ greatly or the particles are large, the required fluid velocity to ensure a fluidized state must be relatively high. In this case fluidization is uneven, and the fluid passes through the bed mainly in the form of large bubbles. These bubbles burst at the surface, spraying solid particles above the bed. Here, the bed has many of the characteristics of a liquid, with the fluid phase acting as a gas bubbling through it. This is called *aggregative fluidization,* in which the gas rises through the bed primarily in the form of bubbles. The value of the *Froude number,* $U_f^2/d_p g$ (in which U_f is the superficial gas velocity, d_p is the particle size, and g is the gravitational constant), is indicative of this type of fluidization. For Froude number values greater than unity, aggregative fluidization prevails. In addition to these classifications, fluidized beds show considerable *bypassing* and *slugging* (i.e., intermittent and unstable flow of large gas bubbles through the bed).

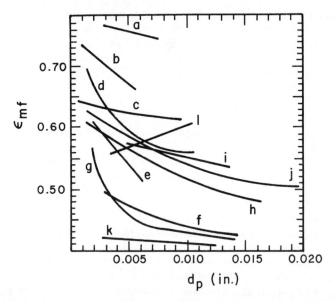

Figure 4-2. Typical values of θ_{mf} in relation to d_p: (a) soft brick; (b) adsorption carbon; (c) broken *Raschig rings;* (d) coal and glass powder; (e) carborundum; (f) sand; (g) round sands, ϕ_s = 0.86; (h) sharp sand, ϕ_s = 0.67; (i) *Fischer-Tropsch catalyst,* ϕ_s = 0.58; (j) anthracite coal, ϕ_s = 0.63; (k) mixed round sand, ϕ_s = 0.86; (l) coke. (ϕ_s is the particle shape factor.)

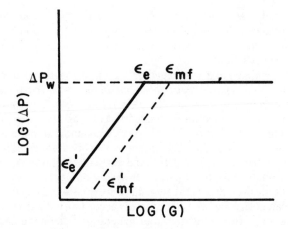

Figure 4-3. Pressure-drop/flow diagram for ideally fluidizing solids.

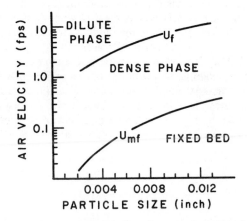

Figure 4-4. Illustration of a typical range of fluidization velocities encountered in industrial practices.

Fluidization may be described as incipient buoyancy because the particles are still so close as to have essentially no mobility; the usual desire is to create bed homogeneity. Such homogeneity can be realized only through violent mixing. This is achieved by increasing the fluid velocity to the point of generating "bubbles" or voids in the bed, which mix the bed as they rise. The increased fluid velocity at which bubbles form first is referred to as the *incipient* (or minimum) *bubbling velocity.*

Fine powders come in a wide range of bulk densities and therefore exhibit substantial variation in fluidizing characteristics. For coarser granular solids, no distinction can be made between *incipient buoyancy* and *incipient bubbling*, as illustrated by the plot shown in Figure 4-5. From a practical standpoint, the incipient bubbling velocity is the more significant parameter when designing fluidized systems with chemical reactions.

The terms "particulate" and "aggregative" are occasionally used to differentiate between *bubbling beds* (aggregative) and *nonbubbling beds* (particulate). In general, *liquid-fluidized beds* are nonbubbling, whereas *gas-fluidized beds* bubble. It is presently recognized that bubbling is related to fluid and particle properties in a manner permitting the prediction of a system's maximum attainable bubble size, which, if negligible, leads to the observation of so-called *particulate fluidization*. Rather than employ the terms aggregative and particulate, it is better to refer to the maximum stable bubble size for a particular system.

Although properties and thus fluidizing characteristics of materials differ greatly, it is possible to categorize the behavior of solids according to their fluidizing behavior. Geldart[20] has classified solids into four general groups on the basis of particle size and density relative to the fluid medium. Group A solids are those materials where fluidization is of the bubbling type (aggregative, heterogeneous), although these powders may exhibit particulate fluidization (homogeneous, nonbubbling) over a limited range of velocities near the minimum fluidization point. With these materials, the bed uniformly expands as the gas velocity is increased, reaches a maximum height at the velocity where the bubbles first appear, and gradually collapses to a minimum height with further increases in velocity. As described earlier, beyond this point, bubbly flow exists, and the bed again expands with the increasing velocity. A typical example of a material falling in Group A is commercial silica-alumina cracking catalyst. Solids that are coarser and more dense have different fluidizing characteristics. In this case, bubbles begin to form at the minimum fluidization point, and the bed expands in a nonuniform manner. These materials are classified as Group B solids. Group C solids consist of powders which are too

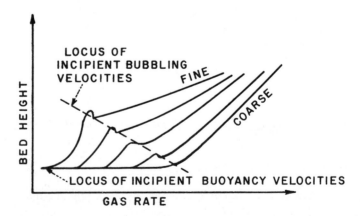

Figure 4-5. Illustration of the dramatic effect of particle size on the minimum fluidization and bubbling velocities.

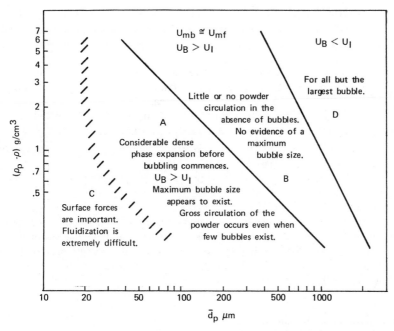

Figure 4-6. Geldart's[20] particle classification diagram.

fine for normal fluidization because of their cohesive properties. Finally, Group D is composed of very large and/or dense particles which can produce spouted beds. Figure 4-6 shows Geldart's classification diagram.

MINIMUM FLUIDIZATION VELOCITY

A layer of solids begins to fluidize when the pressure drop across the layer equals the weight of the bed per unit cross-section, thus allowing for the buoyant force of the rising fluid (Equation 4-23).

Occasionally, particles begin to move and the bed appears fluidized before the pressure drop reaches the critical value. This means that only a portion of the solids is supported by the fluid. At a slightly higher velocity, complete fluidization is obtained, and the pressure drop does indeed equal the weight of bed. To avoid the uncertainty associated with either the onset of fluidization or the velocity at which "complete" fluidization is achieved, the minimum fluidization velocity is generally determined by extrapolating the plot of pressure drop for a fixed bed until it reaches the horizontal line corresponding to the weight of the bed per unit area or the final value of the pressure drop.

A reasonable extrapolation for the Ergun equation for estimating ΔP is to the loosest state of a packed bed (i.e., the minimum fluidization condition). Hence, Equations 4-18 and 4-24 may be combined to give the following quadratic formula for U_{mf}:

$$\frac{1.75}{\phi_s \epsilon_{mf}^3} \left(\frac{d_p U_{mf} \varrho_f}{\mu}\right)^2 + \frac{150(1 - \epsilon_{mf})}{\phi_s^2 \epsilon_{mf}^3} \left(\frac{d_p U_{mf} \varrho_f}{\mu}\right) = \frac{d_p^3 \varrho_f (\varrho_p - \varrho_f)g}{\mu^2} \tag{4-26}$$

From accurate information on particle size, shape, and ϵ_{mf}, the minimum fluidization velocity can be estimated.

Many of the correlations reported in the literature (References 21–33) for ϵ_{mf} stem from this equation.

The functional form of this correlation is justified by the following analysis. Since the pressure drop across a fluidized layer of solids is equal to the particle layer weight, G_p, divided by the cross-sectional area, F, then the volume of the layer is $F\ell$, where ℓ is the layer height. For a porosity ϵ, the volume occupied by the particles in the layer is $F\ell(1-\epsilon)$, and taking into account the gas lifting force, the particles' weight is:

$$G_p = F\ell(1 - \epsilon)(\varrho_p - \varrho)g \tag{4-27}$$

where the pressure drop of the fluidized bed is given by Equation 4-23.

The height of the layer and its *porosity* increase with an increase in the fluid's superficial velocity. The value $1-\epsilon$ decreases, but the product $\ell(1-\epsilon)$ remains constant because the pressure drop across the bed is independent of the superficial gas velocity.

If the height of a fixed layer is ℓ_0 and its porosity is ϵ_0, then

$$\ell(1 - \epsilon) = \ell_0(1 - \epsilon_0)$$

and

$$\epsilon = 1\frac{\ell_0}{\ell}(1 - \epsilon_0) = 1 - \frac{(1 - \epsilon_0)}{K}$$

where $K = \dfrac{\ell}{\ell_0}$ $\tag{4-28}$

where K is the *expansion coefficient* of the fluidized layer. The fluidization velocity may be found by equating the pressure drop of a fixed bed to that of the fluidized bed.

$$\frac{3}{4} \lambda \frac{\ell(1 - \epsilon_0)\varrho U_0^{0.5}}{d_p \phi_s \epsilon_0^3} = \ell(\varrho_p - \varrho)g(1 - \epsilon_0) \tag{4-29}$$

or upon rearranging in terms of an appropriately defined Reynolds number:

$$\lambda(Re_0')^2 = \frac{4}{3}\phi_s\epsilon_0^3\frac{gd_\varrho^3(\varrho_p - \varrho)}{\mu^2} = \frac{4}{3}\phi_s\epsilon_0^3 \, Ar \tag{4-30}$$

where λ = dimensionless coefficient (friction factor)
Re_0' = *modified Reynolds number* based on the minimum fluidization velocity

The important dimensionless groups to recognize are the Galileo number:

$$Ga = \frac{Re^2}{Fr} = \frac{g\ell^3\varrho_f^2}{\mu^2} = \frac{g\ell^2}{\nu^2} \tag{4-31}$$

and the Archimedes number:

$$Ar = Ga\frac{\varrho_p - \varrho_f}{\varrho_f} = \frac{g\ell^3\varrho_f(\varrho_p - \varrho_f)}{\mu^2} = \frac{g\ell^3}{\nu^2}\frac{\varrho_p - \varrho_f}{\varrho_f} \tag{4-32}$$

Upon examining the extrapolated form of the Ergun equation (4-26), the Archimedes and Reynolds number groups are identified.
Wen and Yu[31] have found for a wide variety of systems that:

$$\frac{1}{\phi_s\epsilon_{mf}^3} \simeq 14 \text{ and } \frac{1 - \epsilon_{mf}}{\phi_s^2\epsilon_{mf}^3} \simeq 11 \tag{4-33}$$

From which, Equation 4-26 reduces to the form:

$$Re_{mf} = \frac{d_pU_{mf}\varrho_f}{\mu} = [(33.7)^2 + 0.0408 \, Ar]^{0.5} - 33.7 \tag{4-34}$$

where Ar is written in terms of the average particle diameter:

$$Ar = \frac{d_p^3\varrho_f(\varrho_s - \varrho_f)g}{\mu^2} \tag{4-35}$$

Equation 4-34 provides a very simple expression for estimating the minimum fluidization velocity. Figure 4-7 shows a plot of the expression.
Other approximate forms of Equation 4-26 have been suggested. Some of these are summarized in Table 4-2. The last two equations in Table 4-2, proposed by Wen and Yu,[31] are flow regime dependent. For very small particles, only the laminar flow ($Re_p < 20$) term is important and hence the simpler equation is obtained. Several investigators have presented correlations for U_{mf} that are based on this equation

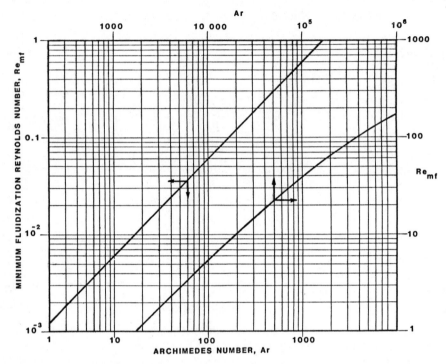

Figure 4-7. Plot of approximate form of extrapolated Ergun equation for estimating the minimum fluidization velocity.

(Table 4-2) but do not contain ϵ_{mf} or ϕ_s. For example, the equation given by Davidson and Harrison[29] in Table 4-2 corresponds to the Wen and Yu[31] expression for $Re_p < 20$ with $\epsilon_{mf} = 0.42$ and $\phi_s = 1.0$. A similar expression with a coefficient of 0.001065 was given by Frantz.[32] Geldart et al.[33] claim, however, that the Davidson-Harrison[29] equation applies to a wide range of Group A materials.

Other investigators have presented empirical correlations for U_{mf} with exponents for d_p, μ, and $\varrho_p - \varrho$ that differ slightly from the values given for the Wen and Yu correlation. A review by Grewal and Saxena[30] shows that Leva's[22] correlation (also given in Table 4-2), fits published data for U_{mf} about as well as any. Note that the exponent of 1.82 rather than 2.0 for the particle size probably comes partly from the tendency for smaller size fractions of most solids to have higher values of ϵ_{mf}. Interparticle forces tend to become more important for small sizes, leading to agglomeration and formations of pockets that would not exist in beds of large solids. Deviations from the expected exponents may also be attributed to the inclusion of data slightly beyond the laminar flow range.

Table 4-2
Various Correlations for Minimum Fluidization Velocity

Correlation	Units/Definitions	Investigators
$$U_{mf} = k_m \left[\frac{\epsilon_{mf}^3}{(1 - \epsilon_{mf})^{n+1}} \right]^{\frac{n+1}{3}} d_p^n$$ $$k_m = k_k^{\frac{-(n+1)}{3}} \left[\frac{(\varrho_p - \varrho_f)}{\varrho_f} \right]^{\frac{n+1}{3}} \left(\frac{\mu}{\varrho_f} \right)^{\frac{1-2n}{3}} g^{\frac{n+1}{3}}$$	k_k = Kozeny's constant when n = 2	Hatch[23]
$$U_{mf} = 0.000850 \left[\frac{\epsilon_{mf}^3}{(1 - \epsilon_{mf})^{0.973}} \right]^{0.973} d_p^{1.92}$$	U_{mf}(cm/s); $d_p(\mu m)$	Rowe and Yacono[26]
$$U_{mf} = 0.000512 \, d_p^{1.77}$$	U_{mf}(cm/s); $d_p(\mu m)$	Yacono[25]
$$U_{mf} = 0.0008 \, g(\varrho_p - \varrho_f) d_p^2 / \mu$$	All units in SI	Davidson and Harrison[29] and Geldart et al.[33]
$$U_{mf} = \frac{0.0093 \, d_p^{1.82}(\varrho_p - \varrho_f)^{0.94}}{\mu^{0.88} \varrho_f^{0.06}}$$	All units in SI	Leva[22]
$$U_{mf} = \frac{d_p^2(\varrho_p - \varrho_f)g}{1,650\mu} \, (Re_p < 20)$$	Applicable for small particles (all units cgs, U_{mf}(cm/s))	Wen and Yu[31]
$$U_{mf}^2 = \frac{d_p(\varrho_p - \varrho_f)g}{24.5\varrho_f} \, (Re_p > 1{,}000)$$	Applicable for large particles (all units cgs, U_{mf}(cm/s)) $Re_p = \frac{d_p \varrho_f U_t}{\mu}$	

It is recommended that for particles with a size distribution, the surface-volume mean, d_{sv}, should be used for d_p. For nonspherical particles, the product of the nominal size and the sphericity or shape factor, ϕ_s, is used to give the equivalent diameter. It is difficult, however, to determine ϕ_s from inspection of irregular solids, and it is usually determined from the pressure drop through a fixed bed or from the equation of minimum fluidization velocity.

We should note that a fluid's motion through a fluidized bed is limited on the one hand by U_{mf} and on the other by the entrainment of solids by the fluid. When entrainment occurs these solids must be replaced by fresh material to maintain a steady-state system. This upper limit to the fluid flow rate can be approximated by the terminal or free-fall velocity of the particles, which can be estimated from the fluid mechanics by an appropriately defined drag coefficient.[34]

The following criteria[35] are used to determine the frictional resistance to flow:

$$\lambda = 220/\text{Re, for Re} < 50 \tag{4-36A}$$

$$\lambda = 11.6/\text{Re}^{0.25}, \text{ for } 50 < \text{Re} < 7,200 \tag{4-37A}$$

$$\lambda = 1.26, \text{ for Re} > 7,200 \tag{4-38C}$$

A dimensionless shape factor can be defined as:

$$\psi' = \frac{\phi_s^3 \epsilon_0^3}{(1 - \epsilon_0)} \tag{4-39}$$

The following regimes of flow based on a modified Reynolds number are defined:

At ψ' Ar $< 18,500$:

$$\text{Re}_0' = \frac{0.00404(1 - \epsilon_0)}{\phi_s} (\psi' \text{Ar}) \tag{4-40}$$

At ψ' Ar $= 18,500 - 1.1 \times 10^8$:

$$\text{Re}_0' = \frac{0.275(1 - \epsilon_0)}{\phi_s} [\psi' \text{Ar } \varrho(0.57)] \tag{4-41}$$

At ψ' Ar $> 1.1 \times 10^8$:

$$\text{Re}_0' = \frac{1.03(1 - \epsilon_0)}{\phi_s} [\psi' \text{Ar } \varrho(0.5)] \tag{4-42}$$

In general, the resistance force acting against the flow is:

$$R_f = \xi F \varrho \frac{U_0^2}{2} \tag{4-43}$$

where ξ = *resistance coefficient*
   F = surface area normal to particle motion (m^2)
   ϱ = density of fluid (kg/m^3)
   U_0 = velocity (m/s)

For spherical particles, we may write:

$$R_f = \frac{F d_p^2}{4} \left(\frac{\varrho U_0^2}{2} \right) \tag{4-44}$$

where d_p = particle diameter

Hence,

$$R_f = \phi U_0^2 d_p^2 \varrho \tag{4-45}$$

where

$$\phi' = \frac{R_f}{U_0^2 d_p^2 \varrho} \tag{4-46}$$

$$\phi' = \xi \frac{\pi}{8} = \text{resistance coefficient}$$

The resistance coefficient can be defined in the usual manner: For the laminar regime (Stokes equation, where $Re_p < 2$):

$$\phi' = \frac{3\pi}{Re_p} \tag{4-47}$$

For the intermediate regime (Allen's equation, where $2 < Re_p < 500$):

$$\phi' = 7.27/Re^{0.6} \tag{4-48}$$

And for the turbulent regime (Newton's equation, where $Re_p > 500$):

$$\phi' = 0.173 \tag{4-49}$$

Note that for nonspherical particles the resistance coefficient depends on both Re and a shape factor ϕ_s:

$$\phi_s = \left(\frac{f_{sph}}{f_p}\right) \tag{4-50}$$

where f_{sph} = sphere surface area
f_p = particle surface area

The porosity of the fluidized layer can be estimated from the following:

$$\epsilon = \frac{18Re_0' + 0.36Re_0'}{Ar} \tag{4-51}$$

Note that $P' - R_f = ma$, where a is particle acceleration and P' is the force exerted on the solids.

When $U_0 = 0$, $R_f = 0$, and $R_f = P'$, $a = 0$, where initially $a = P'/m$. When $P > R_f$, the condition of sedimentation is satisfied. This means that:

$$U_0 = \frac{1}{d_p}\left(\frac{P'^{0.5}}{\phi'\varrho}\right) \tag{4-52}$$

Or upon rearranging terms:

$$\frac{P'\varrho}{\mu^2} = \phi'\frac{U_0^2 d_p^2 \varrho^2}{\mu^2} = \phi' Re^2 \tag{4-53}$$

When a particle of diameter d_p is falling under the influence of gravity, force P' is equal to the weight of a particle in gas:

$$P' = \frac{\pi d_p^3}{6}g(\varrho_p - \varrho) \tag{4-54}$$

Thus,

$$\phi' Re^2 = \frac{\pi d_p^3 g(\varrho_p - \varrho)}{6\mu^2} = \frac{\pi}{6}Ar \tag{4-55}$$

Equation 4-55 along with Equations 4-47 through 4-49 for ϕ', provides three expressions that allow estimates of the particle settling velocity, U_t, as first reviewed in Chapter 1.

At $Re_p < 2$ or $Ar < 36$:

$$Re = 0.056 Ar \tag{4-56}$$

At $Re_p = 2 - 500$ or $Ar = 36 - 83 \times 10^3$:

$$Re = 0.152Ar^{0.715} \tag{4-57}$$

At $Re_p > 500$ or $Ar > 83 \times 10^3$:

$$Re = 1.74Ar^{0.5} \tag{4-58}$$

Starting with Equation 4-6, we may write:

$$\left(\frac{U_t}{U_t}\right)^2 a\, U_{mf}^2 \left(\frac{d_p\varrho_f}{\mu}\right)^2 + b\, U_{mf}\left(\frac{d_p\varrho_f}{\mu}\right) = Ar$$

or

$$a\left(\frac{U_{mf}}{U_t}\right)^2 Re_p^2 + b\left(\frac{U_{mf}}{U_t}\right) Re_p = Ar \tag{4-59}$$

where $a = \dfrac{1}{\phi_s\epsilon_{mf}^3}$

$$b = \frac{1 - \epsilon_{mf}}{\phi_s^2\epsilon_{mf}^3}$$

$$Re_p = \frac{U_t d_p\varrho_f}{\mu}$$

Replacing Re_p by the appropriate expression corresponding to the three regimes of flow (Equations 4-56 through 4-58), a quadratic expression describing the ratio of U_{mf} to U_t is obtained:

$$a'\left(\frac{U_{mf}}{U_t}\right)^2 + b'\left(\frac{U_{mf}}{U_t}\right) + c' = 0 \tag{4-60}$$

Coefficients a', b', and c' are given in Table 4-3 for the three flow regimes, in which the Wen and Yu[31] approximation (Equation 4-33) has been used.

Equation 4-60 is presented graphically in Figure 4-8 as a plot of U_t/U_{mf} versus Ar for all three regimes. As shown, the ratio of U_t/U_{mf} lies between 10 and over 90, which indicates the flexibility of fluidized systems. Experimentally, it is observed that U_t/U_{mf} is small for large-sized particles, suggesting less flexibility than for smaller particles. This ratio also provides an indication of the maximum possible height of the fluidized bed. The reason for this being that the pressure drop through the bed results in an increase in the fluid's velocity through the bed. Consequently, the maximum bed height corresponds to when the bed is just fluidized at the bottom and where U_t is just reached at the top.[34] These conclusions are strictly based on gas-fluidized beds, since in liquid-fluidized beds, the fluid density remains practically unchanged.

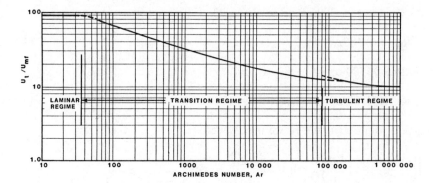

Figure 4-8. Plot of ratio of particle terminal velocity to minimum fluidization velocity.

Table 4-3
Coefficients for Equation 4-60

Flow Regime	a'	b'	c'	Reynolds Number Range	Archimedes Number Range
Laminar	1.37 Ar	1,650	−17.86	<2	<36
Transition	3.72 Ar$^{0.715}$	1,650	−6.58 Ar$^{0.285}$	2–500	36–83 × 10^3
Turbulent	42.63 Ar$^{0.5}$	1,650	−0.575 Ar$^{0.5}$	>500	>83 × 10^3

MINIMUM BUBBLING VELOCITY

Materials in Group A when fluidized, are characterized by conditions of relatively profuse bubbling, as illustrated in Figure 4-9A. Bubbles are formed at the
orifice where the fluidizing gas enters the bed. They form because the velocity at
the interface of the bed, just above the orifice, represents a gas input rate in excess
of the amount that can pass through the interstices at a frictional resistance less than
the bed weight. Hence, the layers of solids above the holes are pushed aside until
they represent a void through whose porous surface the gas can enter at the *incipient
fluidization velocity.*

If the void grows larger, the interface velocity becomes insufficient to support the
walls of the void. Hence, the walls cave in from the sides, cutting off the void and
presenting a new surface of solids to the incoming gas. This sequence is illustrated
in Figure 4-9B. The size of the initial bubble resulting from a detached void is typically on the order of about half the penetration depth (discussed later). Bubbles or

gas voids rise in a fluidized bed by being displaced with an inflow of solids from their perimeters. The superficial fluid velocity at which bubbles first appear to freely form and rise through the bed is referred to as the minimum bubbling point or velocity, U_{mb}. The minimum bubbling velocity is usually very close to $\overline{U}_{mf}$ for many Group A powders. The determination of U_{mb}, as well as U_{mf}, is subject to uncertainty since they are both based on visual observation. In particulate fluidization, a few bubbles may be observed while the bed is still expanding, however, these may be due to wall

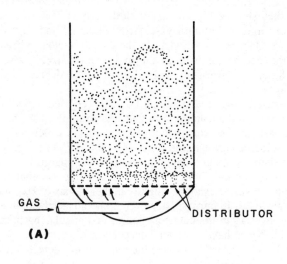

(A)

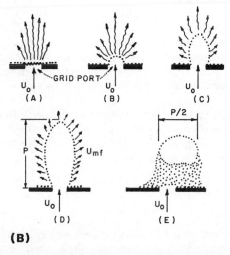

(B)

Figure 4-9. (A) Freely bubbling gas-fluidized bed; (B) illustration of the formation of bubbles by introducing gas through a single orifice.

effects and/or irregularities in the column. Harriott et al.[36] suggest that the definition of U_{mb} be taken to be the velocity at which the maximum bed height is observed. This definition appears to be most appropriate when obtaining U_{mb} values from the literature (see, for example, Reference 37).

The principal parameter affecting the bubble point is particle size. In this regard, Geldart et al.[33] proposed a linear correlation between U_{mb} and the mean volume surface diameter. Harriott and Simone[36] point out that Geldart's data for catalyst particles has a better correlation fit at a lower slope, with a separate line for larger particles of diakon polymer tested. Using their own data obtained from both wide and narrow size distribution cracking catalysts[38] and data reported by other investigators,[37,39-43] they showed U_{mb} to vary with d_p to the 0.7 power.

It is of interest to note that unlike Geldart,[33] Simone[38] and others[43,21] found little effect of the size distribution on U_{mb}. In the case of Geldart's[33] work this can be explained by the fact that he includes a term $\bar{d}_p$ exp $(0.716\ \mathring{F})$, where $\mathring{F}$ is the fraction of fines. Since $\mathring{F}$ is large for small values of d_p, the data are equally well fitted by $d_p^{0.7}$ and no term for the fines fraction.

Much of the discrepancy found among U_{mb} data reported in the literature may be due to irregularities in the materials studied. For example, beds may contain weak aggregates of particles and some cavities or channels, which tend to stabilize the bed to higher velocities prior to the onset of bubbling.[41] There may also be effects due to particle shape, surface roughness, and/or static charges, which tend to influence interparticle forces. Donsi,[41] for example, reports that particles with a strongly corrugated surface showed slightly higher values of U_{mb} and ϵ_{mb} than relatively smooth particles. In fairness, however, it should also be pointed out that there is considerable overlap in the data for spheres and angular particles, even though the latter are known to have stronger interparticle effects.

Goddard and Richardson[39] examined the effect of gas density on U_{mb} by fluidizing solids in air at different pressures. They found that U_{mb} varies with density to a power of 0.06 (also confirmed by Abrahamsen and Geldart[44]). The effect of higher pressures was found to slightly decrease U_{mb}. In one study,[45] coal particles were observed to exhibit particulate fluidization over the entire range of gas velocities tested, but at lower pressures a transition to bubbling fluidization was found.

As will be shown later, high pressure fluidization of fine powders tends to produce smaller gas bubbles in the bubbling regime, as well as lower dense-phase viscosities.[46,47]

The effect of viscosity on U_{mb} can be studied by conducting fluidization tests with different gases, once the dependency on gas density is known. It has been observed that a significant increase in gas viscosity results in lower U_{mb} and U_{mf} values. Abrahamsen and Geldart[44] reported that:

$$U_{mb}/\varrho^{0.06} \propto \mu^{2-0.347} \tag{4-61}$$

Mutsers and Rietema[37] conducted fluidization tests with cracking catalyst and other solids using four gases of widely different viscosities. They observed that ϵ_{mb} was significantly higher at high viscosities. Harriott and Simone[36] estimated U_{mb} data from this study by assuming $\epsilon^3/(1-\epsilon)$ was proportional to the gas velocity. By comparing these estimated data with other literature values of U_{mb}, they obtained the following empirical correlation for the minimum bubbling velocity:

$$U_{mb} = a' d_{vs}^{0.7} \varrho^{0.06} \mu^{-0.4} \qquad (4\text{-}62)$$

where a' is a coefficient that appears to be specific to the solids. For silica-alumina cracking catalyst, Harriott et al. report a value of 4.23×10^{-3} for the coefficient. The units in Equation 4-62 are mm/s for U_{mb}, mm for d_{vs}, kg/m³ for ϱ and Pa-s for μ.

As suggested by Geldart et al.[33] and others,[36] the ratio of U_{mb}/U_{mf} provides a relative index for the range of particulate fluidization. Using the equation given by Davidson et al.[29] (see Table 4-2), an estimate for this index is:

$$\frac{U_{mb}}{U_{mf}} = 0.042 \frac{\mu^{0.6} \varrho^{0.06}}{g d_{vs}^{1.3} (\varrho_p - \varrho)} \qquad (4\text{-}63)$$

where the coefficient for silica-alumina catalyst has been included and all units are in SI.

The range of particulate fluidization is greatest for fine powders, although it is somewhat reduced by channeling and bypassing effects. In general, however, the range increases slightly at high pressures but is significantly greater when the gas viscosity is high as seen by the 0.6 power exponent in Equation 4-63.

BED EXPANSION

Empirical Correlations

The expansion of a bed of Group A solids (i.e., materials which we would normally expect to form freely bubbling beds) can be expressed in terms of the change in bed height, bed density, or voidage. For laminar flow between particles, the pressure drop through a slightly expanded bed (in the region between U_{mf} and U_{mb}) shows approximately the same dependence on ϵ as for a fixed bed. As such, the term $\epsilon^3/(1-\epsilon)$ is roughly proportional to the superficial velocity, from which is derived:

$$\frac{\epsilon}{1 - \epsilon} = U_0 \frac{150\mu}{g(\varrho_p - \varrho)(\phi_s d_p)^2} \qquad (4\text{-}64)$$

Harriott et al.[36] have shown that Equation 4-63 gives a good fit for cracking catalyst data on a log-log plot. Such a plot yields straight lines; however, their slopes are observed to vary from 0.79 to 1.0, with lower values for the smaller fractions. Similar results were obtained by DeJong et al.,[43] whose exponents of 1.2 to 1.0 for the group $\epsilon^3/(1-\epsilon)$ are the reciprocals of the slopes of log-log plots obtained by Harriott.

When the slopes of these lines are less than 1.0, less bed expansion than is predicted by Equation 4-63 occurs; that is, the bed is actually more permeable. Rowe[26] suggests that such deviations could result from small differences in local porosity due to the bed structure. A bed with some channels or cavities larger than the average has a higher permeability than a bed with uniform channels. Massamilla et al.[42] demonstrated this from photographs of 100-μm powder fluidized with air at velocities below the bubble point. The photographs revealed cavities and micro-channels at the wall as large as twice the particle size, but the size and frequency of cavities in the bed interior is not known.

There is also a more fundamental reason for the deviation of experimental fits from Equation 4-64; namely, $\epsilon^3/(1-\epsilon)$, which is derived from the Ergun or Carman-Kozeny models for flow in parallel channels, is not entirely appropriate for a highly expanded bed. Harriott et al. observed the lowest slopes for the smallest-sized fractions, which have the highest maximum values of ϵ. They suggest that more precise data might reveal a gradual decrease in slope as ϵ is increased.

The most widely referenced correlation for bed expansion in particulate fluidization is the Richardson and Zaki[48] equation:

$$\frac{U_0}{U_i} = \epsilon^n \tag{4-65}$$

From liquid-solid fluidization studies, the value of exponent n was regressed to a range of values varying from 4.65 for small particles to 2.4 for large particles. Correlations were also developed to predict n as a function of the particle Reynolds number,[48] where U_i was approximated by the terminal velocity for single particles.

Particulate fluidization using gases can also be described by the Richardson-Zaki equation but with values of n generally larger than for liquids at the same Reynolds number. Harriott et al.[36] report values of n to range from 5.6 for small-size cracking catalyst, to 4.3 for large sizes. In comparison, the value of the exponent for liquid fluidization at comparable particle Reynolds numbers ranges from 4.65 to 4.1. The higher than expected values of n means simply that bed expansion with gases is not quite as great as with liquids. The values of U_i are not equal to U_t, but no particular significance is attached to the exact value of U_i/U_t. Goddard et al.[35] found n for diakon powder fluidized with air at 1 atmosphere was 4.7 to 5.5, but n approached the values for liquid fluidization at higher pressures. With a low density phenolic resin, n was found to be 8.5, indicating much less expansion than for liquid fluidization. Values of n (in the range of 7 to 20) were reported for particulate fluidization of coal with gases at high pressure by Crowther.[45]

Oltrogge and Kadlec[49] review several approaches to predicting bed expansion, which lead to semi-empirical correlations. A simple correlation based on a Froude number criterion is postulated as follows. First, bed expansion is assumed to be described as laminar flow up to some critical Froude number value. Secondly, the gas density is neglected relative to the density of the solids. Wilhelm and Kwauk[50] define the critical Froude number based on the superficial gas velocity and particle diameter to be 0.1. This value makes the distinction between particulate and bubbling fluidization. That is:

$$Fr = \frac{U_0^2}{gd_p}$$

$$Fr = \frac{U_{mb}^2}{gd_p} = 0.1 \tag{4-66}$$

Incorporating this definition into Equation 4-64 gives:

$$\frac{\epsilon_{mb}^3}{1 - \epsilon_{mb}} = \frac{47.4\mu}{g^{0.5}d_p^{1.5}\varrho_p} = 47.4 \ Ga^{-0.5} \tag{4-67}$$

Where the Froude number has been written in terms of the Galileo number,

$$Ga = \frac{G\bar{d}_p^2\varrho_p^2}{\mu^2} = \frac{Re^2}{Fr} \tag{4-68}$$

The correlation is shown compared to data for cracking catalyst[36] and for glass beads and char particles obtained by the authors in Figure 4-10. As shown, Equation 4-67 gives a reasonably good prediction, although Harriott does note that the power dependency on viscosity may be off.

Other expansion correlations have been proposed by various investigators and several that have been found to provide reasonable predictions are listed in Table 4-4.

As described earlier, with Group A materials, the bed expands uniformly as the gas velocity is increased, reaches a maximum height at approximately U_{mb}, and gradually collapses to a minimum height with further increases in gas velocity. Bubbly flow eventually dominates and the bed again expands with increasing velocity. Although the dense phase collapses once bubbling starts, the voidage remains significantly higher than that of the settled bed throughout the bubbling regime. Dense-phase expansion can be readily measured by stopping the gas flow, allowing a few seconds for bubbles to escape through the bed, and recording the bed height.

Changes in height of the dense phase are observed to be typically about half of that measured for the bed at the bubble point. If the expansion occurs uniformly, with increasing velocity, then it is obviously due to the increase in bubble holdup, from which we may write:

$$\Delta h/\Delta h_{mf} = \frac{(V_B/F)}{\bar{U}_B - (V_B/F)} = \frac{U_D - U_i}{\bar{U}_B - (U_D - U_i)} \tag{4-69}$$

where V_B = volumetric flow of gas in form of bubbles
F = bed's cross-section,
$\bar{U}_B$ = average bubble rise velocity
U_D = mean gas velocity across distributor plate
U_i = superficial gas velocity through dense phase

Equation 4-69 suggests an alternate approach to estimating bed expansion, through either measurement or estimate of the average rise velocity of bubbles. This in turn depends on the size and shape of bubbles, and most certainly whether the bed is freely bubbling, channeling or slugging. Discussions of the latter flow regimes, as well as bubble characteristics are described in subsequent sections in this chapter.

For now, we note simply that the expansion of the dense phase is caused by resulting changes in fluidity, bubble stability, and bubble velocity. The interaction between these various effects is complex and varies significantly for different solids even of the same group. King et al.[47] and Matheson et al.[51] have shown that the viscosity of a fluidized bed of fine catalyst is significantly less than for a bed of coarser solids; consequently, bubbles of a given size tend to rise more rapidly when the bed is composed of fine solids. Also, bubbles tend to be smaller when fluidizing

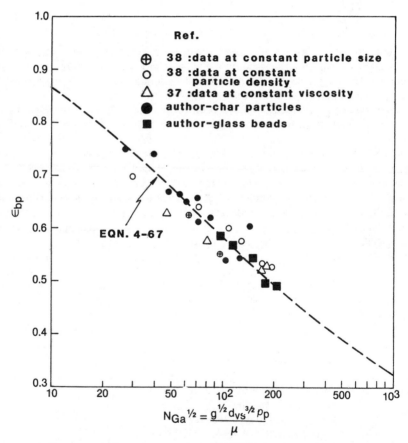

Figure 4-10. Comparison of voidage at maximum bed height to predictions of Equation 4-67.

Table 4-4
Correlations for Maximum Bed Voidage
(or Relative Bed Expansion Height)

Correlation	Comments	Investigator
$\dfrac{\epsilon^3_{mb}}{(1 - \epsilon)_{mb}} = \dfrac{150\, a'\, \mu^{0.6}\varrho^{0.06}}{g\, \varrho_p\, d_p^{1.3}}$	Derived from Equation 4-62 and Davidson and Harrison's[29] equation for U_{mf} (see Table 4-2).	Harriott and Simone[36]
$\epsilon_{mb} = f(F_o) = f\left(\dfrac{\varrho_p^3 \bar{d}_p^4 g^2}{\mu^2 E}\right)$	E is an elasticity coefficient, which accounts for interparticle forces on bed expansion and must be determined for specific powder. F_o is the dimensionless fluidization number.	Mutsers and Rietema[37]
$\dfrac{\epsilon_{mb}}{\epsilon_{mf}} = \left(\dfrac{U_{mb}}{U_{mf}}\right)^{0.22}$	Empirical correlation established from data for alumina, ballotini, and cracking catalyst fluidized with different gases. Has also been tested for various catalyst fractions and polymer particles and shown to provide good predictions.	Abrahamsen and Geldart[44]

fine particles;[52] and the effect of high pressures tends to produce smaller bubbles in beds of fine powders with less pronounced effects in beds of coarse solids.[53,54] Bubble characteristics (i.e., size, shape, rise velocity, and number of bubbles per unit volume of bed per unit time) play dominant roles in the exchange of heat and mass and in promoting chemical reactions in fluidized-bed reactors. It is clear that a more theoretical basis is needed to describe these effects. This more fundamental approach is needed in predicting such parameters as bed expansion as well. Although the correlations presented in this subsection are sufficient for engineering calculations, they do not provide insight into understanding phenomena during fluidization.

Energy Balance Method

A theoretical model for describing the expansion of the dense phase was recently set forth by Azbel and Cheremisinoff.[55] The model, outlined below, attempts to describe the bubbling regime of an infinite medium, and hence from a practical standpoint, is strictly applicable to large columns and where the bed expands uniformly due to freely rising bubbles (i.e., Group A materials).

The following assumptions constitute the basis for the model:

1. The two-phase flow system is sufficiently removed from the vessel walls and the gas distributor, and there are no bed internals.
2. The flow system is considered to be one-dimensional.

3. The solids are considered as a continuum phase and can be approximated as an incompressible fluid.
4. The energy dissipation of the fluidized system is due to the effective viscosity of the bed and its turbulence.

From an energy balance over a unit cross-section of a differential layer of the fluidized bed we may write:

$$dE = dE_1 + dE_2 + dE_3 \tag{4-70}$$

where dE = total energy of the layer
     dE_1 = layer's potential energy
     dE_2 = dissipative energy
     dE_3 = surface tension energy of the bubbles in the layer

The potential energy of the solid layer per unit cross-section of column is:

$$dE_2 = (1 - \epsilon)\varrho_f \, gx \, dx \tag{4-71}$$

where ϱ_f = continuum-phase density
     g = gravitational acceleration
     x = vertical distance
     ϵ = void fraction

The dissipative energy term, dE_2, is a function of the bubble velocity. In turbulent flow, large-scale eddies may entrain bubbles; however, since their density is considerably smaller than that of the solid phase, inertial forces differ by orders of magnitudes, and we can conclude that this entrainment is not complete. At the other extreme, the small-scale eddies cannot entrain a bubble, and as such, bubbles may be considered to be stationary bodies. Solids associated with this small-scale motion tend to flow around a gas bubble.

Levich[56] gives the following equation for the scale of eddies that can entrain a single rising bubble:

$$(\varrho_g + k\varrho_f)V \frac{d\nu_r}{dt} = (\varrho_f - \varrho_g)V \frac{d\nu_t}{dt} - F_D \tag{4-72}$$

where ϱ_g = gas density
     V = volume of a single bubble
     ν_r = velocity of bubbles relative to the solid phase
     F_D = drag force
     ν_t = solid layer's velocity
     k = coefficient of "apparent additional mass," which is basically a bubble shape factor.

The first term on the right hand side of Equation 4-72 expresses the inertial effect of the surrounding turbulent solids, and the second term is the drag force. By convention F_D is assumed equal to the drag imposed on a freely rising bubble of moderate size (Re $\simeq$ 800);

$$F_D = 12\pi\mu_f\, r_b\, \nu_r \tag{4-73}$$

where μ_f = dynamic viscosity of the contiuum phase
$\quad\ r_b$ = bubble radius

In mass-bubbling, however, turbulent motion is generated by the bubbly flow, and each bubble is influenced by its neighbor. Obviously, the drag on a bubble in a real fluid bed differs from that on a single-rising bubble.

Lamb,[57] Golovin et al,[58,59] Miasnikov and Levich,[60] Gupalo[61] and Leva[22] provide various empirical and semi-empirical formulas for estimating the drag exerted on an individual bubble immersed in a bubble swarm.

In an attempt to develop a theoretical description of drag on bubbles in a swarm, Happle,[62] Uchida,[63] and Marucci[64] developed the spherical compartment model. The assumption of uniform bubble size distribution in the layer's volume is applied. Furthermore, the bubble swarm is approximated by assuming that every bubble is located in the center of a spherical compartment formed by adjacent bubbles. Expressions describing the bubble velocity may then be written in spherical coordinates. In writing these expressions the two-phase motion is visualized as a continuum phase (solids) flowing between two concentric spheres, the inner surface being the bubble and the outer constituting a free surface boundary condition.

The radial and tangential velocity components of the enclosed solid phase can be written as follows (see Lamb[57] and Marucci[64] for details):

$$v_R = \frac{v_r}{1-\phi}\left(1 - \frac{r_b^3}{r^3}\right)\cos\theta \tag{4-74}$$

$$v_\theta = \frac{v_r}{1-\phi}\left(1 - \frac{r_b^3}{2r^3}\right)\sin\theta \tag{4-75}$$

where r = radial coordinate
$\quad\ \theta$ = polar angle

The drag on the bubbles can be estimated from the energy dissipation:

$$\frac{dE_f}{dt} = \mu_f \int (\text{curl } \nu_i)^2 dV + \mu_f \int \frac{d\nu_i^2}{dr}ds + 2\mu_f \int (\nu_i \text{ curl } \nu_i)ds \tag{4-76}$$

where ν_i denotes the velocity vector whose components are given by Equation 4-75 and the first integral is a volume integral (the last two integrals are surface integrals). Combining Equations 4-75 and 4-76 gives:

$$\frac{dE_f}{dt} = 9\mu_f\left(\frac{\nu_r}{1-\phi}\right)^2 r_b^6 \int_0^\pi \int_{r_b}^{r/\phi^{0.333}} \frac{1 + 2\cos\theta^2}{r^8}\, 2\pi r^2 \sin\theta\, d\theta\, dr \tag{4-77}$$

Note that as an upper boundary condition on the radial coordinate r, we have $r = r_b \epsilon^{0.333}$, so that the value of the integration and the volume of the bubble are consistent with the flow system void fraction. Upon integrating:

$$\frac{dE_f}{dt} = 12\pi\mu_f r_b \nu_r^2 \frac{1 - \epsilon^{1.666}}{(1 - \epsilon)^2} \tag{4-78}$$

Thus, the drag force on a bubble in a bubble swarm is:

$$F_D = 12\pi\mu_f \nu_r r_b \frac{1 - \epsilon^{1.666}}{(1 - \epsilon)^2} \tag{4-79}$$

Note that the difference between Equation 4-79 and the drag expression for a single freely rising bubble (Equation 4-73) is a factor that accounts for the flow system's void fraction.

Akselrod et al.,[65] Azbel,[66] Gal-Or et al.,[67] and Marucci[64] have found good agreement between the spherical compartment model and experimental data obtained from liquid-liquid and gas-liquid systems.

The energy dissipation of the bubble is obtained from Equation 4-75:

$$dE_2 = 12\pi\mu_f r_b \nu_r^2 \frac{1 - \epsilon^{1.666}}{(1 - \epsilon)^2} \tau \, n dx$$

where τ is the time scale of the turbulent eddies, and the number of bubbles per unit volume is

$$n = \epsilon / \frac{4}{3}\pi r_b^3$$

The energy dissipation produced by the motion of the bubbles in the layer is thus

$$dE_2 = \frac{9\mu_f \nu_r^2 \epsilon (1 - \epsilon^{1.666})}{r_b^2 (1 - \epsilon)^2} \tau \, dx \tag{4-80}$$

Azbel[68] gives an expression for the time scale of the eddies most likely to have an effect on the bubble motion:

$$\tau = \frac{kr_b^2 (1 - \epsilon)^2}{9\nu_f (1 - \epsilon^{1.666})} \tag{4-81}$$

From continuity ($\nu_s = \nu\epsilon$), and substituting τ into Equation 4-80 we obtain:

$$dE_2 = k\varrho_f \frac{\nu_s^2}{\epsilon} dx \tag{4-82}$$

At present assume k to be a constant.

The surface tension energy is defined as follows:

$$dE_3 = 4\pi r_b^2 \sigma \; ndx = \frac{3\sigma}{r_b} \epsilon dx \tag{4-83}$$

Substituting the appropriate expressions for dE_1, dE_2, and dE_3 into the energy balance (Equation 4-70), we get:

$$dE = \left[(1 - \epsilon)\varrho_f gx + k\varrho_f \frac{v_s^2}{\epsilon} + \frac{3\sigma}{r_b} \epsilon \right] dx \tag{4-84}$$

Consequently, the total energy of a two-phase layer of height x, is:

$$E = \int_0^{x_1} \left[(1 - \epsilon)\varrho_f gx + k\varrho_f \frac{v_s^2}{\epsilon} + \frac{3\sigma}{r_b} \epsilon \right] dx \tag{4-85}$$

Now, it is a fundamental axiom that for any steady-state system, the available energy is at a minimum. Thus to find ϵ it is necessary to determine the minimum of the integral in Equation 4-85. Smirnov[69] reduced this problem to that of evaluating the minimum of the integral E under the condition of invariability of the amount of material in the system; in other words with

$$h = \int (1 - \epsilon)dx = \text{constant} \tag{4-86}$$

where h is the static bed height. Equation 4-75 is a boundary condition on the variation of Equation 4-86.

From the method of the calculus of variations, we begin with the following function of a function:

$$E = \int f[\epsilon(x), \; \epsilon'(x), \; x]dx \tag{4-87}$$

where   f = some known function of its argument
$\epsilon(x)$ = unknown function
$\epsilon'(x)$ = derivative

The calculus of variations is a method to obtain a function $\phi(x)$ such that the variation of E is zero.

$$\delta E = 0 \tag{4-88}$$

which also means that the function E is at a minimum (or possibly a maximum) for that function $\epsilon(x)$. This is done subject to the constraint that

$$\epsilon(\epsilon_1 x) = 0 \tag{4-89}$$

where ϵ is some known function. Using the method of variations on Equations 4-87, 4-88, and 4-89, we obtain the Euler equation:

$$\frac{\partial f}{\partial \epsilon} - \frac{d}{dX}\left(\frac{\partial f}{\partial \epsilon'}\right) + \lambda\frac{\partial \psi}{\partial \epsilon} - \lambda\frac{d}{dx}\left(\frac{\partial \psi}{\partial \epsilon'}\right) = 0 \qquad (4\text{-}90)$$

where λ is the Lagrange multiplier and is determined by the constraint equation 4-89. Equation 4-90, which is usually differential but is sometimes algebraic, is then used to obtain that function $\phi(x)$ which gives the minimum of E.

When this analysis is applied to Equation 4-91 with the constraint equation 4-36, the following is obtained:

$$f(\epsilon, \epsilon', x) = (1 - \epsilon)\varrho_f gx + k\varrho_f\frac{v_s^2}{2\phi} + \frac{3\delta}{r_b}\epsilon \qquad (4\text{-}91)$$

$$\psi(\epsilon, x) = 1 - \epsilon \qquad (4\text{-}92)$$

and for the Euler equation we obtain

$$-\varrho_f gx - k\varrho_f\frac{v_s^2}{\epsilon^2} + \frac{3\delta}{r_b} - \lambda = 0 \qquad (4\text{-}93)$$

We have ignored the variation due to the unknown upper limit, x_1, in the calculus-of-variation analysis. This upper limit is the point where the two-phase nature of the flow breaks down—in other words when $\epsilon = 1$. The following discussion shows that it is acceptable to ignore the variation due to x_1.

The problem of the floating limit of an integral is a problem with natural boundary conditions (see Smirnov[69]):

$$E = \int_0^{x_1} f(\epsilon, \epsilon', x)dx \qquad (4\text{-}94)$$

We need to find the $\phi(x)$ that gives an extremum of E when $\epsilon(0) = \epsilon_0$ is set (i.e., the lower limit is fixed) and $\mu(x_1)$ is not set (i.e., no condition is made on the upper limit). Then the value of δE will be given not only by the variation of f under the integral but also by the variation at the upper limit. The most general expression of the variation δE can be written as:

$$\delta E = (f\epsilon', \delta\epsilon)\Big|_0^{x_1} + \int_0^{x_1}\left[f\epsilon - \frac{d}{dx}(f\epsilon')\right]\delta y \, dx \qquad (4\text{-}95)$$

where the system constraints are not taken into account. In the case now under consideration, $f = f(\epsilon, x)$; in other words, we do not have a term $\epsilon' = d\epsilon/dx$, $f\epsilon' \equiv 0$, and the term integrated in brackets is equal to zero, $[f\epsilon', \delta\epsilon]_0^{x_1} = 0$. Therefore, the floating limit of x has no effect, and Euler's equation is as shown in Equation 4-90.

Since the derivative ϵ' does not enter into Equation 4-90, Equation 4-92 is not differential, but algebraic, and thus

$$\epsilon(x) = \left[\frac{k\varrho_f v_s^2}{(3\sigma/r_b) - \lambda - \varrho_f gx}\right]^{0.5} \tag{4-96}$$

Further, since the derivative $\epsilon'(x)$ does not appear in Equation 4-93 no additional conditions can be imposed on the values of $\epsilon(x)$ at the limits of the interval to x_1, and therefore this function may become discontinuous at the ends of the interval. However, from physical considerations it must be the case that the function $\epsilon(x)$ is continuous at all values of x between the limits, and therefore, it can be determined from Equation 4-96. The value of x_1 can now be determined from the equality

$$1 = \left[\frac{k\varrho_f v_s^2}{(3\sigma/r_b) - \lambda - \varrho_f gx_1}\right]^{0.5} \tag{4-97}$$

To eliminate the undetermined Lagrange multiplier, ϵ (from Equation 4-96) is applied in constraint equation 4-86

$$h = \int_0^{x_1} (1 - \epsilon)dx = \int_0^{x_1} \left\{1 - \left[\frac{k\varrho_f v_s^2}{(3\sigma/r_b) - \varrho_f gx - \lambda}\right]^{0.5}\right\}dx \tag{4-98}$$

Integration of this expression yields:

$$h = x_1 + \frac{kv_s^2}{g} - \frac{2}{\varrho_f g}(k\varrho_f v_s^2)^{0.5}(\varrho_f gx_1 + k\varrho_f v_s^2)^{0.5} \tag{4-99}$$

Solving with respect to x_1, an equation suitable for calculating the height of a dynamic two-phase flow is obtained, assuming a constant drag coefficient of 0.5 for turbulent flow conditions.

$$x_1 = h[2(kFr)^{0.5} + 1] \tag{4-100}$$

It follows from this equation that the height of the two-phase flow is a linear function of the superficial gas velocity v_s.

The gas void fraction for the bed can now be solved for from Equation 4-97 where it follows that

$$\lambda = \frac{3\sigma}{r_b} - \varrho_f g\left(x_1 + \frac{kv_s^2}{g}\right) \tag{4-101}$$

Substituting for x_1 (Equation 4-100) into this equation, we obtain

$$\lambda = \frac{3\sigma}{r_b} - \varrho_f g\left[h(4kFr)^{0.5} + h + \frac{kv_s^2}{g}\right] \tag{4-102}$$

Since

$$\frac{kv_s^2}{gh}h = khFr \tag{4-103}$$

we may write

$$\frac{3\sigma}{r_b} - \lambda = \varrho_f gh \left[(4kFr)^{0.5} + 1 + kFr\right] \tag{4-104}$$

And from Equation 4-96, we obtain:

$$\epsilon(x) = \left[\frac{k\varrho_f v_s^2}{\varrho_f gh[(4kFr)^{0.5} + 1 + kFr] - \varrho_f gx}\right]^{0.5} \tag{4-105}$$

Equation 4-105 simplifies to the following:

$$\epsilon(x) = \left[\frac{kFr}{(kFr)^{0.5} + kFr + 1 - x/h}\right]^{0.5} \tag{4-106}$$

The striking observation in Equation 4-106 is that the gas content does not depend on the shape and the size of the gas bubbles, since the radius does not appear in the equation.

The average void fraction ϵ_{av} can now be determined by noting that:

$$\epsilon_{av} = \frac{\int_0^{x_1}\epsilon(x)dx}{\int_0^{x_1}dx} = \int_0^{x_1}\frac{(kFr)^{0.5}dx}{x_1[(4kFr)^{0.5} + kFr + 1 - x/h]^{0.5}}$$

$$= -\frac{2h(kFr)^{0.5}}{x_1}\left[(4kFr)^{0.5} + kFr + 1 - \frac{x_1}{h}\right]^{0.5}$$

$$- [(4kFr)^{0.5} + kFr + 1]^{0.5}] \tag{4-107}$$

Substituting x_1 from Equation 4-100 and simplifying, we obtain

$$\epsilon_{av} = \frac{2(kFr)^{0.5}}{1 + 2(kFr)^{0.5}} \tag{4-108}$$

Equation 4-108 provides a simple formula for the mean void fraction in terms of the Froude number, where dissipative forces have been accounted for.

The relative density of the two-phase flow is:

$$\psi = \frac{h}{x_1} \tag{4-109}$$

and on substituting the expression for x_1 from Equation 4-100, we find that:

$$\psi = \frac{1}{1 + 2(kFr)^{0.5}} \tag{4-110}$$

Equations 4-100, 4-108, and 4-109 imply that the main hydrodynamic parameters of the flow in a bubbling process depend neither on the physical properties of the solid and gas nor on the geometric characteristics of the gas-distributing device. They are determined strictly by the ratio of the continuing phase and gas flow rates (where ν_s is a characteristic gas velocity) and are characterized by the ratio between the inertia forces and the gravity forces; in other words, they are functions only of the Froude number.

The above model describes expansion at standard conditions, in which case the coefficient of added mass, k, is considered to be a constant. However, at elevated pressures, bubble shape and size vary with the density of the fluidizing gas.

A somewhat simplified approach is to assume:

$$k \propto (\varrho_2/\varrho_0)_g \qquad\qquad\qquad (4\text{-}111)$$

That is, the added mass term is considered simply as a correction term accounting for variations in bubble characteristics in terms of gas density or pressure through the ideal gas law.

The model was tested against measurements of the bed expansion obtained in 76.2, 305, and 609 mm diameter columns. The intermediate-size column was a high pressure vessel housed at the Institute of Gas Technology and the system is described by Knowlton.[70] The largest diameter column was an ambient pressure unit housed at Exxon Research & Engineering Co. and is described in Reference 55.

In addition, Knowlton[70] reports bed expansion data at high pressures for a variety of solids ranging from coal char to siderite. Lewis et al.[71] also report data for glass spheres of varying sizes and miscellaneous solids in 63.5 and 114 mm diameter columns for ambient conditions. The fluidizing gas used in all experiments was either nitrogen or air.

The range of experimental conditions and physical properties of the solids used to validate the model are summarized in Table 4-5. Solids' bulk densities and average particle sizes ranged from 480 to 2,500 kg/m³ and 40 to 570 microns, respectively. Column pressures for all data ranged from ambient to 69 bars with superficial gas velocities from 0.05 to 1 m/s.

The bed expansion equation (Equation 4-100) was found to correlate with data over the entire range of conditions tested with a single exponential coefficient fitted to the added mass expression (Equation 4-111) ($k = (p_2/p_0)_{gas}^n$). The value of the empirical coefficient n was evaluated to be 0.34. Figure 4-11 shows a plot of the relative bed expansion (x_1/h) predicted from Equation 4-100 along with the experimental values. For 104 data points obtained from the large columns (609 mm and 305 mm diameters) the predicted relative bed expansion has an average absolute deviation from experiment of 10% with approximately 72% of this data having an absolute deviation of 5%.

The small column data (111 data points) show an absolute average deviation of 20% between predicted and experimental relative bed expansion, with 79 of these data points within 10%. The additional scatter associated with the small column data is due to wall effects, which the model does not account for.

Table 4-5
Materials' Properties and Range of Test Conditions

Material	Particle Density (kg/m³)	Bulk Density (kg/m³)	Mean Particle Size (μm)	Minimum Bubbling Velocity (m/s)	Range of Superficial Gas Velocity (m/s)	Pressure Range (bars)	Column Diameter (mm)	Number of Data Points	Symbol	Investigator
Bituminous coal	1,290	830	287	.005-.027	0.05-0.23	1.03-68.9	305	7	■	Knowlton[70]
Coke breeze	1,571	692	320	0.005-0.03	0.06-0.34	1.03-68.9	305	6	⬢	Knowlton[70]
Gasified coal char	993	481	150	0.04	0.09-0.24	3.45-34.5	305	15	◄	Azbel and Cheremisinoff[55]
FMC char	1,154	647	115, 180	0.002, 0.02	0.09-0.24	3.45-34.5	305	17	►	Azbel and Cheremisinoff[55]
Hydrogasified lignite	1,179	468	244	0.004-0.023	0.06-0.11	1.03-68.9	305	7	▶	Knowlton[70]
	1,120	683	229	0.004-0.022	0.03-0.10	1.03-68.9	305	7	▲	Knowlton[70]
Lignite	1,170	747	267	0.005-0.026	0.06-0.28	1.03-68.9	305	7	▼	Knowlton[70]
Alumina-pellets	2,907	1,011	~830	0.09	0.10-0.40	1.03	609	7	●	Azbel and Cheremisinoff[55]
Siderite	3,910	2,503	290	0.005-0.026	0.09-0.35	1.03-68.9	305	7	+	Knowlton[70]
Cracking catalyst	1,282	761	80	0.001	0.10-0.49	1.01	609	8	◆	Azbel and Cheremisinoff[55]
					0.002-0.10		76.2	7	◇	Azbel and Cheremisinoff[55]
Aerocat microspheres	~497	994	150	0.017	0.02-0.28	1.01	114	9	△	Lewis et al.[71]
Glass spheres	~1,210	~2,420	40.6-569	.0007-0.01	0.03-0.99	1.01	63.5, 114	95	○	Lewis et al.[71]
Sand	2,596	1,683	95, 171	0.03,0.08	0.12-0.24	3.45-31.0	305	16	*	Azbel and Cheremisinoff[55]

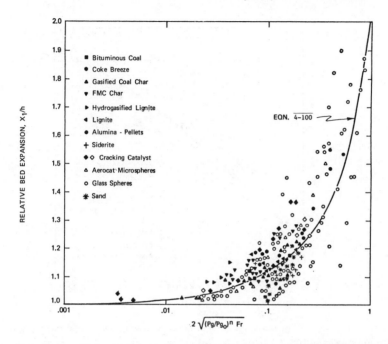

RELATIVE BED EXPANSION, x_1/h

Legend:
- ■ Bituminous Coal
- ● Coke Breeze
- ▲ Gasified Coal Char
- ▼ FMC Char
- ► Hydrogasified Lignite
- ◄ Lignite
- ● Alumina - Pellets
- + Siderite
- ◆◇ Cracking Catalyst
- △ Aerocat Microspheres
- ○ Glass Spheres
- ✳ Sand

EQN. $\overline{4\text{-}100}$

$2\sqrt{(Pg/Pg_0)^n}\ Fr$

Figure 4-11. A comparison of relative bed expansion data to the predictions of Equation 4-100.

A sampling of the void fraction data obtained from the large columns is shown plotted against $(k^n Fr)^{0.5}$ in Figure 4-12. As shown, the experimental values scatter about the predicted curve from Equation 4-108 with an absolute average deviation of 20%.

The effect of pressure (and hence gas density) on bed expansion is shown in Figure 4-13. The curves represent predictions of the relative bed expansion x_1/h for various values of the Froude number over a range of pressures from Equation 4-100. The expansion data for different materials are shown to scatter about these predictions. Note that the effect of pressure on bed expansion (and hence bed voidage) appears pronounced only at large Froude number values (that is, at high gas superficial velocities).

A severe limitation with the model is that it is applicable only to freely-bubbling solids (aggregative, heterogeneous fluidization). Therefore, the fluidization characteristics of the material must be known before applying the model to predictions.

Although the energy balance model shows good correlation with bed expansion data, the absence of the roles of gas and solid physical properties is certainly contrary to the more empirical models reviewed in the previous subsection. The model should therefore be viewed as a limiting case of ideally bubbling deep beds, even though data reported from small diameter columns appear to be as well correlated by Equation 4-100 as with the empirical equations in Table 4-4.

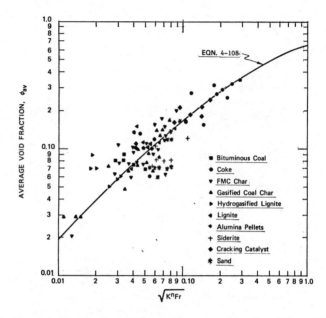

Figure 4-12. Comparison of the large column average void fraction data and the predicted curve from Equation 4-108.

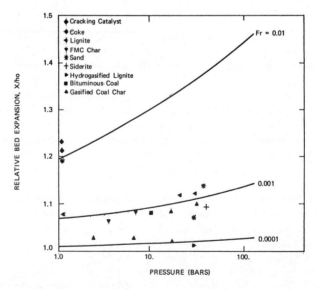

Figure 4-13. Illustration of the effect of pressure on bed expansion for different Froude number values (i.e., different gas superficial velocities).

HYDRODYNAMICS OF BUBBLES

Jet Penetration

Gas is normally introduced to the bed through a grid or distributor located at the bottom of the column. There are a variety of distributor designs, the choice of which depends on the desired quality of application and process requirements. Figure 4-14 illustrates common configurations. Flat perforated plates (a) are often employed in laboratory-scale units. They have the disadvantage that fines are likely to fall through the orifices when the gas flow is stopped. The staggered perforated plate design (b) tends to overcome this problem. Figure 4-14 (c) and (d) show curved plate distributors which are designed to handle heavy loads and thermal stresses in large-diameter columns. The concave perforated plate (c) tends to counteract tendencies towards preferential channeling near the axis of the fluidized bed. The convex plate (d) achieves good contacting with a higher concentration of orifices situated at the perimeter.

The sandwiched packed-bed distributor (e) consists of a packed bed of granular material encased between two perforated plates. This has the advantages of providing good gas-solids contact and thermal insulation to low temperature inlet gases from the hot bed of solids. The packing also provides premixing of feed gases.

Figure 4-14 (f) shows an arrangement of slits between grate bars. This design has approximately the same characteristics as the flat perforated plate, but gives slightly less uniform gas distribution.

Nozzles (g) and bubble caps (h) are used in a variety of commercial fluid-bed reactors and have the advantage of preventing solids from falling through the distributor. There are problems associated with these designs; namely, particle dead zones tend to exist on the flat bottom surface where solids can sinter.

Multiple filter plates (i) and pipe grid arrangements (j) are employed in pthalic anhydride production. They tend to provide better gas contact than bubble caps; however, special precautions are needed to ensure that the feed gas is free of filter-clogging materials.

Two other designs are shown in Figure 4-14. In (k), the gas is injected through nozzles arranged along the side walls—a design that has been used in the roasters of pelletized zinc blends. In (l), the gas is introduced through side-mixing nozzles into a teetered bed.

There is some controversy over whether the type of distributor does indeed significantly affect the quality of gas-solids contacting in vigorously bubbling beds. Simone et al.,[38] Lehmann et al.,[72] and others[44] observed that the distributor configuration does not significantly affect dense-phase properties when the bed is deep. This observation lends some support to the energy balance model for bed expansion described earlier. This would further imply that for very deep beds, only a few or perhaps a single orifice is required to achieve a bubbling state throughout the column, provided that the solids are susceptible to mass bubbling. Although the analogy to gas bubbling in a liquid column is certainly not exactly appropriate because of the absence of surface tension forces, this is clearly observed for gas-liquid systems.

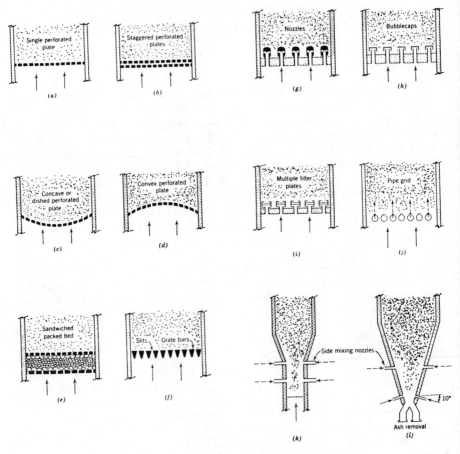

Figure 4-14. Examples of distributor configurations.

A number of experimental investigations (see References 73–83, for examples) have been aimed at studying jet penetration into fluidized beds. These studies have largely been limited to gas introduction through single orifices and therefore do not reflect the interactions caused by perforated plates, bubble caps, or multinozzle configurations. Despite this, such studies are instructive in the understanding of bubble formation. Jet penetration is a function of the solids and gas physical properties, nozzle diameter, and system pressure. Table 4-6 lists several jet penetration correlations developed by different investigators in two-dimensional, semi-cylindrical and cylindrical columns.

The discharge of a gas jet into a fluidized bed is not unlike gas being sparged into a liquid column; however, in the former case, the jet retains its stability over a considerably greater penetration depth. A typical gas jet will appear as a continuous

Table 4-6.
Correlations for Jet Penetration*

Correlation	Bed Geometry	Bed Dimension (cm)	Bed Pressure	Parameters Varied	Investigator(s)
$\dfrac{L_{max}}{d_o} = 19.3\left(\dfrac{\rho_g V_o}{\rho_p(gd_p)^{0.5}}\right)^{0.83}\left(\dfrac{V_B}{V_{cf}}\right)^{-0.54}$	Semi-cylindrical	35-i.d.	50–750 psig	ρ_p, d_p, d_o, V_o, P	Hirsan et al.[83]
$\dfrac{L_B}{d_o} = 26.6\left(\dfrac{\rho_p V_o}{\rho_p(gd_p)^{0.5}}\right)^{0.67}\left(\dfrac{V_B}{V_{cf}}\right)^{-0.24}$	3D	28 and 50	Atmos.	V_o, d_o, d_p	Basov et al.[73]
$\dfrac{L}{d_o} = \left(\dfrac{0.919d_p}{0.0007 + 0.566d_p}\right)\dfrac{V_o^{0.35}}{V_o^{0.35}}$					
$\dfrac{L}{d_o} = 5.2\left(\dfrac{\rho_f d_o}{\rho_p d_p}\right)^{0.3}\left[1.3\left(\dfrac{V_o^2}{gd_o}\right)^{0.2} - 1\right]$	2D	30 × 1.2	Atmos.	V_o, d_p	Merry[74]
$\dfrac{L}{d_o} = 814.2\left(\dfrac{\rho_p d_p}{\rho_f d_o}\right)^{-0.585}\left(\dfrac{\rho_f V_o d_o}{\mu}\right)^{-0.654}\left(\dfrac{V_o^2}{gd_o}\right)^{0.47}$	2D	30.5 × 1.2 30.0 × 1.5 30.0 × 0.5	Atmos.	V_o, d_p, d_o, ρ_p	Wen et al.[77]
$\dfrac{L}{d_o} = 6.5\left[\left(\dfrac{\rho_f}{\rho_p - \rho_f}\right)\left(\dfrac{V_o^2}{gd_o}\right)\right]^{0.5}$	Semi-cylindrical	28.6-i.d.	Atmos.	V_o, d_o	Yang and Keairns[78]
$0.01447\dfrac{L}{d_o} + 1.3 = 0.5\log(\rho_f V_o^2)$	2D	121.9 × 5.1	Atmos.	V_o, ρ_p, d_p, d_o	Zenz[79]

* All units in cgs except Zenz correlation where ρ_f — lb/ft^3, V_o — fps.

stream containing a dilute suspension of entrained solids. At some critical penetration depth, the jet becomes unstable, breaking up into a series of bubbles. Hirsan et al.[83] have observed from tests in a semicylindrical column, that the dilute-phase portion of the jet fluctuates between a minimum and maximum penetration. At the minimum penetration of the dilute phase, the appearance of a series of coalescing bubbles with periodic necks are observed.[83,76]

Hirsan and co-workers[83] define three jet penetration distances as illustrated in Figure 4-15. The greatest penetration, L_B, is defined as the deepest penetration of the jet bubbles into the bed before they lose their momentum. They determined this length from visual measurements of the distance that bubbles from the end of the jet penetrated into the bed before the bed's momentum could divert the bubbles significantly from their vertical path. This last definition has relevance to beds containing internals in the sense that the internals should be located at a distance beyond L_B to avoid being sandblasted. Clearly though, it is L_{max} which should cause more serious difficulties for bed internals.

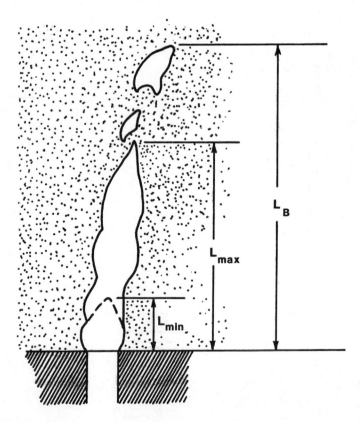

Figure 4-15. Jet instability and penetration depths as defined by Hirsan et al.[83]

Hirsan's correlations are further distinguished from the others listed in Table 4-6 by the complete fluidization velocity. The complete fluidization velocity, V_{cf}, is defined as that velocity at which the entire bed is perceived as being fluidized. This distinction from U_{mb} is apparently only significant when the solids have a very wide particle size distribution and segregation effects are likely to occur at minimum bubbling conditions. Also, V_{cf} is observed to be quite sensitive to pressure.

The interaction between rising gas jets also impacts on jet penetration. A jet will tend to entrain both gas bubbles or portions of neighboring jets as well as solids. This action is observed near the base of the jet. Bubbles from the fluidized bed passing upward near the jet are observed to flow into the jet. This influx of gas bubbles creates additional instabilities or fluctuations in the jet.

Close examination of the correlations listed in Table 4-6 reveals the following observations. In general, jet penetration length tends to decrease as particle density is increased. A jet introduced to a liquid column will tend to penetrate deeper into a lower density medium than a dense one before its momentum is expended. By analogy to a gas-liquid column, jet penetration would be greater in beds comprising low-particle-density materials than in beds of higher density.[83,82] Jet penetration length is observed to increase as particle size decreases. This observation is most pronounced with small particle sizes. Above approximately 200 μm sizes, the effect of particle size on jet penetration is less pronounced.[74,80,83] All the correlations show that jet penetration increases with an increase in bed pressure. By increasing system pressure, gas density increases, and thus, the momentum of the jet becomes greater. It should be further noted that jet penetration increases most dramatically with pressure rises at low pressure, and increases at a slower rate with pressure increments at higher values. The reason for this being that the fractional change in pressure decreases for the same differential pressure change as the system pressure increases. Finally, some differences among the correlations appear for changes in orifice diameter, d_0. Zenz,[79] Shakhova,[80] and Hirsan et al.[83] show that L/d_0 does not change as the nozzle diameter is increased although the actual jet penetration length does increase with larger d_0. The correlations of Yang and Keairns,[78] Wen et al.,[77] and Merry[74] show an added effect of d_0 on the jet penetration.

The correlations of Zenz,[79] Merry,[74] and Wen et al.[77] were derived from data obtained in two-dimensional beds, and although the aspect ratios (i.e., bed-width-to-diameter ratio) were large, wall effects are still significant. Hence, one would not expect these correlations to provide comparable predictions to those correlations derived from test data from semi-cylindrical and cylindrical columns. The only correlation developed in a cylindrical column is that of Basov et al.,[73] which unfortunately does not include the effect of pressure on jet penetration through a gas density term. This leaves the correlations of Hirsan et al.[83] and Yang and Keairns[78] to provide estimates of jet penetration in fluidized beds, where the latter appears to provide an average penetration length.

A comparison of Hirsan's correlations to Yang and Keairns is shown in Figure 4-16 for sand fluidized by nitrogen gas.[83] Yang et al.'s correlation is recommended for an estimate of the average penetration length, and a graphical summary of the plot is given in Figure 4-17 as L/d_0 versus Froude number, where,

$$Fr = V_0^2/gd_0 \qquad (4\text{-}112)$$

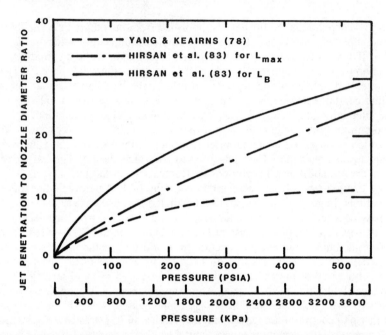

Figure 4-16. Comparison of Hirsan et al., correlations to Yang and Keairns.[78] Conditions: material—sand; fluidizing velocity $\sim V_{cf}$; average particle size—0.0438 cm; jet ID—2.54 cm; jet velocity—762 cm/s. Data of Hirsan et al.[83]

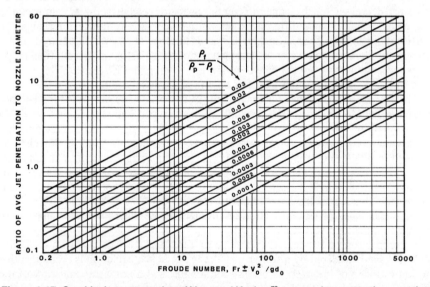

Figure 4-17. Graphical representation of Yang and Keairns[78] average jet penetration equation. Correlation should be applied to fluidizing gases whose viscosities are close to that of air at ambient temperature.

The parameter in this plot is the dimensionless density group $\varrho_f/\varrho_p - \varrho_p$. The correlations of Hirsan et al. and Yang and Keairns show an absolute deviation of approximately 30% on a predicted-versus-experiment L/d_0 parity plot.

Bubble Characteristics

Thus far, the gross behavior of fluidized beds has been described; however, characteristics such as pressure drop, bed expansion, or average fluid-bed voidage do not provide guidance in nor an understanding of the design for the rate processes of heat and mass transfers and reactions. These processes are dependent on the detailed interaction between gas and solids within the bed as well as the degree of solids circulation on both micro and macro scales.

The degree of interaction between gas and solids—i.e., the quality of fluidization—depends on the specific characteristics and behavior of bubbles. The principal characteristics of bubbles important to the two-phase phenomenon are bubble shape, velocity of flow, and size. Their behavior in the bed can be described in terms of frequency (i.e, number of bubbles passing through a given flow area per unit time) and the dynamics of bubble coalescence and breakup. In the discussions that follow, we shall adopt the terminology used by Kunii et al.[34] and others; namely, regions of high solids density in a fluid bed are referred to as the *emulsion phase*, whereas, those of low solids density are referred to as gas pockets or voids.

In an attempt to explain the reported observations on heat transfer, mass transfer, and solid-catalyzed chemical reactions, a considerable amount of attention has concentrated on the movement of particles and gas associated with isolated bubbles rising in fluidized beds.[84-90] This approach has led to some rather eloquent analyses of bubble flow behavior, but the warning "the buyer beware" is most appropriate when searching for a flow model. Bubble dynamics are complex, as shown by the photographs in Figure 4-18. Although considerable distortion of the bubble shape is due to wall effects in the two-dimensional bed in which these photos were taken, clearly bubble breakup and coalescence greatly influences shape and behavior.

In a well-controlled laboratory environment, single, noninteracting bubbles rising through a bed show more uniform characteristics. The shapes of these bubbles appear quite similar: close to spherical when small, flattened and distorted when larger, and spherical cap-shaped when large. Such observations have been made using x-ray photography by various investigators.[91,92]

Theoretical studies have shown that the critical parameter establishing the characteristics of fluid motion near the bubble is the ratio of the velocity of a bubble, U_b, to the interstitial fluid velocity, U_0. The studies further predict that when this ratio exceeds unity, gas passing out of the bubble will tend to remain within a region close to it by the solid particles moving relative to the bubble, and hence, the gas will circulate within this region. The existence of this cloud around a rising bubble (at $U_b/U_0 > 1$) has been confirmed from experiments using colored tracer gas. Figure 4-19B shows a sketch of a photograph of a fast two-dimensional bubble with the well-defined cloud as described by Rowe[93] and others.[94] Figure 4-19A shows bubbles coalescing and breaking up as stalactites of falling particles rain through rising bubbles, causing them to split into smaller ones.

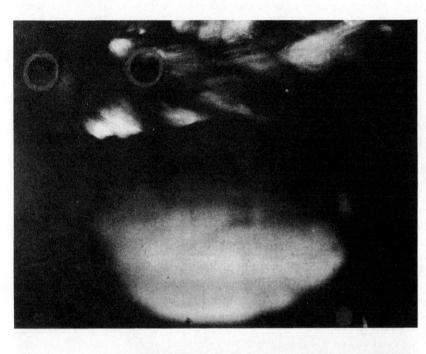

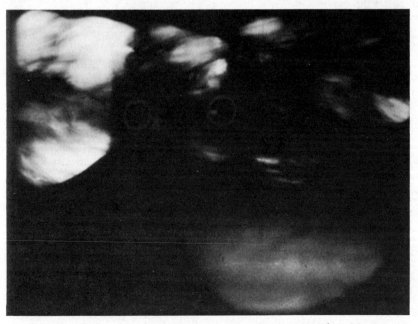

Figure 4-18. Photographs of bubbles rising through a two-dimensional bed containing coal char particles. Solids are shown to rain down through large bubbles, causing them to split into smaller ones. The circular marks on the foreground denote the location of capacitance probes.

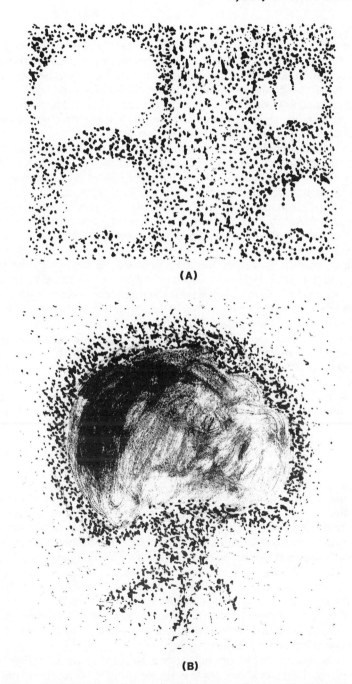

(A)

(B)

Figure 4-19. (A) Sketch of bubbles coalescing and breaking up; (B) sketch of a "cloud" of emulsified solids surrounding a rising bubble.

The leading theoretical models[29,84-86,88,90] describing the dynamics of single bubbles in fluidized beds all give predictions of the size and shape of the circulating gas clouds for different values of $U_b/U_0 > 1$. Furthermore, each model implies a specific pressure distribution in the fluidizing gas. Stewart[95] has compared the various models and found that predictions of the thickness of the cloud surrounding a bubble by different models cover a range of two to one, and predicted pressure changes differ by more than five to one. Even so, a review of these models is warranted here as they still provide a good starting basis for flow analyses.

The differences in model predictions stem from different assumptions applied by the various investigators. Davidson[29,84] as well as Collins[85] makes the assumption that the gas pressure distribution in the vicinity of a bubble is independent of the solid particles motion. In contrast, Jackson[86] and Murray[90] make the implicit assumption that particle momentum considerations play a dominant role in establishing the magnitude and form of pressure and gas velocity changes. The principal differences between the theoretical analyses were summarized by Stewart[95] and are restated in Table 4-7.

Davidson's[84] analysis is perhaps the most idealized, assuming that the bubble is spherical and that particles flow around it as if they were elements of an incompressible, inviscid fluid. In this analysis, the fluidizing gas is considered to be incompressible and to have negligible inertia. Also, the pressure gradient in the gas at any point is assumed to be proportional to the relative rise velocity of gas and particles. The pressure within the bubble is assumed to be approximately uniform, and that throughout any horizontal plane well removed from the bubble, it is constant (refer to Figure 4-20A). The pressure gradients in excess of those required for fluidization exist close to the bubble, as gas seeking an easy path through the bubble generates increased gas velocities in this region. Other investigators[93,85] lend support to Davidson's view that particle flow behavior is similar to that of an ideal fluid.

Figure 4-20B illustrates Collins'[85] concept of a rising bubble in a fluidized bed. A transformation is used to convert the circular cross-section into a kidney shape which is a closer approximation to actual bubble contours. Collins' analysis uses assumptions which are identical to that of Davidson. Gas and particle flows are described in relation to the transformed bubble contour. This viewpoint is, however, unrealistic from the solid's motion viewpoint. Stewart[94] further comments that the solids should be viewed as flowing relative to the circular cross-section which just encloses the entire deformed bubble. Apart from the bubble shape considerations, both Stewart and Collins employ Davidson's[84] assumptions.

Murray[90] has derived a series of complex equations which are greatly simplified to solve for a stream function for the motion of the gas. Similarly to Davidson, he assumes constant porosity in the particulate phase, negligible gas momentum, and a circular bubble cross-section. He does however include a solids momentum equation which must be linearized because of the constant porosity assumption, in order to obtain a consistent set of equations.

Jackson[86] also assumes a circular bubble cross-section; however, unlike Davidson, the porosity of the particulate phase is allowed to vary. This provides an additional degree of freedom which permits more complex equations of motion to be formulated. In addition, this approach does not require the assumption that solid

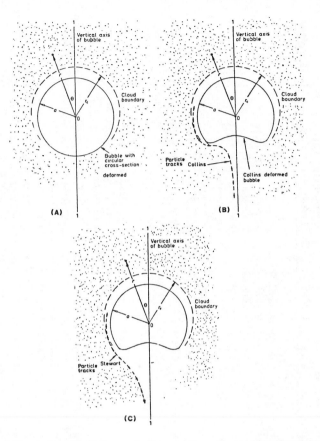

Figure 4-20. Illustration of bubble coordinates and theoretical bubble shapes proposed by different investigators.

particles behave like an ideal incompressible fluid. This assumption appears only to be approached when the fluidizing gas momentum is negligible. A major departure from Davidson's model is that Jackson assumes that the pressure gradient in the gas above the bubble (i.e., in excess of that required to fluidize the bed) is equal to the rate of change of particle momentum approaching the bubble. This implies that the drag exerted by the gas on the particle and the porosity needed to generate it are equivalent to those required to cause particle motion relative to the rising bubble. Computed changes in porosity from that at incipient fluidization are in general, small. As such, the particle motion does indeed resemble that of an ideal incompressible fluid around a solid object with the same shape as the bubble at the extreme. Jackson's assumption that the motion of a fluidizing gas will be influenced by the momentum of the particles relative to a bubble is justified. Furthermore, he concludes that bed porosity increases close to the upper boundary of a bubble; an ob-

Table 4-7
Various Assumptions Made in Theoretical Analyses of Bubble Motion as Summarized by Stewart[95]

Bubble Shape (vertical cross section)	Properties of Particulate Phase	Properties of Fluidizing Gas	Particle Motion	Fluidizing Gas Pressure Changes	Investigator
Circular	Inviscid; incompressible, i.e. constant porosity	Incompressible; negligible inertia	As for an ideal fluid, i.e. potential flow, around a solid sphere or cylinder	Local pressure gradient proportional to interstitial gas velocity. Pressure in bubble uniform and pressure constant in any horizontal plane well removed from bubble	Davidson[29,84]
Indented at base ("kidney" shaped)	Inviscid; incompressible, i.e. constant porosity	Incompressible; negligible inertia	Potential flow relative to indented shape	Local pressure gradient proportional to interstitial gas velocity. Pressure in bubble uniform and pressure constant in any horizontal plane well removed from bubble	Collins[85] (two-dimensional bubble only)
Indented at base ("kidney" shaped)	Inviscid; incompressible, i.e. constant porosity	Incompressible; negligible inertia	Potential flow relative to smallest cylinder enclosing the deformed bubble	Local pressure gradient proportional to interstitial gas velocity. Pressure in bubble uniform and pressure constant in any horizontal plane well removed from bubble	Stewart[90] (two-dimensional bubble only)

Table 4-7 (continued)
Various Assumptions Made in Theoretical Analyses of Bubble Motion as Summarized by Stewart[95]

Bubble Shape (vertical cross section)	Properties of Particulate Phase	Properties of Fluidizing Gas	Particle Motion	Fluidizing Gas Pressure Changes	Investigator
Circular	Inviscid; incompressible, i.e. constant porosity (for actual solution)	Incompressible; negligible inertia	As Davidson[84]	Pressure changes in gas given by linearized particle momentum equation	Murray[90]
	Inviscid; variable porosity	Incompressible; negligible inertia	Shown to be potential flow relative to the bubble with small deviations due to porosity changes close to the bubble	Coefficient relating interstitial gas velocity and pressure gradient, sensitive to local porosity. Pressure changes given by particle momentum changes	Jackson[86]
Indented at base	Viscosity 2–30 poise; porosity changes of the order of 0-1 up to one radius from the bubble	Negligible inertia, approximately incompressible for small pressure changes	Similar to potential flow solution relative to the cylinder or sphere enclosing the bubble. Viscous as well as inertial forces are important in determining particle velocities and trajectories	Pressure gradients above those required for fluidization are the principal driving force for the bubble motion. At any point the gradient is dependent on interstitial gas velocity and porosity. Pressure changes are roughly proportional but not equal to particle momentum changes as interparticle viscous stresses are also significant	Actual behaviour in a fluidized bed —observed or deduced (Stewart[95])

servation which is supported by Reuter's[96,97] experiments showing a region of reduced porosity beneath the bubble.

Cloud penetration is defined as the ratio of the cloud radius to the bubble radius. It is well known that the rise velocity of bubbles in gas-fluidized systems is in close agreement with gas-liquid systems. For comparatively isolated and undisturbed bubbles it is generally agreed that

$$U_b = k_v(gD_b)^{0.5} \tag{4-113}$$

This expression stems from the theoretical analysis of Davies and Taylor.[98] In terms of the bubble radius, r_b, theoretical expressions for the rise velocity are:

$$U_b = 0.5(gr_b)^{0.5} \text{ (for two dimensions)} \tag{4-114A}$$

$$U_b = 2/3(gr_b)^{0.5} \text{ (for three dimensions)} \tag{4-114B}$$

Stewart[95] derived formulae relating the cloud penetration, α, on the vertical axis above the bubble (i.e., at $\theta = 0°$ in Figure 4-20) to U_b/U_0, based on the models described. The expressions are given in Table 4-8. The group β/β_0 represents the ratio of the particle/gas drag coefficient at any point to the drag coefficient in the incipiently fluidized bed. A comparison of the predictions from the various models is given in Figure 4-21.

The data of Rowe et al.[93,26] and others shows that Davidson's theory tends to overestimate the actual penetrations for two-dimensional bubbles. Also, there seems to be little theoretical justification to choose between the theories of Jackson and Murray, both of which tend to provide good fits of the data. For three-dimensional bubbles, the scatter in both literature-reported data and the authors' own data is so great that it is not possible to assess which model is best applicable.

Following Stewart,[95] comparisons of the pressure gradients generated by the presence of a bubble may be made by subtracting the hydrostatic pressure term from the distribution. Limiting the analysis to $\theta = 0$, the pressures of interest then are differences that exist between points on the vertical axis of the bubble and points in the same horizontal planes well removed by the bubble. The following dimensionless expressions are described by Stewart:

For the Davidson and Harrison model:[29]

$$P/\varrho_p ga = \pm 1/\alpha \qquad \text{(two dimensions)} \tag{4-115A}$$

$$P/\varrho_p ga = \pm 1/\alpha^2 \qquad \text{(three dimensions)} \tag{4-115B}$$

where the negative sign applies below the bubble.

For the model of Jackson:[86]

$$P/\varrho_p ga = + \frac{1}{4\alpha^2}\left(1 - \frac{1}{2\alpha^2}\right) \qquad \text{(two dimensions)} \tag{4-116A}$$

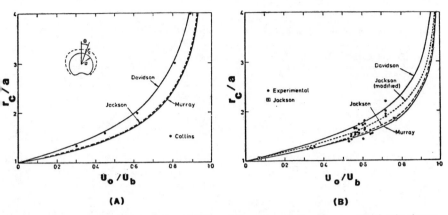

Figure 4-21. Comparison of model predictions of cloud penetration along vertical axis above: (A) two-dimensional bubbles; (B) three-dimensional bubbles.

$$P/\varrho_p ga = +\frac{2}{ga^3}\left(2 - \frac{1}{\alpha^3}\right)$$

$$P/\varrho_p ga = +\frac{1}{2\alpha^3}\left(2 - \frac{1}{\alpha^3}\right)$$

(three dimensions)   (4-116B)

No solution is given for the region below the bubble.
For the model of Murray:[90]

$$P/\varrho_p ga = +\frac{1}{4\alpha^2}$$ (two dimensions)   (4-117A)

$$P/\varrho_p ga = +\frac{1}{3\alpha^3}$$ (three dimensions)   (4-117B)

Again, no solution is given for the region below the bubble.
Finally, the following expression derived from stream functions is given for Collins'[85] model:
(for the region above the bubble):

$$P/\varrho_p ga = \frac{1}{2}\left\{\alpha + 0.54 + [(\alpha + 0.54)^2 + 0.32]^{0.5}\right.$$

$$\left. + \frac{3.50}{\alpha - 0.77 + [(\alpha + 0.54)^2 + 0.32]^{0.5}}\right\}$$ (4-118A)

Table 4-8
Summary of Formulae for U_b/U_o Along Vertical Axis Above Bubble

Two-Dimensional Bubbles	Three-Dimensional Bubbles	Investigator
$\dfrac{\alpha^2 + 1}{\alpha^2 - 1}$	$\dfrac{\alpha^3 + 2}{\alpha^3 + 1}$	Davidson et al.[29,84]
$\dfrac{\alpha^2 + \dfrac{1}{2\alpha}}{\alpha^2 - 1}$	$\dfrac{\alpha^3 + \dfrac{1}{\alpha}}{\alpha^3 - 1}$	Murray[90]
$\dfrac{\alpha^2 + \dfrac{1}{2\alpha}\left(1 - \dfrac{1}{\alpha^2}\right)}{\alpha^2 - 1}\left(\dfrac{\beta_o}{\beta}\right)$	$\dfrac{\alpha^3 + \dfrac{4}{3\alpha}\left(1 - \dfrac{1}{\alpha^3}\right)}{\alpha^3 - 1}\left(\dfrac{\beta_o}{\beta}\right)$	Jackson[86]
$\dfrac{[\alpha - 0.77 + (A^2 + 0.32)^{0.5}]^2 + 3.50}{[\alpha - 0.77 + (A^2 + 0.32)^{0.5}]^2 - 3.50}$		Collins[85]
$\left\{\alpha^2 + \dfrac{3.50\alpha^2}{[\alpha - 0.77 + (A^2 + 0.32)^{0.5}]^2}\right\}$		Stewart[94]
	$\times \left[\dfrac{1 + \dfrac{\alpha + 0.54}{(A^2 + 0.32)^{0.5}}}{2}\right]$	

where $A = \alpha + 0.54$
β = percolation coefficient relating interstitial gas velocity to pressure gradient
β_o = value of β at incipient fluidization
α = nondimensional cloud radius ($= r_c/a$)

(for the region below the bubble):

$$P/\varrho_p ga = -\frac{1}{2}\left\{\alpha - 0.54 - [(\alpha - 0.54)^2 + 0.32]^{0.5}\right.$$

$$\left. + \frac{3.50}{\alpha + 0.77 + [(\alpha - 0.54)^2 + 0.32]^{0.5}}\right\} \tag{4-118B}$$

Comparisons of the model predictions for three-dimensional bubbles along with the data of Reuter[96] obtained from a two-dimensional fluidized bed are given in Figure 4-22. The equations from Murray's and Jackson's models are shown to underpredict the pressure difference. Reuter does, however, report the following empirical bubble rise velocity expression:

$$U_b = 1.0(gr_b)^{0.5} \tag{4-119}$$

which, when used in Jackson's analysis, is shown to provide better predictions (curve 2).

For both experiments and Jackson's analysis, the pressure increase ahead of the bubble occurs over a shorter distance than that predicted by Davidson's analysis. Since Jackson's expression for gas pressure is the only one derived from a particle momentum equation, including allowance for porosity changes, the similarities between curve 2 and experiments suggest that the development of fluid pressure approaching the bubble is controlled by the rate of change of particle momentum. In other words, porosity changes of the sort predicted by Jackson are therefore, reasonable.

Measurements of pressure in the bubble wake[96] show that, close to the bubble, the slope of the pressure curve is very close to zero. By analogy with conditions at the nose of the bubble it is likely that there are also regions of reduced porosity in the bubble wake. It can be concluded that the theories of Davidson and Collins forecast pressure changes of the right magnitude and that Jackson correctly assumes that particle momentum and gas pressure changes are directly related.

The reader is referred to Kunii and Levenspiel[34] and Wen et al.[99] for further discussions on classical single-bubble models and extensions to analyzing rate processes. Some of these concepts are discussed in Chapter 9.

The study of comparatively isolated and undisturbed bubbles has produced useful analyses which seem to apply to mass bubbling conditions. Actually, because of the

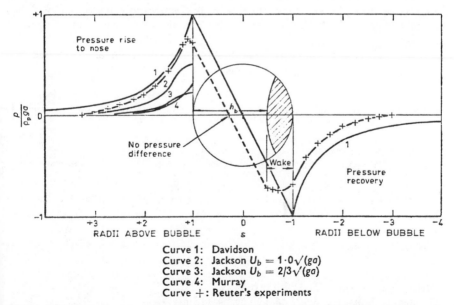

Curve 1: Davidson
Curve 2: Jackson $U_b = 1 \cdot 0\sqrt{(ga)}$
Curve 3: Jackson $U_b = 2/3\sqrt{(ga)}$
Curve 4: Murray
Curve +: Reuter's experiments

Figure 4-22. Illustration of predicted dimensionless pressure gradient between points on vertical bubble axis and points in same horizontal plane well removed from bubble, as reported by Stewart.[94]

wide variability of bubble velocity, shape and size data in mass bubbling situations, it has not been possible to evaluate the merits of such models. All that is clear is that they predict approximately the same trends and at roughly the proper magnitudes. For example, it is generally agreed that Equation 4-113 adequately describes single rising bubbles, with a value for coefficient k_v of 0.71 being appropriate for three-dimensional bubbles, and 0.5 for two-dimensional bubbles. Since this is a limiting case, we denote the single bubble velocity is $U_{b(\infty)}$.

In an actual fluid bed, velocity increases with bubble concentration and can be described as follows:[29]

$$U_b = U_{b(\infty)} + (U_D - U_{mf}) \qquad (4\text{-}120)$$

where U_D is the mean gas velocity across the distributor plane (i.e., the gas superficial velocity). Velocity data tend to be widely scattered, and it is difficult to establish any relationship. It is observed, however, that the centroid velocity is more reliable than that of the apex, and reported values should therefore be reviewed as an arithmetic average of the former.

The lateral velocity component is small. Very close to the column distributor, bubble motion is almost entirely vertical. Above this, an average motion can be observed towards the center of the column as moderately-sized bubbles coalesce. This action dies away with increasing height as the bubble number frequency or concentration decreases, and at some point in the bed the motion is again almost entirely vertical. The average vertical velocity component increases both with bed height and gas velocity. It also increases, but less sensitively, with decreasing particle size.

Rowe[28] has reported the variation of bubble size with height and flow rate, and adequately correlated an average bubble size as follows:

$$D_b = g^{-0.25}(h + h_0)^{0.75}(U_d - U_{mb})^{0.5} \qquad (4\text{-}121)$$

where h = bed height above the distributor
h_0 = a constant that characterizes the distributor ($h_0 \simeq 0$ for a porous plate).

Note that Equation 4-121 can be expressed in terms of a modified Froude number:

$$D_b/(h + h_0) = Fr_{mb}^{0.25} \qquad (4\text{-}122)$$

where $Fr_{mb} = (U_D - U_{mb})^2/g(h - h_0)$.
Combining Equations 4-121, 4-120 and 4-113 gives:

$$\overline{U}_b = k_v(1/2)^{0.5}(g)^{0.375}(h + h_0)^{0.375}(U_D - U_{mb})^{0.25} + (U_D - U_{mf}) \qquad (4\text{-}123)$$

Alternatively, this expression can be written in terms of modified Froude numbers:

$$Fr_b^{0.5} = \frac{k_v}{(2)^{0.5}} Fr_{mb}^{0.03125} + Fr_{mf}^{0.5} \tag{4-124}$$

where $Fr_b^{0.5} = \overline{U}_b/[g(h + h_0)]^{0.5}$
$Fr_{mf}^{0.5} = (U_D - U_{mf})/[g(h + h_0)]^{0.5}$

Equation 4-123 or 4-124 gives the average velocity of a bubble that will be observed at a height h above the distributor at superficial gas velocity U_D. Note that these are mean velocities for all bubbles that cross a plane height h above the distributor. Note, however, that

$$\overline{U}_b = \overline{U}_b^* + (U_D - U_i) \tag{4-125}$$

where U_i is the superficial velocity through the dense phase and can be estimated from the bed expansion expression (Equation 4-69); and $\overline{U}_b^*$ is the average rising velocity near minimum bubbling conditions. This expression refers to an average velocity with which all bubbles travel between the distributor and the plane at height h. Rowe[28] therefore, notes that the height term in Equation 4-123 must be appropriately averaged:

$$\int_0^h (h + h_0)^{0.375} / (h + h_0) = \frac{8}{11} (h + h_0)^{0.375}$$

from which is obtained:

$$\overline{U}_b^* = g^{0.375} \frac{k_v}{(2)^{0.5}} \left(\frac{8}{11}\right) (h + h_0)^{0.375}(U_D - U_{mb})^{0.25} \tag{4-126}$$

The h in this expression now refers to the total height of the bed from which expansion measurements were made.

In terms of the modified Froude numbers:

$$\overline{Fr}_b^* = C^2 Fr_{mb}^{0.5} \tag{4-127}$$

Equation 4-126 is normally plotted as $\overline{U}_b^*$ versus $(U_D - U_{mb})$, where the latter term refers to the excess gas velocity above incipient fluidization. The generalized Froude numbers are shown plotted in Figure 4-23, where $C = (8/11) K_v/(2)^{0.5} = 0.366$, using a value of 0.711 for k_v.

Note that the above analysis shows that $\overline{U}_b^*$ is not constant for a given bed height, but rather is a slowly varying function of gas velocity. A constant value can be concluded if it is assumed that the dense phase voidage remains constant and if the bed expands linearly with gas velocity.

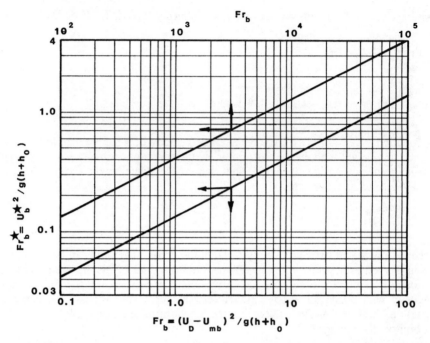

Figure 4-23. Generalized plot for estimating average bubble rise velocity in a three-dimensional fluid bed.

Two-Phase Theory for Bubble Flow

The simplest form of the two-phase theory[100] can be stated as:

$$\frac{V_B}{F} = U_D - U_{mf} \tag{4-128}$$

For very fine powders, $U_i \simeq U_{mf} \simeq U_{mb}$. However, there is general agreement[101] that U_i is not always U_{mf}, where U_i is usually greater. Various modifications to the theory are listed in Table 4-9. Equation 4-128 represents, then, the ideal two-phase theory. Rowe[28] makes the distinctions between theories as follows. "Modified two-phase theory" refers to considerations when interstitial flow is admitted to vary from Equation 4-128 but is in some way related to U_{mf}. When the added mass is accounted for in bubbles (see Table 4-9) or volume changes as a result of chemical reaction, models are referred to as "true volume two-phase theory."

We note that if permeability varies with voidage in a manner similar to the expressions of Hatch[23] or Rowe and Yacono[26] (refer to Table 4-2), then

$$\frac{U_i}{U_{mf}} = \frac{\epsilon^3}{(1 - \epsilon)} \cdot \frac{(1 - \epsilon_{mf})}{\epsilon_{mf}^3} \qquad (4\text{-}129)$$

Experiments using narrow-cut sizes of fine powders confirm that U_i/U_{mf} is independent of particle size, however, the voidage change required to bring about this change in permeability is sensitive to size. Also voidage can be observed to decrease with height in step with the reduced interstitial flow, and this change is much more dramatic with fine powders.

We can conclude this subsection with the following observations. First, fine powders tend to expand at gas velocities in excess of U_{mf} but do not bubble and become completely fluidized until some higher velocity. Between U_{mf} and U_{mb}, fine powders can be observed to expand erratically, usually because of channeling effects. At the higher gas velocities, uniform bubbling conditions are restored because of

Table 4-9
Various Modifications to The Two-Phase Theory

Modification to Two-Phase Theory	Comments/Justification	Investigator(s)
$\frac{V_B}{F} = U_D - kU_{mf}$; $k = 1 + 2F_B$	k is bubble geometric factor, which accounts for spacing between bubbles where F_B is fraction of space occupied by bubbles.	Davidson and Harrison[101] and Lockett et al.[102]
$\frac{V_B}{F} = (U_D - U_i)/f(k_T)$	k_T is correction factor which accounts for net flow via bubbles. Correction k_T is small when $U_b > U_{mf}$.	Yacono[25]
$\frac{V_B}{F} = U_D(1 + k_\varrho h) - U_{mf}$	k_ϱ accounts for the added mass of gas to bubbles as gas expands due to pressure decreases with height. Expression given is for an isothermal expansion and Rowe has shown that $k_\varrho = g\varrho_s\epsilon/1.01 \times 10^6$ for discharge under atmospheric pressure.	Azbel and Cheremisinoff[55]
$\frac{V_B}{F} = U_D - k'U_{mf}$ $k' = 1 + CF_B$	Same as Davidson[101] and Lockett et al.[102] but C > 2 to fit their experimental results.	Grace and Harrison[103]

better solids mixing (i.e., particle segregation effects are reduced at higher gas velocities). The size and shapes of bubbles are independent of particle sizes. Note, however, that bubble velocities do increase as particle size decreases. Finally, there is wide variation in the behavior and characteristics of individual bubbles and in predictions on an individual basis. Therefore such predictions are meaningless. Fluidized-bed behavior is best described in terms of average bubble properties.

Channeling and Slugging

Many solids do not show the properties characteristic of freely bubbling beds, or if they do, they also exhibit channeling tendencies at conditions close to minimum bubbling. The pressure-drop/flow relationship for moderately channeling solids typically appears as shown in Figure 4-24. This abnormality is characterized by the establishment of preferential flow paths in the bed through which large quantities of gas flow. Branch $\epsilon_e' - \epsilon_e$ denotes the relationship for a fixed bed. As noted earlier, the point of initial bed expansion usually occurs at a somewhat higher pressure drop than computed from the buoyant weight of the bed.

As particles "unlock" from each other, the pressure drop decreases rather suddenly. After the minimum pressure drop (point C in Figure 4-24) has been passed, there is always a pressure drop recovery, but in *channeling beds* the theoretical value is never quite reached. The amount by which the pressure drop is lower is indicative of the channeling tendencies of the solids.

There are two common cases of channeling. In *through channeling* the flowpaths extend through the entire bed, whereas *intermediate channeling* involves only a portion of the bed. Intermediate channeling beds result in higher fluidizing pressure

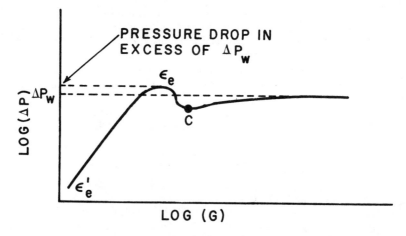

Figure 4-24. Typical pressure-drop/flow curve for moderately channeling solids.

drops with increasing gas rates. Because with channeling the resulting bed density is not homogeneous, there will be local space velocities inside the bed that greatly differ from the overall planned space velocity. This will lead to erratic temperature profiles, as well as contact and reaction conversion inefficiencies in large-scale equipment.

The shape and density of solids are factors that affect channeling, as well as the overall bed diameter. In general, an increase in channeling occurs with decreasing particle size. Furthermore, the specific configuration of the gas-inlet device has a profound effect on whether channeling occurs and on channeling magnitude. With porous plates the gas distribution into a bed tends initially toward uniformity. Channeling tendencies are always smaller with multiorifice distributors. In this arrangement the gas is introduced through a relatively small number of geometrically spaced holes.

Slugging is an abnormality frequently encountered in fluidization. It is considerably affected by the choice and design of the equipment. Characteristics of particles also are involved, although to a lesser extent than in channeling. Slugging is described as the condition in which bubbles of gas coalesce to a size approaching the order of magnitude of diameter of the confining vessel. Solid particles form layers or slugs between the large gas pockets and tend to move upward in a piston-like fashion, and upon reaching a certain height, they then disintegrate and fall downward in a raining fashion. Local space velocities may differ widely from the overall velocity in this situation. This has an erratic effect on yields and temperature distributions. In addition, *slugging* may accelerate the rate of *mechanical attrition* of particles.

The pressure-drop/flow diagram also reflects slugging behavior. Figure 4-25 shows the particles to approach ideal behavior up to and considerably beyond the point of the incipient fluidization. Beyond a certain flow range, however, the pressure drop will increase above the value calculated from the weight of the bed (point S). This condition denotes the *onset of slugging.*

The pressure drop excess over the theoretical value is due to friction between the solid slugs and the wall of the fluidized bed. This implies that the height-to-diameter ratio of the bed is an important parameter.

The particle size effect on slugging is shown in Figure 4-26. Smooth operation increases very markedly as particle size decreases. There is a wealth of correlations in the literature for predicting the onset of slugging; however, many are specific to the type of solids and exact system in which experiments were performed. One correlation for fluidizing particles is:

$$U_s = 6.8 \frac{U_{mf}}{L_e^{0.8}} \tag{4-130}$$

where U_s = gas velocity for *incipient slugging* (fps)
   U_{mf} = gas velocity at minimum fluidization (fps)
   L_e = bed height (ft)

Equation 4-130 is based on tests using 72-100-mesh coal with a maximum bed height of 6 in.

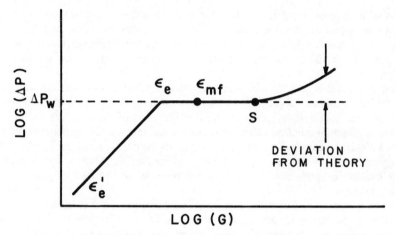

Figure 4-25. Typical pressure-drop/flow diagram for slugging solids.

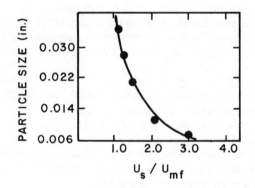

Figure 4-26. Illustration of a typical trend observed for slugging velocities as function of particle size. Data are for coal particles in a 1.64-in. diameter column with a bed depth of 10 in.

NOMENCLATURE

a   acceleration
a,b   parameters defined in Equation 4-59
A_r Archimedes number
C   coefficient
D_b Bubble diameter

d_e equivalent diameter or dimension
d_p particle diameter
d_{vs} surface volume diameter
E   energy of solids layer
F   cross-sectional area
F_b cross-sectional area of bed
F_0 drag force
F_0 fraction of fines
f_p particle surface area
f   friction factor
Fr   Froude number
g   gravitational constant
Ga   Galileo number
G_p weight of solids in bed or layer
h_0 distributor constant
k   coefficient of added mass
k_v constant in Equation 4-124
K   expansion coefficient (see Equation 4-28)
ℓ level or height of bed
ℓ_c pore channel length
ℓ_{mf} expanded bed height at minimum fluidization
n   number of bubbles per unit volume, or exponent
P'   force
P   pressure
Q   volumetric flow rate
r   radius
Re   Reynolds number
Re_p Reynolds number based on particle diameter
R_f resistance force
R_H hydraulic radius
S   solids surface area per unit volume of bed
S_p particle surface area
U   superficial velocity
U_B average bubble rise velocity
U_f superficial gas velocity
U_{mb} minimum bubbling velocity
U_{mf} minimum fluidization velocity
U_s incipient slugging velocity
U_t particle terminal velocity
U_0 velocity m/s
V_B gas volumetric flow rate as bubbles
V_{cf} complete fluidization velocity
V_p particle volume
W   bouyant weight of bed
x_i weight or number fraction of material in size interval i

Greek Symbols

α cloud penetration
β, β_o particle and gas drag coefficients
ϵ void fraction
θ polar angle
λ friction factor or Lagrange multiplier
μ_f viscosity
ν kinematic viscosity
ν_r relative velocity of bubbles
ν_R radial velocity component
ν_s superficial gas velocity
ν_θ tangential velocity component
$\bar{\nu}$ average fluid velocity
ξ resistance coefficient
ϱ density
σ surface tension of bubbles.
τ time scale of turbulent eddies
ϕ_s particle shape factor
ϕ' resistance coefficient
ψ relative bed density
ψ' shape factor defined by Equation 4-39

REFERENCES

1. Carman, P. C., *Trans. Inst. Chem. Engrs.* (London), 15: 150 (1937).

2. Carman, P. C., *J. Soc. Chem. Ind.* (London), 57: 225 (1938).

3. Kozeny, J., *Sitzber. Akad. Wiss. Wien,* Math-naturw. kl (Abt. IIa), 136: 271 (1927).

4. Oman, A. O., and K. M. Watson, *Natl. Petrol. News,* 36: R795 (1944).

5. Meyer, W. G. and L. T. Work, *Trans. American Inst. Chem Engrs.,* 33: 13 (1937).

6. Leva, M., et al., U.S. Bur. of Mines, Bull. No. 504 (1951).

7. Hiles, J. and R. A. Mott. *Fuel,* 24: 135 (1945).

8. Hatch, L. P., *J. Appl. Mech.,* 7: 109 (1940).

9. Hatch, L. P., *Trans. Am. Geophys. Union,* 24: 537 (1943).

10. Happel, J., *Ind. Eng. Chem.,* 41: 1,161 (1949).

11. Hancock, R. T., *Mining Mag.* (London), 67: 179 (1942).

12. Fehling, R., *Feurungstechnik,* 27: 33 (1939).

13. Fair, G. M., and L. P. Hatch, *J. Am. Water Works Assoc.,* 25: 1,551 (1933).

14. Diepschlag, E., *Feuerungstechnik,* 23: 133 (1935).

15. Chilton, T. H., and A. P. Colburn, *Ind. Eng. Chem.,* 23: 913 (1931)

16. Blake, C. F., *Trans. American Inst. Chem. Engrs.,* 14: 415 (1922).

17. Bakhmeteff, B. A., and N. V. Feodoroff, *J. Appl. Mechanics,* 4: A97 (1937).

18. Ergun, S., *Ind. Eng. Chem.,* 41: 1,179 (1949).

19. Ergun, S., *Chem. Eng. Progr.,* 48: 89 (1952).

20. Geldart, D., *Powder Technology,* 7: 285 (1973).

21. Richardson, J. F., in *Fluidization,* J. F. Davidson and D. Harrison, (Eds.), Academic Press (London) (1971).

22. Leva, M., *Fluidization,* McGraw-Hill Book Co., New York (1959).

23. Hatch, L.P., *J. Appl. Mech.,* 7: 109–112 (1940).

24. Richardson, J. F., and W. N. Zaki, *Trans. Inst. Chem. Engrs.,* 32: 35–53, (1954).

25. Yacono, C. X. R., Ph.D. Thesis, University of London, (April 1975).

26. Rowe, P. N., and C. Yakono, *Trans. Inst. Chem. Engrs.,* 53: 59–60 (1975).

27. Rowe, P N., and A. J. Widmer, *Chem. Eng. Sci.,* 28: 980–981, (1973).

28. Rowe, P. N., *Chem. Eng. Sci.,* 31: 285–288 (1976).

29. Davidson, J. F., and D. Harrison, *Fluidized Particles,* Cambridge Press, London, (1963).

30. Grewal, N. S., and S. C. Saxena, *Powder Technology,* 26: 229 (1980).

31. Wen, C. Y., and Y. H. Yu, *AIChE J.,* 12: 610 (1966).

32. Frantz, J. F., *Chem. Eng.,* 69: 161 (Sept. 17, 1962).

33. Geldart, D., and A. R. Abrahamsen, *Powder Technology,* 19: 133–136 (1978).

34. Kunii, D., and O. Levenspiel, *Fluidization Engineering,* Robert E. Krieger Pub. Co., Huntington, NY (1977).

35. Azbel, D., and N. P. Cheremisinoff, *Fluid Mechanics and Unit Operations,* Ann Arbor Science/Butterworth Pub., Ann Arbor, MI (1983).

36. Harriott, P., and S. Simone, "Fluidizing Fine Powders," in *Handbook of Fluids in Motion,* N. P. Cheremisinoff and R. Gupta (Eds.), Ann Arbor Science/Butterworth Pub., Ann Arbor, MI (1983), pp. 653–663.

37. Nutsers, S. M. P., and K. Rietema, *Powder Technology,* 18: 233 (1977).

38. Simone, S., and P. Harriott, *Powder Technology,* 26: 161 (1980).

39. Goddard, K., and J. F. Richardson, *Ind. Chem. Eng. Symp. Series,* 30: 126 (1968).

40. Rowe, P. N., L. Santoro, and J. G. Yates, *Chem. Eng. Sci.*, 33: 133 (1978).

✱41. Donsi, G., and L. Massimilla, *AIChE J.*,19: 1,104 (1973).

42. Massamilla, L., G. Donsi, and C. Zucchini, *Chem. Eng. Sci.*, 27: 2,005 (1972).

43. DeJong, J. A. H., and J. F. Nomden, *Powder Technology*, 9: 91 (1974).

44. Abrahamsen, A. R., and D. Geldart, *Powder Technology*, 26: 35 (1980).

45. Crowther, M. E., and J. C. Whitehead, *Fluidization*, J. F. Davidson and D. L. Keairns (Eds.), Academic Press (1978). p. 65.

46. Guedes de Carvalho, J. R. F., and D. Harrison, *Fluidized Combustion*, Inst. Fuel Symp. Ser., 1, (1975).

47. King, D. F., F. R. G. Mitchell, and D. Harrison, *Powder Technology*, 28: 55 (1981).

48. Richardson, J. F., and W. N. Zaki, *Trans. Inst. Chem. Eng.*, 32: 35, (1954).

49. Oltrogge, R. D., and R. H. Kadlec, Detroit AIChE. Meeting, (June 1973).

50. Wilhelm, R. H. and M. Kwauk, *Chem. Eng. Prog.*, 44: 201 (1948).

51. Matheson, G. L., W. A. Herbst, and P. H. Holt, *Ind. Chem. Eng.*, 41: 1,099 (1949).

52. Tsutsui, T., and T. Miyauchi, *Trans. Inst. Chem. Eng.*, 20: 386 (1980).

53. Guedes de Carvalho, J. F. R., *Chem. Eng. Sci.*, 36: 413 (1981).

54. Kawabata, J., et al., *Journ. Chem. Eng. Japan*, 14 (2): 85–89 (1981).

55. Azbel, D., and N. P. Cheremisinoff, "Mathematical Model of Freely-Bubbling Fluidized Bed," in Proceedings of 4th International Conference on Mathematical Modelling, Zurich, Switzerland (August 1983).

56. Levich, V. G., *Physicochemical Hydrodynamics*, Prentice-Hall, Englewood Cliffs, NJ (1962).

57. Lamb, G., *Hydrodynamics*, Dover Publications, NY (1945).

58. Golovin, A. M., and V. G. Levich, Tolmachev, *Prikl. Mat. Teor. Fiz.*, Moscow, 2: 63 (1966).

59. Golovin, A. M., *Prikl. Mat. Teor. Fiz* (Moscow) 6 (1967).

60. Miasnikov, V. P., and V. G. Levich, *Khim. Prom.* (Moscow) 6 (1966).

61. Gupalo, Yu. P., *Inzh-Fiz. Zh.*, (Moscow) 1: 16 (1962).

62. Happle, J., *AIChE J.*, 4: 197 (1958).

63. Uchida, S., *Ind. Eng. Chem.*, 46: 1,194 (1958).

64. Marucci, G., *Ind. Eng. Chem. Fund.*, 2: 224, (1965).

65. Akselrod, L. S., and V. V. Dilman, *Khim. Prom.*, (Moscow) (1): 8, (1954).

66. Azbel, D., *Khim. Prom.*, (Moscow) (11): 854, (1962).

67. Gal-Or, B., and H. E. Hoelscher, *AIChE J.*, 3(12): 499 (1966).

68. Azbel, D., *Two-Phase Flows in Chemical Engineering*, Cambridge Univ. Press, New York (1981).

69. Smirnov, V. I., *Kurs Vysshey Matematiki*, Gostelchizadert, (Moscow) Vol. 4, (1941).

70. Knowlton, T. M., paper no. 96 in 67th Annual Meeting of AIChE, Washington, DC (Dec. 1–5, 1974).

71. Lewis, W. K., E. R. Gilliland, and W. C. Bauer, *Ind. & Eng. Chem.-1*, 41 (6): 1,104–1,117 (June 1949).

72. Lehmann, J., H. Ritzmann, and B. Schugerl, Int. Symp. Fluidization (Toulouse), (1973), p. 107.

73. Basov, V. A., et al., *Int. Chem. Eng.*, 9: 263 (1969).

74. Merry, J. M. D., *AIChE J.*, 21: 507 (1975).

75. Knowlton, T. M., "High Pressure Fluidization Characteristics of Several Particulate Solids, Primarily Coal & Coal-Derived Materials," *AIChE Symposium Series*, 73: 22 (1977).

76. Rowe, P. N., H. J. MacGillvray, and D. J. Chessman, "Gas Discharge from an Orifice into a Gas Fluidized Bed," paper presented at AIChE Meeting in Miami, FL (November 1978).

77. Wen, C. Y., et al., "Jetting Phenomena and Dead Zone Formation on Fluidized Bed Distributors," Proceedings of the Second Pacific Chemical Engineering AIChE, NY (1977).

78. Yang, W. C., and D. L. Keairns, "Design and Operating Parameters for a Fluidized Bed Agglomerating Combustor/Gasifier," in *Fluidization*, J. Grace and J. Matsen (Eds.), Plenum Press, NY (1978).

79. Zenz, F. A., *Inst. Chem. E. Symp. Ser.*, 30: 136 (1968).

80. Shakhova, N. A., *Inzh. Fiz. Zh.*, 14: 61 (1968).

81. Behie, L. A., et al., *Can. Journ. of Chem. Eng.*, 48: 158–160 (April 1970).

82. Knowlton, T. M., and I. Hirsan, "The Effect of Pressure on Jet Penetration in Semi-Cylindrical Gas-Fluidized Beds," in *Fluidization*, J. Grace and J. Matsen (Eds.), Plenum Press, NY (1980). p. 315.

83. Hirsan, I., C. Sishtla, and T. M. Knowlton, "The Effect of Bed and Jet Parameters on Vertical Jet Penetration Length in Gas Fluidized Beds," paper presented at 73rd Annual AIChE Meeting, Chicago, IL (Nov. 16–20, 1980).

84. Davidson, J. F., *Trans. Inst. Chem. Engrs.*, 39: 320 (1961).

85. Collins, R., *Chem. Eng. Sci.*, 20: 747 (1965).

86. Jackson, R., *Trans. Inst. Chem. Engrs.*, 41: 22 (1963).

87. Davies, R. M., and G. I. Taylor, *Proc. Roy. Soc.*, A200: 375 (1950).

88. Davidson, J. F., et al., *Trans. Inst. Chem. Engrs.*, 37: 323 (1959).

89. Kunii, D., and O. Levenspiel, *Ind. Eng. Chem. Fund.*, 7: 466 (1968).

90. Murray, J. D., *J. Fluid Mech.*, 22: 57 (1965).

91. Rowe, P. N., and B. A. Partridge, *Trans. Inst. Chem. Engrs.*, 43: T157 (1965).

92. Toei, R., et al., *Chem. Eng. Japan*, 29: 851 (1965).

93. Rowe, P. N., United Kingdom Atomic Energy Agency, Research Group Report AERE-R 4383 (1963); *Chem. Engr. Progr.*, 60: 75 (March 1964).

94. Stewart, P. S. B., Ph.D Thesis, University of Cambridge, England (1965).

95. Stewart, P. S. B., *Trans. Inst. Chem. Engrs.*, 46: T60-66 (1968).

96. Reuter, H., *Chemie-Ingr. Tech.*, 35: 98, 219 (1963).

97. Reuter, H., Dissertation, Technischen Hochschule Aachen, Germany (1963).

98. Davies, R. M., and G. I. Taylor, *Proc. Roy. Soc.*, A200: 375 (1950).

99. Wen, C. Y., and L. M. Chen, "Flow Modelling Concepts in Fluidized Beds," in *Handbook of Fluids in Motion*, N. P. Cheremisinoff and R. Gupta, (Eds.), Ann Arbor Science Pub., Ann Arbor, MI (1983), pp. 665-690.

100. Toomey, R. F., and H. F. Johnstone, *Chem. Eng. Prog*, 48: 220-226 (1952).

101. Davison, J. F., and D. Harrison, *Chem. Eng. Sci.*, 21: 731-738 (1966).

102. Lockett, M. J., J. F. Davidson, and D. Harrison, *Chem. Eng. Sci.*, 22: 1,059-1,066 (1967).

103. Grace, J. R., and D. Harrison, *Chem. Eng. Sci.*, 24: 497-508 (1969).

5

Hydrodynamics of Entrainment

CONTENTS

INTRODUCTION, 207

MECHANISMS AND OBSERVATIONS OF ENTRAINMENT, 208

PHYSICAL PARAMETERS AFFECTING ENTRAINMENT, 216

    Bed Diameter, 216
    Bed Depth, 216
    Baffles, Stirrers, and Internals, 216
    Dispersed Phase Density, 217

ENTRAINMENT CORRELATIONS AND MODELING, 219

NOMENCLATURE, 232

REFERENCES, 232

INTRODUCTION

A fluidized column of solids may be divided into three distinct zones. Near the bottom of the column is the distributor or grid zone in which vertical and/or horizontal small-size gas bubbles form and begin their ascent. Above this region is the bubbling zone of the bed, where bubbles grow by coalescence and if the bed is deep enough, achieve some dynamic equilibrium between coalescence and breakup into smaller bubbles. At the surface of the bed bubbles burst, throwing particles above the bed surface. These solids become entrained by the upward flowing gas stream. This region above the bed is referred to as the freeboard zone. Some of the particles in this zone are carried a significant distance above the bed surface and are elutriated, whereas others simply fall back to the surface. The height at which the rate of entrainment appears nearly constant is referred to as the transport disengaging height (TDH).

The freeboard zone is important to the designer not only from the standpoint that it must be of sufficient height to allow entrained solids to disengage and return to the bed surface, but because it affords the opportunity for lean-phase reactions to take place. For example, in a fluidized-bed coal combustor (FBC), entrainment of carbon from the freeboard represents the principal source of combustion efficiency losses. In many reactor systems it therefore becomes necessary to recycle entrained fines back to the fluidized bed or in the case of the FBC, to include a carbon burnup cell to increase combustion efficiency.

In an FBC, the magnitude of fines loading in the freeboard not only affects NO_x reduction, SO_2 adsorption, CO and hydrocarbon emissions, etc., but contributes to such physical phenomena as tube heat transfer and solids attrition.

The subject of entrainment has been extensively studied as witnessed by the overabundance of correlations on entrainment rates in the literature. Despite this avid interest, the state-of-the-art for estimating entrainment rates in design and freeboard modeling is at best poor. The lack of reliable design procedures stems partly from not fully understanding the important mechanisms and in part from the difficulty in obtaining accurate entrainment rate data. Many of the experimental findings reported were based on tests in small-diameter columns or were conducted over narrow conditions of low gas rates and with relatively narrow particle size distributions containing only small amounts of fines. Data from large-scale beds are scarce, and the effects of bed diameter and internals on entrainment appear significant but have not been clearly established.

MECHANISMS AND OBSERVATIONS OF ENTRAINMENT

Entrainment generally is expressed in terms of the mass of solids per unit volume of gas flowing upward through the freeboard. Experimental observations have shown that the rate of entrainment is proportional to different variables in the following manner:

- Superficial gas velocity to the 4th-6th power
- Particle density to the −4th power
- Particle size to the −2nd power
- Gas density to the 1st power
- A factor of 10 in raising disengaging heights from 5 ft to 25 ft above which height negligible change is observed

A major problem encountered with entrainment data is its poor reproducibility. A range of $\pm 30\%$ is very common in a series of replica experiments in the same apparatus with identical charges of particles. Scatter is slightly less at high gas velocities and is typically greatest at low entrainment rates or low disengaging heights. Commercial entrainment data do not provide a good basis for general correlations, although they are of limited value in validating correlations specific to the particular equipment. Most of the entrainment studies have not included disengaging height, and it is believed that various literature-reported data were calculated for conditions above the *transport disengaging height* (TDH), at which point entrainment becomes constant with increasing height.

Column diameter greatly affects entrainment. Gas velocity and disengaging height also have significant effects on entrainment changes with bed diameter. At bed diameters greater than a few feet, wall effects are small and entrainment above TDH probably does not significantly vary with increasing diameter. Geometric factors are of secondary importance compared to the wide variations of effects of operating and physical properties. The particle properties important to entrainment are average size, size distribution, shape, and density.

Particles comprising narrow size ranges up to about 1,800 μm average diameter, have been studied by various investigators. Entrainment of very large particles at high velocities is of interest in *fluid-bed combustion*. Entrainment of single-sized particles is important from the viewpoint of generating various correlations and to theoretical understanding. Tables 5-1 and 5-2 summarize various entrainment studies and ranges over which experiments were conducted by different investigators.[1-24]

A number of investigators have observed that entrainment rates of narrow cut sizes of particles high above a bed are proportional to the weight percent of that fraction in the bed. It also has been found that the entrainment rate of any size fraction decreases with height until the TDH is reached. The entrainment rate of the fines fraction decreases with height in proportion to its concentration in the bed, even though there are essentially no coarse particles in the dilute phase. The single-particle terminal velocity, U_t, often plays a prominent role in the correlations. For uniform suspensions, particle slip velocity becomes progressively less than the *terminal velocity* as the *void fraction* decreases. It is also possible that particles can cluster in dilute suspensions and achieve velocities higher than a single-particle terminal velocity. According to definition, however, entrainment occurs at voidages less than 1. Further, with the possibility of *cluster formation*, it is clear that particle *slip velocity* could be expected to depart from predicted U_t values. With particles of mixed sizes, the flow phenomenon becomes more complex because different-size particles tend to move at different velocities, while exerting drag effects on each other.

When gas bubbles erupt at the surface of a fluidized bed, particles are ejected upwards. How particles are actually thrown into the freeboard is still subject to controversy. It is believed that a combination of factors are responsible; two common interpretations are:

1. Some of the solids in the wakes of fast-rising bubbles are thrown upward as bubbles burst at the surface (see Leva and Wen,[25] George and Grace,[26] Lin[27]).

(text continued on page 214)

Table 5-1
Summary of Entrainment Studies in Fluidized Beds Without Internals

Description of Experiments	Column Diameter, D_c Bed Height, L Freeboard, H(m)	Gas	Distributor	Particles	Size of Fines To Be Entrained (μm)	Size of Coarse Solids in Bed (μm)	Initial Weight Fraction of Fines (%)	Range of Superficial Gas Velocity (m/s)	Investigator
Elutriation, two components batch operation	D_c = 0.035, L + H = 1.22	Air	Perforated plate	Sand and Iron catalyst	41–67	110–230	20	0.21–0.41	Leva[1]
Elutriation two components, batch operation	D_c = 0.076, L = 0.14–0.29	Air, CO_2 He, Freon-12	Sintered steel plate	Glass spheres	19–36	590–1,450	0.4–5.6	0.04–0.18	Osberg and Charlesworth[2]
Entrainment, one component batch operation	D_c = 0.0508, L = 0.648, H = 0.305–0.914	Air, H_2	—	Pulverized coal	76	—	—	0.049–0.259	Jolley and Stantan[3]
Elutriation, two and multi-components, batch operations	D_c = 0.052–0.071, L = 0.031–0.12	Air	Fixed bed of steel balls	Sand, glass, seed refactory	85–500	310–1,640	5–20	0.92–1.62	Yagi and Aochi[4]
Entrainment of FCC catalyst, steady state operation	D_c = 0.051 × 0.61, H = 0.254–2.80	Air, mean pressure 8 atm	Grid	FCC catalyst with size distribution	20–150	—	—	0.30–0.72	Zenz and Weil[5]
Entrainment, one component, batch operation	D_c = 0.0965, 0.0305, H = 0.305–3.96	Air	—	3A catalyst	50, 60	—	—	0.518–0.368	Andrews[6]

Table 5-1 (continued)
Summary of Entrainment Studies in Fluidized Beds Without Internals

Description of Experiments	Column Diameter, D_c, Bed Height, L, Freeboard, H(m)	Gas	Distributor	Particles	Size of Fines To Be Entrained (μm)	Size of Coarse Solids in Bed (μm)	Initial Weight Fraction of Fines (%)	Range of Superficial Gas Velocity (m/s)	Investigator
Elutriation, two and multi-components batch operation	D_c = 0.051, 0.102; L + H = 2.08, 1.83	Air, He	Filtercloth	Glass spheres, coal powder	40–140	100–280	6–100	0.22–1.32	Wen and Hashinger[7]
Elutriation, two components, batch operation	D_c = 0.102; L = 0.15–0.92; l + H = 1.83	Air	Sintered bronze plate	Glass beads	6–79	800–300	2–20	0.06–0.38	Thomas et al.[8]
Elutriation, multicomponents, batch operation	D_c = 0.076; L + H = 1.37	Air	Filter cloth	Glass spheres	88–250	250–420	—	1.65–2.10	Hanesian and Rankell[9]
Elutriation, two components, batch operation	D_c = 0.067; L/D_c = 1–2; L + H = 0.60	Air	Fixed bed of glass beads (conical shape)	Sand, salt, coke, magnetite ammonium sulphate	277–359	459–677	35–80	U_o/U_{mf} = 7–9	Guha et al.[10]
Elutriation, two components, batch and continuous	D_c = 0.067; L + H = 1.80	Air	Perforated plate	Glass beads, sand, stainless balls, lead balls, Neobeads	60–800	141–2,300	—	1.28–2.70	Tanaka et al.[11]

Table 5-1 (continued)
Summary of Entrainment Studies in Fluidized Beds Without Internals

Description of Experiments	Column Diameter, D_c Bed Height, L Freeboard, H(m)	Gas	Distributor	Particles	Size of Fines To Be Entrained (μm)	Size of Coarse Solids in Bed (μm)	Initial Weight Fraction of Fines (%)	Range of Superficial Gas Velocity (m/s)	Investigator
Entrainment, steady state operation	D_c = 0.061 L + H = 7.92	Air	Grid	FCC catalyst with size distribution	20-150	—	—	0.11-0.22	Fournol et al.[12]
Elutriation, steady state operation	D_c = 0.90 × 0.45 L = 0.61-.122 L + H = 3.96	Air	—	Coal ash with size distribution	0-1,400	1,400-3,170	—	0.61-2.44	Merrick and Highley[13]
Entrainment, steady state operation	D_c = 0.61 L + H = 7.92	Air	Grid	FCC catalyst with size distribution	20-150	—	—	0.091-0.335	Nazemi et al.[14]
Entrainment steady state	D_c = 0.61 L + H = 7.92	Air	Grid	Sand with size distribution	37-250	—	—	0.20-0.30	Large et al.[15]
Entrainment, multicomponents, steady state operation	D_c = 0.1524 L = 0.23-0.25	Air	Perforated plate	Sand	22-180	Coarse: 443-1095 Medium: 22-1095	10-20	0.61-1.25	Bachovchin et al.[16]
Elutriation, multicomponents, batch operation	D_c = 0.076 L = 0.35-0.45 L + H = 3.80	Air	Filter paper covered by wire mesh	Sand, shot, Alumina	38-327	150-355	5-75	0.60-3.00	Geldart et al.[17]
Entrainment and elutriation, multicomponents, steady state operation	D_c = 0.60 × 0.60 L = 0.25 H = 0.63-3.27	Air	Grid	Sand/char with size distribution	0-125 (char)	125-419 (sand)	0.01-1	0.10-0.30	Lin et al.[18]

Table 5-2
Summary of Entrainment Studies in Fluidized Beds with Internals

Description of Experiments	Column Diameter, D_c Bed Height, L Freeboard, H(m)	Gas	Distributor	Particles	Size of Fines To Be Entrained (μm)	Size of Coarse Solids in Bed (μm)	Initial Weight Fraction of Fines (%)	Range of Superficial Gas Velocity (m/s)	Description of Internals	Investigator
Entrainment, one component, steady state operation	D_c = 0.019–0.146 L = 0.102–0.71 H = 0.92–3.16	Air	Wire mesh screen on fixed bed	Glass, polystyrene, iron, cracking catalyst	51–361	—	—	0.28–4.76	With and without stirrer or wire obstruction	Lewis et al.[19]
Entrainment, one component, batch operation in conical vessels	upper D_c/lower D_c = 15/6, 50/20	Air	Wire mesh screen on fixed bed	Sand	100–1000	—	—	0.40–1.70	Grids above dense bed	Blyakher and Pavlov[20]
Entrainment, multicomponents steady state operation	D_c = 0.165 $1/D_c$ = 1.3–2.6 H = 0.254–2.03	Air	Grid	Sand	104–208	—	—	0.60–0.96	Screen packing above dense bed	Tweddle et al.[21]
Elutriation, two components, steady state operation	D_c = 0.22 L = 0.31 H = 2.14	Air	Grid	Sand	63–76	425–500	20	0.44	Baffles above dense bed	Harrison et al.[22]
Elutriation, multicomponents, batch operation	D_c = 0.90 × 0.90 L + H = 6.30	Air	Perforated plate	Sand with size distribution	37–356	356–2360	10	0.90–3.60	With and without immersed heat transfer tubes	Colakyan et al.[23]
Elutriation multicomponents		Air (300°K–445°K)	Perforated plate	Silica sand	30–90	90–272	50	0.2–1.3	With and without tube bundle	George and Grace[24]

2. Solids at the surface become a part of the erupting dome of a bubble and are thrown upward as the dome breaks (see Do et al.[28]).

The first scenario appears to provide the dominating mechanism. Solids that are ejected either return to the bed against the upward gas stream or are carried out of the bed. Larger particles that return to the bed will acquire trajectories depending on their size, initial projection velocity, the background superficial velocity, etc. Actually, erupting gas bubbles can and do splash solids far into the freeboard region above the average surface of the bed. If the gas exit is situated immediately above the bed top, a large amount of solids become entrained in the gas flow. The amount of entrainment is considerably smaller when the gas exit is higher. Eventually, a level is reached above which entrainment becomes almost constant. The amount of entrainment can range from negligible to large amounts, especially if the solids contain a significant quantity of fines or if the gas velocity is very high.

The location of the TDH for different solids in a rectangular column is illustrated by the plot given in Figure 5-1. Very little information is available on the TDH. For known solids and vessel geometries, entrainment is very sensitive to gas velocity, varying approximately as $U^{2.5}$ to U^4. However, the TDH is not nearly as sensitive to gas velocity; it increases by about 75% for a doubling in the gas velocity. For a given gas velocity the TDH increases with vessel size, in a manner similar to that

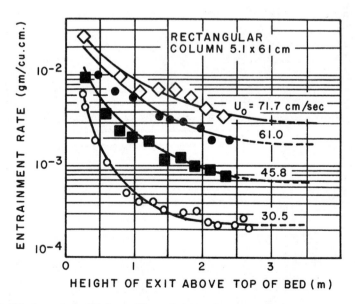

Figure 5-1. Entrainment of solids from different heights above upper surface of dense bubbling fluid bed (Zenz and Othmer[29]).

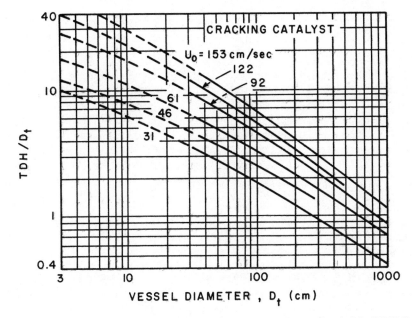

Figure 5-2. Empirical correlation for estimating the *transport disengaging height* (TDH) (from Zenz and Weil[5]).

shown in Figure 5-2. For a freeboard height less than the TDH, the size distribution of entrained solids varies with position, and entrainment decreases as the freeboard height approaches the TDH. When the gas stream is discharged above the TDH, both the entrainment rate and the size distribution appear constant and are governed by the saturation-carrying capacity of the gas stream under *pneumatic transport* conditions. This also appears applicable to describing entrainment above the TDH for monosize solids. In addition, another phenomenon may occur either below or above TDH; that of *elutriation,* which is the separation or removal of fines from a mixture. These various terms involved are defined in Figure 5-3.

Leva and Wen[25] give the following expression for estimating the TDH for the case of freely bubbling beds.

$$TDH = \frac{\varrho_s d_{pi}^2}{18\mu} \{U_{i0} - (U_{ti} - U) \ln [1 + U_{i0}/(U_{ti} - U)]\} \qquad (5\text{-}1)$$

where U_{i0} denotes the initial velocity of the fine particles having diameters d_{pi}.

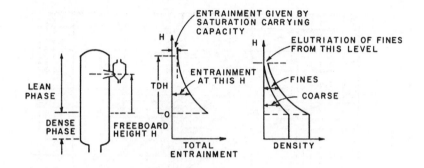

Figure 5-3. Terms which describe the removal of solids from a bed.

PHYSICAL PARAMETERS AFFECTING ENTRAINMENT

Clearly, entrainment is a complex flow phenomenon. To complicate matters further, entrainment is highly dependent on vessel geometry, size, bed depth, and the presence of internals.

Bed Diameter

Figure 5-4 shows the effect of bed diameter on entrainment for a given U_0 and bed depth. The sharp rise in entrainment in small bed diameters is associated with slugging conditions, while the minimum in entrainment at intermediate bed diameters is associated with gas *channeling*. For bed diameters greater than 8–10 cm, the entrainment rate becomes constant and independent of vessel diameter.

Bed Depth

For fine solids, entrainment appears to be insensitive to the depth of the dense bed, except for very shallow beds, where the size of bubbles reaching the surface becomes smaller and entrance effects intrude. Entrainment increases with deeper beds containing dense solids, which fluidize poorly, giving rise to severe *channeling* and *slugging*.

Baffles, Stirrers, and Internals

The effective diameter of a bed is reduced by the presence of baffles and wire obstructions, which can result in an increase in entrainment. Entrainment rates may, however, decrease if the average bubble size is reduced. When the obstructions are just under the upper surface of the dense bed, entrainment diminishes. The presence of stirrers decreases entrainment, their effect being more pronounced at high gas velocities. Table 5-2 lists various studies on entrainment rates where different internals were immersed in the dense bed.

Dispersed Phase Density

The density of the dispersed phase in the freeboard region is observed to decrease with height. With a rise in freeboard height, density increases. If the freeboard is above the TDH, or high enough so that entrainment is negligible, then the density at

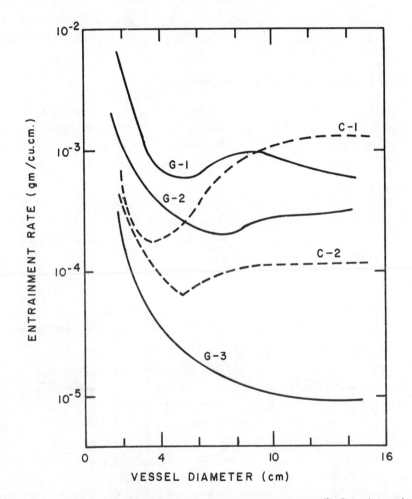

Figure 5-4. Effect of vessel diameter on entrainment rate (Lewis et al[19]). G-1: glass spheres (0.051 mm), 52 cm/s; G-2: glass spheres (0.074 mm), 52 cm/s; G-3: glass spheres (0.094 mm), 58 cm/s; C-1: cracking catalyst (0.070 mm), 39.6 cm/s; C-2: cracking catalyst (0.162 mm), 79.5 cm/s.

any level becomes a maximum, $\bar{\varrho}_R$. This condition is referred to as *complete reflux.* At complete reflux conditions, the density at any level, ℓ, above the dense phase is described by:

$$\bar{\varrho}_R = \bar{\varrho}_{R0}e^{-a_1\ell} \tag{5-2}$$

where $\bar{\varrho}_{R0}$ = density of the lean phase just above the surface of the dense bed
    a_1 = constant

For conditions different from complete reflux, Lewis et al.[19] observed that the density is some fixed value which is less than that at complete reflux, and is independent of the level in the bed, i.e.,

$$\bar{\varrho}_R - \bar{\varrho} = \text{constant throughout the freeboard} \tag{5-3}$$

Figure 5-5 illustrates these observations. Qualitatively, entrainment varies in a manner similar to the density of the lead phase. For a given U_0, entrainment and *freeboard height* are related as follows:

$$F_t = F_0e^{-a_1H} \tag{5-4}$$

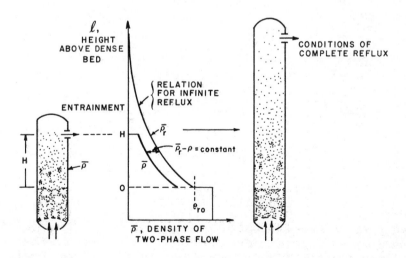

Figure 5-5. Density of lean phase as a function of level in the bed and the freeboard height.

Table 5-3
Values of B′ for Equation 5-5

Column Diameter (cm)	Cracking Catalyst 0.070 mm	Glass Spheres, 0.075 mm
5.1		0.036
7.1	0.031	0.053
14.6	0.020	0.083

where H is the freeboard height, and F_0 and a_1 are constants. Constant a_1 is the same as in Equation 5-2. The overall effect of gas velocity and freeboard height on entrainment (g/cc) is defined by the following equation:

$$\frac{F_t}{A_b U_0} = B' \exp \left\{ - \left[\left(\frac{b}{U_0} \right)^2 + a_1 H \right] \right\} \tag{5-5}$$

where $b = 8.86 \times 10^4 \varrho_s^{0.5} d_p$ (cm/s) and B′ values are given in Table 5-3.

ENTRAINMENT CORRELATIONS AND MODELING

Several models and correlations for estimating entrainment rates are reported in the literature. The entrainment rate can be expressed by the following equation, as follows from the description in Figure 5-3:

$$F_i = F_{i\infty} + (F_{i0} - F_{i\infty}) \exp(-a_f h) \tag{5-6}$$

where F_i = entrainment rate at a point h above bed surface
    a_f = a constant in freeboard
    $F_{i\infty}$ = rate of elutriation of the fines with diameter d_{pi} above the TDH

$$F_{i\infty} = E_{i\infty} X_i \tag{5-7}$$

where $E_{i\infty}$ is the elutriation rate constant for which numerous correlations have been reported. Table 5-4 lists various published correlations for the elutriation rate constant.

The constant, a_f, in Equation 5-6 is independent of the bed's composition (see Large[15]) and can be evaluated from experimental data for F_i as a function of h. Fol-

Table 5-4
Published Elutriation Rate Constant Correlations*

Correlations	Investigator(s)
$\dfrac{E_{i\infty} g d_p^2}{\mu(U_0 - U_{ts})^2} = 0.0015\, Re_t^{0.6} + 0.01\, Re_t^{1.2}$	Yagi and Aochi[4]
$\dfrac{E_{i\infty}}{\varrho_g U_0} = 3.91 \times 10^2 \left(\dfrac{U_0^2}{g d_p \varrho_s^2}\right)^{1.87} \quad ; \quad \dfrac{U_0^2}{g d_p \varrho_s^2} \leq 581.8 \times 10^{-3}$	Zenz and Weil[5]
$\dfrac{E_{i\infty}}{\varrho_g U_0} = 7.02 \times 10^3 \left(\dfrac{U_0^2}{g d_p \varrho_s^2}\right)^{1.15} \quad ; \quad \dfrac{U_0^2}{g d_p \varrho_s^2} \geq 581.8 \times 10^{-3}$	
$\dfrac{E_{i\infty}}{\varrho_g(U_0 - U_{ts})} = 1.52 \times 10^{-5} \left[\dfrac{(U_0 - U_{ts})^2}{g d_p}\right]^{0.5} Re_t \left(\dfrac{\varrho_s \varrho_g}{\varrho_g}\right)^{1.15}$	Wen and Hashinger[7]
$\dfrac{E_{i\infty}}{\varrho_g(U_0 - U_{is})} = 4.6 \times 10^{-2} \left[\dfrac{(U_0 - U_{ts})^2}{g d_p}\right]^{0.5}$	Tanaka et al.[11]
$\dfrac{E_{i\infty}}{\varrho_g U_0} A + 130 \exp\left[-10.4 \left(\dfrac{U_{ts}}{U_0}\right)^{0.5} \left(\dfrac{U_{mf}}{U_0 - U_{mf}}\right)^{0.25}\right]$	Merrick and Highley[13]
$\dfrac{E_{i\infty}}{\varrho_e U_0} = 23.7 \exp\left(-5.4 \dfrac{U_{ts}}{U_0}\right) ;$	Geldart et al.[17]
$\varrho_e = \varrho_g + \Sigma \varrho_i;$ where $\varrho_i =$ solid loading of ith size fraction in exit gas.	

Table 5-4 (continued)
Published Elutriation Rate Constant Correlations*

Correlations	Investigator(s)
$E_{i\infty} = 33\left(1 - \dfrac{U_{ts}}{U_0}\right)^2$	Colakyan et al.[23]
$E_{i\infty} = 3.35 \times 10^{-5}\left(\dfrac{U_0}{(d_p g)^{0.5}}\right)^{4.67}\left(\dfrac{\varrho_g}{\varrho_s}\right)^{1.62}\left(\dfrac{\mu}{\bar{d}_p}\right)\left(\dfrac{D_c(X_s)^{0.5}}{\bar{d}_p}\right)^{1.15}$	Bachovchin et al.[16]
where $\bar{d}_p$ = average size of particle elutriated	
x_s = fraction of fines at bed surface	
$\dfrac{E_{i\infty}}{\varrho_g U_0} = 9.43 \times 10^{-4}\left(\dfrac{U_0^2}{gd_p}\right)^{1.65}$	Lin et al.[18]
$E_{i\infty} = 20G \exp\{-32.6(U_t/U_0)^{0.5}[U_{mf}/(U_0 - U_{mf})]^{0.25}\}$ (bubbling bed)	Chen and Wen[30]
$E_{i\infty} = 13G \exp\{-10.4(U_t/U_0)^{0.5}[U_{mf}/(U_0 - U_{mf})]^{0.25}\}$ (slugging bed)	

* Symbols defined in Nomenclature.

lowing Chen et al.,[30] F_{i0} is the entrainment rate of particles at the bed surface where:

$$F_{i0} = E_0 X_i \tag{5-8}$$

where E_0 = elutriation rate constant at bed surface
X_i = weight fraction of the particle cut size d_{pi}.

The following correlations can be used to estimate E_0:[30]

For a bubbling bed:

$$E_0 = 0.3 D_b d_p^{-1.17} (U_0 - U_{mf})^{0.66} \tag{5-9}$$

For a slugging bed:

$$E_0 = 36.8 D_e d_p^{-2.47} (U_0 - U_{mf})^{1.69} \tag{5-10}$$

where D_b and D_e are the bubble and column diameters, respectively, and d_p is the average particle size.

The disadvantage of Equation 5-9 is that it requires knowledge of the average bubble size at the bed surface. Equations for the bubble diameter are given by Cranfield and Geldart[31] and Mori and Wen.[32] Also, there is some uncertainty whether Equation 5-10 applies to very large columns. The definition of a slugging bed is somewhat subjective in that it is a wall-controlled phenomenon. As a rule of thumb, slugging is believed to occur when the bubble diameter exceeds about 30% of the column diameter. At this size, wall effects distort bubble shape and rise velocity, and clearly Equation 5-10 would not apply.

Chen and Wen[33] have extensively reviewed the literature pertaining to entrainment and elutriation and compared many of the correlations listed in Table 5-4.

Most correlations for determining the elutriation rate constant are limited to the experimental conditions employed by each of the investigators (Yagi and Aochi;[4] Zenz and Weil;[5] Wen and Hashinger;[7] Tanaka et al.;[11] Merrick and Highley;[13] Bachovchin et al.;[16] Colakyan et al.;[23] Geldart et al.[17]). Extrapolation of these correlations to different operating conditions (different column diameters) often leads to very strange results as noted by Matsen[34] and Lin et al.[35]

Following Wen et al.[33] with particles of a single size elutriated above the TDH, the saturation carrying capacity of the gas stream reaches pneumatic transport conditions. The rate of elutriation from a bed composed of a single-sized particle can be viewed to be independent of a hydrodynamics prevailing inside the bed, and a material balance of elutriating particles in such a condition can be expressed as:

$$E_{i\infty} = \varrho_s (1 - \epsilon_i) U_{si} \tag{5-11}$$

where ϱ_s = solid density of elutriated particles

ϵ_i = voidage in the freeboard when the single-sized particles are being elutriated

U_{si} = the solid velocity of a given particle size (approximated by the difference between the gas velocity and the single particle terminal velocity as $(U_0 - U_{ts})$

Leung et al.[36] calculated the solid flow rate at the onset of choking in a vertical pneumatic transport system by the same equation and assumed the voidage was equal to 0.97. However, the voidage in the freeboard, ϵ_t, can be obtained from the force balance on the wall as shown by Wen;[33] and Yang;[39] as:

$$U_{si} = U_0 - U_{ts}\left[\left(1 + \frac{\lambda U_{si}^2}{2gD_c}\right)\epsilon_i^{4.7}\right]^{0.5} \tag{5-12}$$

Replacing the approximated solid velocity, U_{si}, with $(U_0 - U_{ts})$, and rearranging terms, an expression for ϵ_i is obtained:

$$\epsilon_i = \left\{1 + \frac{\lambda(U_0 - U_{ts})^2}{2gD_c}\right\}^{-1/4.7} \tag{5-13}$$

where λ is the friction coefficient due to the bouncing of the particles against the wall and against each other and is defined as:

$$dF_f = \pi D_c dh\ (\tau_s) = \frac{\lambda U_{si}^2}{2g_c D_c}\ (dW_s) = \frac{\lambda U_{si} G_s}{2g_c D_c} dh \tag{5-14}$$

Wen et al.[33] correlated λ with the system parameters, as:

$$\frac{\lambda \varrho_s}{d_p^2}\left(\frac{\mu}{\varrho_g}\right)^{2.5} = 5.17\ Re_p^{-1.5}(D_c^2)\ (\text{for } Re_p \leq Re_{pc}) \tag{5-15}$$

$$\frac{\lambda P_s}{d_p^2}\left(\frac{\mu}{\varrho_g}\right)^{2.5} = 12.3\ Re_p^{-2.5}(D_c)\ (\text{for } Re_p \geq Re_{pc}) \tag{5-16}$$

where,

$$Re_{pc} = 2.38/D_c \tag{5-17}$$

and

$$Re_p = \varrho_g(U_0 - U_{ts})(d_p/\mu) \tag{5-18}$$

A comparison of this relation with the experimental data (Leva;[25] Yagi and Aochi;[4] Andrews;[6] Wen and Hashinger;[7] Lewis et al.;[19] Tanaka et al.;[11] and others[13,23,35]) showed wide variation.

Comparisons between calculated rate constants based on the above relation with the experimental data were made by Wen et al.[33] Approximately 80% of the experimental data that can be represented by this correlation is within $\pm 50\%$ deviation. Wen et al. noted that the deviation of some of the experimental data is greater than $\pm 50\%$. In view of the diversity of the experimental conditions and the difficulty in obtaining accurate elutriation data, the deviation of this magnitude can be considered within the experimental accuracy.

When the bed is not fully entrainable at the gas/superficial velocity (i.e., when the superficial velocity is lower than the *settling velocity* of the coarse particles), then the large particles will remain in the bed and in the dilute phase up to the TDH. These particles thus have sufficient residence times to undergo reactions. The fines, on the other hand, spend very little time in the bed and consequently have a significant effect on reaction yields if they constitute a significant portion of the bed. Their main contribution is probably in maintaining small bubble sizes in the grid region. Thus, in systems where the solids take part in the chemical reaction, such as in *coal combustion* and *gasification,* fines are difficult to react.

Entrainment at and above the TDH has been studied by several investigators with narrow- or mono-size particles. It is known that entrainment from a bed of closely sized solids is not significant until a superficial velocity, U_0, considerably in excess of the terminal velocity, U_t, is reached. Under entrainment conditions, the bed can be considered as a saturation feed device such that the freeboard above the TDH is a *pneumatic conveying* tube for the transportation of solids. Several results are shown in Figure 5-6. In pneumatic conveying there is a maximum particle concentration which can be held in suspension by the flowing gas without collapse of solids into a dense slugging mass. This limiting condition is shown in Figure 5-7. The saturation carrying capacity of tubes can be used to determine the entrainment rate, $F_s(g/s)$ above the TDH. The entrainment per unit volume of gas is given as $F_s/A_b U_0$ (grams of solids transported per cm^3 of fluidizing gas), where A_b is the cross-sectional area of the bed.

For a bed of solids composed of a wide size distribution under flow conditions where $U_0 > U_t$, the following method can be used to estimate entrainment rates:

1. Divide the size distribution into narrow intervals and determine which of these intervals has $U_t < U_0$. Solids of this interval will be entrained.
2. Assume that each size is present alone in the bed and determine its entrainment rate.
3. Assume that the incoming gas divides into separate parallel streams, each passing through solids of one size alone, and which are of the same gas velocity. Then the total entrainment rate (g/s) is given by:

$$
F_t = \begin{pmatrix} \Sigma \\ \text{all fraction} \\ \text{of solids where} \\ U_t < U_0 \end{pmatrix} \begin{pmatrix} \text{entrainment rate} \\ \text{for a particular} \\ \text{size} \end{pmatrix} \begin{pmatrix} \text{fraction of that} \\ \text{size in the bed} \end{pmatrix} \tag{5-19}
$$

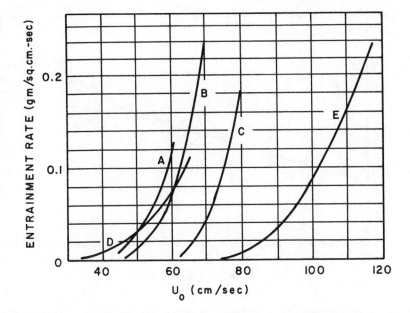

Figure 5-6. Entrainment versus superficial air velocity, U_o, in a bed with single-size solids (Lewis et al[19]); vessel diameter, 5.08 cm; static bed height, 10.2 cm; freeboard, 112 cm. Glass spheres: (A) 0.051 mm; (B) 0.074 mm; (C) 0.094 mm. Cracking catalyst: (D) 0.070 mm; (E) 0.162 mm.

An even simpler approximation method is to take the 50 wt % particle size of those solids where $U_t < U_0$. Estimate the entrainment rate for this size and then multiply the rate by the weight fraction of solids that have $U_t < U_0$. A comparison between experimental and predicted entrainment rates at different pressures based on this procedure is shown in Figure 5-8.

Wen and Chen[33] present a simplistic model for estimating entrainment rates. Their proposed model is based on the assumption that the entrainment rate of particles decreases exponentially along the freeboard. The value of TDH is not required in estimating the amount of solids being entrained. The amount of solids entrained at different heights in the freeboard, F, can be estimated from the entrainment rate at the bed surface, F_0, and from the elutriation rate, F_∞. The entrainment rate at the bed surface is calculated from information on the bubble size at the bed surface. The elutriation rate can be estimated from an elutriation rate constant correlation that is related to the saturation carrying capacity of the gas stream but is independent of the bed hydrodynamics. The freeboard height required can be estimated from:

$$F = F_\infty + (F_0 - F_\infty)[\exp(-ah)] \tag{5-20}$$

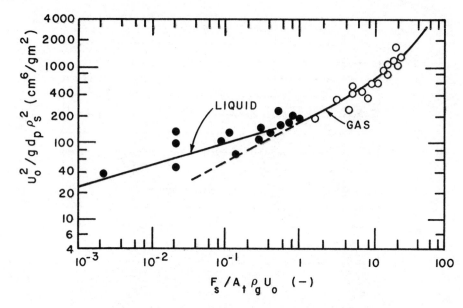

Figure 5-7. Empirical correlation of the saturation carrying capacity with superficial gas velocity, U_g, for uniformly sized particles in either horizontal or vertical cocurrent dispersed flow (taken from Zenz and Weil[5]).

where   F = entrainment rate of particles in freeboard at a height h above the bed
surface

F_∞ = elutriation rate (or entrainment rate above the TDH)

It can be assumed that the entrainment rate at the freeboard outlet is within a small percentage more than the amount of particles elutriated. Wen et al.[33] give the example that if the entrainment rate is within one or more percent of elutriation rate, the freeboard height required is estimated to be:

$$TDH = (1/a) \ln (F_0 - F_\infty)/(0.01F_\infty) \tag{5-21}$$

The value of "a" in the entrainment equation (Equation 5-20) is reported to vary from 3.5 to 6.4 m^{-1}. Table 5-5 lists average values obtained by Wen and Chen[33] using literature-reported data. An average value of 4.0 m^{-1} may be used for a system in which no information is available on entrainment rates.

Lewis et al.[19] formulated an entrainment model that describes the appearance of the entrainment process. Bursting bubbles of gas project agglomerates of particles into the space above the bed, and as the air flow rate is increased, this action becomes more evident with agglomerates projected successively higher into the freeboard. These agglomerates are broken up many times to form a dispersed phase, as well as streams of particles in a random motion. Measurable entrainment occurs only if $U_0 > > U_{mf}$. Under these conditions practically all the gas passes through the bed in the form of large bubbles with velocities considerably in excess of U_t. A rather simple model showing various aspects of entrainment for a dense bubbling bed is illustrated in Figure 5-9. There are three distinct phases in the freeboard above the dense fluidized bed.

- Phase 1: The gas stream containing completely dispersed solids where the solids velocity is U_1.
- Phase 2: Projected agglomerates moving upward with velocity U_2.
- Phase 3: Descending agglomerates and a thick dispersion moving downward with velocity U_3.

At any level in the bed the rate of dissipation of agglomerates to form the dispersed solid of Phase 1 is proportional to the concentration of agglomerate solids at that level. Upward-moving agglomerates occasionally reverse direction and move downward. The frequency of this change from Phase 2 to Phase 3 is proportional to the solids concentration in Phase 2. Denoting F_1, F_2, F_3 (g/s) as the mass flow rate

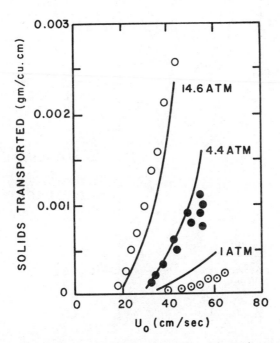

Figure 5-8. Comparison between calculated and experimental entrainment at various pressures (from Zenz and Weil[5]). Solid lines are predicted.

Table 5-5
Typical Values of the Entrainment Rate
Constant Reported by Wen et al.[33,37]

Average Particle Size Range Tested (μm)	Solids Density (kg/m³)	Column Diameter (m)	Average a (m⁻¹)	Range Gas Velocity (m/s)	Investigator
445–450	2,630	0.1524	4.0	0.73–0.90	Bachovchin et al.[16]
76	1,330	0.0508	3.5	0.12–0.25	Jolley and Stantan[3]
123–136	2,650	0.61	6.4	0.2–0.30	Large et al.[15]
59	840	0.61	3.6	0.091–0.335	Nazemi et al.[14]
163	1,370	0.1651	6.1	0.762	Tweddle et al.[21]
60	940	0.0508 × 0.61	4.2	0.305–0.6096	Zenz and Weil[5]

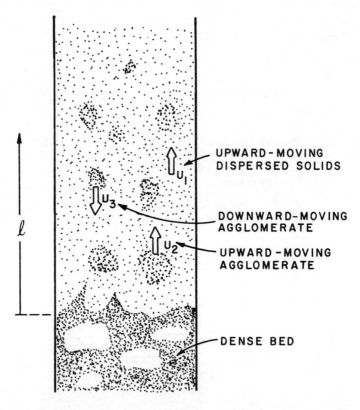

UPWARD-MOVING DISPERSED SOLIDS

DOWNWARD-MOVING AGGLOMERATE

UPWARD-MOVING AGGLOMERATE

DENSE BED

Figure 5-9. Model to account for elutriation and entrainment from dense fluidized beds.

of each phase and C_{s1}, C_{s2}, C_{s3} (g/cc) as the weight of each phase per unit volume of freeboard, the net upward flow of solids F is:

$$F = F_1 + F_2 - F_3 \qquad (5\text{-}22)$$

where

$$F_1 = A_b C_{s1} U_1$$

$$F_2 = A_b C_{s2} U_2$$

$$F_3 = A_b C_{s3} U_3 \qquad (5\text{-}23)$$

the average solids concentration is:

$$\bar{\varrho} = C_{s1} + C_{s2} + C_{s3} \qquad (5\text{-}24)$$

Mass balances for various phases are as follows:

- Phase 1: Increase of solids in Phase 1
  = transfer of solids from Phases 2 and 3 into 1
- Phase 2: Decrease of solids in Phase 2   (5-25A)
  = transfer of solids from Phase 2 to 1 and 3
- Phase 3: Increase of solids in Phase 3
  = transfer of solids from Phase 2 to 3 and from Phase 3 to 1.

Symbolically, the mass balances are:

$$U_1 \frac{dC_{s1}}{d\ell} = \hat{K}(C_{s2} + C_{s3})$$

$$-U_2 \frac{dC_{s2}}{d\ell} = (\hat{K} + K^*)C_{s2}$$

$$U_3 \frac{dC_{s3}}{d\ell} = \hat{K} C_{s3} - K^* C_{s2} \qquad (5\text{-}25B)$$

where $\hat{K}(s^{-1})$ is the mass transfer coefficient for the transfer of solids from Phases 2 and 3 to 1, and $K^*(s^{-1})$ is the mass transfer coefficient for the transfer of solids from Phase 2 to Phase 3. At the freeboard height, H, the gas stream leaves the vessel and so there is no downward flow. Thus

$$F_3 = 0$$

and

$$C_{s3} = 0 \text{ at } \ell = H \tag{5-26}$$

And since,

$$C_{s1} = 0,$$
$$C_{s2} = \frac{F_0}{A_b U_0} \text{ at } \ell = 0 \tag{5-27}$$

where F_0 is the flow rate of solids projected from the bed surface. Solving Equations 5-25B using Equations 5-26 and 5-27, we obtain:

$$\frac{1 - F/F_0}{1 - F_s/F_0} = 1 - e^{-H} \tag{5-28}$$

where

$$\frac{F_s}{F_0} = \frac{F_K}{1 + F_K} \tag{5-29}$$

$$F_K = \frac{\left(1 + \dfrac{U_2}{U_3}\right)\hat{K}}{K^*} \tag{5-30}$$

$$a_1 = \frac{K^*}{U_2}\left[1 + \left(1 + \frac{U_2}{U_3}\right)\frac{\hat{K}}{K^*}\right] \tag{5-31}$$

where F_s is the mass flow rate corresponding to the saturation capacity of the flowing gas stream.

For normal entrainment, a large quantity of solids projected from the bed returns to the surface. Therefore:

$$\frac{F_s}{F} << 1 \tag{5-32}$$

Hence, from Equation 5-29, F_K is approximately zero and Equation 5-28 simplifies to:

$$F = F_0 C^{-a_1 H}$$

$$a_1 = \frac{K^*}{U_2} \tag{5-33}$$

Assuming U_2 to be proportional to U_0, then $a_1 \propto U_0^{-1}$; from which the following formula is obtained from the above analysis:

$$F_0 = A_b U_0 B' \exp\left[-\left(\frac{b}{U_0}\right)^2 \right] \tag{5-34}$$

It has been found that for a new process, even with a perfect correlation of laboratory-determined parameters, entrainment cannot be predicted for large-size equipment with a high degree of confidence. Better correlations are needed for scale-up purposes. Specific examples where better correlations are needed include:

1. Entrainment predictions, where operation without cyclones is desired. Most beds have cyclones, giving a design that is insensitive to entrainment rate. However, there are situations such as fluid-bed combustion processes that operate without cyclones. Such designs are very sensitive to carryover.

2. Confirmation of effects at very high gas densities and viscosities is needed. New processes such as pressurized fluid-bed combustion and coal gasification operate at gas properties greatly different from existing entrainment data bases and correlations.

3. Prediction of dilute-phase holdup, which surely must be linked intimately with entrainment is needed. With fast reactions, such as riser cat cracking, a very substantial fraction of catalyst is present in the dilute phase.

NOMENCLATURE

a_1 constant in the entrainment equation
A   cross-section area of bed
b, b_1 constants
d_P, d_{pi} particle diameter of close cut particle, i
$\bar{d}_p$ average particle diameter in bed
D_B bubble diameter at bed surface
D_c column diameter
$E_{i\infty}$ elutriation rate constant of particle size i
F   total elutriation rate of particles
F_f frictional force of particles
F_i entrainment rate of particle size i
$F_{i\infty}$ elutriation rate of particle size i
F_0 total entrainment rate at bed surface
F_∞ total elutriation rate of particles
g   gravitational acceleration constant
g_c gravitational conversion constant, $m\text{-}kg/s^2kg\text{-}force$
G_s solids flow rate
h   height above dense bed surface
Re_p particle Reynolds Number $= \varrho_g(U_0 - U_{ts})d_p/\mu$
Re_t $dp\,U_{ts}\varrho g/\mu$
t   time
U_{mf} minimum fluidization velocity
U_0 superficial gas velocity
U_{si} solid velocity (upward)
U_{ts} single particle terminal velocity of particle size i
W   weight fraction of bed
W_s weight of solid particles in vertical pipe having length h
X_i weight fraction of particle size i in bed
X_{io} initial weight fraction of particle size i in bed

Greek Symbols

ϵ voidage in freeboard
ϵ_1 voidage in freeboard for system having only particle size i
λ solid friction coefficient
ϱ_g gas density
ϱ_p particle density

REFERENCES

1. Leva, M., *Chem. Eng. Prog.*, 47 (1): 39 (1951).

2. Osberg, G. L., and D. H. Charlesworth, *Chem. Eng. Prog.*, 47 (11): 566 (1951).

3. Jolley, L. T., and J. E. Stantan, *J. Appl. Chem.*, Vol. 2, Supplementary Issue, (1): 562 (1952).

4. Yagi, S., and T. Aochi, paper presented at the Society of Chemical Engineers (Japan), Spring Meeting (1955).

5. Zenz, F. A., and N. A. Weil, *AIChE J.*, 4 (4): 272 (1958).

6. Andrews, J. M., *I&EC Fund.*, 52 (1): 85 (1960).

7. Wen, C. Y., and R. F. Hashinger, *AIChE J.*, 6 (2): 220 (1960).

8. Thomas, W. J., P. J. Grey, and S. B. Watkins, *British Chem. Eng.*, 6 (2): 176 (1961).

9. Hanesian, D., and A. Rankell, *I&EC Fund.*, 7 (3): 452 (1968).

10. Guha, S. K., A. Kumar, and P. Sen Gupta, *Can. J. Chem. Eng.*, 50 (5): 602 (1972).

11. Tanaka, I., et al., *J. of Chem. Eng. of Japan*, 5 (1): 51 (1972).

12. Fournol, A. B., M. A. Bergougnou, and G. G. J. Baker, *Can. J. Chem. Eng.*, 41: 401 (1973).

13. Merrick, D., and J. Highley, *AIChE Symp. Series*, 70 (137): 366 (1974).

14. Nazemi, A., M. A. Bergougnou, and G. G. J. Baker *AIChE Symp. Series*, 70 (141): 98 (1974).

15. Large, J. F., Y. Martinie, and M. A. Bergougnou, Intl. Powder Bulk Solids Handling & Processing Conf. (May 1976).

16. Bachovchin, D. M., J. M. Beer, and A. F. Sarofim, AIChE 72nd Meeting, San Francisco (1979).

17. Geldart, D., et al., *Transactions of I. Chem. Eng.*, 57: 269 (1979).

18. Lin, L., J. T. Sears, and C. Y. Wen, *Powder Technology*, 27: 105 (1980).

19. Lewis, W. K., E. G. Gilliland, and P. M. Lang, *CEP Symp. Series*, 58 (38): 65 (1962).

20. Blayakher, I. G., and V. M. Pavlov, *Intl. Chem. Eng.*, 6 (1): 47 (1966).

21. Tweddle, T. A., C. E. Capes, and G. L. Osberg, *I&EC Process Design and Development* 6 (1): 85 (1970).

22. Harrison, D., P. N. Aspinall, and J. Elder, *Trans. Inst. Chem. Engrs.*, 52: 213 (1974).

23. Colakyan, M., et al., AIChE 72nd Meeting, San Francisco (1979).

24. George, S. E., and J. R. Grace, 3rd Intl. Conf. on Fluidization, Henniker, New Hampshire (August 1980).

25. Leva, M., and C. Y. Wen, in *Fluidization*, J. F. Davidson and D. C. Harrison, (Eds.), Academic Press, Inc., London (1971).

26. George, S. E., and J. R. Grace, *AIChE Symp. Series*, 74 (176): 67–74 (1978).

27. Lin, L,. "The Elutriation of Char from a Large Fluidized Bed," MS Thesis, West Virginia University, Morgantown, WV (1978).

28. Do, H. T., J. R. Grace, and R. Chift, *Powder Technology*, 6: 195 (1972).

29. Zenz, F. A., and D. Othmer, *Chem. Eng.*, 84 (27): 81 (1977).

30. Chen, L. H., and C. Y. Wen, paper presented at METC (1979).

31. Cranfield, R. R., and D. Geldart, "Large Particle Fluidization," *CES*, 29: 935 (1974).

32. Mori, S., and C. Y. Wen, *AIChE J.*, 21 (1): 109 (1975).

33. Wen, C. Y. and L. H. Chen, *AIChE J.*, 28 (1): 117–128 (Jan. 1982).

34. Matsen, J. M., "Entrainment Research: Achievements and Opportunities," presented for the NSF Workshop on Fluidization and Fluid-Particle Systems, Troy, NY (Oct. 1979).

35. Lin, L., J. T. Sears, and C. Y. Wen, *Powder Technology*, 27: 105 (1980).

36. Leung, L. S., R. J. Wiles, and D. H. Nicklin, *I&EC Process Design and Development* 10 (2): 183 (1971).

37. Wen, C. Y., "Dilute and Dense Phase Pneumatic Transport," paper in *Bulk Materials Handling*, Vol. 1, M. C. Hawk, (Ed.), Univ. of Pittsburgh, (1971) p. 258.

38. Yang, W. C., *AIChE J.*, 21 (5): 1,013 (1975).

39. Tanaka, I., and H. Shinohara, *Intl. Chem. Eng.*, 18 (2): 276 (1978).

6

Commercial Fluid Bed Processes

CONTENTS

INTRODUCTION, 235

REACTORS IN THE PETROLEUM INDUSTRY, 236

Early Developments, 236
Reaction Kinetics and Catalysts, 239
Fluid Bed Operations, 247

DRYING AND PROCESSING OPERATIONS, 255

REFERENCES, 269

INTRODUCTION

Fluid bed technology is widely used throughout the petroleum and allied industries in such applications as petroleum refining, plastics and chemicals preparations, lime mud reburning, roasting operations, waste incineration, and many others. This chapter presents an overview of conventional process operations.

REACTORS IN THE PETROLEUM INDUSTRY

Early Developments

In the early years of the petroleum industry, distillers discovered the benefits of thermal cracking to produce benzene by forcing their stills to the limits. One of the most successful early catalytic cracking processes was the Houdry process, of which the first commercial unit was placed into operation in 1936. This development significantly increased gasoline yields from crude. The early Houdry process employed a silica alumina catalyst, which at high temperature cracked gas oils to gasoline. The principal drawback with this process was the regeneration of the catalyst. A byproduct of the cracking reaction is coke, which deposits onto the catalyst and blinds or deactivates the active catalytic sites. Coke can be burned off in air; however, a considerable amount of heat is liberated, which if not removed, can melt the catalyst.

Catalytic cracking in the Houdry process was originally performed in fixed beds. Temperature control in these reactors was achieved using a molten salt heat removal scheme as the catalyst was regenerated. The heat of reaction and some of the required feed preheat were supplied by circulating the molten salt through vertical tubes distributed through the reactor bed. A typical reaction cycle for an individual reactor was about ten minutes. At the end of this cycle, feed was automatically switched to another reactor that had been regenerated. The spent reactor was steam purged for several minutes and then isolated by an automatic cycle timer. Regeneration air was then introduced and the carbon was burned off at a rate at which the bed temperature could be controlled by the recirculation of the molten salt stream. The regenerated bed had to be purged of oxygen before being returned into cracking service. A typical operation consisted of three to six reactors. The main difficulty with the fixed-bed catalytic cracker was that equilibrium was never achieved. The gas oil conversion (i.e., the amount of feed converted to lighter components) was initially high at the start of the reaction and gradually diminished as carbon deposited onto the catalyst until regeneration was needed. To minimize this effect multiple parallel reactors were employed; however, true steady-state operation was never actually achieved. Reaction-bed temperatures during reaction and regeneration cycles fluctuated considerably.

The next major development in gasoline production was a moving bed operation (process flow sheets of two early units are shown in Figure 6-1). In the moving bed processes, the hot salt heat transfer and cycle time systems were eliminated. The catalyst was transferred to the top of the unit and flowed by gravity down through the vessel. These systems were first commercialized around 1943. The catalyst was pelletized into about one eighth-in. diameter beads and allowed to flow by gravity from the top of the vessel, down through a seal zone to the pressurized reactor vessel. The catalyst then flowed down through another sealing section and a countercurrent stripping zone. From there, catalyst flowed to the regenerator or kiln, which operated close to atmospheric pressure. The Socony Vacuum Oil Co.'s unit (Figure 6-1A) injected the regeneration air near the center of the regenerator bed. The gas flowed upward and then downward. The upflowing gas combusted about

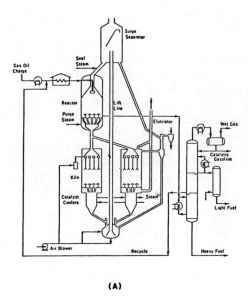

(A)

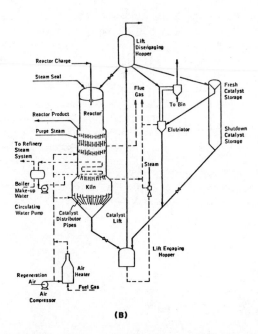

(B)

Figure 6-1. Moving-bed catalytic crackers: (A) Thermofor moving-bed process developed by Socony Vacuum Oil Co.; (B) Houdriflow catalytic cracking process.

60% of the coke, and heated the downward flowing catalyst. The downward flowing gas completed the combustion process. The principal difference between the Socony Vacuum process (Figure 6-1A) and the modified Houdry process (Figure 6-1B) was that the latter consisted of a single vessel with reaction and stripping zones separated by intermediate vessel heads. Also, flue gas rather than air was used for catalyst lifting in the Houdry design. This allowed for a higher circulation rate. The Socony Vacuum design consisted of separate vessels for reaction and regeneration.[1,2] Units constructed in the late 1940s employed a pneumatic lift design which allowed for high catalyst circulation rates. A typical design is shown in Figure 6-2, which allowed for a primary air stream to convey the catalyst. A secondary air stream is injected through an annulus into which the catalyst can flow. By varying the secondary gas flow, the catalyst circulation rate can be varied. This design permitted the injection of all liquid feeds and feeds of higher boiling ranges.[3]

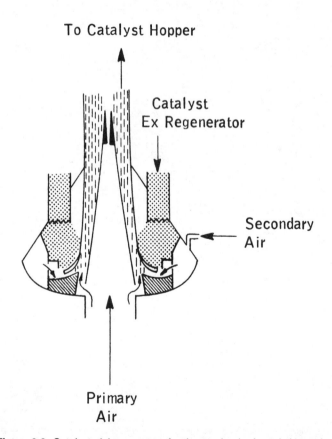

Figure 6-2. Catalyst pick-up system for the moving-bed catalytic cracker.

The lift pipe design was tapered to a larger diameter at the top. This minimized the effects of erosion and catalyst attrition, and also prevented the instantaneous total collapse of circulations when the saltation concentration, or velocity, of solids is experienced (i.e. the slump velocity—that velocity below which particles drop out of the flowing gas stream). In a typical operation, 2% to 4% coke can be deposited on the catalyst in the reactor and burned in the regenerator. Catalyst circulation is generally not sufficient to remove all the heat of combustion. This facilitated the need for steam or pressurized water coils to be located in the regeneration zone to remove excess heat.

The application of fluidized solids techniques to catalytic cracking resulted in a major technological and process advancement in the petroleum industry. This technology made it possible to transfer all the regeneration heat to the reaction zone. In addition, much larger units could be constructed and heavier liquid feeds could be processed. The development of the fluid solid catalytic cracking process was accelerated by the need for aviation fuel by the Allied nations during World War II. The growth of the fluid-bed process for gasoline and petroleum products manufacture has grown steadily over the years. Before discussing specific process operations and designs, a brief discussion of catalytic cracking chemisty and catalyst properties is warranted.

Reaction Kinetics and Catalysts

The primary product differences between catalytic cracking and thermal cracking are summarized in Table 6-1. The major products of catalytic cracking lie in the distribution of light gases (i.e., C_3's and C_4's), whereas C_1 and C_2 products are obtained from thermal cracking.

With the risk of oversimplifying the chemistry, catalytic cracking reactions can be classified into primary and secondary reactions. Primary reactions involve an initial carbon/carbon breaking into the following reactions:

$$
\left.
\begin{array}{l}
\text{Paraffin} \longrightarrow \text{paraffin} \ + \ \text{olefin} \\
\text{Alkylnaphthene} \longrightarrow \text{napthene} \ + \ \text{olefin} \\
\text{Alkylaromatic} \longrightarrow \text{aromatics} \ + \ \text{olefin}
\end{array}
\right\}
\qquad (6\text{-}1)
$$

These reactions proceed through a carbonium ion mechanism resulting in several products other than a single olefin and single saturated component.

The secondary reactions include a large number of reactions of olefins and a group of independent reactions. Major secondary reactions include olefins cracking, double bond shift, geometrical or skeletal isomerization, hydrogen transfer to an olefin from naphthenes to produce cyclic olefins and aromatics, hydrogen transfer from another olefin to produce diolefins, polymerization to produce higher molecular weight olefins, aromatization, and the alkylation of aromatics. Some of these reactions proceed further, producing coke deposits on the catalyst. The coke forming reactions include extended polymerization of olefins or diolefins, aromati-

Table 6-1
Comparison of Reaction Characteristics of Catalytic and Thermal Cracking[4]
(Based on pure hydrocarbons in a temperature range of 400°C–550°C and atmospheric pressures)

Hydrocarbon	Catalytic Cracking	Thermal Cracking
n-Paraffins	Breakdown to C_2 and larger fragments. Product largely in C_2 to C_6 range and contains branched aliphatics. Few normal α-olefins above C_4	Extensive breakdown to C_2 fragments, with much C_1 and C_2. Prominent amounts of C_4 to C_{n-1} normal α-olefins. Aliphatics largely unbranched.
Isoparaffins	Cracking rate relative to n-paraffins increased considerably by presence of tertiary carbon atoms.	Cracking rate increased to a small degree by presence of tertiary carbon atoms.
Naphthenes	Crack at about same rate as those paraffins with similar numbers of tertiary carbon atoms. Aromatics produced, with much hydrogen transfer to unsaturates.	Crack at lower rate than normal paraffins. Aromatics produced with little hydrogen transfer to unsaturates.
Unsubstituted aromatics	Little reaction; some condensation.	Little reaction; some condensation.
Alkyl aromatics (substituents C_3 or larger)	Entire alkyl group cracked next to ring and removed as olefin. Crack at higher rates than paraffins.	Alkyl group cracked to leave one or two carbon atoms attached to ring and at lower rate than paraffins.
n-Olefins	Product similar to that from n-paraffins, but more olefinic.	Product similar to that from n-paraffins, but more olefinic.
All olefins	Hydrogen transfer is an important reaction, especially with tertiary olefins. Crack at much higher rates than corresponding paraffins.	Hydrogen transfer is a minor reaction, with little preference for tertiary olefins. Crack at about same rate as corresponding paraffins.

zation to form polycyclic aromatics, and cyclization and/or condensation of alkylated aromatics.

The mechanisms involved in the catalytic cracking can be explained through the carbonium ion theory.[3-7] Carbonium ions are generated by three routes. The first involves the reversible addition of a proton from the acidic catalyst to an olefin, thus forming a carbonium ion:

$$R-CH_2-CH=CH-CH_2-R + H^+ \rightleftharpoons R-CH_2-CH^+-CH_2-CH_2-R \quad (6-2)$$

A second route by which carbonium ions may be formed is by the abstraction of a hydride ion (H^-) from a saturated molecule by the catalyst acidic site:

$$
\begin{array}{ccc}
CH_3 & & CH_3 \\
| & & | \\
CH_3-CH & \rightleftharpoons CH_3-C & + \text{ Acid Site: } H^+ \\
| & & | \\
CH_3 & & CH_3
\end{array}
\qquad (6\text{-}3)
$$

Finally, carbonium ions may be formed by the extraction of a hydride ion from a saturated molecule by another carbonium ion.

$$
\begin{array}{ccc}
CH_3 & & CH_3 \\
| & & | \\
CH_3-CH & + R-CH^+-R \rightleftharpoons CH_3-C & + R-CH_2-R \\
| & & | \\
CH_3 & & CH_3
\end{array}
\qquad (6\text{-}4)
$$

The carbonium ion is extremely reactive and undergoes a variety of reactions according to specific rules of formation, rearrangement, and reaction. The principal rules as described by Voge[5] are summarized as follows:

STEP 1. A carbonium ion is readily rearranged by methyl or hydrogen and shifts to form isomerized ions:

$$
\begin{array}{ccc}
H & & \\
| & & \\
R-C-CH_2-R & \rightarrow R-CH-CH_2^+ \rightarrow R-C^+-R \\
| & \qquad | \qquad | \\
+ & \qquad R \qquad CH_3
\end{array}
$$

The order of carbonium ion stability is

teritiary > secondary > primary

STEP 2. A carbonium ion can extract a hydride ion from a saturated molecule to form a new carbonium ion

STEP 3. A carbonium ion can transfer a proton to an olefin and, thus, form a new carbonium ion and a new olefin:

$$R-CH^+-CH_3 + C_4H_8 \rightarrow C_4H_9^+ + R-CH=CH_2$$

STEP 4. If a carbonium ion is sufficiently large, it can split at the bond beta to the positive charge and form an olefin and a new carbonium ion:

$$CH_3-CH^+-CH_2-R \rightarrow CH_3-CH=CH_2 + R^+$$

STEP 5. The propagation of carbonium ions is terminated by the donation of a proton to the catalyst surface and production of an olefin from the carbonium ion.

Isoparaffins are cracked by mechanisms similar to those for paraffins. The rate of cracking of isoparaffins is generally higher than that of paraffins primarily due to the high rates of removal of hydride ions from tertiary and secondary carbon atoms relative to primary carbons (approximately 20 and 2, respectively) compared to unity for primary carbon.

Cracking reactions of napthenes are probably similar to those of paraffins. The rates of cracking of naphthenes are believed to be determined by the types of carbon atoms present (e.g. primary, secondary, or tertiary carbon atoms, rather than by a ring structure).

Alkyl aromatics with side chains of three more carbon atoms react rapidly during catalytic cracking. The high reactivity is attributed to a proton attack at the ring carbon atom which carries a propyl or higher substituent to and from a denuded aromatic and carbonium ion fragment.

N-paraffin cracking is characterized by the production of large quantities of gas that are predominantly composed of C_3's and C_4's, along with low coke yields. Secondary reactions, such as polymerization and cyclization of olefins, and condensation of olefins with aromatics, are primarily responsible for the small production of coke and aromatics. Cracking characteristics of isoparaffins resemble those of n-paraffins, however, C_3 and C_4 yields are typically lower. Naphthenes tend to crack faster and produce more liquid products and less coke than paraffins. Naphthenes also tend to undergo extensive dehydrogenation. In the case of monocyclic naphthenes, monocyclic aromatics are produced and a high quality gasoline rich in aromatics results. Dehydrogenation to the less desirable polycyclic aromatics occurs with polynuclear naphthenes at high severity conditions. Dehydrogenation reactions typically occur when the catalyst is poisoned by nickel, vanadium, and/or iron.

With monocyclic aromatics, the breaking of side chains results in relatively stable aromatics in the gasoline boiling range. The breaking of larger side chains with diaromatics produces methyl- or ethyl-substituted naphthalenes which are a major constituent of the light oils generated from aromatic or naphthenic feeds. Similar bond-breaking reactions of triaromatics and higher polycyclics produce the corresponding aromatic with only short side chains left. Denuded polycyclic aromatics concentrate in the heavier cycle oils. A significant amount of the aromatic carbon in these structures does, however, deposit as coke on the catalyst.

The formation of coke is a key component in gasoline production. It not only reduces catalyst activity due to the buildup of carbonaceous deposits, but is an important factor in the heat balance for the process. Consequently, coke yield influences the regenerator design as well as the need for feed-preheat or heat-recovery facilities.

Coke formation in catalytic cracking is a complex phenomenon that is governed by several reactions. There are three types of coke formed: catalytic coke, "cat-to-oil" coke, and "Conradson carbon" coke. Catalytic coke is formed when hydrocarbons are cracked over an acidic catalyst. It is the byproduct of a variety of secondary reactions, such as the polymerization of olefins and diolefins, aromatization to form polynuclear aromatics, cyclization and/or condensation of alkylated aromatics, and dehydrogenation to form polycyclic aromatics. The controlling mechanisms in catalytic coke formation are thought to be adsorption of polynuclear aromatic structures followed by condensations and reactions with olefins to generate intermediate structures. Polynuclear aromatic constituents in the feedstock are the primary contributors to catalytic coke formation.

The "cat-to-oil" coke arises from portions of the feed being trapped in the pores of the catalyst as it leaves the reactor and flows to the regenerator. It is usually related to the catalyst/oil ratio, catalyst porosity, and the efficiency of steam stripping.

"Conradson carbon" coke is attributed to feedstocks that contain small amounts of high boiling or nonvolatile hydrocarbons that arise from inefficient fractionation or contamination of the feed. Fractions are deposited on the catalyst resulting in coke formation. The coke yield from these nonvolatile constituents has been correlated with the Conradson carbon content of the feed.

Larger amounts of coke are generated on catalysts that have been contaminated with metals such as nickel, vanadium, and iron. This is attributed to the dehydrogenation of naphthenic structures and polynuclear aromatics that form additional coke. Coke yields in catalytic cracking reflects feedstock properties, reactor conditions, physical and chemical properties of the catalyst, and stripper variables. Catalytic cracking yields and product quantities are controlled by a large number of operating variables and conditions. These include the reactor temperature, recycle of unconverted feed fractions, feed preheat temperature, and catalyst and feedstock residence times. In addition, catalyst activity plays a dominant role.

Cracking catalyst activity can differ markedly and thus establish the cracking reaction and the quality of the products obtained from cracking the gas oil feeds (i.e. selectivity). Activity can be related directly to the total number of active sites per unit weight of catalyst and the acidic strength of these sites. It is the differences in activity and acidity that establish the extent of various secondary reactions occurring and thus differences in product quality.

In general, cracking catalysts consist of mixed metal oxides, such as SiO_2—Al_2O_3, SiO_2—MgO, and crystalline alumino-silicate zeolites, among others.

Early cracking catalysts consisted of acid-leached montmorillonite clays. The purpose of the acid leach was to remove various metal impurities, such as iron, copper, and nickel, that could adversely affect the cracking performance. These first catalysts were manufactured by Houdry and later by the Filtrol Corporation and were employed in fixed-bed and moving-bed systems in the form of shaped pellets. With the advent of the fluid catalytic cracking process, clay catalysts were prepared in the form of a ground, sized powder. Clay catalysts are relatively inexpensive and have been widely used.

Synthetic catalysts were developed because of the need to have uniform composition and catalytic performance. The first synthetic cracking catalyst consisted of 87% SiO_2 and 13% Al_2O_3 and were manufactured by the Houdry Corporation in pellet form. They were extensively used in fixed-bed units in the 1940s. Catalysts of this composition were ground and sized for use in fluid catalytic cracking units. By the mid 1940s catalysts in the form of beads (about 2.5–5.0 mm diameter) were introduced by the Socony-Mobil Co. These catalysts consisted of about 90% SiO_2 and 10% Al_2O_3 and were extremely durable.

Other combinations of mixed oxides were found to be catalytically active and were developed during the 1940s. These included silica-magnesia, silica-zirconia, silica-alumina-magnesia, silica-alumina-zirconia, and alumina-boria, however, only silica-magnesia was used in commercial units.

The commercial cracking catalysts used most widely up until about 1962 were the acid-leached clays and silica-alumina. The latter was manufactured in two forms; low alumina (about 13% Al_2O_3), and high alumina (about 25% Al_2O_3) content. High alumina content catalysts are characterized by a higher equilibrium activity level and surface area.

A semi-synthetic grade of silica-alumina catalyst consisting of about 25% to 30% kaolin dispersed throughout the silica-alumina gel was also introduced by the 1960s. These catalysts could be offered at a lower price, but were marked by a lower catalytic activity and greater stack losses because of increased attrition rates. An advantage of this catalyst grade was that a lesser amount of adsorbed, unconverted, heavy products on the catalyst were carried over to the stripper zone and regenerator. As a result, a higher yield of more valuable products and also smoother operation of the regenerator was achieved.

During the late 1950s crystalline zeolites were introduced as selective adsorbents. The Socony-Mobil Co. introduced the first commercial cracking catalyst which contained crystalline zeolites. Its predecessor was a spray-dried version for use in fluid catalytic cracking units. Zeolite catalysts have an intrinsically higher activity than conventional amorphous silica-alumina catalysts, coupled with much higher yields of gasoline and decreased coke and light ends yields.

Crystalline alumino-silicates also have catalytic cracking properties. These include synthetic faujasite (X and Y types), offretite, mordenite, and erionite. Of these, the faujasites have been most widely used. Faujasite is synthesized in the sodium form; however, the sodium is removed by base exchange with other metal ions that for cracking catalysts include magnesium, calcium, rare earths (mixed or individual), and ammonium. The mixed rare earths alone, or in combination with ammonium ions, have been the most commonly used forms of faujasite in cracking catalyst formulations. The X-type faujasite has a stoichiometric formula of $Na_2O \cdot Al_2O_3 \cdot 2.5\ SiO_2$, whereas the Y-type faujasite is $Na_2O \cdot Al_2O_3 \cdot 4.8\ SiO_2$. Slight variations in the SiO_2/Al_2O_3 ratio exist for each of the types. Rare-earth-exchanged Y-type faujasite retains much of its crystallinity after steaming at 1520°F with 20% steam for about 12 hours. The rare earth form of X-faujasite, is thermally stable in dry air but tends to lose its crystallinity at these temperatures in the presence of steam.

The general procedure involved in the manufacture of silica-alumina catalyst, consists of

1. The gelling of dilute sodium silicate solution ($Na_2O.3 \cdot 25\ SiO_2 \times H_2O$) by the addition of an acid (H_2SO_4, CO_2) or an acid salt such as aluminum sulfate
2. Aging the hydrogen under controlled conditions

3. Adding the prescribed amount of alumina as aluminum sulfate and/or sodium aluminate
4. Adjusting the pH of the mixture
5. Filtering the composite mixture

After filtering, the filter cake can either be washed free of extraneous soluble salts by a succession of reslurrying, filtration steps, and spray drying, and then washed free of extraneous soluble salts before flash drying the finished catalyst. There are several critical factors which affect the physical and catalytic properties of the finished catalyst; principal ones are the concentration and temperature of the initial sodium silicate solution, the amount of acid added to effect gelation, the length of time of aging the gel, the method and conditions of adding the aluminum salt to the gel, and its incorporation therein.

Zeolite cracking catalysts are manufactured by dispersing or imbedding the crystals in matrix form. The matrix is generally amorphous silica-alumina gel and may also contain finely divided clay. The zeolite content of the composite catalyst is typically in the range of 5–16 wt%. If clay is used in the matrix, it is present in an amount of 25–45 wt%, while the remainder is composed of silica-alumina hydrogel "glue," which binds the composite together. The zeolite may be preexchanged to the desired metal form and calcined to lock the exchangeable metal ions into position before introducing other ingredients. An alternative approach involves combining sodium form zeolite with the other components, which are then washed and treated with a dilute salt solution of the desired metal ions before the final drying step. The matrix generally consists of silica-alumina, but several catalysts have been commercialized which contain either silica-magnesia/kaolin or synthetic montmorillonite-mica and/or kaolin as the matrix for faujasite.

Most manufacturers provide several grades of zeolite catalysts. Although the exact formulations are proprietary, the general manufacturing scheme is composed of the following steps:

1. Dilute sodium silicate solution is blended with kaolin
2. The blended slurry is treated with alum solution to lower the pH to around 10 and effect gelation
3. Mixed gel is aged under controlled conditions
4. Alum solution is added to provide the necessary amount of alumina in the silica-alumina hydrogel
5. A slurry of sodium faujasite (Y type) is added
6. The pH is adjusted to the desired level
7. The composite slurry is filtered
8. The mix is spray dried
9. The catalyst is washed free of sodium with a dilute ammonium sulfate solution
10. The catalyst is reslurryed in a dilute solution of mixed rare earths

These steps are followed by filtering, rinsing, and flash drying the finished catalyst.

Differences between catalyst activities of the mixed oxide type lie in the relative action toward promoting the individual reaction types included in the overall cracking operation. Silica-magnesia catalyst under a given set of cracking conditions will give a higher conversion to cracked products than silica-alumina catalyst for example. The products from SiO_2-Mg catalyst have a higher average molecular weight, hence, a lower volatility, and lesser amounts of highly branched/acyclic isomers, but more olefins among the gasoline boiling range products (C_4-430°F) than the products from $SiO_2-Al_2O_3$ catalyst. Such changes in composition produce a gasoline from cracking with SiO_2-MgO catalyst which is of a lower octane number. The differences between catalysts are perhaps best described by the differences in the intensity of the action at the individual active catalytic sites. Catalysts such as $SiO_2-Al_2O_3$ give greater intensity of reaction than SiO_2-MgO, as observed from the yields of the individual cracked products and the motor gasoline octane number. Titrations of these two catalysts show $SiO_2-Al_2O_3$ to have a lower acid titre than SiO_2-MgO, but the acid strength of the sites is higher.

The individual components in these catalysts are essentially nonacidic; however, when mixed together they result in a titratable acidity. Many secondary reactions occurring in the cracking process may also be promoted with strong mineral acids, such as concentrated sulfuric and phosphoric acids, aluminum halides, hydrogen fluoride, hydrogen fluoride-boron trifluoride mixtures, and others. This lends support to the concept of the active catalytic site as being acidic. Zeolites have a much higher active site density than the amorphous mixed oxides, which accounts for their extremely high cracking propensity. Furthermore, they promote complex hydrogen transfer reactions among the primary products so that the recovered cracked products have a much lower olefin and higher paraffin content than is obtained with amorphous mixed oxide catalysts. The hydrogen transfer propensity of zeolites to saturate primary cracked product olefins to paraffins minimizes the reaction of polymerizing the olefins to form a coke deposit. This accounts for the lower coke yields with zeolite catalysts as opposed to amorphous catalysts.

Catalyst activity varies with faujasite content. Selectivity of the catalyst to coke and naphtha also varies with faujasite content. When the faujasite content falls below 5%, the catalyst begins to show some cracking properties of the matrix. In contrast, for zeolite contents of 10% or higher, very little change in the selectivity pattern is observed. Also, the various ion-exchanged forms of the faujasite can result in slightly different cracking properties. Examples include using high-cerium-content, mixed rare earths to improve carbon burning rates in the regenerator; using H-form faujasite or H+/RE+3 form faujasite to improve selectivity to C_3-C_5 fractions; and using trace amounts of copper forms of faujasite to increase light olefin yields and naphtha octanes.

The ideal cracking catalyst will retain its cracking activity, showing no change in product selectivity as it ages in the reactor. Unfortunately, there are several factors which contribute to a loss in catalyst activity. These include the combination of high temperatures, steam partial pressure, and time; impurities present in the fresh catalyst; and impurities acquired by the catalyst from the feedstock. Catalysts typically experience temperatures in the range of 900°F-960°F in the reactor and steam stripper zones, and temperatures of 1150°F-1325°F and higher in the regenerator, accompanied by a substantial partial pressure of steam. In the case of mixed oxide amorphous gel catalysts, the surface area and pore volume decreases abruptly during the first few days of operation. After this initial stage, the rate at which surface and pore properties change is much slower. This is accompanied by a loss in the number and strength of the active catalytic sites.

Zeolite catalysts degrade from instabilities of the gel, and also from loss in their crystalline structure. The latter also results from the combined effects of time, temperature, and steam partial pressure. When this occurs, the amorphous residue is relatively low in activity, approximating that of the amorphous gel matrix. The rate of degradation of the amorphous gel component is not necessarily the same as that of the zeolite crystals. The gel may degrade rapidly, and through thermoplastic flow effectively coat the crystals and interfere with the diffusion of hydrocarbons to the catalytic sites in the zeolite.

Sodium and sulfates constitute the main residual impurities found in freshly manufactured catalysts. These result from the use of sodium silicate and aluminum sulfate in the production of the silica-alumina gel matrix and subsequent washing of the composite catalyst with ammonium sulfate to remove sodium. The sodium content of the amorphous gel is typically less than 0.1 wt% (as Na_2O), and less than 0.5 wt% for sulfate.

The residual sodium found in zeolite catalysts may be primarily associated with the zeolite itself. Sodium levels typically range from about 0.2% to generally under 0.5%. Excessive amounts of sodium react with the silica in the matrix under regenerator operating conditions. This serves as a flux to increase the rate of surface area and pore volume loss. Sodium faujasite is not as hydrothermally stable as other metal exchanged forms, such as mixed rare earths.

As noted earlier, catalysts can degrade as a result of impurities acquired from the feed processing. These impurities are typically sodium, nickel, vanadium, iron, and copper. Sodium tends to neutralize active acid sites and thus reduces catalyst activity. It also acts as a flux to accelerate matrix degradation. Freshly deposited metals are much more effective "poisons" than aged metal deposits. The reason for this is that the metal deposited on the active exterior surface of the matrix is "buried" with time due to the thermoplastic flow of the matrix gel. Zeolite catalysts are less responsive to metal contaminants than amorphous gel catalysts. Thus, equilibrium catalysts can tolerate low levels of these metals provided they have sufficient time to become buried. A sudden deposition of fresh metals can cause adverse effects on yields. Metal levels on equilibrium catalysts reflect the metals content of the feeds being processed. Typical values for vanadium are 200–1,200 ppm, for nickel, 150–500 ppm, and for copper, 5–45 ppm. Sodium levels are typically in the range of 0.25–0.8 wt% as Na_2O. References 8 through 23 provide further readings on catalytic cracking and catalyst properties.

Fluid Bed Operations

The first commercial fluidized-bed catalytic cracking reactors were put into operation at the beginning of World War II. Figure 6-3A shows an early design consisting of a complex multivessel arrangement. Catalyst flowed up through the reaction and regeneration sections in a riser type of flow regime. These systems were

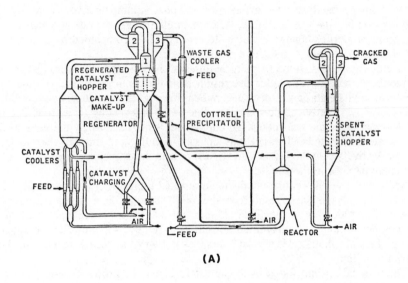

(A)

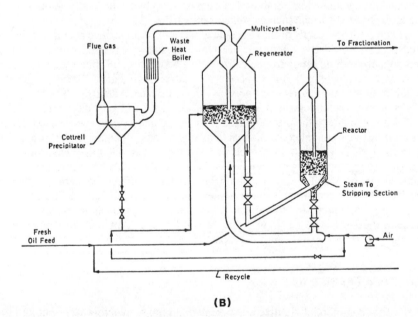

(B)

Figure 6-3. Illustration of older catalytic crackers: (A) a typical catalytic cracking system of World War II vintage (downflow unit); (B) upflow catalytic cracking unit still used in older plants today.

designed to feed a reduced crude to a vaporizer furnace where the gas oil was vaporized and fed in a vapor-state to the reactor. The unvaporized bottoms bypassed the cracking section. A unique feature about these systems was that regenerator pressure was very low (typically 2 to 3 psig), primarily because high discharge pressure, centrifugal blowers were scarce at that time. Cracked oil vapors and entrained catalyst exited the top of the reactors, which were equipped with enlarged sections to allow for large catalyst holdup. Typical gas velocities in these sections were 4 to 6 fps. The overhead catalyst captured by cyclones was returned to a hopper where it was fluidized with steam to recapture any entrained hydrocarbon vapors. The catalyst was then discharged from the hopper, down through a standpipe. The solids flow through the standpipe was controlled by a slide valve located at the base. From there, the solids went into a riser where they were carried by a stream of air to the regenerator vessel.

The regenerator operation in these older plants resembled that of the reactor except for the system's use of air instead of oil vapor. A portion of the catalyst from the regenerated catalyst hopper was returned to the regenerator through catalyst fresh feed exchangers. This action controlled the regenerator temperature and served to preheat the feed. Another bypass line from the hopper to the regenerator was used to control the dense bed level or holdup in the regenerator. Flue gas exiting the cyclones was sent through the heat recovery equipment into electrostatic precipitators that recovered additional entrained catalyst fines. Catalyst from the regenerated catalyst hopper flowed through a standpipe back into a riser where the oil feed was injected.

The next significant development in the evolution of fluid cat crackers was the downflow unit (Figure 6-3B); many of which are still operating today. By lowering the vessel velocity to 1.5 to 2 fps, a relatively dense bed of catalyst was formed in the reaction zone. The bed was sufficiently large to provide adequate catalyst holdup to complete reaction and regeneration. The lower gas velocity used in downflow designs resulted in increased vessel diameters which greatly simplified mechanical design since the cyclones could now be housed inside the reactor and regeneration vessels, which in turn eliminated the need for peripheral catalyst hoppers.

Significant changes to fluidized cat crackers came about in the late 1950s. The typical design seen in many refineries today resembles that shown in Figure 6-4. Catalyst is transferred between vessels via U-bends. This design does not require the use of controlling valves for catalyst circulation. Insead, catalyst circulation is controlled by pressure balance or process flows, which are accomplished by varying the density of the catalyst on the upflow side of the spent U-bend by injecting regeneration air. Typical bed densities in the "control riser" vary between 10 and 20 lb/ft³ by adjusting the gas velocity between 6 and 15 fps. The regenerator is equipped with an overflow weir so that the rate of catalyst leaving is automatically balanced by the incoming flow. Catalyst holdup in the reactor is maintained constant during operation and is established by the overall system inventory. Catalyst circulation can be altered by either changing differential pressures between the reactor and regenerator vessels or by varying the amount of air in the spent catalyst riser. Designs prevalent in the late 1950s had reactor and regenerator zones designed to operate at 4 to 6 fps, which resulted in relatively low bed densities and

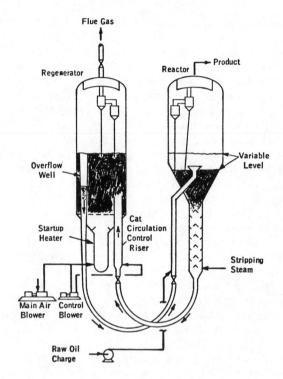

Figure 6-4. The Exxon Model IV fluid-bed cat cracker.

fairly efficient conversion and regeneration zones. The vessels were tapered to a larger diameter in the upper portion to provide space for mounting the catalyst recovery cyclones in the same unit.

Because catalysts today are much more active, the configuration in Figure 6-4 has been modified to run with no reactor bed. The catalyst level is maintained below the reactor grid in the stripper zone. Hence, the catalyst in the reactor-process flow stream contacts the oil only in the dilute phase of a riser. Today, grass roots designs are primarily based on riser cracking only. Many licensed units feature riser or transfer line contacting. Improvements in catalyst activities have made all riser cracking practical in many applications. In fact, many of today's catalysts are so active that overcracking to undesirable product is possible when a bed is used with some cracking feeds.

Other designs are illustrated in Figures 6-5 through 6-9. The M. W. Kellogg Co. concentrated on the Orthoflow design which employs plug valves and stacked vessels (Figure 6-5). The design incorporates staged regeneration, which reduces the regeneration holdup needed and/or carbon on regenerated catalyst. Typical designs in the past have included vertical feed risers for efficient riser cracking. More recent designs include external feed riser lines consisting of right angle bends which extend riser lengths and minimize erosion problems.

Figure 6-6A shows the Universal Oil Products (UOP) stacked unit design, consisting of a long riser reactor that terminates in the reactor vessel at the top of the unit. The riser is supported on the regenerator vessel. The reactor vessel normally contains only a single stage of cyclones for returning solids to the unit. Additional catalyst fines are scrubbed out in the lower portion of the fractionator. After being concentrated in the slurry product, the catalyst is returned to the unit along with a portion of the slurry. More recent UOP designs include a reactor configuration composed of an all-riser section with no bed holdup (Figure 6-6B). One of the most recent UOP designs incorporates riser regeneration, which operates with a catalyst that promotes carbon monoxide conversion in the regeneration step (Figure 6-6C).[24,25]

Figure 6-7 shows the Texaco process, which features a dual reactor system where fresh feed and recycle are cracked separately. The reactor has a tear-drop configuration, which promotes good contacting when a bed is retained in the vessel. The regenerator has a tapered shape, which provides a high velocity bed and low velocity dilute-phase zone. The catalyst is fed through the side of the regenerator vessel and has a swirl type flow imparted to it to provide more efficient contacting and regeneration. Catalyst circulation is controlled by a slide valve.[26]

The Gulf process is illustrated in Figure 6-8. The design incorporates vertical riser contacting, and relatively efficient conversion of feed is achieved by injecting different components of feed at various points in the riser. This has the advantage of allowing optimization of the yield patterns.[27]

Cat cracking of poor or dirty feedstocks has become economical. Residuum, for example, can be cracked in specially designed cat-cracking processes. Companies

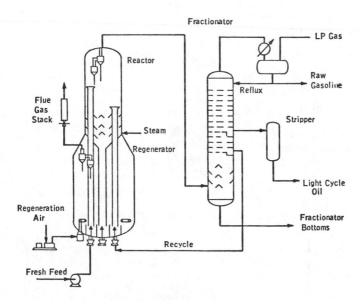

Figure 6-5. The Kellogg Othoflow unit.

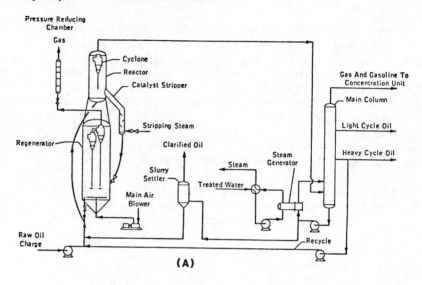

(A)

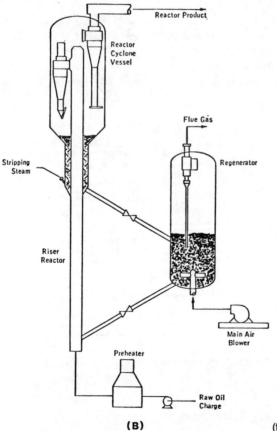

(B)

(figure continued on next page)

Figure 6.6. Continued.

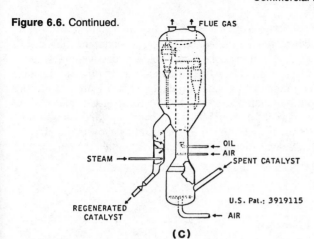

FLUE GAS

OIL
AIR
SPENT CATALYST
STEAM →
U.S. Pat.: 3919115
REGENERATED CATALYST
AIR

(C)

Figure 6-6. Illustration of UOP cat-cracker designs: (A) UOP stacked fluid cat cracker unit; (B) UOP fluid catalytic cracking unit; (C) UOP riser-regenerator design.

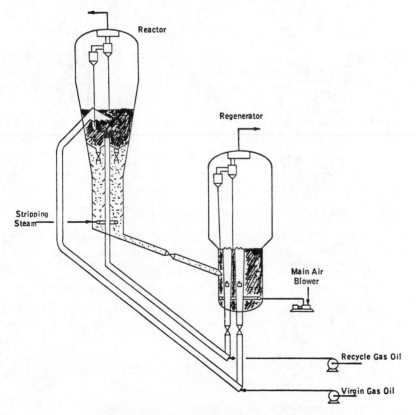

Reactor

Regenerator

Stripping Steam

Main Air Blower

Recycle Gas Oil

Virgin Gas Oil

Figure 6-7. The Texaco fluid catalytic cracking system.

such as Kellogg, Gulf, and UOP license such systems. In some applications, the residuum feed is hydrotreated to reduce the concentration of contaminating metals and to improve feed quality, thus keeping coke yields below excessive levels. Other applications require a relatively high catalyst replacement rate in order to maintain the catalyst quality within a range that provides product yields. Figure 6-9 shows a residuum cracking unit jointly developed by the M. W. Kellogg Co. and Phillips Petroleum Co. Eighty-five percent conversions have been reported on an atmospheric residuum.[28,29] As shown in Figure 6-9, the catalyst flows from the regenerator, through a plug valve which controls the flow to maintain the reactor tem-

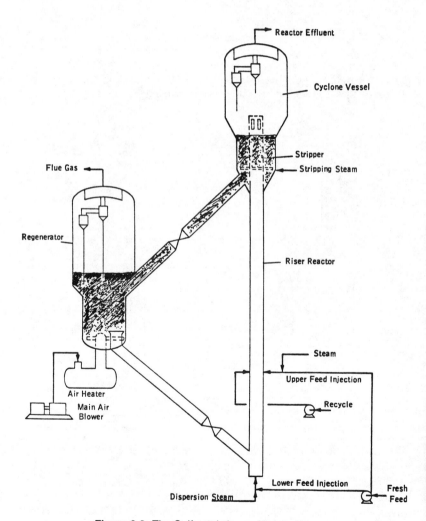

Figure 6-8. The Gulf catalytic cracking system.

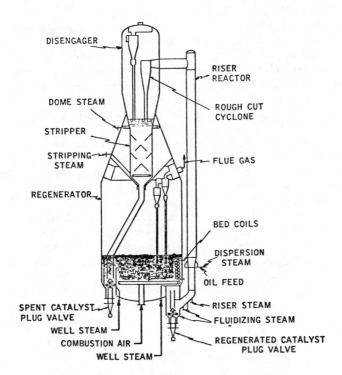

Figure 6-9. The Kellogg residuum cracker.

perature. Steam injection is done upstream of the feed point to accelerate the catalyst and disperse it. The reason for this is to avoid high rates of coke formation at the feed injection. The feed, which is atomized by steam, is then injected into this stream via a multi-nozzle arrangement. Flow rates are adjusted to control residence times in the riser, primarily because the effects of metals poisoning on catalyst are a function of the time catalyst and oil are in contact. The reaction cycle is terminated by sending the flow through a cut cyclone.

DRYING AND PROCESSING OPERATIONS

Fluidized-bed systems are employed in a multitude of processing operations in a variety of industries. Examples of fluidized-bed processes include drying, roasting, calcining, incineration, and many others.

Fluidized-bed (fluid-bed) drying applications have been successfully used for many years in a variety of applications, such as potash production, coal drying, and polymers and chemicals drying. In the case of potash manufacturing, there are two basic flowsheets for production. One type is principally chemical in nature and includes various phases of leaching, evaporation, solution purification, selective crystallization, dewatering, drying, and product classification. The second method is a flotation process whereby ore mineral is separated physically from gangue material. A typical flowsheet of the second type is shown in Figure 6-10. As shown, milling phases include crushing, screening, hydraulic classification, selective flotation, thickening, filtering, and drying. Older technology traditionally used rotary-type dryers in potash milling operations. These systems in general experienced problems of internal scaling, resulting in lengthy and expensive shut-downs, and product degradation through attrition. In addition they were high energy consumption devices. Relatively high thermal efficiencies are required in this drying application. Figure 6-11 shows the relationship between heat requirement and windbox temperature for one operation. In a standard drying arrangement, coal, oil, or gas is fired to an air heater. The products of combustion pass through a constriction plate to contact and dry the potash in the fluid bed. Feed is continuously metered into the dryer at a point above the bed and is classified and dried by the hot gases. The fine, dried product, is carried aloft with the gas to be recovered in a dust collection system. Coarse product flows across the constriction plate and is discharged. The solids discharge rate and bed level can be controlled by a differential

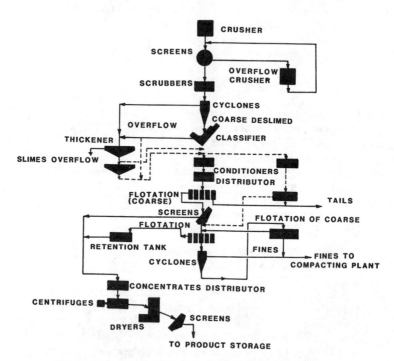

Figure 6-10. Process flowsheet for potash flotation method.

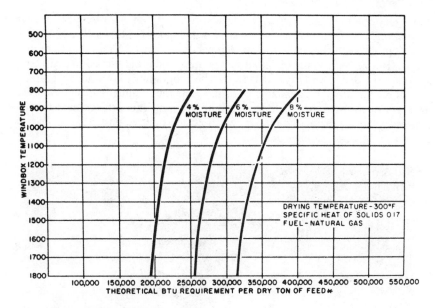

*ADD 5-10% FOR SYSTEM RADIATION LOSSES

Figure 6-11. Illustration of the theoretical heat requirement per dry ton of potash at various moisture contents of feed.[30]

control system. Instrumentation can provide close control of drying temperature, retention time, and product moisture.

An example of a small batch fluid bed unit is shown in Figure 6-12, and the key features of operation are illustrated in Figure 6-13. Sizing of these units is based on the wet weight of the material to be dried per hour, which determines the container capacity. Fan selection depends upon the pressure drop of the system. The control system plays an important role in drying efficiency.

Some of the more sophisticated systems employ programmable microprocessor controllers to provide sequenced start/stop functions as well as complete temperature and flow regulation of the dryer. Inlet and outlet air temperatures, system pressures, and time are the parameters used to control the drying process and the length of the dry cycle. These systems can automatically lock the container into place, seal the lower plenum, start the fan, open the damper, start the agitator drive, and control the temperature and air flow until the process is complete. Then, the dryer goes through a sequenced shut down and alerts the operator that the cycle is complete. Control systems can be equipped with alarm indications and shut-down schemes. Temperatures and pressures are monitored continually, and if predetermined limits are exceeded, the dryer will automatically shut down. The unit shown in Figure 6-12 contains four proportional controllers with reset, integral, and derivative action that compare monitored process conditions against programmed requirements and signal dryer control devices to adjust accordingly. Inlet air temperature can be programmed to follow a profile as shown in Figure 6-14, which can be altered based upon monitoring the outlet air temperature. Thus a blended system of control, reflecting both actual outlet air temperature and programmed inlet air temperature is provided. Similarly, air flow can be programmed to follow a profile.

Coal drying units are available as turnkey operation units. Normally these systems are under pressure in the combustion section. This arrangement minimizes power on the fluidizing air blower, and reduces fugitive dust leaks in the under section in the dryer compartment.

Figure 6-12. A fluid-bed drying unit and control panel. (Courtesy of The Fitzpatrick Co., Elmhurst, IL)

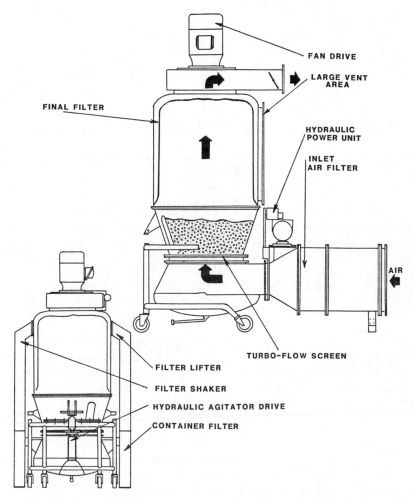

FAN DRIVE

LARGE VENT
AREA

FINAL FILTER

HYDRAULIC
POWER UNIT

INLET
AIR FILTER

AIR

TURBO-FLOW SCREEN

FILTER LIFTER

FILTER SHAKER

HYDRAULIC AGITATOR DRIVE

CONTAINER FILTER

Figure 6-13. The principal design features of the fluid-bed unit shown in Figure 6-12.

Pulverized-coal firing heats the air in the lower section of the air heater, and tempering air is introduced through a bustle located midway up the heater. The preheated air passes through a refractory constriction plate into the dryer. Wet coal, fed into the dryer, is fluidized in a deep fluid bed by the drying gases and is brought to the desired drying temperature, thus driving off the moisture. Finer coal is carried out of the dryer by the gas and collected in large cyclones. Larger coal particles are continuously and automatically discharged from the dryer. Bed temperatures are controlled automatically by feed rate, and this together with the deep fluid bed results in maintaining the moisture content of the cyclone and coarse product within

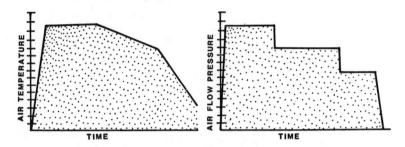

Figure 6-14. Typical program profiles used in controllers.

narrow limits. The elimination of temperature fluctuations, common in other types of dryers, yields a uniform product dried within the specified limits.

The deep fluid bed typically results in good heat transfer so that the gases leaving the bed are essentially the same temperature as the bed product and are typically over 80% saturated with water vapor. This high humidity results in extremely high collection efficiencies in the cyclones. An exhaust fan is normally located after the cyclones to maintain the drying compartment at negative pressure and to push the gas through a venturi scrubber for final clean-up to conform to emission regulations.

A system designed for plastics- and chemicals-drying applications is shown in Figure 6-15. This particular drying system is used for materials containing recoverable solvents. The feed is metered into the fluid bed, which is maintained at optimum drying temperature. This temperature can be within a few degrees of the material's critical temperature (i.e. its softening, melting, degradation temperature, etc.). The bed is maintained in a fluidized state and is dried by the action of filtered warm air passing through the constriction plate. The air preheat is accomplished by an external heat exchange system, however, it is also possible to use heat exchange coils in the fluid bed to provide a portion of the heat. Direct combustion products may be employed if product specifications so permit. Note that this is a closed system, where the fluidizing-drying gas, which may be solvent, and/or inert gas is recycled. The gas exiting from the dust collector is introduced to a scrubber-condenser, where temperature is controlled so as to condense the proper quantity of solvent. Some of the condensed solvent may be cooled in an external heat exchanger and recycled back to the condenser. The vapor exiting the condenser is recompressed, superheated in a steam heated external heat exchanger, and returned to the dryer as fluidizing gas.

In addition to drying applications, fluidized-bed operations extend into the areas of roasting, calcining, and incineration. Table 6-2 provides a breakdown of applications areas, and Figures 6-16 through 6-19 show specific process examples.

Figures 6-16 and 6-17 show two versions of a sulfide roasting operation. During operation (Figure 6-16), feed is introduced to the reaction chamber either wet or dry. The slurry feeding arrangement is preferred due to its simplicity. Starting burners are employed only to bring the bed to ignition temperature, where the strongly exothermic roasting reaction takes place or internal combustion is achieved, depending upon the material being processed. After this point has been

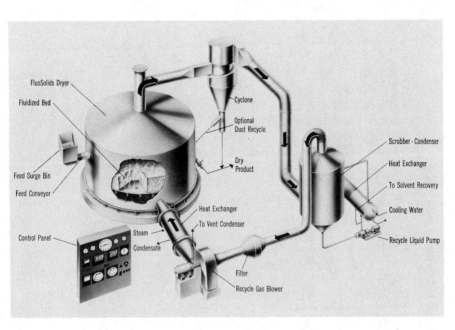

Figure 6-15. The Dorr-Oliver FluoSolids plastics drying system with recycle. (Courtesy of Dorr-Oliver, Inc., Stamford, CT)

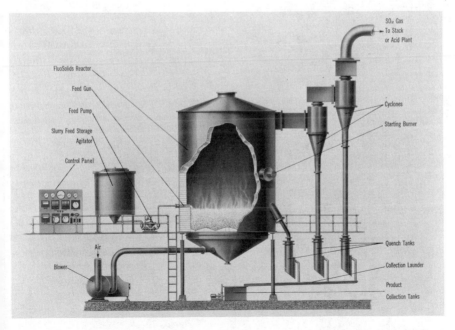

Figure 6-16. A wet system (Dorr-Oliver FluoSolids) for sulfide roasting. (Courtesy of Dorr-Oliver, Inc., Stamford, CT)

Table 6-2
Breakdown of Fluid-Bed Operations for Different Applications

Industry	Drying • Low temperature • Single compartment • Uses fuel (coal, gas, oil)	Roasting • High temperature • Single compartment • Uses no fuel	Calcining • High temperature • Multicompartment • Uses fuel (coal, gas, oil)	Incinerating • High temperature • Single compartment • Little or no fuel
Metals and minerals	Phosphate rock Coal and coke Sand Iron ore Limestone-dolomite Potash Sulfide concentrates	Pyrite-pyrrhotite Zinc sulfide Copper sulfide Sulfur ore Arsenopyrite Cobalt Nickel	Phosphate rock Copperas Iron ore reduction Manganese ore reduction Caliche Bauxite Limestone	Spent machinery oil Paint wastes Rolling oil waste Steel mill waste
Petroleum and chemicals	Polymers Synthetic rubber Detergents			API bottoms Biological sludge Flotation skimmings Tank bottoms Spent caustic Carbon black Waste activated sludge
Pulp and paper		Pyrite-pyrrhotite	Lime mud	NSSC liquor Primary clarifier sludge Waste activated sludge Black liquor Bark
Foods and pharmaceuticals	Food additives		Carbon reactivation	Coffee grounds Biological sludge Anti Biotic-broth Animal wastes Other solid wastes
Foundry	Reclaimed sand Raw sand		Shell molding sand Resin bonded sand	

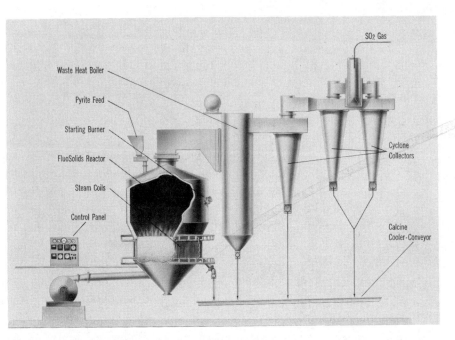

Figure 6-17. A Dorr-Oliver FluoSolids roaster with dry feed for steam production. (Courtesy of Dorr-Oliver, Inc., Stamford, CT)

reached, extraneous fuel is seldom required. Low-pressure air is introduced into the windbox and passes through a distribution plate, where it mixes with the feed solids in the fluidized bed. The finer-sized particles of the calcine are entrained with the fluidizing gases and recovered in a suitable dust collection system with or without heat recovery in a waste heat boiler. The SO_2 gas then goes through the usual gas cooling and cleaning steps prior to the manufacture of sulfuric acid. Coarse product moves across the bed, overflows, and is collected either wet or dry, dependent upon further treatment requirements.

Figure 6-17 shows a dry system arrangement for sulfide roasting. Close air control and intimate mixing of the gas and the solids result in complete oxidation of the solids with a minimum of excess air—as little as 5%–10% excess in the case of pyrite roasting. Consequently, in the roasting of sulfide ores, autogenous (or self supporting) operations are achieved with minimum sulfur contents—as low as 20% in some cases. Operating at high temperatures minimizes the formation of SO_3, increases steam recovery, and promotes the complete oxidation of the solids. In cases where maximum steam production is a necessity, temperature control is accomplished by the use of recycled cool gas or cooling coils in the bed. The ability to roast sulfides with minimal excess air also results in a stronger sulphur dioxide gas, cutting down gas processing equipment size.

Figure 6-18 shows a multicomponent system designed for applications involving endothermic reactions. The multicompartment reactor consists of a reaction bed

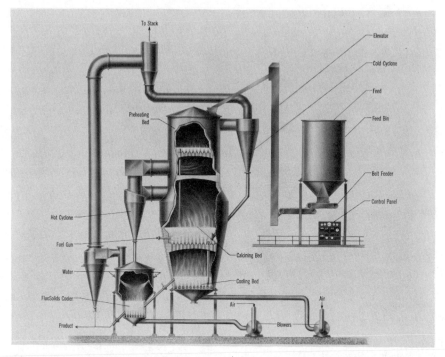

Figure 6-18. A multicomponent system design for endothermic reactions. (Courtesy of Dorr-Oliver, Inc., Stamford, CT)

and one or more heat exchange beds for heat recovery. The unit shown in Figure 6-18 contains three beds, however, systems incorporating as many as five beds are possible. In operation, feed metered from the feed bin is introduced into the top (preheating) bed of the reactor. Here it is dried and heated by hot gases from the reaction or calcining compartment. The coarse portion is discharged to the reaction compartment. The fine fraction entrained in the gas is carried over to the cyclone where it is collected and discharged to the reaction bed. Here, fuel is injected and the desired reaction is effected. Again, size separation takes place with coarse material passing to the cooling compartment, where it serves to heat incoming air before discharge to the spray cooler. Flow of heated gas through the system is the reverse of that of the solids thereby accomplishing countercurrent heat exchange. The fine fraction from the reaction compartment is collected in cyclones and is also discharged to the spray cooler where the temperature is reduced to approximately 200°F for ease of handling.

The last example is illustrated in Figure 6-19, where a fluid bed system is used for sludge incineration. Fluid beds are particularly well adapted to this application because they provide the ideal environment for the thermal oxidation of most biological wastes, particularly sewage sludge. Silica sand or another inert material serves as the bed material. Air, supplied by a fluidizing air blower, becomes the fluidizing gas medium. Biological wastes are introduced to the sand bed. The wastes are quickly mixed with the bed because of its boiling, turbulent action. Water contained in the wastes is rapidly evaporated, and the waste's combustible solids and vapors contact and react with the oxygen in the fluidizing air stream. This produces complete combustion with a minimum of excess oxygen, at minimum temperature. The fluid bed of sand acts as a thermal sink, or flywheel, and ensures uniform temperature and consistent operation.

The conventional design consists of a carbon steel vessel with a flat bottom and conical top, supported on grillage beams. The vessel interior is lined with insulating and refractory brick. Dewatered sludge is fed to the bed by pumps or screw feeders and the moisture is evaporated from the sludge, while the organic components react with oxygen in the fluidizing gas. Steam from the sludge mixture, plus the gaseous byproducts of organics and fuel combustion, plus the fine inert particles, exit from the reactor's top. Deodorized exhaust gases can be cleaned and cooled in a venturi scrubber and multitray cooling section before release into the atmosphere.

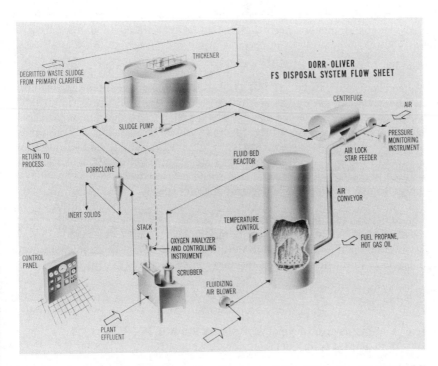

Figure 6-19. A fluid-solids disposal system. (Courtesy of Dorr-Oliver, Inc., Stamford, CT)

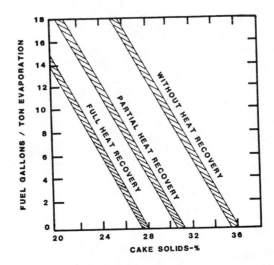

Figure 6-20. Typical throughput capacities for a fluid-solids incineration system.

The combustion process can be combined with a waste recovery system that has the advantage of increased thermal efficiency. A typical operation proceeds as follows:

Cold air from the fluidizing air blower is heated by the gas-to-gas heat exchanger in a range from 600°F–1,000°F, extracting some of the sensible heat in the reactor exit gases. The reactor exit gas temperature is cooled to 1000°F. The heat recovered from the exit gases is supplied to the incinerator to evaporate sludge water. This heat is recovered without burning fuel or consuming any oxygen. With the system shown in Figure 6-19, only 2,500 to 2,600 Btus are required to evaporate one pound of water compared to 3,700 to 4,100 Btus without preheated air. Moreover, the waste heat recovery system provides a higher sludge burning and water evaporation capacity.

Figure 6-20 shows typical throughput capacities for such a system. The basis for these plots assumes that conventional domestic sewage can be dewatered to a sludge cake at 75% volatile solids with 9,500 Btu/lb volatile solids. To estimate the evaporation rate in lb/hr, the following formula can be used:

$$\xi = \frac{A(100\%)}{B} - A \tag{6-5}$$

where A = the lb/hr of dry solids to the incinerator
       B = percent of dry solids in the dewatered cake.

Table 6-3 provides a rough guide to size selection and Table 6-4 provides some operating experienced data reported by one manufacturer for different installations.

Table 6-3
Approximate Sizing Chart for Waste Incineration
(Courtesy of Dorr-Oliver Inc., Stamford, CT)

| | Full Heat Recovery | | | Partial Heat Recovery | | | Without Heat Recovery | |
Reactor Diameter	Evaporation Rate (lb/hr)	Operating Horsepower	Reactor Diameter	Evaporation Rate (lb/hr)	Operating Horsepower	Reactor Diameter	Evaporation Rate (lb/hr)	Operating Horsepower
9'	2,800	77	9'	2,550	77	9'	2,240	72
10'	3,470	99	10'	3,175	99	10'	2,770	91
11'	4,200	114	11'	3,830	114	11'	3,350	107
12'	4,950	144	12'	4,520	144	12'	3,990	134
13'	5,800	162	13'	5,280	162	13'	4,620	151
14'	6,750	183	14'	6,150	183	14'	5,350	171
15'	7,750	206	15'	7,060	206	15'	6,150	193
16'	8,760	236	16'	8,000	236	16'	7,000	216
17'	9,900	269	17'	9,050	269	17'	7,900	246
18'	11,100	296	18'	10,050	296	18'	8,700	276
19'	12,350	324	19'	11,220	324	19'	9,750	303
20'	13,600	366	20'	12,400	366	20'	10,800	333
21'	15,100	397	21'	13,710	397	21'	11,900	375
22'	16,550	430	22'	15,050	430	22'	13,100	406
23'	18,180	465	23'	16,450	465	23'	14,300	440
24'	19,700	512	24'	17,880	512	24'	15,500	475
25'	21,400	551	25'	19,380	551	25'	16,800	512

Table 6-4
Performance Data Reported on Dorr-Oliver's
FluoSolids Waste Incineration System
(Courtesy of Dorr-Oliver Inc., Stamford, CT)

Plant	Types of Sludge	FS Reactor Diameter	Heat Recovery	Capacity (#/hr disposable solids)		Aux. Fuel (gal/ton disposable solids)		Power (Includes Dewatering) (kwh/ton disposable solids)		% Volatile in Ash		Stack Emissions (Grains/scf)	
				Design	Actual	Design	Actual	Design	Actual	Design	Actual	Design	Actual
Liberty, NY	Prim+T.F.	6'	No	282	338	10.28	53.3	—	—	3.0	0.31	—	—
Ocean City, MD	Prim	6'	No	350	445	48.0	22.9	—	—	3.0	0.85	—	—
Barstow, CA	Prim	7'	No	500	552	36.0	31.9	239	210	—	—	0.1	0.025
Northwest Bergen, NJ	Prim+WAS	12'	Yes	1,100	1,169	41.5	57.0	267	243	4.0	0.59	0.1	0.018
Upper Merion Twp. PA	Prim+T.F.	9'	Yes	865	918	18.4	14.4	—	—	—	—	—	—
Port Washington, NY	Prim+T.F.	9'-6"	No	860	865	64.5	85.5	252	261	3.0	0.4	0.1	0.025
Arlington, NY	Prim+WAS	9'	No	700	742	—	—	—	—	3.0	0.3	—	—
New Windsor, NY	Prim+T.F.	7'	No	570	666	56.6	75.5	—	—	3.0	0.4	—	—
Bath, NY	Prim+WAS	9'-6"	No	605	657	113.9	85.5	400	344	3.0	0.4	0.1	0.044
Lorain, OH	Prim+WAS	14'	No	1,400	1,635	40.0	32.2	274	181	3.0	0.7	—	—
Somerset-Raritan, NJ	Prim+WAS	12'	Yes	1,170	1,376	55.0	23.8	247	247	3.0	0.5	0.2	0.047
Bayshore, NJ	Prim+WAS	15'	Yes	1,170	1,376	55.0	23.8	247	247	3.0	0.5	0.2	0.047

REFERENCES

1. Danner, A., *Petroleum Refiner,* 29 (9): 179–182 (1950).

2. Holiman, J. B., "Mechanical Aspects of Hydroflow Catalytic Cracking Process", in *Advances in Petroleum Chemistry and Refining,* Vol. 2, J. J. McKetta, Jr., (Ed.), Interscience, New York (1959).

3. Hobson, G. D., *Mod. Petroleum Technol.,* 4th Ed., Wiley and Sons, New York (1973), pp. 288–309.

4. Greensfelder, B. S., "Theory of Catalytic Cracking", in *Chemistry of Petroleum Hydrocarbons II,* Reinhold Pub. Co., New York (1955).

5. Voge, H. H., "Catalytic Cracking", in *Catalysis,* V1, P. H. Emmett, (Ed.), Reinhold Pub. Co., New York (1958).

6. Hansel, V., "Catalytic Cracking of Pure Hydrocarbons", *Advances in Catalysts* III, Academic Press, New York (1951).

7. Hansford, R. C., "Chemical Concepts of Catalytic Cracking", in *Advances in Catalysts and Related Subjects,* IV, Academic Press Inc., New York (1952).

8. Weekman, V. W., Jr., and M. D. Nace, *AIChE. J.,* 16 (3): 397–404 (1970).

9. Gary, J. H., and G. E. Handwerk, *Petroleum Refining Technology and Economics,* Marcel Dekker Inc., New York (1975), pp. 100–108.

10. Letzch, W. S. et al., *Oil & Gas J.* 74 (4): 130–144 (January 26, 1975).

11. Blazek, J. J., et al., *Proceedings American Petroleum Inst.,* 42 Section III: 277–286 (1962).

12. Ashley, K. D., and W. B. Innes, *Ind. Eng. Chem.,* 44: 2,857 (1952).

13. Thomas, C. L., in *Catalytic Process and Proven Catalysts,* Academic Press, New York (1970), Ch. 4.

14. Voltz, S. E., et al., *Ind. Eng. Chem. Process Design and Development,* 10(4): 538–541 (1971).

15. Oblad, A. G., T. H. Milliken and G. A. Mills, "The Effects of the Variables in Catalytic Cracking", in *The Chemistry of Petroleum Hydrocarbons II,* Reinhold Pub. Co., New York (1955), pp. 165–188.

16. Montgomery, J. A., "The Effect of Operational Variables", in *The Davison Chemical Guide to Catalytic Cracking,* Petroleum Chemicals Dept., W. R. Grace and Co., Baltimore, MD (1975), pp 15–21.

17. Pholenz, J. B., *Oil & Gas J.,* 61 (13): 124–143 (April 1, 1963).

18. Mooran, J. W., *Oil & Gas J.,* 53 (36): 63–73 (January 10, 1955).

19. Haunschild, W. M., D. O. Chessmore, and D. G. Spars, "A Pilot Plant Comparison of Riser and Dense Bed Cracking of Hydrofined Feedstocks", paper— AIChE 79th National Meeting, Houston, Texas (March 16–20, 1975).

20. Blanding, F. H., *Ind. Eng. Chem.,* 45 (6): 1,186, 1,197 (1953).

21. Blazek, J. J., "High Temperature Regeneration", in *Catalgram* No. 48, Davison Chemical Co. (1975).

22. Nelson, W. L., *Oil & Gas J.*, 60 (24): 161 (June 11, 1962).

23. Whittington, E. L., et al., "Catalytic Cracking—Modern Designs," ACS Div. Pet. Chem., reprints, 17 (3): B 66–82 (July 1972).

24. Helmer, C. L. and W. L. Vermilion, "Developments in Fluid Catalytic Cracking", 1973 Technology Conference, Univ. Oil Products, Des Plains, Ill. (1973).

25. Vermilion, W. L., "Modern FCC Design: Evaluation and Revolution," paper—Belgium Petroleum Institute Meeting, Antwerp, Belgium (Nov. 4, 1974).

26. Bunn, D. P., et al., "The Development and Operation of the Texaco Fluid Catalytic Cracking Process", paper—AIChE 64th National Mtg., New Orleans, LA (March 16–20, 1969).

27. Bryson, M. C., et al., "Gulf's FCC Process", *Proceedings*, 37th API Division Ref. Mtg. (May 1972), pp. 277–386.

28. Finneran, J. A., et al., "Application of Heavy Oil Cracking in a Fuels Refinery", paper—AIChE 74th National Mtg., New Orleans, LA (March 11–15, (1973).

29. Hildebrand, R. E., et al., "Desulfurization and Catalytic Cracking of Residua," paper—Delaware Valley Section Mtg. AIChE, Drexel Univ., Philadelphia, PA (March 19, 1974).

30. Tyler, G. W. and H. F. Hart, "Fluo Solids Drying of Canadian Potash", Fluo Solids "Par 3" Seminar, Dorr-Oliver, Inc. Pub., paper at New York meeting (May 3, 1968).

7

Coal Gasification

CONTENTS

INTRODUCTION, 271

OVERVIEW OF REACTOR TYPES, 272

MAJOR GASIFICATION PROCESSES, 273

Slagging Lurgi Process, 273
Texaco Coal Gasification Process, 281
Combustion Engineering Process, 284
Shell-Koppers Process, 286
COGAS Process, 286

KINETICS OF COAL GASIFICATION, 294

NOMENCLATURE, 307

REFERENCES, 308

INTRODUCTION

Considerable effort has been expended in the development of technology for efficient gasification of coals to yield high quality methane gas suitable as a substitute for natural gas. The principal types of gasifiers are classified as fixed bed, entrained bed, and fluid bed. A gasification process must satisfy certain chemical constraints based on the stoichiometry of the coal gasification reactions and the energy requirements to produce those reactions. Low-temperature processes are thermally efficient and maximize methane formation, but have low throughput and produce unwanted byproducts such as tars. Higher-temperature processes avoid these problems, but must recover more of the coal energy in a heat recovery boiler. Process efficiency is improved by using smaller amounts of steam, but these processes have proved more difficult to operate. High steam usage produces a high ratio of hydrogen to carbon monoxide in the output gas. The process selected must be matched to its intended use.

The reaction kinetics in coal gasification are not well understood. Rate constants vary significantly with the rank of coal, the catalytic activity of the mineral matter, and pretreatment methods used. In a fixed-bed gasifier the feed coal is slowly warmed by the product gas stream and undergoes drying and devolatilization. Significant methane production occurs before the char is oxidized with air and reacted with steam. The heating value of the gas that is produced will increase to 150 Btu/scf (and slightly higher) as the gasification temperature is increased to about 1700°F (920°K).

The conversion of carbon to CO and the production of H_2 increases as gasification temperature rises, while the production of CH_4, H_2O, and CO_2 decreases. The production of trace elements and minor chemical species varies with temperature in a complete fashion.

This chapter provides an overview of coal gasification processes. In-depth discussions of operational experiences in pilot- and demonstration-size facilities are given by Mangold et al.[1]

OVERVIEW OF REACTOR TYPES

Mangold et al.[1] describe five major gasification processes which are the slagging Lurgi process, the Texaco process, the Shell-Koppers process, the Combustion Engineering (CE) process, and the COGAS process.

The slagging Lurgi process is primarily a methane and fuel gas producer, with the higher-temperature operation giving throughput- and thermal-efficiency advantages over the established dry-ash Lurgi process. The pressurized gasifier operates at a high temperature and produces a larger quantity of gas containing a substantial concentration of methane.

The Texaco and Shell-Koppers processes were developed from petroleum refinery experience to produce a chemical synthesis gas. Texaco employs a water slurry injection system to produce a high hydrogen-to-carbon-monoxide ratio in the product gas. The Shell-Koppers process is a pressurized version of the Koppers-Totzek process, which uses the minimum amount of steam for high thermal efficiency and produces a low hydrogen-to-carbon-monoxide ratio. The intended application of the gas can determine the preferred gas composition. Both the Texaco and Shell-Koppers units require a high-temperature heat exchanger that represents a difficult technical problem. Both processes give about half of the available energy in the form of steam from the waste heat boiler, which is easily utilized in a refinery or chemical plant, but may be of limited value in other applications.

The Combustion Engineering (CE) two-stage gasifier produces at a lower temperature and utilizes a heat-exchanger design like a utility boiler. Because of the atmospheric pressure operation and a design that gives quick access for maintenance of the components, unit availability should be high. The CE gasifier is designed as a high-volume producer of low-Btu gas to be fed directly into a utility boiler.

The COGAS process was designed to utilize the char produced from the COED pyrolysis process for producing liquids. The low-temperature process gives high thermal efficiency and is the only one utilizing the fluid-bed principle. The gas is reformed into synthetic pipeline gas.

Table 7-1 summarizes some of the characteristic differences among these gasification processes. The selection of the optimum process for a given application requires careful analysis in which the characteristics of the gasifiers are often designed to fit the application and type of coal used. Many potential applications prefer to minimize tar and oil productions because of the difficulty of removing this material from the gas. Steam produced from high-temperature raw gas may have a use, depending on the application. The chemical composition of the gas produced varies with the types of coal, gasifier conditions, and design of the cleanup system.

MAJOR GASIFICATION PROCESSES

Slagging Lurgi Process

The slagging Lurgi gasification process manufactures synthetic natural gas (SNG) from caking and noncaking coals. The technical feasibility of the process has been demonstrated in a series of runs conducted in the British Gas Corporation (BGC) 300-ton/day (270-metric ton/day) pilot plant located at Westfield, Scotland. In addition to the gasifier, a shift converter, gas cooler, and purification methanation, drying, and compressing units are incorporated in the integrated system shown in Figure 7-1. The gasifier used in this process is a pressurized, oxygen-blown, fixed-bed, dry-ash Lurgi gasifier which has been modified to operate at temperatures above the clinkering point of most coal ashes (1500°C). At this temperature the influence of the coal's reactivity is negligible, and it is possible to operate with steam-to-oxygen ratios ranging from 1.1 to 1.5 mol/mol.

The slagging Lurgi differs from the conventional Lurgi by allowing the ash to melt before it is collected at the bottom of the unit. The dry-ash Lurgi works with steam/oxygen ratios of 8 to 10 mol/mol. Excess steam is required to cool the ash down below its melting point to avoid clinkering effects and thus clogging of the slag retrieval mechanism. In this process, the gas flow is directed downward, close to the exit, to permit the ashes to leave the gasifier while still in a molten state. In

Table 7-1
Characteristics of Gasification Processes[1]

Process	Gasifier Type	Product Gas Temperature	Tar and Oil Production	H$_2$/CO Ratio	Application
Slagging Lurgi	Moving bed	Low	Yes	Medium	Methane and fuel gas
Texaco	Entrained bed	High	No	High	Chemical synthesis gas
Shell-Koppers	Entrained bed	Highest because steam injection is limited	No	Lowest	Chemical synthesis gas
Combustion Engineering	2-stage entrained bed	Medium	No	Medium	Low Btu atmospheric pressure fuel gas for utility boiler
COGAS	Multiple fluidized beds with char recycle	Low	Liquid fuel production is an objective	High	Combination of liquid fuels and synthetic pipeline gas

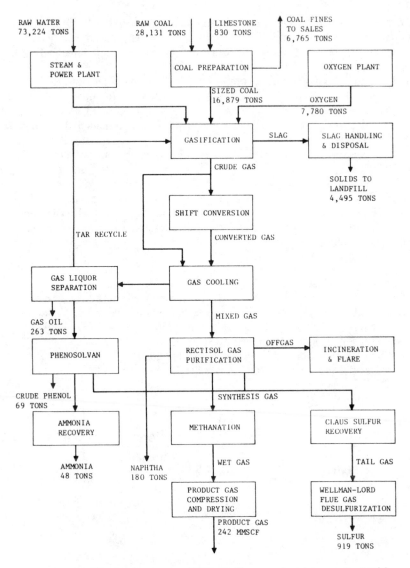

Figure 7-1. Conceptual slagging Lurgi pipeline gas plant (stream-day basis).

the dry-ash Lurgi process, the gases flow upward, well above the exit, to permit the ashes to cool below the clinkering point before they exit the gasifier.

Mangold et al.[1] describe the conceptual design of the slagging Lurgi process as comprising nine operating gasifiers plus three spares feeding into three trains of purification and methanation equipment. Additional plant facilities will include administration facilities; security, water, and power stations; cooling towers; utility connections; product storage tanks; and shipping and receiving facilities. The size of the facility may be determined from Table 7-2 which defines the daily input and output. The properties of the synthetic natural gas are listed in Table 7-3.

1. Coal and flux handling and preparation
2. Air separation
3. Gasification
4. Shift conversion
5. Gas cooling
6. Rectisol
7. Methanation
8. Product gas compression and drying
9. Sulfur recovery
10. Slag handling and disposal
11. Gas liquor separation
12. Phenol extraction
13. Ammonia recovery
14. Water treatment and steam generation
15. Cooling water system
16. Plant and instrument air system
17. Wastewater treatment
18. Flare and incinerator facilities
19. Tankage and fuel oil system
20. Shipping and receiving facilities

Proprietary processes used in the plant include:
• Gasification: British Gas Corporation, International Consultancy Service
• Shift conversion , gas cooling, Rectisol, gas liquor separation, phenol extraction, ammonia recovery: Lurgi Kohle and Mineraloeltechnik, GmbH
• Methanation: Conoco Methanation Company
• Sulfur recovery: Standard Oil Company (Indiana)
• Flue gas desulfurization: Davy Powergas, Inc.

Table 7-2
Commercial-Size Gasification Plant Inputs and Products[1]

Material	Amount/Stream-Day	
	English Units	Metric Units
Input		
Coal (Illinois No. 6)	16,879 tons	15,313 metric tons
Flux (limestone)	830 tons	753 metric tons
Steam at 550 psig		
(37 atm) and 750°F (400°C)	5,540 tons	5,026 metric tons
Oxygen (98%)	7,779 tons	7,057 metric tons
Recycle tar	1,224 tons	1,110 metric tons
Products and byproducts		
SNG, 960 Btu/scf		
(36 MJ/normal m^3)	242 million scf	6.9 million normal m^3
Coal fines	6,764 tons	6,136 metric tons
Crude phenols	69 tons	63 metric tons
Naphtha	180 tons	164 metric tons
Tar oils	262 tons	238 metric tons
Anhydrous ammonia	48 tons	44 metric tons
Sulfur	919 tons	834 metric tons

Table 7-3
SNG Properties

Property	English Units	%	Metric Units
Gross heating value	960 Btu/scf		36 MJ/normal m^3
Molecular weight	16.22		
Water content	7 lb/10^6 scf		0.1 kJ/normal m^3
H$_2$S, maximum	0.25 gr/100 scf		5.2 mg/normal m^3
Total sulfur, maximum	1.0 gr/100 scr		20 mg/normal m^3
Composition (vol %)			
Methane		94.29	
Hydrogen		2.45	
Carbon monoxide		0.00	
Carbon dioxide		0.80	
Nitrogen		2.46	
Total		100.00	

Operating conditions are more stringent in the slagging Lurgi since higher temperatures are required to facilitiate slag formation. Both the dry ash gasifier and a demonstration-size unit built in Westfield can operate at much higher temperatures and pressures, with overall better performance. A demonstration plant has been designed to operate principally with Illinois No. 6 coal.

Gas outlet temperatures for the two gasifiers differ because of the longer gas-solid contact time encountered in the demonstration gasifier; the coal bed temperature is the same for both as the slag is removed from the units by the same technique. The demonstration gasifier operates at higher pressures to increase its coal processing rate (throughput). The demonstration plant exhibits a somewhat lower overall efficiency than the Scotland pilot plant because Illinois No.6, the coal feedstock contains smaller amounts of volatiles and fixed carbon than do the coals used in the pilot plant.

In this process, coal sized to 2 by 0.25 in. (5 by 0.6 cm), recycled tar, and a flux agent (limestone) are fed, batchwise, through lock hoppers to the gasifier. The function of the limestone is to control the slag viscosity so as to enhance the tapping operation. The tar is added to enhance the process economics, to help control coal and char dust carryover with the product gases, and to dispose of solids which accumulate in the tar. When the loading operation is completed, the pressure in the coal lock is raised to that of the gasifier with recycle lock gas before the coal is dropped into the distributor and stirrer section of the gasifer. On unloading, the coal lock is depressurized by venting the gas into the lock gas holder and made ready for the next batch. The coal mixture is distributed evenly over the entrained coal bed by means of the distributor. The formation of large voids and coal agglomerates is minimized by the use of a rotating stirrer.

Oxygen (98% pure) and superheated steam at 550 psig (37 atm) are injected as one stream through tuyeres located at the bottom of the gasifier. The coal entering the reactor moves to the bottom of the gasifier in a slowly moving bed. As it travels countercurrent to the rising product gases, volatile matter and the moisture in the coal is driven off and carried away by the hot rising product gases. Gasification of the coal occurs closer to the bottom of the gasifier. The coal first reacts with the oxygen being injected to generate the necessary heat needed for the reaction of the carbon with steam to produce the synthesis gas (CO, H_2).

$$C + H_2O \rightarrow CO + H_2 \tag{7-1}$$

The gasification process is completed by reacting carbon monoxide with steam to produce more hydrogen, and by reacting the carbon still unreacted with the hydrogen produced.

$$CO + {}^{'}H_2O \rightarrow CO_2 + H_2 \tag{7-2A}$$

$$C + 2H_2 \rightarrow CH_4 \tag{7-2B}$$

For high-Btu gas manufacture, the raw gas needs to be shifted and methanated. In the demonstration plant the raw gas is passed through a waste heat exchanger before it is treated in the shift conversion section. The incoming gas to this unit is divided into two streams. The smaller of the two is sent to the gas cooling section for the removal of heavy hydrocarbons via condensation. The other stream is sent to the shift conversion unit to adjust the hydrogen-to-carbon monoxide ratio. This stream is divided into three sections and sent into three reactors operating in this section. The stream going to the first reactor is cooled and scrubbed with injection water from the gas liquor separation section. Gas from the first reactor is mixed with clean condensate to control the temperature of the gas before it enters the second reactor. Steam at 550 psig (37 atm) and 750°F (339°C) in excess of the stoichiometric requirements is injected to drive the equilibrium toward production of carbon dioxide and hydrogen.

The operation is carried over a cobalt-molybdenum catalyst fixed-bed reactor. The conversion proceeds according to the reaction:

$$CO + H_2O \rightarrow CO_2 + H_2 \tag{7-3}$$

Due to the nature of the fluids processed through the unit, the catalyst used in the reactors must be regenerated periodically. The length of time between regeneration is dependent on the properties of the gas impurities. Catalyst contamination is indicated by increases in pressure drops across the unit and a decrease of catalyst activity.

The shifted and bypass gases are cooled in the gas cooling unit to remove the condensables and to utilize the sensible heat in the raw gases. The usuable heat removed from the gases is used to superheat high-pressure steam, to produce high- and medium-pressure steam, and to heat turbine condensate and boiler feed water. The heat recovery operation is performed in seven stages, with the sixth and seventh stages not recovering useful heat.

The outputs from this section consist of a mixed gas stream at 95°F (35°C) going to the Rectisol section and an oily gas liquor stream at 226°F ((107°C) going to the gas liquor recovery section.

The gases from the Rectisol unit are sent to the methanation unit for conversion into pipeline quality gas. The following reactions take place over nickel catalyst, temperature-controlled, fixed-bed reactors:

$$CO + 3H_2 \rightarrow CH_4 + H_2O \tag{7-4A}$$

$$CO_2 + 4H_2 \rightarrow CH_4 + H_2O \tag{7-4B}$$

$$C_nH_m + (2n - m/2)H_2 \rightarrow nCH_4 \tag{7-4C}$$

The heat from the above reactions is used to produce saturated 600 psig steam for use in the boilers.

Prior to releasing the gas for distribution, it is necessary to remove environmentally objectionable sulfur oxides. This operation is accomplished by passing the gas through the sulfur recovery unit. In this unit, the following reaction takes place:

$$2H_2S + SO_2 \rightarrow 3S + 2H_2O \tag{7-5}$$

Before the above reaction can take place, it is necessary to have the hydrogen sulfide/sulfur dioxide in a 2:1 mol/mol ratio to obtain maximum sulfur recovery. The ratio is achieved by burning some of the hydrogen sulfide with oxygen from the air.

The sulfur recovery unit is fed by streams coming from four sections of the plant: the Rectisol acid gas, phenol extraction acid gas, boiler fuel gas SO_2, and the gas liquor separation expansion gas.

The liquid sulfur flows by gravity to a central collection unit where the temperature is maintained at 275°F (135°C) to facilitate pumping to a storage area.

The dusty and oily gas liquors from the gasification and shift conversion sections, respectively, are collected in the gas liquor separation unit, and the dust, tars, oils, phenol, and ammonia contained in those gases are removed sequentially.

The slagging Lurgi gasification process is a modification of the older, commercially proven Lurgi dry-ash process that has been in worldwide operation since the 1940s. Developmental work was initiated by the Lurgi Mineraloeltechnik GmbH on a small pilot plant shortly after the end of World War II. The plant was located at the Holten Works of Ruhrchemie AG, Federal Republic of Germany. The unit was sold to the British Gas Corporation which further developed the technology at its Midlands Research Station at Solihull, England, on an experimental basis in the late 1950s and on a 100-ton/day pilot-plant unit in the early 1960s. These trials demonstrated the feasibility of the slagging concept.

The gasification program was restarted by the British Gas Corporation in 1974 with sponsorship from Conoco and a consortium of 15 U.S. oil and gas firms. The $10 million program was carried out over a 3-year period and was conducted with the active collaboration of Lurgi Mineraloeltechnik of Frankfurt-am-Main, Federal Republic of Germany.

In late 1977 the U.S. Department of Energy (DOE) awarded a contract to Conoco Oil Company for the design, construction, and operation of a commercial-scale plant. Conoco is presently waiting for DOE to decide whether to proceed with the construction of the plant.

The design of the plant is based on data obtained from trials of the pilot plant at the Westfield Development Centre located near Cardenden, Scotland. These trials demonstrated that the gasifier could operate with caking coal such as the Pittsburgh No. 8 coal. Operability of the gasifier was demonstrated also with Ohio No. 9 coal, although experience with this coal is somewhat less detailed than with the less-caking Pittsburgh No. 8 coal.

Most of the component equipment in the pilot plant has been in commercial operation for a number of years, and there is a wealth of information about the processes' performance and confidence in operability on the commercial scale.

Texaco Coal Gasification Process

This process manufactures either low- or medium-Btu synthesis gas via a procedure analogous to the synthesis gas generation process. There are more than 75 petroleum residue plants operating around the world, constituting a large amount of operating experience. The technical feasibility of the Texaco Coal Gasification process has been demonstrated on a 15-ton/day (14-metric ton/day) pilot plant located at Montebello, CA.

The gasifier is illustrated in Figure 7-2. As shown, it consists of a cylindrical pressure vessel, the upper section of which is refractory lined and serves as the gasification section. The lower portion extends into a water reservoir and has a restricted orifice through which slag from the gasification section exits along with the raw gas. Immediately below the lower section of the gasifier, the water reservoir acts as a slag quencher, gas washer, and gas seal to prevent pressure drops due to gas leaks in the slag removal section. The gas exit ports are located below the lower edge of the refractory lined section. This location prevents the raw gas from coming into contact with the oxygen in the feed.

The gasification process takes place in a flame-type environment with inadequate oxygen to consume the coal, according to the reaction:

$$C + O_2 \rightarrow CO_2 \tag{7-6}$$

Heat liberated by this reaction provides the energy need to drive the steam/carbon and carbon/CO_2 reactions, which are endothermic:

$$C + H_2O \rightarrow CO + H_2 \tag{7-7A}$$

$$C + CO_2 \rightarrow 2CO \tag{7-7B}$$

Due to the high temperatures in the gasifier, nitrogen contained in the coal is converted to ammonia (NH_3) or free nitrogen (N_2). Most of the sulfur is converted to hydrogen sulfide (H_2S) or COS compounds.

The gasifier is capable of operation using air or oxygen and does not require any additional steam because the coal is injected as a coal-water slurry. If the tempera-

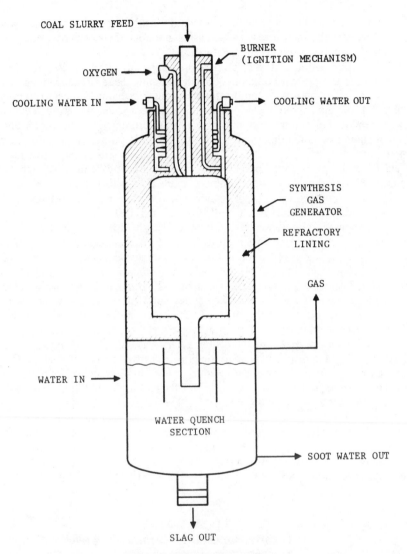

Figure 7-2. The Texaco gasifier.

ture in the reactor is above what is desirable, a moderator (usually steam), is injected to control the temperature.

Coal is normally ground to a carefully controlled size (less than 1.5 in. (3.8 cm)) and mixed with water. The slurry is then injected into the gasifier through a specially designed nozzle. The use of water to feed the coal to the gasifier bypasses the problem of continuous coal feeding to the pressurized gasifier. It does, however, introduce a thermal penalty in its operation, since some of the heat of combustion from the reaction of the coal with the oxidant must be used to convert the water to steam. The penalty increases with increasing amounts of water in excess of the stoichiometric amount required for gasification.

The gasifier operates in the temperature range of 2300°F–2600°F (1260°C–1430°C) and at a pressure of about 600 psig (41 atm). Feed residence time is on the order of a few seconds with combustion reactions proceeding almost to completion. Table 7-4 lists the operating parameters of the gasifier when operating in the air and oxygen mode. For comparison, the same data are presented for the pilot-plant gasifier. It should be noted that there has been very little pilot-plant activity in the air mode, and that the coal residence time in this mode is still under active research. Data from the pilot-plant operations have been used by Texaco Montebello Research Laboratory and by Fluor Engineers and Constructors, Inc. in the conceptual design of a combined-cycle plant, which would operate on 10,000 ton/day (9,901 metric ton/day) of Illinois No. 6 coal to produce 1,100–1,200 MW.

The composition of Illinois No. 6 coal used as feed is given in Table 7-5. The gasifier products when processing Illinois No. 6 are summarized in Table 7-6. For comparison, results of operation at the pilot plant are also shown. There is essentially no production of tars or phenols, and the synthesis gas (CO, H_2) yield is about 80%. The heating value for the gas is about 320 Btu/scf (11.9 MJ/normal m^3).

The Texaco gasification process began development in the 1940s on natural gas and has been in operation since 1946. The feedstock has been expanded to include a large number of high-sulfur petroleum waste materials and, finally, to coal.

One of the largest experimental coal gasifiers was built at the Morgantown, WV, plant of Olin Mathieson. It was an air-blown gasifier processing 84 ton/day (70 metric ton/day) of Pittsburgh seam coal to be used in the synthesis of ammonia and methanol. The unit was large, measuring 27 ft (9 m) high and 8 ft (2.7 m) in diameter and operated at 450 psig (30.6 atm). It is known that problems were encountered with heating of the slurry and wear in the nozzle, but data on parameters such as general plant performance, gas quality, heat losses, and refractory durability are unavailable. Operations began in August 1956 and terminated in 1958.

In addition to two 15- to 20-ton/day (13.5- to 18-metric-ton/day) pilot plants using coal in Montebello, CA, a 150-ton/day (135-metric-ton/day) plant has operated

Table 7-4
Gasifier Operating Parameters[1]

Parameter	Pilot Plant Oxygen	Combined Cycle Plant* Oxygen	Combined Cycle Plant* Air
Cold gas efficiency (%)	66–73	75	68
Gas production rate [scf/lb (10^5 cm^3/kg)]	26–36 (16–22)	34.3 (21)	30.5
Offgas temperature [°F (°C)]	400–500 (200–260)		
Gasification temperature [°F (°C)]	200–2,500 (1,100–1,370)	2,360 (1,300)	2,300 (1,260)
Gasification pressure [psig (atm)]	350–2,000 (24–140)	600 (20)	815 (55)
Residence time (min)	< 1	< 1	
Percent coal in slurry	48–66	60	
Throughput [lb/hr-ft² (kg/hr-cm²)]	300 (0.15)		
Steam/coal ratio (wt/wt)	0.24–0.43		
Oxygen/coal ratio (wt/wt)	0.98–1.00	0.953	1.03

* Estimated by Texaco, Inc.

Table 7-5
Coal Analysis (Illinois No. 6)[1]

Components	Balance
Proximate Analysis (wt %)	
Moisture	4.2
Ash	9.6
Fixed Carbon	52.0
Volatile Matter	34.2
Total	100.0
Ultimate Analysis* (wt %)	
Carbon	77.26
Hydrogen	5.92
Oxygen	11.14
Nitrogen	1.39
Sulfur	4.29
Total	100.00
Heating Value—as Received	
Higher Heating Value	12,235
Net Heating Value	11,709

* Dry, ash-free basis.

Table 7-6
Gasifier Performance (Volume %)[1]

Component	Combined Cycle Plant Air	Combined Cycle Plant Oxygen	Pilot Plant Oxygen
CH_4	0.10	0.10	0.03
H_2	11.61	35.07	35.78
CO	19.46	51.62	44.62
CO_2	7.68	10.72	17.97
H_2S	0.52	1.22	1.02
COS	0.05	0.07	0.05
N_2	59.74	0.80	6.48*
Ar	0.71	0.15	
NH_3	0.11	0.24	

* N_2 and Ar.

for a year and a half in West Germany. The Tennessee Valley Authority has constructed an ammonia plant using a 180-ton/day gasifier. Because of the unique properties of the Texaco coal gasifier when integrated into a combined cycle gas turbine/steam turbine electric generating plant, a 90-MW facility is now being designed for Coolwater, CA. Before the gasifier output is connected to the gas turbine, it will be used for one year to supply fuel to an existing boiler. The total plant capacity of 1,000 ton/day (900 metric ton/day) will be supplied by seven 150-ton/day (136-metric-ton/day) gasifiers.

Combustion Engineering Process

The Combustion Engineering (CE) entrained-bed atmospheric pressure coal gasification process began from studies conducted in the early 1970s. A gasifier for power-plant applications was determined to have the optimum cost, maintenance, and operational advantages when air blown and operated at atmospheric pressure, using construction methods and firing techniques similar to those of a pulverized coal boiler. A 5-ton/hr (4.5-metric-ton/hr) pilot plant contains coal handling, gas cleanup, and char recycle facilities and is a complete but smaller version of the next phase in the development of the process, a demonstration plant supporting a 150-MW utility boiler.

The CE entrained-bed gasifier uses a two-stage combustor. Coal is pulverized and about one third is injected into a combustor where it is burned with preheated air producing a gas temperature of 3200°F (1750°C). The hot gas rises into a reduction zone where additional coal is added with little additional air. Approximately two thirds of the coal added in the reduction zone gasifies with the endothermic reducing chemical reactions, dropping the temperature to 1700°F (930°C). The coal exits in a stream with char and H_2S. Char separated from the gas stream is recycled to the combustor, giving the process a high carbon utilization efficiency. The coal ash is melted into slag and removed from the bottom of the combustor. The product gas is cooled in a heat exchanger to 300°F (147°C), the char is removed for reinjection into the gasifier, and the product gas is spray-washed to remove particulates and desulfured using the Stretford process. In the pilot plant the clean gas is burned to preheat the incoming air. In a utility plant the gas would be reheated and burned in any of several steam or combined cycles to produce electricity.

A flow chart diagram of the CE coal gasification process is shown in Figure 7-3. Coal from receiving and storage is pulverized to 200 mesh following standard utility practice. One third of the coal is pneumatically injected into the combustor, producing the heat required to drive the gasification process, and the remaining feed is injected into the reducing zone to complete the gasification reaction. The hot gas and char flowing out of the reducing zone is cooled in a steam generator that is constructed using normal utility boiler practice. The steam that is produced would be utilized in the steam turbine cycle of a commercial power plant; the design parameters of the boiler must therefore be integrated into the overall design of the plant that the gasifier serves. The gas is passed through a char separator and liquid spray scrubber for removal of particulates and ammonia, from which it passes into a gas absorber section of a sulfur removal plant operating with the Stretford process.

The Stretford process consists of four basic steps:

1. Absorption of H_2S in an alkaline solution of Na_2CO_3 and Na_2VO_3
2. Formation of elemental sulfur by an oxidation/reduction reaction with a vanadium compound
3. Regeneration of the absorbing solution
4. Recovery of elemental sulfur

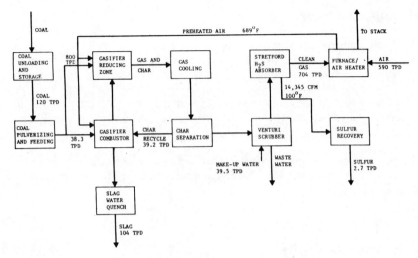

Figure 7-3. The Combustion Engineering entrained-bed coal gasification process.

After absorption in the sodium carbonate solution:

$$Na_2CO_3 + H_2S \rightarrow NaHS + NaHCO_3 \tag{7-8}$$

the products of the reaction participate in an oxidation/reduction reaction in which sodium metavanadate and anthraquinone disulfonic acid produce a sulfur froth

$$4NaVO_3 + 2NaHS + H_2O \rightarrow Na_2V_4O_9 + 2S + 4NaOH \tag{7-9}$$

Sulfur is removed from the froth that is skimmed from the holding tank using a rotary vacuum filter. The solution is regenerated by blowing air through a holding tank to reoxidize the vanadium into $NaVO_3$, which is then recirculated to the absorption tower. The Stretford process works well at atmospheric pressure and low CO_2 concentrations, but does not remove COS and CS_2.

After sulfur removal, the gas produced in the pilot plant is incinerated and used in preheating the gasifier air. In a utility installation the gas would be reheated using a low-temperature hot-water circulation loop from the gasifier heat recovery section and burned in a steam boiler operating at atmospheric pressure using burner heads modified to utilize low Btu gas. An alternative electric power generating cycle is the compression of the gas from atmospheric pressure to a pressure of 167–259 psig ($488.6 - 757.8$ kg/cm^2) for injection into a gas turbine used in a combined cycle generating system.

The reader should refer to References 2 through 19 for more in-depth discussions of the processes described thus far.

Shell-Koppers Process

The Shell-Koppers development program is a joint venture of Shell Internationale Research Mij. and Krupp-Koppers, aimed at the commercialization of a coal gasification process operating in the entrained-bed mode at elevated pressures. Depending on the moisture content of the coal, little or no steam is utilized. A 6-ton/day (5.4 metric-ton/day) process development unit and a 150-ton/day (136-metric ton/day) pilot plant located at Shell's Amsterdam laboratory is providing the necessary operating experience to proceed with the commercialization phase of the project.

The gasification reactions occur in a flame-like environment in the presence of excess carbon to ensure the formation of synthesis gas. Gasification proceeds according to the reaction:

$$C + 0.5O_2 \rightarrow CO \tag{7-10A}$$

$$CO + H_2O \rightarrow CO_2 + H_2 \tag{7-10B}$$

$$CO + 3H_2 \rightarrow CH_4 + H_2O \tag{7-10C}$$

At high temperatures and pressures, the routes described by Equations 7-10A and 7-10B are favored.

In this process, oxygen and finely ground and dried coal, 90% of which is smaller than 3.6×10^{-3} in. (90 μm), is fed through nozzle burners placed directly opposite each other. A schematic diagram of the process is shown in Figure 7-4. The gasifier operating parameters are listed in Table 7-7. The ash flowing out of the reactor is collected in a water-filled compartment at the bottom of the reactor.

The hot raw gases are passed through a proprietary system consisting of a cyclone and scrubbers to remove the entrained matter in the gasifier. Table 7-8 shows the composition of the raw gas resulting from the gasification of four different coals whose compositions are shown in Table 7-9. Note that the moisture content varies from 10 to 50 wt%. Steam consumption is inversely proportional to the moisture content varying from 50% of the base case to 0%. Coal input increases as the rank of the coal decreases. The efficiency of the gasifier is reported to be minimally affected by the different feedstocks.

The Shell-Koppers is a relatively new process that has not been extensively developed. Only a few years of experience with the gasifier has been obtained with a 150-ton/day (136-metric-ton/day) installation.

COGAS Process

The COGAS process consists of three subprocesses: multistage fluidized-bed pyrolysis, char gasification, and processes for upgrading the raw product to synthetic crude oil and synthetic natural gas.

The technical feasibility of the processes has been demonstrated separately. The pyrolyzing process has been demonstrated in a 36-ton/day (32.7-metric-ton/day) pilot plant located in Princeton, NJ, used to demonstrate the feasibility of the COED

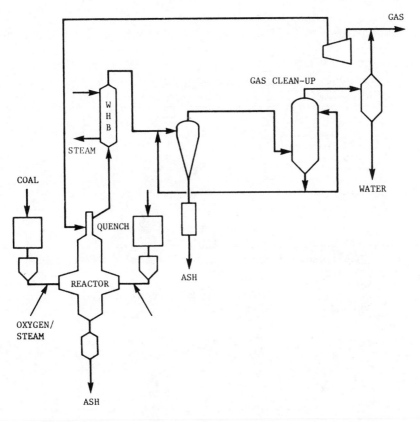

Figure 7-4. Schematic flow diagram of the Shell-Koppers process.

Table 7-7
Shell-Koppers Gasifier Operating Conditions[20]

Parameters	Balances
Temperature [°F (°C)]	> 2,550 (1,400)
Coal size [in. (cm)]	3.6×10^{-3} (90×10^{-4})
Oxygen feed (ton/ton coal)	0.7–1.0
Steam, ton/ton coal	0.0–0.07
Gas production rate* [scf/lb (m^3/metric ton)]	34.95 (2,000)
CO/H_2 ratio	2.0–2.4
Heating value [Btu/scf (kcal/m^3)]	303 (2,700)
Thermal efficiency (%)	77–80
Cold gas efficiency (%)	92–94
Offgas temperature [°F (°C)]	< 2,700 (1,500)

* For good quality bituminous coals.

Table 7-8
Shell-Koppers Coal Gasification Dry Synthesis Gas Composition (vol. %)[20]

Component	West German Bituminous Low-Ash	High-Ash	Wyodak Lignite	Australian Brown Coal (Yallourn)
H_2	31.3	30.2	30.1	28.6
CO	65.6	66.5	66.1	65.8
CO_2	1.5	1.8	2.5	4.7
CH_4	0.4	0.3	0.4	0.1
H_2S	0.4	0.4	0.2	0.1
N_2	0.6	0.6	0.5	0.5
A	0.2	0.2	0.2	0.2

Table 7-9
Shell-Koppers Coal Gasification Coal Feed Analyses[20]

Components	West German Bituminous Low-Ash	High-Ash	Wyodak Lignite	Australian Brown Coal (Yallourn)
Carbon	66.5	51.4	44.6	33.0
Hydrogen	4.3	3.3	3.5	2.3
Oxygen	8.0	6.2	9.9	13.1
Nitrogen	1.0	0.8	0.6	0.3
Sulfur	1.1	0.9	0.4	0.1
Ash	9.	27.4	6.0	1.2
Moisture	10.0	10.0	35.0	50.0
Heating Value (LHV)				
kcal/kg	6,300	4,860	4,100	2,680
Btu/lb	11,300	8,700	7,400	4,800

process. The gasification process has been demonstrated in a 50-ton/day (45.4-metric-ton/day) pilot plant located in Leatherhead, England. Chars from the COED pilot plant were used as feedstock for the gasification pilot plant. Data from the operation of both pilot plants (summarized in Table 7-10) have been used by the COGAS Development Corporation, of Princeton, NJ, in the conceptual design of a commercial plant based on the COGAS process.

The pyrolysis section of the process is similar in its operation to the COED process shown in Figure 7-5. The difference between the processes lies in how the heat required for pyrolysis is generated. In the COED process, this is accomplished by reacting some of the char with oxygen to produce hot synthesis gas. This gas is passed through the other stages of the process in a countercurrent fashion. In the COGAS process, heat is provided from synthesis gas generated in the gasifier. The gasifier does not generate its products as a result of chemical processes. The principal mechanism at work in the pyrolysis is devolatilization, a physical process that

Table 7-10
Summary of COED Process Development Unit: Results on All Coals Tested[21]

Components	Utah A-Seam	Illinois No. 6	Colorado Bear	New Mexico McKinley	Wyoming Rock Springs	Wyoming Glenrock	Montana Colstrip	Indiana No. 5	Indiana No. 6	W. Kentucky Paradise No. 9
Moisture as received (wt %)	5.0	10.0	0.5	15.0	9.0	24.0	23.0	6.0	10.0	6.0
Proximate analysis (wt % dry)										
Volatile matter	42.9	38.6	36.5	41.8	44.6	40.3	36.2	37.0	36.8	38.9
Fixed carbon	51.0	50.0	53.6	49.6	52.1	39.8	52.5	51.2	51.4	53.9
Ash	7.1	11.4	9.9	8.6	3.3	19.9	11.3	12.8	11.8	7.2
Heating value as received [Btu/lb (kcal/kg)]	12,700 7,048	10,900 6,050	12,800 6,100	10,000 7,100	12,480 6,926	7,500 4,162	8,720 4,840	11,660 6,471	11,370 6,310	12,770 7,087
Product yields, per ton										
Char (tons)	0.375	0.40	0.432	0.289	0.368	0.297	0.368	0.448	0.426	0.545
(metric tons)	0.340	0.362	0.392	0.262	0.334	0.270	0.334	0.406	0.386	0.494
Crude oil (bbl)	1.37	1.04	1.40	0.93	1.14	0.425	0.373	1.13	0.98	1.06
Gas (scf, CO₂-free) (normal m³)	7,900 224	7,720 219	8,470 240	11,100 314	8,290 235	5,250 149	4,250 120	5,770 163	6,910 196	

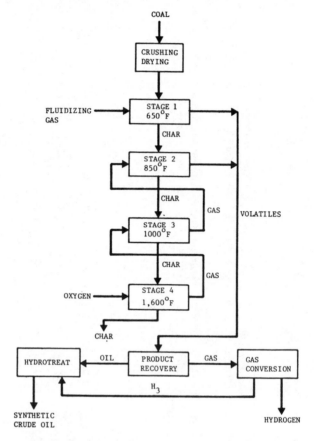

Figure 7-5. COED process flow diagram. (Source: Bloom and Wisdom.[22])

results from the action of heat on the feedstock. Figure 7-6 shows a schematic diagram of the pyrolysis and char combustion processes.

The gasification section generates synthesis gas by reacting carbon with steam:

$$C + H_2O \rightleftharpoons CO + H_2 \qquad (7\text{-}11)$$

The preceding reaction described by Equation 7-11 is endothermic and needs heat to proceed. Heat for the reaction is provided by circulating chars through a combustor as shown in Figure 7-7. The heat transfer between the flue gas and the chars occurs in the lift tube. The chars are separated from the flue gas in the disengager and returned to the gasifier to react with steam. In this process, crushed coal is pressurized with synthesis gas from the process and sent to pyrolysis, where it is devolatilized by countercurrent-flowing synthesis gas. This section of the plant consists of several cylindrical steel vessels. The required number of vessels depends on the coal used; the more agglomerating the coal, the greater the number of stages required. For most coals, complete pyrolysis is accomplished in three stages. The key feature of the process is that each stage is operated at a temperature below the coal-softening temperature, which eliminates the problems associated with the removal of molten ash and high carbon losses. The process avoids agglomeration by processing the coal in several stages, each operating at sequentially higher temperatures. The problem of coal agglomeration is also controlled by recycling some of the chars from the higher-temperature stages to dilute the potentially agglomerating chars and to control the temperature. In the low-temperature stages, the oil partial pressure is controlled to accelerate the rate at which matter is removed from the chars.

The commercial plant is schematically illustrated in Figure 7-8. The flowsheet shows the processing of Illinois No. 6 coal and water as feedstock and the production of synthetic natural gas and fuel oil as principal products. Table 7-11 summarizes the composition of Illinois No. 6 coal. The composition of SNG, fuel oil, naphtha, and light hydrocarbons are summarized by Mangold et al.[1]

The naphtha is produced as a result of upgrading the raw pyrolysis oil. The light hydrocarbons form during the pyrolysis and upgrading operation of the fuel oil; it is a mixture of alkanes and alkenes, with ethane and butane as the principal constituents.

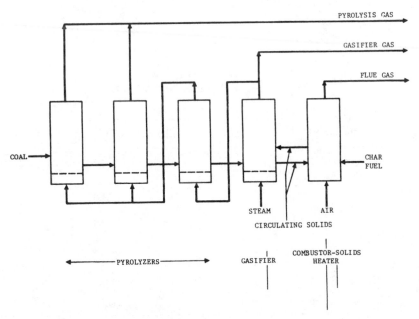

Figure 7-6. The pyrolysis-gasification process. (Source: Bloom and Wisdom.[22])

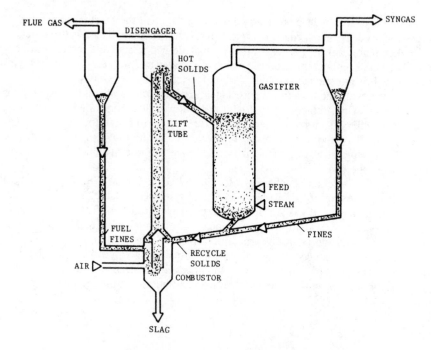

Figure 7-7. Gasification-combustion system.

Table 7-11
Properties of Illinois No. 6 Coal

Property	wt %
Proximate Analysis	
Moisture	12.08
Ash	13.27
Volatiles	30.80
Fixed Carbon	43.85
Total	100.00
Ultimate Analysis*	
Carbon	76.55
Hydrogen	5.26
Oxygen	10.92
Nitrogen	1.11
Sulfur	5.95
Chlorine	0.21
Total	100.00

* Dry ash-free basis.

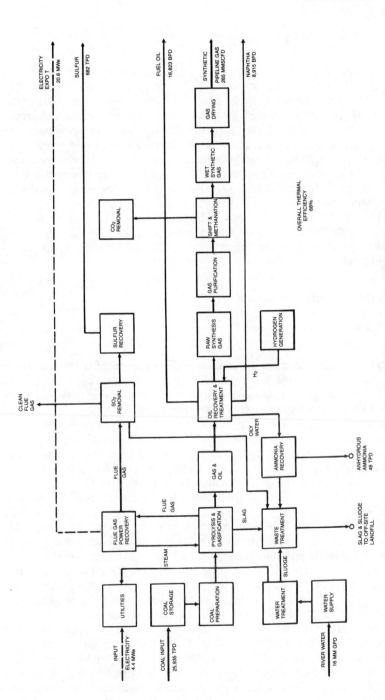

Figure 7-8. Illinois coal gasification group, COGAS commercial plant concept.

KINETICS OF COAL GASIFICATION

During the initial gasification stage, coal undergoes devolatilization reactions leading to the formation of carbon oxides, water, oils, tars, and significant quantities of light hydrocarbons in the presence of hydrogen at elevated pressures. The problem of optimization of methane yields requires a kinetic characterization of the relevant processes coupled with a good understanding of the important chemical and physical phenomena that occur during the transition of coal to coal char and during the subsequent gasification of the coal char itself. There is some evidence that heterogeneous interactions play an important role in initial methane formation reactions; however, considerable variation exists in proposed mechanisms and the kinetic representations used to correlate experimental behavior.

Table 7-12 lists the range of experimental conditions reported in the literature, over which the initial reactions during coal gasification in hydrogen-containing gases were studied. As noted earlier, three types of experimental systems appear of most interest:

1. Fixed coal bed flowing gas
2. Fluidized coal bed
3. Dilute solid-phase transport (entrained bed), or free-fall systems

In addition to differences in the coal type and the range of conditions employed, there are also differences in the methods for characterizing experimental results. In fixed-bed studies for example, gasification behavior is often characterized on the basis of total coal weight loss or coal-to-carbon conversion.

The gasification process occurs in two fairly well defined stages: an initial rapid stage associated with devolatilization processes and a second, much slower stage associated with the char-hydrogen reaction. The first stage for practical purposes is considered to be instantaneous, relative to the amount of time required for significant char-hydrogen reactions. The reason for this is that the first-stage reaction involves rapid reaction of hydrogen with the more reactive parts of the coal structure such as oxygen-containing functional groups and aliphatic hydrocarbon side chains.

In general, methane yields are observed to increase with increasing hydrogen partial pressure. The maximum yield during the initial stage is stoichiometrically limited and is independent of the hydrogen pressure. In the case of brown coal, this maximum yield is typically about 28% conversion of the carbon feed to methane and 12% to other volatiles. The amount of solid carbon remaining after completion of the first reaction stage corresponds fairly closely to that known to be present in aromatic ring structures in brown coal. At temperatures above 700°C, methane yields reported by Blackwood et al.[23] during the first-stage reaction are dependent only on hydrogen partial pressure up to the maximum yield possible, which was obtained at a hydrogen partial pressure of 30–40 atm (refer to Figure 7-9).

Blackwood and McCarthy[23] suggest that there is a fixed fraction of reaction carbon in the raw coal structure that can potentially be converted to methane, once sufficient time has elasped to complete the devolatilization process.

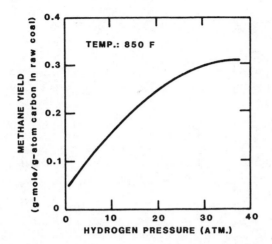

Figure 7-9. Illustration of the effect of hydrogen pressure on first-stage methane yields obtained for gasification of brown coal in a fluidized bed. (Data from Blackwood and McCarthy.[23])

Mosley and Patterson[24] report that the high yields of methane during the initial gasification stages in hydrogen resulted not only from the hydrogenation of a limited amount of coal volatile matter, or potentially volatile matter, but also from direct hydrogasification of an active intermediate that would otherwise form relatively unreactive char or fixed carbon. Their data, along with that of Blackwood et al.,[23] suggest that at sufficiently high hydrogen pressures substantial fractions of potential fixed carbon is gasified within a matter of a few seconds. Furthermore, Moseley et al. suggest that at elevated temperatures, the hydrogenation of evolved volatile matter to form methane is essentially complete at a hydrogen pressure of less than 100 atm. At higher pressures, methane yield increases linearly with hydrogen partial pressure due solely to the gasification of potential fixed carbon in the intermediate coal structure.

When the hydrogen reaction with volatile matter is complete, methane formation is due solely to the attack by hydrogen on transient, unstable structures in the pyrolyzing coal char and to this reaction competing effectively with normal thermal stabilization processes leading to unreactive carbon residues.[24] Moseley and Patterson[24] propose the following overall reaction scheme:

$$
C_0(coal) \xrightarrow{K_A} V(volatiles) + I(active\ intermediate) \xrightarrow{K_B} \left.\begin{array}{l} Cross\text{-}linked, \\ less\ active \\ structure, \\ not\ easily \\ gasified\ by \\ hydrogen \end{array}\right\} \quad (7\text{-}12)
$$
$$
+ 2nH_2 \quad \downarrow \quad K
$$
$$
I + nCH_4
$$

Table 7-12
Range of Investigations of Initial Coal-Gasification Reactions in Hydrogen-Containing Gases

Coal Type	Primary Particle Diameter Range (μ)	Feed Gases	Temperature Range (°C)	Pressure Range (atm)	Residence Time at Temperature (s) Solids	Gas	Solids Heat-up Rate (°C/s)
Fixed-bed studies							
Low-temperature bituminous coal char	420–1,190	H_2, H_2O, H_2-H_2O	900–1,150	70	0–1,500		~20
Pittsburgh high-volatility bituminous coal	250–590	H_2	800–1,200	5–70	0–1,800	< 1	~10
Pittsburgh high-volatility bituminous (air-preheated) coal	420–840	N_2, H_2, H_2O, H_2-H_2O, H_2-CH_4	450–900	10–70	60–3,600		~10
Pittsburgh high-volatility bituminous coal, Montana lignite	50–80	H_2, He, N_2, H_2-He	400–1,100	0.001–71	0–20		60–10⁴
Illinois high-volatility bituminous coal	< 40	H_2, N_2	650–1,000	100	2–65	0.2–23	20–1,400
North Dakota lignite	40	H_2	550–850	10–280	0.3–10	03.10	~10⁴
Fluidized-bed study							
Brown coal	300–760	H_2, H_2-N_2, synthesis gas	500–950	2–40	900–6,500	6	

Table 7-12 (continued)
Range of Investigations of Initial Coal-Gasification Reactions in Hydrogen-Containing Gases

Coal Type	Primary Particle Diameter Range (μ)	Feed Gases	Temperature Range (°C)	Pressure Range (atm)	Residence Time at Temperature (s) Solids	Residence Time at Temperature (s) Gas	Solids Heat-up Rate (°C/s)
Dilute solid-phase transport studies							
British high-volatility bituminous coal	100–150	H$_2$	840–930	50–500	0.5–5	60–120	
Pittsburgh high-volatility bituminous coal	150–300	H$_2$–CH$_4$	730	100–200	1–2	120–240	
North Dakota lignite	70–150	Synthesis gas	940–970	70–85	2–10	2–10	
Pittsburgh high-volatility bituminous coal, Illinois high-volatility bituminous coal, North Dakota lignite	70–300	H$_2$, H$_2$–CH$_4$	650–900	35–140	1–2	30–200	
Montana lignite, Montana subbituminous coal, North Dakota lignite	70–90	H$_2$, He, H$_2$–He	450–850	20–50	5–15	5–15	30–~10^4
North Dakota lignite, New Mexico subbituminous coal	< 50, < 150	H$_2$	700	70–100	15–40	10–70	

where K, K_A, and K_B are rate constants. Assuming first-order reaction processes, the following rate equation was derived to describe the rate of methane formation under isothermal conditions:

$$\frac{dY_{CH_4}}{dt} = \frac{KK_AC_oC^{-K_At}}{K_B} P_{H_2}M \tag{7-13}$$

where C_o = initial concentration of structures in the coal capable of forming the active intermediate
M = effective char concentration

Clearly this is an oversimplification of the kinetics, suggesting that not only do C_o, K_A, and K_B depend on the original coal and the temperature of hydrogenation, but also that K_A and K_B are unlikely to remain strictly constant at any one temperature, since devolatilization and linking require larger activation energies to overcome the hindrance of previous cross-linking. The solid carbon concentration, M in Equation 7-13 does not vary significantly with time as compared to changes in the concentration of the active intermediate. In other words, the solid carbon is always in excess kinetically even when a large portion of it has been gasified. The total methane yields after complete conversion of the active intermediate either to methane or to inactive char is:

$$Y_{CH_4} = \frac{Y^o_{CH_4} + bP_{H_2}}{1 + bP_{H_2}} \tag{7-14}$$

where $Y^o_{CH_4}$ = methane yield resulting only from devolatilization
b = kinetic parameter, proportional to the ratio of rate constants for methanation and deactivation of the active intermediate

Excessive carbon conversion due to rapid-rate methane formation at final reaction temperatures above 800°C (hydrogen partial pressures up to 70 atm) is correlated as follows:[25]

$$S = 1 - \exp\left(-f_R 0.0092P_{H_2}\right) \tag{7-15}$$

where f_R = reactivity factor used to characterize coal type ($f_R \simeq 1.0$ for high volatility bituminous coals)
P_{H_2} = hydrogen partial pressures (in atm)

This correlation describes yields obtained above 800°C, at which temperature devolatilization and those processes leading to rapid-rate methane formation are completed in relatively short times. For gasification at lower temperatures, a more detailed model and correlation to describe methane yields has been proposed,[25] where Equation 7-13 is modified by replacing the term $K_A C^{-K_A{}^t}$ by the following:

$$\int_0^\infty K_A C^{-K_A{}^t} f(E) dE$$

where

$$K_A = K_A^\circ C^{-E/RT} \tag{7-16}$$

$f(E)$ is the distribution function, defined as:

$$f(E) = \frac{4\alpha^{1.5}(E - E_1)^2}{\pi} \exp\left(-\alpha(E - E_1)^2\right) \text{ for } E > E_1 \tag{7-17}$$

and

$$f(E) = 0 \text{ for } E < E_1$$

Evaluation of the kinetic parameters is as follows:

$$E_1 = 18.2 \text{ kcal/gmol}$$
$$\alpha = 0.111 \text{ (kcal/gmol)}^{-2}$$
$$K_A^\circ = 150 \text{ s}^{-1}$$
$$C_o K/K_B = 0.0092 \text{ } f_R, \text{ atm}^{-1}$$

This produces the plots shown in Figures 7-10 and 7-11.

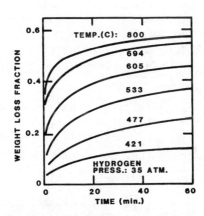

Figure 7-10. Illustration of the effect of temperature and residence time on weight loss obtained for hydrogen gasification of air-pretreated high-volatility bituminous coal in thermobalance. (Data from Pyrioch, Feldkirchner, et al.[26])

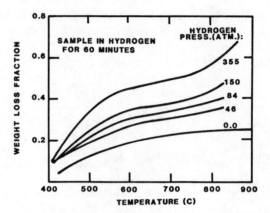

Figure 7-11. Illustration of the effect of pressure and temperature on gasification of air-pretreated high-volatility bituminous coal in thermobalance. (Data from Pyrioch, Feldkirchner, et al.[26])

A material balance for the reactive volatiles within the coal particles results in the following expression:

$$\frac{dV_r'}{dt} = \frac{k_c}{P}C + k_1C + k_2P_{H_2}C + \frac{dC}{dt} \tag{7-19}$$

where

    C = concentration of reactive volatiles in particles

    k_c = overall coefficient for mass transfer of reactive volatiles out of particle

    k_1 = overall rate constant for deposition of reactive volatiles within particle

    k_2 = overall rate constant for stabilization of reactive volatiles within particle, by gaseous hydrogen

    dV_r'/dt = rate of formation of reactive volatiles

    P_{H_2} = hydrogen partial pressure

    P = total pressure

If $dc/dt \simeq 0$, then the ratios of rate constants and transfer coefficients are independent of temperature. Hence, for reaction times approaching infinity, the total yield of evolved reactive volatiles is:

$$V_r^* = \frac{V_r^{**}[(1/P) + (k_2/kc)P_{H_2}]}{[(1/P) + (k_2/kc)P_{H_2} + (k_1/kc)]} \tag{7-20}$$

where V_r^* = reactive volatiles lost from particles up to time $t \simeq \infty$ (i.e., the ultimate yield)

        V_r^{**} = reactive volatiles formed up to $t \simeq \infty$ (i.e., the potential ultimate yield)

This expression suggests that the total yield of evolved reactive volatiles is independent of the time-temperature history, but that it increases with increasing hydrogen partial pressure due to stabilization of reactive volatiles and decreases with increasing total pressure due to increased diffusion resistance.

Additional interest concerns the kinetics of the initial-stage methane-plus-ethane formation for different coals as a function of hydrogen partial pressure and coal time-temperature history. The total methane-plus-ethane yields obtained in coal gasification with hydrogen result primarily from three overall reaction processes: direct hydrogenation, thermally activated coal-decomposition reactions, and secondary hydrogenation of C_3^+ gaseous hydrocarbons.

The kinetics of direct coal hydrogenation depend on the contributions of coal-decomposition reactions and secondary hydrogenation reactions to total methane-plus-ethane yields. Simplifying approximations and assumptions can be made to obtain first-order estimates. Methane-plus-ethane obtained from coal decomposition can be assumed to occur in two stages: below 600°C a fixed fraction is instantaneously evolved; and above this temperature, yields increase linearly with increasing temperature up to 780°C when conversion is complete. The assumption that the kinetics of this reaction are independent of coal residence time implies a wide distribution of activation energies for the decomposition steps leading to methane-plus-ethane formation. Figure 7-12 shows yields of C_3^+ gaseous hydrocarbons obtained in hydrogen and helium for gasification of Montana lignite at a coal heat-up rate of 30°C/s. In helium, the C_3^+ hydrocarbons initially formed do not undergo pyrolysis at higher temperatures up to 810°C, whereas in hydrogen the yield of this fraction begins to decrease above about 600°C due to hydrogenation to methane and ethane.

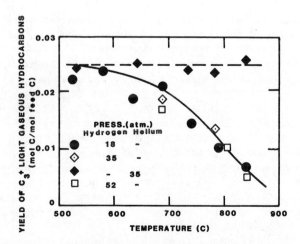

Figure 7-12. Yields of C_3^+ light gaseous hydrocarbon from gasification of Montana lignite in hydrogen or helium (constant gas-coal heat-up rate = 30°C/s).[26]

The overall hydrogenation reactions occurring were assumed to be equivalent to a single first-order reaction:[26]

$$C_3^+ \text{ gaseous hydrocarbons } \xrightarrow{k_4} \text{methane + ethane} \tag{7-21}$$

The complete correlation to describe methane-plus-ethane formation from coal thermal decomposition and hydrogenation of C_3^+ hydrocarbons has the following form:

$$N = N_o(\alpha' X + \alpha'' X'' + \alpha''' X''') \tag{7-22}$$

where X' = conversion fraction of thermal decomposition reactions below 600°C

X'' = conversion fraction of thermal decomposition reactions above 600°C

X''' = conversion fraction of C_3^+ hydrogenation reactions

N_o = total carbon in methane-plus-ethane that can be formed from thermal decomposition and C_3^+ hydrogenation reactions (in g-atom/g-atom feed carbon in coal)

N = carbon in methane-plus-ethane formed from thermal decomposition and C_3^+ hydrogenation reactions at any time (in g-atom/g-atom feed carbon in coal)

$\alpha', \alpha'', \alpha'''$ = coefficients defining the distribution of carbon that can be converted to methane-plus-ethane from the three reactant groups considered

The previous model is an oversimplification but still provides an approximate basis consistent with literature data obtained to numerically adjust methane-plus-ethane yields to correspond only to direct coal hydrogenation.

It should be noted that a strong correlation exists between adjusted methane-plus-ethane yields and coal-hydrogen evolution during the secondary devolatilization stage. This behavior is illustrated in Figure 7-13 where methane-plus-ethane yields at constant hydrogen partial pressure are directly proportional to the secondary coal hydrogen evolved, independent of the time-temperature history. The slopes of the lines drawn in Figure 7-13 increase with increasing hydrogen pressure, which is consistent with qualitative observations reported in the literature for the rapid-rate methane formation. Variations in coal hydrogen evolution with increasing temperature are illustrated in Figure 7-14. For a given time-temperature history the amount of coal hydrogen evolved is essentially independent of gaseous hydrogen pressure, and the results obtained with Montana lignite (Figure 7-14A) show similar behavior in both helium and hydrogen atmospheres.

Figures 7-13 and 7-14 suggest that the formation of active sites, which promote methane-plus-ethane formation through interaction of gaseous hydrogen with the coal is directly related to the processes in which coal hydrogen is evolved; this lat-

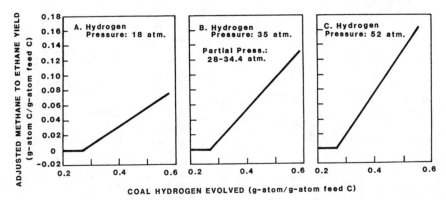

Figure 7-13. Stoichiometric relationship between adjusted methane-plus-ethane yield and coal-hydrogen evolution.

ter process involves only thermally activated phenomena occurring independently of gaseous atmosphere and dependent only on time-temperature history. This model can be represented as:

$$CH_x^o \xrightarrow{\hspace{5cm}} CH_y^* \qquad (7\text{-}23)$$

semi-char   (thermally activated   active
               coal-hydrogen evolution) inter-
                                        mediate

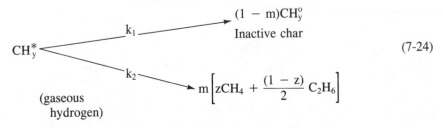

$$(7\text{-}24)$$

where x = hydrogen: carbon atomic ratio in CH_x^o
         y = hydrogen: carbon atomic ratio in CH_y^* and CH_y^o
         z = fraction of carbon gasified as methane in reaction (7-24)
k_0, k_1, k_2 = first-order rate constants (s^{-1})
         m = $k_2/(k_1 + k_2)$

And Y = total carbon in adjusted methane-plus-ethane yields
        n_4 = total coal hydrogen gasified at any time (in g-atom/g-atom feed carbon)
        n_4^o = total coal hydrogen gasified during primary devolatilization (in g-atom/g-atom feed carbon)

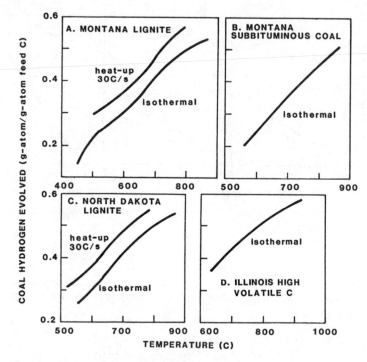

Figure 7-14. Coal-hydrogen evolution during gasification of different coals.

Using the previous model the rate of Reaction 7-23 is assumed to be limiting, with the rate of Reaction 7-24 being very fast. The ratio k_2/k_1 is assumed to be temperature independent. Using these definitions the conversion factor, f, of the semi-char, CH_x^o, to the active intermediate, CH_y^*, is expressed by the relationship:

$$f = \frac{Y}{m_\lambda} = \frac{n_H - n_H^o}{(x - y + my)\lambda} \tag{7-25}$$

Where λ is the fraction of total feed carbon not evolved as primary devolatilization products (closely related to fixed carbon) (in g-atom/g-atom feed carbon).

From Equation (7-24) of the methane-plus-ethane yield, Y, is related to coal hydrogen evolved through the following expressions:

$$Y = \frac{m(n_H - n_H^o)}{(x - y + my)} \tag{7-26A}$$

$$\text{or } Y = S(n_H - n_H^o) \tag{7-26B}$$

$$\text{where } S = \frac{m}{(x - y + my)} \tag{7-27}$$

Equation 7-26B is consistent with the trends shown in Figure 7-13. The slopes, S, of these lines are tabulated in Table 7-13, and the value of n_H^o estimated from Figure 7-13 is about 0.27, corresponding to the value of coal hydrogen evolved due to primary devolatilization reactions. The following independent relationship is obtained from the model

$$Y\left(\frac{1}{S - Z}\right) = \lambda(x - z) \tag{7-28}$$

where z is the hydrogen: carbon atomic ratio in the coal at a given time during gasification. Values of m can be computed as a function of pressure by rearranging Equation 7-27:

$$m = \frac{S(x - y)}{1 - Sy} \tag{7-29}$$

with a value of $y = 0.1$ assumed as a nominal average value based on gasification data for different coals at elevated temperatures. Values of m and corresponding values of k_2/k_1 are given in Table 7-14.

Table 7-13
Variation in S with Hydrogen Pressure

Hydrogen Pressure [atm (bar)]	S (g-atom Carbon/ g-atom Hydrogen)
18 (18.2)	0.24
35 (35.5)	0.41
52 (52.7)	0.56

Table 7-14
Variation of m and k_2/k_1 with Hydrogen Pressure

Hydrogen Pressure [atm (bar)]	m	k_2/k_1
18 (18.2)	0.127	0.145
35 (35.5)	0.225	0.290
52 (52.7)	0.307	0.443

The relationship between k_2/k_1 and hydrogen pressure is linear and can be expressed by:

$$\frac{k_2}{k_1} = 0.0083 \ P_H \tag{7-30}$$

where P_H is hydrogen partial pressure (in atm). The methane-plus-ethane yield is related to the conversion factor, f, of the semi-char through the relationship:

$$Y = m\lambda f = \frac{0.00664 P_H}{1 + 0.0083 P_H} \ f \tag{7-31}$$

The following assumptions are applied to evaluating the kinetic constants for the reaction scheme in Equation 7-23:

1. The compound CH_x^o reacts according to Equation 7-23 by a first-order process, where there is a distribution of activation energies for the first-order rate constant, k_o.
2. The activation energies' distribution function is a constant, i.e., $f(E)dE$ = fraction of total carbon in which the activation energy, E, in the rate constant $k_0 = k_0^0 \exp(-E/RT)$

where $f(E) = 0$ for $E < E_0$
$f(E) = C$ (constant) for $E_0 < E < E_1$
$f(E) = 0$ for $E > E_1$
k_0^0 = preexponential factor (s^{-1}) is between E and $(E+ dE)$.

Thus, we note that

$$\int_{E_0}^{E_1} CdE = 1$$

then

$$C = \frac{1}{E_1 - E_0}$$

Making use of the aforementioned assumptions, the average conversion factor of CH_x^o is expressed by the following relationship for any time-temperature history:

$$1 - f = \frac{1}{E_1 - E_0} \int_{E_0}^{E_1} \left(\exp\left[-k_o^0 \int_{E_0}^{\theta} \left(-\frac{E}{RT} \right) d\theta \right] \right) dE \tag{7-32}$$

For the appropriate time-temperature history then,

$$k_0^0 = 1.97 \ (10^{-10}) \ (s^{-1})$$
$$E_0 = 40.8 \ KCal/g\text{-}mol$$
$$E_1 = 62.9 \ KCal/g\text{-}mol$$

The theoretical implications concerning the detailed mechanisms of coal-hydrogen evolution during secondary devolatilization, seems straightforward based on the values of k_0, E_0, and E_1 given in the preceding notation; however, such considerations should be made with caution.

Simultaneous to the occurrence of devolatilization in the presence of a gas containing hydrogen at an elevated pressure, in addition to thermal pyrolysis reactions, there are coals or coal chars containing volatile matter exhibiting a high, although transient, reactivity for methane formation. However, it has been shown that rapid-rate methane formation occurs at a rate that is at least an order of magnitude slower than devolatilization. When a coal or coal char containing volatile matter is subjected to an elevated temperature, a series of complex physical and chemical changes occur in the coal's structure, accompanied by thermal pyrolysis reactions which result in devolatilization of certain coal components. The amount of carbon gasified to methane during the transient high reactivity increases significantly with increases in hydrogen partial pressure. Above approximately 1700°F the transient reactivity for rapid rate methane formation exists only briefly. For coals or coal chars prepared in inert atmospheres this time frame is on the order of a few seconds.

When stages of devolatilization and rapid-rate methane formation are over, char gasification occurs at a relatively slow rate. Several models to describe the gasification kinetics of this material for various limited ranges of conditions have been proposed.[27,28] The differential rates of reaction of devolatilized coal chars are a function of temperature, pressure, gas composition, carbon conversion, and prior history.

NOMENCLATURE

b	kinetic parameter in Equation 7-14
C	concentration
E	activation energy
f_R	reactivity factor
K, K_A, K_B	overall rate constants
k_0, k_1, k_2	rate constants
k_o	preexponential factor
k_c	overall mass transfer coefficient
M	effective char composition
n	number of moles

P   partial pressure
R   universal gas law constant
T   absolute temperature
t   temperature
V_r' volume of reactive volatiles
x   conversion factor

Greek Symbols

θ dimensionless temperature
λ fraction of total feed carbon not evolved as primary devolatilization products

REFERENCES

1. Mangold, E. C., et al., *Coal Liquefaction and Gasification Technologies,* Ann Arbor Science Pub., Ann Arbor, MI (1982).

2. Allen, D. W., and W. H. Yeu, "Methanator Design and Operations," *Chem. Eng. Prog.,* 69(1): 75-79 (1973).

3. Atlantic Research Corp., "Development of Coatings for Protection of Coal During Transport and Storage," COO-4632-2, prepared for the U.S. Department of Energy (1978).

4. Continental Oil Co., "Phase I: The Pipeline Gas Demonstration Plant. Design and Evaluation of Comercial Plant, Vols. 1-4," prepared for the U.S. Dept. of Energy, FE-2542-10 (1979).

5. Continental Oil Co., "Phase I: The Pipeline Gas Demonstration Plant. Technical Support Program Report," FE-2542-13, prepared for the U.S. Dept. of Energy (1979).

6. Covell, R. B., and M. J. Hargrove, "Power Cycle Evaluation of the C-E Coal Gasification," paper presented at the American Power Conference (April 1979).

7. Dravo Corp., *Handbook of Gasifiers and Gas Treatment Systems,* FE-1772-11, prepared for the U.S. Energy Research Agency (1976).

8. Fluor Engineers and Construction, Inc., "Economic Studies of Coal Gasification Combined Cycle Systems for Electric Power Generation," EPRI AF-642, prepared for the Electric Power Research Institute (1978).

9. Fluor Engineers and Construction, Inc., "Economics of Texaco Gasification Combined Cycle Systems," EPRI AF-753, prepared for the Electric Power Research Institute (1978).

10. MITRE Corp., "Compilation and Evaluation of Leaching Test Methods," MTR-7758, prepared for the U.S. Environmental Protection Agency (1978).

11. MITRE Corp., "Environmental Data for Energy Policy Analysis. Volume I: Summary," M78-74, prepared for the U.S. Dept. of Energy (1978).

12. Patterson, R. C., "Coal Gasification for Power Plant Fuel," paper presented at the VGB Conference on Gasification of Coal in Power Engineering (March 1979).

13. Patterson, R. C., and S. L. Darling, "A Low Btu Coal Gasification System," paper presented at the 72nd Annual Meeting of the AIChE (November 1979).

14. "R&D Status Report: British Gas Corporation Slagging Gasifier," *EPRI J.* (January/February 1979).

15. Savage, P. R., "Slagging Gasifier Aims for SNG Market," *Chem. Eng.*, 84 (19): 108–109 (1977).

16. Sudbury, J. D., "A Demonstration of the Slagging Gasifier," in proceedings of the Eighth Synthetic Pipeline Gas Symposium (1978).

17. TRW, "Environmental Assessment Data Base for High-Btu Gasification Technology: Volume II. Appendices A, B, and C," EPA-600/7-78-186b, prepared for the U.S. Environmental Protection Agency (1978).

18. TRW, "Environmental Assessment Data Base for High-Btu Gasification Technology: Volume II. Appendices D, E, and F," EPA-600/7-78-186c, prepared for the U.S. Environmental Protection Agency (1978).

19. Wilson, H. S., "Procedures for Coal Storage at Industrial Plants," *Plant Engineering* (June 23, 1977), p. 121.

20. Kraayveld, H. J., and M. J. van der Burgt, "Technical and Economic Prospects of the Shell-Koppers Coal Gasification Process," paper presented at the 175th American Chemistry Society National Meeting, Industrial and Engineering Division, Anaheim, CA (1978).

21. Bloom, R., Jr., "The Illinois Coal Gasification Group Project Incorporating the COGAS Process," paper presented at the American Gas Association Eighth Synthetic Pipeline Gas Symposium, Chicago, IL (October 1976).

22. Bloom, R., Jr., and L. I. Wisdom, "Chemical Feedstocks from Coal," paper presented at the meeting of the American Institute of Chemical Engineers, Houston, TX (April 1-6, 1979).

23. Blackwood, J. D., and D. J. McCarthy, *Aust. J. Chem. Eng.*, 20 (9): 2,003–2,004 (1967).

24. Mosley, F., and D. Patterson, *J. Inst. Fuel;* 38 (288): 13–23 (1965).

25. Johnson, J. L., *Amer. Chem. Soc.*, Div. Fuel Chem., Prepr.; 18 (1): 228–268 (April 8, 1973).

26. Feldkirchner, H. L., E. J. Pyrcioch, and E. B. Shultz, *Chem. Eng. Prog.*, Symp. Series; 57 (34): 73–80 (1961).

27. Wen, C. Y. and J. Huebler, *Ind. Eng. Chem.*, Prod. Res. Develop., 4 (2): 142–147 (1965).

28. Feldkirchner, H. L., and J. Heubler, *Ind. Eng. Chem.*, Prod. Res. Develop., 4 (2): 134–142 (1965).

8

Coal Liquefaction

CONTENTS

INTRODUCTION, 312

HYDRODYNAMICS OF THREE-PHASE FLUIDIZATION, 312

Pressure Drop, 313
Solids Holdup and Bed Expansion, 314
Gas and Liquid Holdups, 317
Bubble Properties, 317
Heat and Mass Transfer Characteristics, 318

MAJOR LIQUEFACTION PROCESSES, 318

Exxon Donor Solvent (EDS), 318
H-Coal Process, 326
Solvent Refined Coal Process, 328
Fischer-Tropsch Synthesis, 332
Zinc Halide Hydrocracking Process, 336
Mobile Gasoline Synthesis, 337

NOMENCLATURE, 342

REFERENCES, 342

INTRODUCTION

Three ranks of coal are considered for gasification and liquefaction feedstock; namely: bituminous, subbituminous and lignite. Although the synthetic fuels technologies have been under development for decades, the economics justifying commercialization have been questionable. Until petroleum prices soared in the early and late 1970s, there had been little incentive to accelerate development programs beyond that of an orderly research and development activity. With the projection of stable petroleum prices through the 1980s, development activities in liquefaction are likely to be at a subdued pace. One point, however, must be emphasized—until government policies are firmly established and financial incentives are provided, economic and construction estimates for commercial-scale operations in the United States and Europe will remain indefinite.

The applications of synthetic fuels are diverse and include synthetic pipeline gas; light hydrocarbon gas petrochemical feedstocks; gasoline for motor fuel; intermediate distillate fuels; heavy boiler fuel oils or solids; chemicals, including benzene, xylene, toluene, and phenols; intermediate- and low-Btu gaseous fuels for boilers and various processes; fuel gas for specialized applications, such as combined cycle power plants; and chemical synthesis gas for metallurgical ore reduction, refinery processes, ammonia, and methanol synthesis, and hydrogen production.

This chapter provides an overview of coal liquefaction technology. Since some potential processes involve a three-phase reaction system, a review of hydrodynamic principles is presented first.

HYDRODYNAMICS OF THREE-PHASE FLUIDIZATION

The term "three-phase fluidization" requires explanation, as it can be used to describe a variety of different operations. The three phases are gas, liquid, and particulate solids, although recently investigations have focused on using two immiscible liquids and particulate solids. As in the case of a fixed-bed operation, both cocurrent and countercurrent gas-liquid flow can exist, and for each of these, both bubble flow, in which the liquid is the continuous phase and the gas dispersed, and trickle flow, in which the gas forms a continuous phase and the liquid is more or less dispersed, take place.

A well-established device for countercurrent trickle flow, in which low-density solid spheres are fluidized by an upward current of gas and irrigated by a downward flow of liquids, is variously known as the turbulent bed contactor, mobile bed contactor and fluidized packing contactor, or the "turbulent contact absorber" when it is specifically used for gas absorption and/or dust removal. A more recent variation is the three-phase spouted bed contactor.

Bubble flow, whether cocurrent or countercurrent, is conveniently subdivided into two modes: Liquid-supported solids are the main mode in which the liquid exceeds the minimum liquid-fluidization velocity; bubble-supported solids are the second mode in which the liquid is below its minimum fluidization velocity or is even stationary and serves mainly to transfer to the solids the momentum and potential energy of the gas bubbles, thus suspending the solids.

Countercurrent bubble flow with liquid-supported solids, which can be affected by downward liquid fluidization of particles having a density lower than that of the liquid, has been referred to as "inverse three-phase fluidization." The mass transfer potential of such a countercurrent operation is worthy of study, especially for cases in which dispersion of the gas rather than the liquid is called for and the required gas-liquid ratio and throughputs can be effected without flooding. In contrast, the corresponding cocurrent mode has received more attention than all other cases and constitutes the majority of the literature on three-phase fluidization.

Pressure Drop

For gas-liquid fluidization, the total axial pressure gradient at any bed level is simply the bed weight per unit volume at that level:

$$- \frac{dP}{dz} = (\epsilon_s \varrho_s + \epsilon_\ell \varrho_\ell + \epsilon_g \varrho_g)g \tag{8-1}$$

where the individual phase holdups are interrelated as:

$$\epsilon_s + \epsilon_\ell + \epsilon_g = 1 \tag{8-2}$$

Subscripts s, ℓ, g refer to solid, liquid, and gas, respectively. The total pressure drop across a bed of height H is:

$$- \Delta P = g \int_0^H (\epsilon_s \varrho_s + \epsilon_\ell \varrho_\ell + \epsilon_g \varrho_g)dz \tag{8-3}$$

where $\epsilon_g \varrho_g$ usually can be neglected relative to the other terms. When the liquid is the continuous phase, the dynamic pressure gradient can be measured using a differential manometer where the total pressure gradient is corrected for the hydrostatic head of the liquid:

$$- \frac{dP}{dz} = \left(- \frac{dp}{dz}\right) - \varrho_\ell g \tag{8-4}$$

Substituting Equations 8-1 and 8-2 into Equation 8-3 gives:

$$- \frac{dP}{dz} = [\epsilon_s(\varrho_s - \varrho_\ell) - \epsilon_g(\varrho_\ell - \varrho_g)]g \tag{8-5}$$

when $\epsilon_g = 0$, $\epsilon_s = 1 - \epsilon_\ell$ and Equation 8-5 reduces to:

$$- \frac{dP}{dz} = \epsilon_s(\varrho_s - \varrho_\ell)g = (1 - \epsilon_\ell)(\varrho_s - \varrho_\ell)g \tag{8-6}$$

The frictional pressure gradient is the total pressure gradient corrected for the hydrostatic head of two-phase fluid:

$$- \frac{dP_f}{dz} = \left[- \frac{dP}{dz} \right] - \varrho_f g \tag{8-7}$$

where ϱ_f is the composite fluid density given by:

$$\varrho_f = \frac{\epsilon_\ell \varrho_\ell + \epsilon_g \varrho_g}{\epsilon_\ell + \epsilon_g} = \frac{\epsilon_\ell \varrho_\ell + \epsilon_g \varrho_g}{1 - \epsilon_s} \tag{8-8}$$

Substituting for ϱ_f into Equation 8-6 gives:

$$- \frac{dP_f}{dz} = \left[- \frac{dP}{dz} \right] - \frac{\epsilon_\ell \varrho_\ell + \epsilon_g \varrho_g}{1 - \epsilon_s} g \tag{8-9}$$

The integral form of this expression, neglecting $\epsilon_g \varrho_g$ relative to $\epsilon_\ell \varrho_\ell$ can be used for expressing pressure drop. Substituting Equations 8-1 and 8-7 into Equation 8-8 yields:

$$- \frac{dP_f}{dz} = \epsilon_s (\varrho_s - \varrho_f) g = (\varrho_s - \varrho_f) g \tag{8-10}$$

which has the same form as Equation 8-5, to which it reduces identically in the absence of gas.

Equations 8-1, 8-4, and 8-9 are based on the assumptions that

1. The buoyed weight of the solid particles is supported by the upward fluid drag on these particles
2. The flow of gas causes negligible additional losses by friction
3. Wall friction is negligible

In addition, radial pressure gradients are commonly assumed to be small relative to axial gradients, so that the pressure drop experienced by each fluid phase is essentially the same.

The frictional pressure gradient at minimum fluidization is given by Equation 8-10, with $\epsilon = \epsilon_{mf}$. The upward liquid superficial velocity required to initiate fluidization in the presence of an upward gas flow is lower than in its absence.

Solids Holdups and Bed Expansion

The solids holdup, ϵ_s, is defined as the volume fraction of the fluidized bed occupied by particulate solids, and can therefore be expressed in terms of the expanded bed height:

$$\epsilon_s = \frac{dm/dz}{\varrho_s A_b} \tag{8-11A}$$

and for the bed as a whole by:

$$\epsilon_s = \frac{M}{\varrho_s A_b H} \tag{8-11B}$$

where a uniform solids density, ϱ_s, and a column of constant cross-sectional area, A_b, are assumed. The upper bed surface is distinctly defined, as occurs when relatively coarse and/or dense solids are used. Then H can be measured by direct visual observation or from pressure drop profile data over the column height. For finer and/or lighter solids (e.g., glass beads smaller than 1 mm and fluidized by air or water), the upper bed surface becomes increasingly diffuse at higher fluid flow rates, primarily due to particle entrainment, but also due to stratification of solids by size where a significant particle size variation exists. A reproducible value of H then can be obtained as the intersection of two straight lines, one of positive slope representing the pressure drop profile in the homogeneous portion of the three-phase bed, and the other of negative slope representing the pressure drop profile in the solids-free two-phase region above the bed.

A procedure for measuring ϵ_s locally, thus avoiding the use of Equation 8-11B and the necessity for estimating H, is presented by Begovich and Watson.[2] The method depends on a local measurement of ϵ_ℓ using an electroconductivity technique, and on the local pressure gradient via a pressure profile. Equations 8-1 and 8-2 are then solved simultaneously for ϵ_g and ϵ_s. For a known bed solids mass, M, a check on the local values of ϵ_s can be obtained by integrating Equation 8-11A as follows:

$$\int_0^\infty \epsilon_s dz = \frac{1}{\varrho_s A_b} \int_0^M dm = \frac{M}{\varrho_s A_b} \tag{8-12}$$

Under certain circumstances, the introduction of gas to a liquid-fluidized bed or the increase of gas velocity to a gas-liquid fluidized bed results in a contraction of the bed. This counterintuitive observation has intrigued many investigators and undoubtedly has prompted more studies on bed expansion and solids holdup than on any other aspect of three-phase fluidization. The explanation lies in the fact that some of the liquid that otherwise would give support to the solid particles is diverted to the solids-deficient wakes behind the gas bubbles. (Two models of such wakes have been proposed by Darton and Harrison.[3,4,5]) When the wake flux is large relative to the remaining liquid flux, as in the case of small and/or light particles in viscous liquids, the resulting contraction effect usually overrides the expansion caused by the presence of the gas bubbles. When the bubble wake flux is relatively small, as for large and/or heavy particles in nonviscous liquids, the expansion effect tends to predominate. For glass beads in water as the continuous phase, the transition particle size is about 3 mm when the dispersed fluid is a gas and somewhat smaller when the dispersed fluid is either kerosene or toluene. Other three-phase systems show different transition sizes.

The behavior for wettable solids can be rationalized most consistently by the "generalized wake model" of Bhatia and Epstein,[6,7] which can be reduced to:

$$1 - \epsilon_s = \left[\frac{U_\ell - U_g k''(1 - x)}{V_\ell(1 - \epsilon_g - k''\epsilon_g)}\right]^{1/n} \times$$

$$[1 - \epsilon_g(1 + k' - k'x)] + \epsilon_g(1 + k' - k'x) \qquad (8\text{-}13)$$

where $k'' = \epsilon_\ell/\epsilon_g$
$\quad\quad\quad x = \epsilon_{s\ell}/\epsilon_{sf}$
$\quad\quad\quad u_\ell, u_g$ = liquid and gas superficial velocities, respectively

Many investigators, after measuring ϵ_s and ϵ_g, have calculated k'' from Equation 8-13 on the assumption that $x = 0$, for which the expression reduces to an equation derived by Darton and Harrison:[5]

$$\epsilon_i = \left[\frac{U_\ell - k''U_g}{V_\ell}\right]^{1/n} (1 - \epsilon_g - k''\epsilon_g)^{1-1/n} + k''\epsilon_g \qquad (8\text{-}14)$$

To avoid this arbitrary assumption, El-Temtamy and Epstein[8] computed k'' by treating each bubble wake as the sphere-completing volume of a spherical-cap bubble in a viscous medium with due allowance being made for the hydrodynamic interaction between bubbles. The partition coefficient, x, was then calculated from Equation 8-13. By applying this procedure to a large amount of experimental data on wettable solids, the following empirical, but rational correlation for x was generated:

$$x = 1 - 0.877\frac{V_1}{U_{g\ell}} (0 \leq U_{g\ell} \leq 1.14) \qquad (8\text{-}15A)$$

and when $x = 0$,

$$V_1/U_{g\ell} > 1.14 \qquad (8\text{-}15B)$$

where V_1 = Richardson-Zaki intercept for liquid fluidization
$\quad\quad\quad U_{g\ell}$ = velocity of gas relative to liquid

Equations 8-13, 8-15A and 8-15B have been used to predict the initial expansion or contraction characteristics not only of relatively large and/or heavy particles (e.g., water-fluidized glass beads 1 mm or larger) for which $x \simeq 0$, but also of finer and/or lighter particles for which $0 < x < 1$. Equation 8-13 can be used to predict solids holdup for three-phase fluidization. A simpler approach to the prediction of solids holdup is through the use of empirical equations for ϵ_s or $\epsilon(= 1 - \epsilon_s)$ as a function of fluid fluxes and particle and fluid properties. A more fruitful approach is the use of Equation 8-13, with further refinements on the methods for predicting k'' and x, as well as the gas holdup, ϵ_g.

Gas and Liquid Holdups

If the solids holdup is known (from Equation 8-11B), then a pressure gradient measurement allows simultaneous solution of Equations 8-1 and 8-2 for ϵ_g and ϵ_ℓ. A point-bed-density measurement can be used instead of the pressure gradient. One simple, but elegant method for arriving at ϵ_g employed by El-Temtamy[9] involves measuring the pressure gradient for the three-phase, solid-liquid bed at the same level H (and, therefore, of ϵ_s) using differential manometry. The three-phase pressure gradient, given by Equation 8-5 is substracted from the two-phase gradient, given by Equation 8-6, and the result is $\epsilon_g(\varrho_\ell - \varrho_g)$, from which ϵ_g can be determined. The liquid holdup is, of course, $1 - \epsilon_g - \epsilon_s$.

A more direct method of measuring ϵ_g in the test section is by simultaneously shutting two quick-closing valves and measuring the fraction of the isolated volume occupied by the gas. A precaution must be taken not to include the two-phase gas-liquid volume above the three-phase bed in the isolated section. Other methods of measuring ϵ_g that do not require knowledge of ϵ_s are the use of electroresistivity (or impedance) probes, which yield local measurements of ϵ_g. Alternatively, measurements of ϵ_ℓ may be effected by the electroconductivity technique. The electroconductivity and electroresistivity methods offer the greatest promise.

The most interesting generalization on gas holdup in three-phase liquid-supported beds is that ϵ_g for relatively small particles is lower than ϵ_g for the corresponding (same u_ℓ and u_g) solids-free system, while the reverse is the case for relatively large particles. Characteristics of three-phase and two-phase (gas-liquid) systems are alternated as the liquid flux is increased, i.e., as the bed is expanded, it becomes more dilute in solids. These phenomena are directly related to bubble characteristics.

Bubble Properties

The most striking effects of introducing fluidized solids to an upward-flowing two-phase gas-liquid system are the enhanced bubble growth, which occurs in beds of fine particles, and the increased bubble splitting, which takes place in beds of coarse particles, especially at low bed expansions. The bubble growth effect has been attributed to the fact that when the solid particles are much smaller than the bubbles, a liquid-fluidized bed behaves as a pseudohomogeneous medium having both density and viscosity greater than the density and viscosity of the pure liquid. The bubble disintegration phenomenon has provoked more controversy. Lee et al.[10] state that when the solid particles are similar in size to that of the bubbles, the latter will break up if the particles have sufficient inertia to penetrate the roof of a bubble. The numerical criterion for bubble breaking is that the Weber number, We = $\varrho_s V_b^2 d_p / \sigma$, exceeds about 3. However, different theories have been presented by different investigators.

Heat and Mass Transfer Characteristics

The difference between bubble-coalescing and bubble-disintegrating systems is given by the experimental data of Ostegaard and Suchozebriski[11] on volumetric liquid-phase mass transfer coefficients, $k_\ell a'$, for gas-liquid mass transfer. These data, especially for the larger particles, are in agreement with those of many subsequent studies, most recently with those of Dhanuka and Stepanek.[12,13] According to Nishikawa et al.[14] $k_\ell a'$ for cocurrent gas-liquid spouting of solids is considerably larger than for cocurrent gas-liquid fluidization of solids at comparable conditions of operation.

The volumetric mass transfer coefficient for the dispersed fluid phase has been evaluated along with that of the continuous phase only in the recent liquid-liquid-solid study of Roszak and Gawronski.[15] Solid-liquid mass transfer in three-phase fluidized beds, unlike gas-liquid transfer, has barely been investigated.

For a wall-to-bed heat transfer at low bed expansions, the heat transfer coefficient for a liquid-fluidized bed increases significantly upon the introduction of gas bubbles, presumably due to the stirring effect of the latter. As the gas rate increases the heat transfer coefficient eventually reaches a maximum value.

There are no reported studies of gas-liquid or particle-liquid heat transfer in three-phase fluidized beds, although the mass-heat transfer analogy can be used to generate credible values of volumetric heat transfer coefficients where the corresponding mass transfer coefficients have been determined, as in the gas-liquid case. Further discussions and additional references are given by Epstein.[16]

MAJOR LIQUEFACTION PROCESSES

Exxon Donor Solvent (EDS)

A schematic of the EDS process is shown in Figure 8-1. Feed coal is crushed, dried, and slurried with the hydrogen donor solvent. The role of the solvent is to disperse the coal and transport it through the liquefaction system and to donate hydrogen to the coal to promote liquefaction. The slurry is heated, mixed with hydrogen, and fed into a simple upward plug flow reactor, where it is maintained at constant temperature for a given residence time. The reactor effluent is separated by a series of distillation steps into the donor solvent (which is recycled), light hydrocarbon gases, naphtha, and medium and heavy distillate oils. A heavy vacuum bottoms stream, containing liquids with a boiling point exceeding 1000°F (538°C), unconverted coal, and coal mineral matter, contains half of the weight of the feed coal. Recycle solvent is hydrogenated in a fixed-bed catalytic reactor with conventional petroleum technology using commercially available catalysts. Separation of solvent hydrogenation from coal processing is a unique feature in this process. It prolongs catalyst lifetime by treating a distillate oil which avoids contact with the catalyst-poisoning contaminants in the coal.

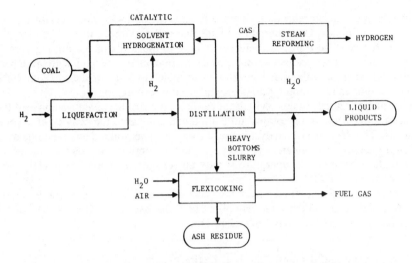

Figure 8-1. Exxon donor solvent process.

The heavy vacuum bottoms stream is processed to produce additional liquids and a low-Btu fuel gas for plant operations. An Exxon commercial petroleum process, Flexicoking, is being adapted to process residual liquids from coal liquefaction. All of the organic material in the bottoms is recovered as liquid product or combustible gases. Hydrogen for the process can be produced by steam reforming of light hydrocarbons produced in the liquefaction process, or partial oxidation of vacuum distillation tower bottoms or raw coal.[17]

The present configuration and process flow scheme were selected from general options on the basis of research performed in experimental equipment ranging in complexity from 100-cm^3 batch units to a continuous 0.5-ton/day (0.45-metric-ton/day) integrated pilot plant. The reactor configurations that were evaluated included stirred tank, recirculated tubular, ebullating bed, and tubular plug flow.

Several recycle solvents were evaluated on bituminous and subbituminous coals, with and without hydrogenation. Ranges of temperatures, pressures, and residence times were evaluated in both the liquefaction and solvent hydrotreating reactors. Based on the results, a hydrogenated recycle process was selected for further development using noncatalytic, tubular-plug-flow liquefaction reactors that eliminated the need for ash-tolerant catalysts. Vacuum distillation was identified as the most promising product separation technique.

During 1974 and 1975, the basic design of a 250-ton/day coal liquefaction pilot plant was established. A 1-ton/day pilot plant was constructed and initially operated. A supporting laboratory and engineering research and development program more closely defined operating conditions for the selected process. Data from the 1-ton/day pilot plant provided scale-up comparisons with smaller units on product yield, coal concentration in the feed slurry, and the effects of mixed-phase (hydrogen plus coal) preheating. Spent solvent feedstock was produced for hydro-treating experiments. Operational problems that had previously limited run lengths were overcome. These included slurry sticking to the walls of the mixing vessel, plugging of the slurry preheater, plugging of the liquefaction reactor with large particles, and wear on valves and nozzles. The high viscosity of the vacuum flash tower bottoms made pumping difficult and produced plugging.

A set of laboratory studies on hydrogenation of the recyle solvent established the effect of mass velocity on catalyst utilization and compared the activity of several catalysts. The decrease of catalyst activity with time was studied and methods used to restore activity investigated. A one-year catalyst lifetime can be obtained by increasing the operational temperature as the catalyst ages, a technique routinely used in the petroleum industry.

On the basis of data obtained from the processing of Illinois No. 6 and Wyoming subbituminous coals in the 1-ton/day pilot plant, the issues identified as critical for the design of the 250-ton/day pilot plant are:

1. Preheating and drying of the liquefaction reactor feed slurry
2. Erosion and entrainment in the vacuum flash separator
3. Corrosion resistance of metals and erosion of pressure letdown valves
4. Design of an onstream solids withdrawal system to prevent reactor plugging by large solids particles

Heating of the coal feed slurry produces complex heat transfer problems that are difficult to model mathematically. Consequently, scale-up of the heater design to a larger size is difficult. Scale-up of the vacuum flash separator is complicated by the entrainment of higher boiling liquids and solids in the lighter boiling liquid vapors. The tower diameter and size of the transfer line to the vacuum tower were varied to study erosion and entrainment effects. Erosion by the abrasive slurry is a design problem requiring features such as tungsten carbide coatings in the pressure letdown valves between the high-pressure liquefaction reactor and the atmospheric fractionation tower. A cold-flow model of the liquefaction reactor was used to identify design parameters associated with particle size distribution and withdrawal rate and frequency.

Processing results have shown that the EDS process can be applied to a wide variety of coal types, including bituminous, subbituminous, and lignites. Illinois No. 6 bituminous coal and Wyoming subbituminous were the initially specified project coals. Other coals have undergone evaluation in small pilot plants.

An analysis of the coals that have been processed in the pilot plant is given in Table 8-1, and their liquid yields are given in Table 8-2. Longer residence times in the reactor increase conversion of the coal to liquids, but also increase hydrocracking of the liquids to gas. As a result, there is an optimum processing time in the liquefaction reactor to maximize liquid yield, although additional liquids may be obtained by recycling or separately processing the bottoms via Flexicoking. The types of coal that produce high yields have low ash content, and contain high quantities of volatile matter, sulfur, and reactive fractions.

Table 8-1
Analyses of Feed Coals Run in RCLU[17]

Operating Parameters	Illinois No. 6 Bituminous		Pittsburgh Seam Bituminous		Australian Black bituminous	Wyoming Sub-bituminous	Texas Lignite	North Dakota Lignite
	Monterey No. 1	Burning Star No. 2	Ireland	Arkwright	Wandoan	Wyodak	Big Brown	Indian Head
Elemental analyses (dry wt %)								
Carbon	70.1	74.0	74.0	78.4	59.8	68.5	62.0	63.8
Hydrogen	5.1	4.9	5.2	5.4	5.0	4.9	4.8	4.7
Oxygen (by difference)	10.6	9.9	6.3	5.1	13.4	17.2	14.5	19.2
Nitrogen	1.2	1.2	1.2	1.5	0.7	1.1	1.1	0.9
Sulfur	4.1	3.1	4.3	2.3	0.3	0.5	1.2	1.2
Ash	8.9	10.5	9.0	7.3	20.8	7.8	16.4	10.2
Total	100.0	100.0	100.0	100.0	100.0	100.0	100.0	100.0
H/C atomic ratio	0.87	0.84	0.84	0.82	1.01	0.86	0.92	0.88
Ash (SO_3-free)	8.8	10.2	8.8	7.0	20.8	6.6	14.0	7.6
Total oxygen	15.1	14.9	10.0	8.5	26.3	23.4	23.8	26.0
Equilibrium moisture (wt %)	14.0	10.4	2.1	1.8	10.5	29.0		33.6
Proximate analyses (dry wt %)								
Volatile matter	42.1	39.0	39.1	36.8	44.6	45.5	44.4	44.1
Fixed carbon	49.0	51.2	51.9	55.9	34.6	46.7	39.2	45.7
Ash	8.9	10.5	9.0	7.3	20.8	7.8	16.4	10.2

Table 8-2
Highest Liquid Product Yields for EDS Program Coals at 1,500 psig[17]
(RCLU Data)

Operating Parameters		Coal						
	Arkwright	Ireland	Burning Star	Monterey	Wandoan	Wyodak	Big Brown	Indian Head
Liquefaction conditions								
Temperature (°F)	840	840	880	800	840	840	840	840
Residence time (min)	100	100	25	140	40	100	25	40
Number of conditions investigated	2	10	7	16	6	10	4	3
Liquefaction yields (lb/100 lb dry coal)								
Hydrogen	−4.2	−4.6	−3.4	−4.6	−3.1	−4.8	−3.1	−4.3
Water	4.6	6.0	8.2	9.8	10.6	15.1	10.4	17.5
Carbon oxides	1.1	1.4	1.5	0.6	3.2	5.8	6.8	7.9
Ammonia	0.7	0.6	0.6	0.7	0.3	0.5	0.4	0.6
Hydrogen sulfide	1.8	3.2	2.4	3.4	0.2	0.5	0.7	0.4
C_1–C_3 gas	13.5	13.5	9.5	9.0	7.1	10.1	6.2	6.8
C_4–1000°F liquid	29.9	32.7	30.4	36.1	27.7	30.9	28.0	28.1
1000°F conversion (lb/100 lb dry coal)	47.4	52.8	49.2	55.0	46.0	58.1	49.4	57.0
Liquid product selectivity (wt %)								
C_4–400°F naphtha	73.2	71.6	48.0	62.7	66.7	80.1	57.6	68.5
C_4–1000°F liquids								

The percentage of volatile material in the coal is the most important coal property used to predict the liquid yield. In performing a single variable regression analysis, 88.5% of the variation about the mean can be removed using this single parameter. Bituminous coals give a total liquid yield of 43%–45%, subbituminous coals give 40% yield, and lignites produce 33%–35% liquid. The products that are produced have higher levels of nitrogen than similar fractions of petroleum and have sulfur levels in proportion to the original sulfur content of the coal. Both sulfur and nitrogen concentrations can be reduced by subsequent processing using standard petroleum hydrotreatment processes. The pilot-plant operations have shown that the younger subbituminous coals and lignites are more difficult to process due to the higher oxygen and organically associated calcium content. Formations of calcium carbonate deposits on the walls of the reactor have proven to be an operational problem. If not removed, these deposits can plug the reactor and foul downstream equipment. Large, solid particles must be periodically withdrawn from the liquefaction reactor, and chemical cleaning will be necessary during turnaround times. This mechanical method is preferred due to simplicity and more favorable economics. An alternate scheme involves pretreatment of the crushed coal with sulfur dioxide, which converts the calcium into calcium sulfate and consequently does not form reactor deposits under the EDS operating conditions. Another problem in processing the younger coals is the high viscosity of the coal liquefaction bottoms. Viscosity is a direct measure of the difficulty in pumping the bottoms from a vacuum fractionator into a coking or gasification reactor. The viscosity of the younger coals can adequately be reduced to pumpable levels by using longer liquefaction residence times.

The principal liquid products to be manufactured in the EDS commercial plant are liquefied petroleum gas, naphtha, and middle distillate to heavy fuel oils. The petroleum gases are a finished product; the naphtha is an unfinished feedstock for a downstream refinery/petrochemical plant; and the fuel oil is suitable for sale to customers having the facilities to receive, handle, and burn it. For Illinois coal, operation of the process at the preferred conditions would produce 37% of the total liquids in the form of 350°F (177°C) naphtha. A distillate fuel oil boiling in the 350°F–650°F (177°C–343°C) range would represent 24% of the liquid output, while 39% would be 650°F and above, heavy fuel oil. The distillate fuel oil and heavy fuel oil have been used in combustion tests to determine if environmental requirements are met and combustion properties are acceptable. Additional treatment, using available technology, will be required to remove nitrogen from the fuel oil to limit oxides of nitrogen emissions.

The use of EDS coal naphtha for reforming into high-octane gasoline blending feedstock will require single- or two-stage hydrotreating facilities to eliminate reforming catalyst poisoning by sulfur, oxygen, and nitrogen in the naphtha. The extent to which the heavy fuel oil market will receive competition from the direct combustion of coal is difficult to predict. Testing of the fuel oils is being performed to determine potential utilization as diesel and jet fuel or home heating oil and industrial fuel oil. High concentrations of aromatic compounds can cause fuel stability and combustion problems, requiring equipment modifications in some existing equipment and applications.

Because half of the coal feed emerges from the reactor as vacuum bottoms, the disposition of this high-ash product is an important process consideration. This stream contains one-third to one-half of the available carbon in the feed coal and will be used to achieve plant hydrogen and fuel balances for the overall process, to convert the available carbon into a useful form, and to minimize costs. Exxon Flexicoking is a commercial petroleum process that employs an integrated coking/gasification sequence in circulating fluidized beds. The heavy vacuum bottoms are fed to the Flexicoking unit with air and steam to produce additional distilled liquid products and a low-Btu fuel gas for the process furnaces. All of the organic material is recovered as a liquid product or combustible gases. Other potential candidates include the production of hydrogen and fuel gas, using either the Texaco or Shell-Koppers partial oxidation processes Another possibility is recycling the bottoms through the donor solvent process to produce additional liquids.

The technical issues on the disposition of the bottoms requiring further investigation are:

Coal Liquefaction Bottoms Properties	Process Development Issues
High ash/solids content	Gasifier slagging; particulate generation/control
High viscosity	Bottoms pumpability
Thermal instability	Feed control and distribution

A mathematical modeling effort has been a part of the hydrogen donor solvent development program. Simple empirical models have been developed to predict the product outputs of the development units as a function of process conditions, as well as a more fundamental model that analyzes the chemical reactions involved in the donor solvent process. The fundamental model

1. Permits correlation and prediction of differences in liquefaction yields due to variations in feed coals.
2. Provides better understanding of the chemistry of coal liquefaction.
3. Allows more precise prediction of the product distribution from coal liquefaction.

A complete model that would define the reaction paths of the individual molecular species and compute the reactions over a wide range of process conditions and hydrogenation feedstocks would be complex. By lumping similar reactions into classes of compounds, rate constants and activation energies have been determined that can predict the concentrations of the key components for typical reactor and catalytic hydrogenation conditions. The chemical species and reactions chosen are based on the known chemistry of coal, coal liquids, and donor solvents. From these reactions, rate equations are derived and integrated numerically to give concentrations of chemical species as a function of reaction time. The results of the calculations are compared to pilot-plant data, and the rate constants, activation energies, and equations adjusted to give a best fit of the data.

The code calculates a material balance summary for nine processing steps and prints out the contents of each stream. The streams are characterized in terms of the nine component fractions shown with representative percentage weight yields.

Fraction	Wt. %
Hydrogen	(−3.7)
C_1–C_3 gas	5.3
Chemical gases (H_2S,NH_3,CO,CO_2)	4.7
C_4-400°F (204°C), naphtha	17.9
400–700°F (204–371°C) liquids	7.6
700–1000°F (371–538°C) liquids	7.6
1000°F+ (538°C+) vacuum bottoms	52.0
Dry feed coal	(−100.0)
Water	8.6
Total	0.0

The yields are computed as a function of the following seven independent variables:

1. Liquefaction temperature
2. Liquefaction residence time
3. Solvent temperature
4. Solvent hydrogen partial pressure
5. Solvent hydrotreater space velocity
6. Solvent/coal ratio
7. Composition and amount of 1000°F (538°C) liquid in bottoms

Exercising the model has duplicated process development unit results and verified one of the strong features of the EDS process: the maximum yield of 400°F–1000°F (204°C–538°C) boiling temperature liquids is insensitive to process temperature. At any temperature in the range 800°F–860°F (426°C–460°C) a liquid yield of approximately 14% can be obtained if the proper liquefaction residence time is chosen. Another positive feature that can be demonstrated is that a wide range of product slates may be obtained by optimizing conditions in the liquefaction and solvent hydrogenation steps. This wide range of products is obtainable without employing extremes of operating conditions and is readily attainable using conventional equipment used in the petroleum processing industry.

A linear programming model based on pilot-plant experience has been used to study process alternatives and their complex interactions to maximize income from the sale of products, while minimizing processing costs and maintaining an optimum blend of product manufacture. The basic relations between product yield and reactor treatment conditions are programmed to evaluate alternative conversion processes for generating the hydrogen and fuel gas required for liquefaction. The possibilities studied included air and oxygen Flexicoking, partial oxidation, and moving-bed gasification of liquefaction bottoms or additional raw coal. The costs and yields of these processes and restrictions due to material balance, feed availability, product demands, equipment cost, and capacity are used by the model to optimize process options. The features of the model include:

- Computerized weight and energy balances
- Simultaneously balanced hydrogen, fuel gas, and bottoms disposition
- Definition of the utilities required for each case, with steam and electric power generation optimized
- Investment estimate calculated for each case
- Each case balanced to minimum overall cost
- Parametric examination of key variables, such as relative product values and volumes
- Feedstock flexibility, with coal available to generate hydrogen, fuel gas, power, and steam as well as feed for liquefaction
- Selection of optimum product slate as a function of price structure (potential products include naphtha, liquefied petroleum gas, low-sulfur fuel oil (several grades), high-, low- and medium-Btu fuel gas and vacuum bottoms)
- Modeling of byproduct processes for sour water stripping and recovery of ammonia, phenols, and sulfur
- Utility costs, including electric power, raw water, recirculating cooling water, demineralized boiler feed water, 600- and 150-psig steam generation costs and steam turbine drivers substituted for electric motors

The process-alternatives model has been used to defend the optimum plant configurations, to select the equipment sizes and to determine capital and operating costs of the configurations.

H-Coal Process[21-27]

The H-Coal process is a direct catalytic hydroliquefaction processing method for converting high-sulfur coal into either a heavy fuel oil that will meet environmental sulfur emission regulations or into a variety of liquid products considered equal to a synthetic crude oil. The process is characterized by an ebullating-bed reactor in which a slurry of coal and recycled oil is brought into direct contact with the catalyst. The reactor uses an upward flow of liquid and hydrogen to expand the catalyst bed and distribute the slurry, gas, and catalyst evenly across the reactor. The ebullating-bed reactor permits a moderate accumulation of solids to be present in the system without plugging the reactors, promotes optimum catalytic activity at a uniform temperature, and achieves a simple and economic equipment configuration for promoting the reactions that liquefy coal.

The H-Coal process was developed from previous work done by the developer, Hydrocarbon Research, Inc., on the liquefaction of petroleum residual oils and tar sands. The process, called H-Oil, utilizes a similar reactor, and has been in operation on a commercial scale for several years. The H-Coal process technically is a descendant of the Bergius process for direct catalytic hydrogenation, but employs a more effective catalyst and operates at lower pressure, with reduced hydrogen consumption.

The properties of the product liquid are determined by the residence time of the coal in the reactor and the amount of hydrogen consumed. Prolonged treatment conditions convert the product into lighter-weight hydrocarbons and remove greater quantities of sulfur and nitrogen. The processing capacity of the reactor decreases as the treatment time of the coal increases.

The H-Coal process is schematically shown in Figure 8-2. Coal is crushed, dried, and slurried with a recycle oil. The slurry is heated to a temperature below the 750°F (404°C) operational temperature of the reactor in a fuel gas-fired preheater and mixed with hydrogen. The reactor temperature is hotter because of heat released in the liquefaction process. The ebullating-bed reactor brings the coal into contact with a cobalt/molybdenum catalyst, where hydrogenation and cracking of the coal molecular structure take place. Sulfur, nitrogen, and oxygen are converted into hydrogen sulfide, ammonia, and water. The hydrocarbon products produced range from heavy fuel oil to naphtha and light gases, depending on the length of time spent in the reactor. Since the hydrogenation reactions are exothermic, the reactor temperature control is maintained at the optimum level by balancing the heat input from the entering preheater slurry and the output to the product separator. Circulation of the reacting mixture of gases, liquids, and solids in the reactor promotes constant reactor temperature, keeps the material in good contact with the catalyst bed, and prevents plugging by solid ash material and undissolved coal.

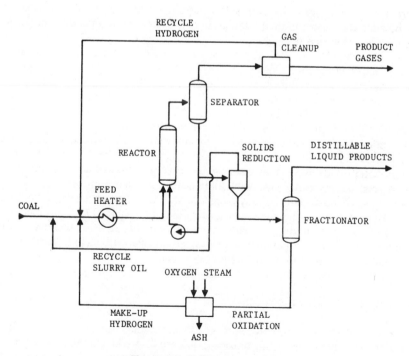

Figure 8-2. H-Coal process.[17]

The product mixture is depressurized into a product separator. A mixture of gases and hydrocarbon vapors is taken off at the top and a slurry of liquids, undissolved ash, and unconverted coal is removed from the bottom. The gases are sent to a recovery plant where hydrogen is separated for recycle to the preheater. Light hydrocarbon gases are removed into several product streams, and a fuel gas is produced for use in plant process heaters and for steam generation. Ammonia and hydrogen sulfide are sent to recovery plants to produce marketable sulfur and anhydrous ammonia. The slurry is depressured to flash into a vapor fraction and a liquid containing recycle oil, unreacted coal, and ash. The liquid is centrifugally separated into a high solids-content and a low solids-content stream in hydroclones. The low-solids stream is used as recycle oil and sent to the slurry preparation system. The high solids-content stream flows to an atmospheric distillation tower. The tower overhead is sent to a products fractionator with other liquid hydrocarbon streams. The bottoms from the atmospheric tower is sent to a vacuum distillation tower. The distillation tower separates hydrocarbon products from the bottoms, which consist of heavy hydrocarbon liquids, unreacted coal, and ash. The bottoms are fed into a partial oxidation unit with steam and oxygen, to produce makeup hydrogen from the process and a fuel gas. The coal ash is then rejected without having to be separated by filtration.

All process hydrocarbon liquids are separated into light gases, naphtha, distillate oil, and heavy fuel oil and subsequently processed with conventional petroleum refining technology to produce a marketable product. Additional hydrotreatment steps can reduce concentrations of sulfur, nitrogen, and oxygen. The product yield can be altered by varying the treatment in the reactor. More than 90% of the feed coal can be converted to liquids.

The advantage of the H-Coal technology is that it is based on a commercially proven petroleum technology that has been thoroughly tested at a size which is within the range of a commercial coal liquids plant. Much of the equipment development technology can be transferred to H-Coal, along with operating and control procedures that have been thoroughly tested. The H-Coal process has been tested successfully on many commercially important American coals.

The pilot plant now being completed at Catlettsburg, KY, will be the largest coal liquefaction plant built in the United States. Operation of the 200- to 600-ton/day facility will provide the data necessary to make a scale-up from a pilot plant to a full commercial facility using experience obtained in petroleum processing.

A proposal for a 50,000-bbl/day commercial H-Coal plant has been submitted to the DOE by Ashland Synthetic Fuels, a subsidiary of Ashland Oil. The objective of this program will be to design, plan, construct, and operate a commercial coal liquefaction plant under a commercialization group that will include corporations, representatives of utilities, and foreign organizations.

Solvent-Refined Coal Process[28-30]

The solvent-refined coal (SRC) process separates the combustible organic material in the coal from the sulfur, nitrogen, and ash to produce a higher-heat-content fuel that can be burned with minimum environmental treatment. Heat and pressure,

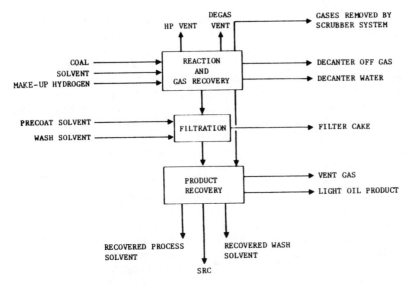

Figure 8-3. SRC process flowsheet.[17]

combined with the catalytic activity of minerals contained in the coal ash, are used to liquefy and desulfur the coal without the extra complicated steps of catalytic processes. Crushed coal is slurried with a recycled solvent having hydrogen donor properties. A schematic of the SRC process is shown in Figure 8-3. Hydrogen gas is added to the mixture, which is heated to 800°F (427°C) and fed into a dissolver operating at 1,400–2,500 psi (98.4–176 kg/cm²). More than 90% of the coal is dissolved in 30-60 min residence time in the preheater and dissolver. The degree of dissolution depends on the reactivity of the coal and competition from other reactions that depolymerize and hydrogenate the coal, hydrocrack the solvent to lower-molecular-weight hydrocarbons, and remove sulfur and oxygen by combination with hydrogen.

The dissolver product stream is depressurized and separated into its components, consisting of light hydrocarbon gases, excess hydrogen, dissolved coal, unreacted coal, and undissolved ash. The gases are scrubbed to remove hydrogen sulfide and carbon dioxide. Some of the hydrogen is separated and recycled to the preheater, while the rest forms a medium-Btu fuel gas for sale or plant process use. Undissolved coal and mineral matter are separated from the SRC solution by filtration. The filtered liquid is distilled to separate the 500°F–800°F (288°C–427°C) boiling point solvent from the SRC product, which is solidified by cooling. Light organic liquid and hydrocarbon gases are separated and recovered as byproducts.

The advantages of the SRC process are that more than 90% of the feed coal is processed into some form of usable fuel, with minimum consumption of hydrogen. The product can be a solid bottoms fraction from distillation, with a solidification temperature of 350°F (177°C), or hydrocracked and hydrotreated to produce heavy oils that are liquids at ambient temperatures. The treatment severity controls the amount of sulfur, oxygen, and nitrogen remaining in the product. Higher conversions reduce the concentrations of sulfur, nitrogen, and oxygen, but increase the hydrogen consumption and residence time in the reactor.

No expensive catalysts nor treatment steps that require additional equipment to handle catalysts are needed. The process does, however, require a reactive bituminous coal. Several bituminous coals have successfully been processed. The yield of SRC can be varied over a large range by varying process conditions. Thermal efficiencies are maximized at 67%–70% when the solvent-refined coal yield is between 15% and 45% of the dry coal feed rate.

The Wilsonville, AL, SRC pilot plant where pulverized coal to −200 mesh is mixed with a process-generated solvent in a slurry blend tank is illustrated in Figure 8-4. The boiling range of the solvent is 450°F–900°F (232°C–482°C). A hydrogen-rich gas may be added to the coal slurry before it enters the preheater, or hydrogen injection may occur between the preheater and the dissolver. The feed gas stream consists of scrubbed recycle gas plus sufficient makeup hydrogen to bring the overall gas composition to 85% hydrogen by volume. The coal slurry and gas are heated in a 600-ft-long (183 m) helical coil of 1.25-in. (3.2-cm) stainless steel pipe by an oil burner located at the bottom of the slurry preheater. The slurry leaving the preheater passes into a 1-ft (0.3 m) diameter, 23-ft (7 m) high dissolver which can be operated at 800°F–875°F (427°C–468°C) and 1,400–2,500 psi (98.4–176 kg/cm^2) and provide residence times of 0.5–1.5 hr.

Because the reactions (hydrogenation of the solvent and coal, hydrocracking of the solvent and coal into lower-molecular-weight compounds, formation of water) occurring in the dissolver are exothermic, the slurry increases in temperature over the value at the preheater discharge. A solids withdrawal system may be operated intermittently or continuously to control the dissolved solids accumulation.

The slurry is depressurized through high-pressure letdown valves into a flash tank, where vapors are separated. The slurry now proceeds to the most critical phase of the process where filtration of the SRC product is performed to separate the high-melting-point hydrocarbon from the ash and unreacted coal, which is in the form of micron-sized solid particles. Filter operations have proven to be the source of numerous mechanical problems and many plant shutdowns. A pressure-leaf filter is used with metal wire screens, having a filtration area of 100 ft^2 (9.3 m^2). The filter is operated at 480°F–580°F (249°C–304°C) and 150–200 psi (10.5–14 kg/cm^2), with a maximum pressure drop of 80 psi (5.6 kg/cm^2) between the slurry inlet and filtrate outlet. An automatic sequence of operations is performed.

1. Precoating of the filter with a high-boiling-point process solvent
2. Filtration of the slurry
3. Washing of the filter with 350°F–450°F (177°C–232°C) boiling-range solvent
4. Blowdown of the filter cake and depressurization with 200°F (92°C) nitrogen
5. Vacuum flash-drying to recover the solvent
6. Discharging of the filter cake
7. Repressurization

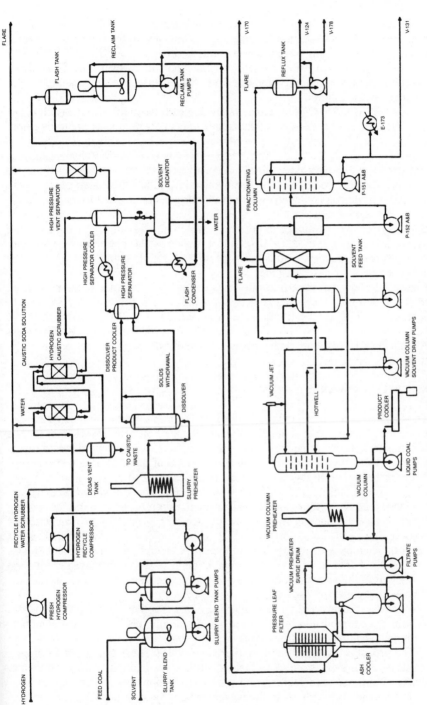

Figure 8-5. Simplified flowsheet for the SRC-II process.

The filtered solution is sent to a vacuum-column preheater to boost the temperature to 600°F (315°C). Recirculated solution is mixed with the filtrate and injected into the vacuum column, where the material is separated into liquid SRC that is drawn off at the bottom, solvent fractions, and vapors in the overhead. The column overhead vapors are condensed and sent with the solvent-decanter stream to a light-solvent recovery column.

Liquid SRC is fed to two vibrating, water-cooled trays in the product cooler. The SRC solidifies into brittle sheets that shatter into small fragments upon vibration. The fragmented SRC is conveyed to storage.

Vapor from the high-pressure vent separator contains 60%–80% hydrogen, plus hydrocarbon gases, hydrogen sulfide, and carbon dioxide. The hydrogen sulfide and carbon dioxide are removed by scrubbing with a dilute solution of caustic soda. Scrubbed recycle gas is blended with pure hydrogen compressed to the inlet pressure of the slurry preheater.

Solvent from the vacuum column is fractionated into a bottoms having a boiling range of 450°F–800°F (232°C–427°C) that is used as the recycle process solvent, and an overhead fraction with a boiling range of 350°F–450°F (177°C–232°C) that is used in filter cake washing.

Figure 8-5 shows an improved pilot-plant design (SRC-II) where the pulverized coal is slurried with unfiltered coal solution rather than with distilled solvent. In this case, the troublesome filters were bypassed. The ash was removed with the bottoms in a vacuum distillation step. The primary product of the SRC-II process was changed to a distillate with a reduced quantity of the solid fuel produced by SRC-I.

Fischer-Tropsch Synthesis[31,32,33]

The Fischer-Tropsch method of indirect hydrocarbon synthesis was originally developed in the 1920s, with commercial plants in operation before World War II. The German petroleum shortage during the war resulted in its greatest utilization, when nine plants using the technology accounted for 12% of the total peak German production of 100,000 bbl/day. By 1962 all of the plants had ceased production because of the availability and low cost of petroleum. The Union of South Africa, when faced with the need for an internal petroleum source, chose to further develop this technology. Production from the Sasol plant began in 1955. A production of 6,000 bbl/day from 6,600 ton/day (5,991 metric ton/day) of coal satisfied about 10% of the country's motor fuel requirements. A second plant, processing 38,000 ton/day (34,496 metric ton/day) began operation in 1980 and increased production to about half of the national consumption. A third plant is being planned as the second process design.

The process gasifies coal into a synthesis gas of carbon monoxide and hydrogen, cleans the gas of impurities, and feeds it into a catalytic reactor, where it combines into long-chain aliphatic hydrocarbons including gasoline, alcohol, waxes, oil, and gas. The products are separated and upgraded, with fuel gas being produced as a byproduct. Additional materials obtained during gasification include ammonia, phenols, sulfur, naphtha, coal tar, and oils. The reaction uses powdered iron catalysts in an Arge fixed bed or, in the newer units, a Synthol entrained-bed reactor.

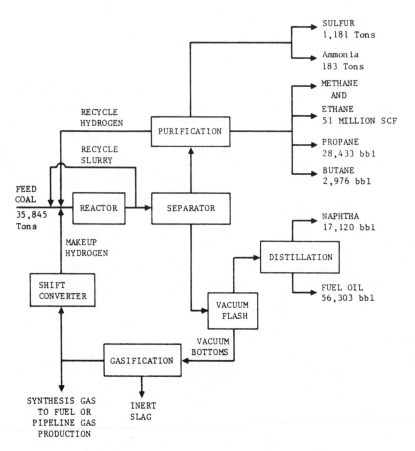

Figure 8-4. Flowsheet for Wilsonville SRC plant.[17]

Advantages of the process include the avoidance of many problems associated with coal handling in the early stages of direct liquefaction by converting it into synthesis gas. Other types of organic matter that could be gasified are also potential feedstock material. A broad range of products is produced from the reactor, some of which do not have ready markets when produced in large quantities. The yield of gasoline and motor fuels per ton of coal consumed is relatively low, and the gasification step and high heat rejection during catalytic synthesis results in a low thermal efficiency.

The coal gasification section of the Fischer-Tropsch plant consists of:

• Coal storage and handling
• Lurgi gasifiers
• Raw gas shift and cooling

- Gas purification
- Gas liquor separation
- Sulfur, phenol, and ammonia recovery

A heavy hydrocarbon recovery unit is used to remove heavy hydrocarbons from the Fischer-Tropsch synthesis purge gas to meet methanation feedstock specifications. A low-temperature heptane wash was selected because of the CO_2 content of the gas.

The Union Carbide pressure-swing process is used to absorb all of the nonhydrogen components of the feed gas to produce 98% pure hydrogen for use in the plant hydrogenation/hydrotreating units. The gases desorbed from the process are recompressed and returned to the synthetic natural gas (SNG) upgrading train as feed to the processing unit. The Lurgi methanation process is used to produce synthetic pipeline gas with a CO content of less than 0.1%. The gas that is produced is reduced in CO_2 content to less than 0.5% by scrubbing with monoethanol amine and reduced in water content by scrubbing with ethylene glycols.

The design of the hydrocarbon synthesis unit is shown in Figure 8-6. Products manufactured include methanol, liquid hydrocarbons and waxes. The products include paraffins, mono olefins, aromatics, alcohols, aldehydes, ketones, and fatty acids with carbon numbers from 1 to more than 35. Small amounts of diolefins and esters can also be produced. The structure is predominantly a single-methyl branched structure when it occurs. Yield, selectivity, and composition are highly dependent on the catalyst, reaction conditions, and reactor type.

Commercial catalysts include cobalt (fixed bed) and iron (fixed and fluid bed). Both are promoted for improved activity and selectivity. Operating conditions range from 392°F–617°F (200°C–325°C) and from 1- to 2-atm pressure, depending on products desired, catalyst, and reactor design. Because the reactions that occur are highly exothermic, the principal problem in designing the reactor is heat removal. Fixed-bed reactors have a heat exchanger, with the catalyst cooled by boiling water or circulating oil. Fluid-bed reactors have internal-tube bundles for removal of the reaction heat. The fluid-bed design gives the following products:

C_1 to C_4	43%
C_5^+	8%
Light oil	35%
Heavy oil	7%
Alcohols	6%
Acids	1%

The design estimates that 85% conversion of CO and H_2 can be obtained at operating conditions of:

- Vapor feed temperature: 320°F (160°C)
- Catalyst and vapor outlet temperature: 644°F (340°C)
- Vapor outlet pressure: 300 psia (21 kg/cm^2)
- Catalyst life: 50 days

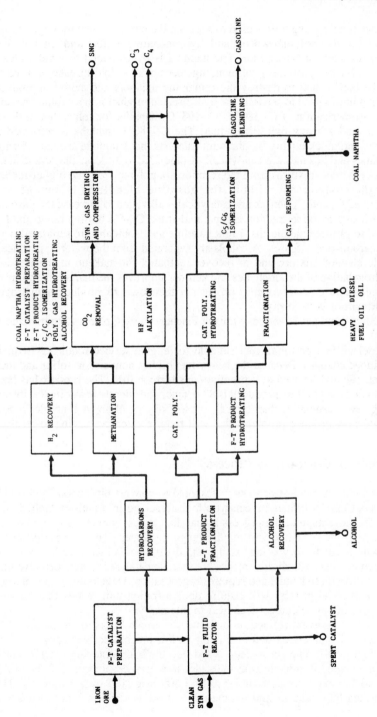

Figure 8-6. Fischer-Tropsch synthesis.[31]

A product-fractionating unit is used to separate the output stream into light gases, feedstocks for the polymerization and hydrogenation units, and an 850°F+ (440°C+) residual for boiler fuel. The naphtha is hydrotreated to yield a clean, saturated, stabilized gasoline pool-blending feedstock. A hydrotreater is used to saturate the olefins and to destroy the remaining alcohols and acids. A product-fractionating unit is used to separate the hydrotreated product into a pentane/hexane stream for isomerization, a C_7-380°F (C_7-193°C) naphtha for reforming, a diesel oil product, and a heavy fuel oil product. The C_7-380°F naphtha is reformed to increase the antiknock quality by platinum catalysts that stimulate aromatic formation. Pentanes and hexanes are catalytically isomerized to increase the octane number. Propene/butene mixtures from the reaction are polymerized into higher-molecular-weight compounds suitable for gasoline blending. Isobutane and unpolymerized C_3 and C_4 olefins are catalytically alkylated to increase the gasoline yield. The heavy gasoline fraction is separated at the C_9-C_{10} boiling range and hydrogenated to saturate the olefins. Light gasoline and isobutane are separated from the hydrocarbon-rich offgases. Alcohols are separated from the water to produce a marketable alcohol mixture and to recover methanol for makeup to the Rectisol unit. Hydrogenation of the aldehydes and ketones improves the marketable value of the alcohol mixture. A cryogenic process is then used to produce a hydrogen makeup stream of 90% purity.

The product yield per stream day for the Fischer-Tropsch plant is summarized in Table 8-3.

The diesel oil is a premium fuel suitable for engine service requiring frequent speed and load changes. Because the heavy fuel oil has nonexistent sulfur and metals content, it could be used as a premium gas turbine fuel. The process has been adjusted so that the gasoline produced is 87 octane, and slightly lower in gravity and containing fewer aromatics than typical, present-day gasoline. A high olefin content of 20% may produce problems that will require extensive testing to resolve.

Zinc Halide Hydrocracking Process[34,35]

The zinc chloride catalyst process is designed to convert bituminous and subbituminous coal into distillates by catalytic hydrocracking in a bath of molten zinc chloride. The advantage of the process is that the catalyst converts a high percentage of the coal into gasoline and middle-range distillates. The process produces gasoline with a satisfactory octane rating and distillate oils that have lower sulfur and nitrogen content. The disadvantages are that the catalyst is a hot corrosive medium that is difficult to handle and requires regeneration. Development into an economical commercial process will require demonstration unit results that provide satisfactory solutions to current technical problems.

Either coal or a solvent refined product may be employed as the feedstock. The coal is dried and pulverized before mixing with a process-derived recycle oil as shown in Figure 8-7. The slurry feed is fed into the hydrocracking reactor which consists of a bath of molten zinc chloride at a temperature of 752°F–842°F (400°C–450°C) and a pressure of 1,500 to 3,500 psig (105 to 246 kg/cm²). The coal is cracked into gasoline and middle-range distillates and is withdrawn into a

Table 8-3
Fischer-Tropsch Commercial Plant Mass Balance[31]

Items	Energy Values	Throughputs
Coal handling facility input (coal as mined)		27,792 tons
Process input		
Moisture- and ash-free coal		18.593 tons
Gasifier input coal		15,264 tons
Boiler input coal		3,329 tons
Raw water input		39,840 tons
Raw iron ore (used as catalyst)		82.2 tons
Process output		
Synthetic pipeline gas		173.3×10^6 scf
Gasoline		13,580 bbl
Diesel fuel		2,307 bbl
Heavy fuel oil		622 bbl
Alcohols		1,825 bbl
Butane		146 bbl
Propane		1,107 bbl
Sulfur		61 tons
Anhydrous ammonia		103 tons
Excess electric power		3.31 MW(e)
Thermal conversion factors		
Coal HHV	12,720 Btu/lb	7060 kg cal/kg
Synthetic gas	1003 Btu/scf	37.6 J/normal m^3
Gasoline	5.0×10^6 Btu/bbl	5.28×10^6 kJ/bbl
Heavy hydrocarbons	5.5×10^6 Btu/bbl	5.80×10^6 kJ/bbl
Butane and propane	4.0×10^6 Btu/bbl	4.21×10^6 kJ/bbl
Alcohols	3.8×10^6 Btu/bbl	4.0×10^6 kJ/bbl
Thermal efficiency		58%

receiver where the gas- and solid-free liquid products are separated by distillation. The spent catalyst contains the ash, nitrogen, and sulfur compounds, and carbonaceous residue. The catalyst is fed to a fluidized-bed combustor where the residual carbon is burned at 1700°F (912°C) to vaporize the catalyst, condense it, and recycle it back to the reactor. The deficiency of recovered catalyst must be made up with expensive fresh zinc chloride.

Mobil Gasoline Synthesis[31,36,37]

The Mobil process has been developed for the production of light hydrocarbons to be reformed into a gasoline motor fuel. The process catalytically dehydrates methanol to selectively produce naphtha, butane, propane, light fuel gases, and water. After reforming, 85% by weight of the hydrocarbon product is gasoline, with

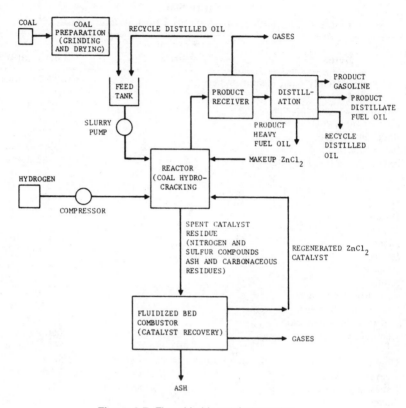

Figure 8-7. Zinc chloride catalyst process.

13% liquefied petroleum gas. The methanol can be produced by the gasification of coal and catalytic synthesis of raw methanol.

The process flowsheet for this system is illustrated in Figure 8-8. Coal, oxygen, and steam are gasified, purified, and shifted to the optimum CO-to-H₂ ratio using commercially available technology. The synthesis gas is used to produce methanol, and the methane produced as a byproduct can be utilized as a synthetic pipeline gas. The crude methanol is then treated to produce water, gasoline, petroleum gas, and a light gas that can be used to synthesize additional methane.

Because the methanol-to-gasoline conversion is separated from the methanol synthesis step, development effort has only concentrated on a process development unit and bench-scale work with the gasoline conversion reactor. No conversion of coal into methanol has been performed by Mobil. A 4-bbl/day fluid-bed reactor was constructed. Present commercial-scale methanol production plants are significantly smaller in size than would be required for synthetic gasoline production.

The advantages claimed in scaling up this process to a commercial size are that it:

1. Produces a high percentage of premium motor fuel.
2. Has an acceptably high thermal efficiency.
3. Has relatively few process steps.
4. Can utilize existing technology for coal gasification and methanol synthesis.
5. Utilizes existing petroleum refining technology for a large part of the plant.

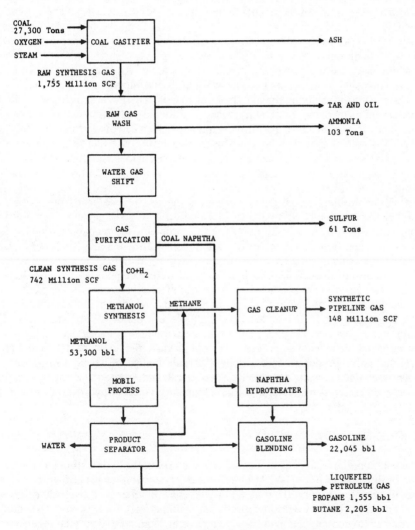

Figure 8-8. Mobil methanol-to-gasoline synthesis.[31]

6. Can consequently be scaled up to commercial plant size with less risk than competing liquefaction technologies.

7. Will be able to utilize alternative processes or future improvements in coal gasification, purification, or methanol synthesis.

Since the process starts with methanol feedstock, which could be directly used as a motor fuel or as a blending stock for gasoline, the advantages of converting it to gasoline should be explained to provide a justification for incurring the additional expenses. The biggest disadvantages are the low energy of methanol and its high water solubility. Since a gallon of methanol has only one half the energy content of gasoline, the volume of motor fuel to be shipped, stored, and transported would be doubled. The mileage that a motorist would obtain from the fuel would be cut in half. Methanol, alone or in gasoline blends, tends to pick up water from the air. Storage conditions can lead to a phase separation that separates the water-alcohol mixture from the fuel, resulting in engine shutdown. Additionally, methanol can prove corrosive to metals and cause swelling in elastomers.

The kinetics involved in the path from methanol to hydrocarbons begins with the conversion of methanol to dimethyl ether. Additional water removal produces olefins that are converted to paraffins, aromatics, and cycloparaffins. A two-stage fixed-bed reactor system is used to limit temperature rise due to the exothermic reactions. The raw gasifier naphtha is hydrotreated under conditions that saturate the raw naphtha olefins with little aromatic-ring hydrogenation to reduce the octane rating as little as possible.

A major problem in the reactor design is the removal of heat from the highly exothermic reaction. Conversion of methanol to hydrocarbons and water releases approximately 740 Btu/lb. To minimize this problem, the reaction is divided into two steps. The first step involves reversibly dehydrating the methanol into dimethylether, releasing about 20% of the heat of reaction. In the second step, the equilibrium mixture of methanol, dimethylether, and water is converted to hydrocarbons and water. In the conversion reactor the Mobil catalyst converts the mixture of methanol and dimethylether first into light olefins and then by polymerization and rearrangement into higher-molecular-weight olefins, paraffins, and aromatics. The reaction terminates at the upper end of the gasoline boiling range due to the unique nature of the catalyst. The process does not produce the heavy paraffins and alcohols that are byproducts of the Fischer-Tropsch method of gasoline synthesis.

The technique is made possible by a zeolite catalyst, called the ZSM-5 class, that selectively converts methanol to the stoichiometric yields of hydrocarbons (44% by weight) and water (56%):

$$nCH_3OH \rightarrow (CH_2)_n + nH_2O \tag{8-16}$$

The action of the catalyst is highly selective in producing hydrocarbons in the gasoline boiling range (C_4–C_{10}). After reforming by conventional petroleum processing, the gasoline produced has an unleaded octane number between 90 and 100 and is chemically similar to gasoline produced from petroleum feedstock. The catalyst is resistant to contamination during operations and can periodically be regenerated. After two weeks of operation enough coke accumulates on the catalyst to require regeneration. Combustion of the coke at a controlled temperature restores the activity. Since the catalyst is tolerant of water, crude methanol can be used without any purification.

The equipment used in the process is similar to a two-stage petroleum hydrotreater. A schematic of the Mobil pilot plant is shown in Figure 8-9. Crude methanol is first passed through a dehydration reactor and then into the conversion reactor. Recycle gas provides a heat sink to absorb the heat of reaction and limit the temperature rise. The gasoline-conversion-reactor inlet temperature is typically 680°F and with a 9-to-1 recycle ratio; the adiabatic temperature rise is about 100°F. The reactor effluent is condensed, water and liquid hydrocarbon phases are separated, and the gas is recycled. Liquid and gaseous hydrocarbons are processed through a conventional gas plant to produce additional gasoline. Propene, butenes, and isobutane are separated and alkylated using conventional technology.

The gasoline produced by the process is of very high quality, consisting of highly branched paraffins and olefins, naphthenes, and aromatics. The gasoline does not contain sulfur or nitrogen since there is none in the methanol feed. A gasoline yield of 85% by weight is achieved with 13.6% by weight of liquefied petroleum gas produced.

The thermal efficiency of the process using methanol produced from coal is slightly less than the efficiency that can be achieved by other coal liquefaction technologies with an efficiency of about 88%. The overall process efficiency does depend on the coal gasification process and the byproducts that are produced. Three options for plant design are being considered. The first option is the production of synthetic pipeline gas plus byproducts such as naphtha and tar by the Lurgi process.

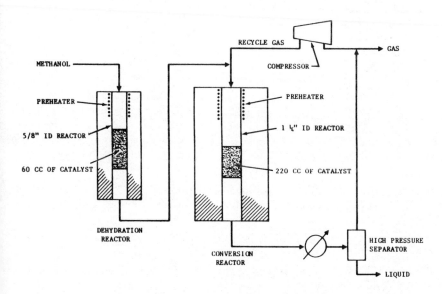

Figure 8-9. Schematic of Mobil fixed-bed pilot plant.

The second is to produce methanol plus synthetic pipeline gas and byproducts. The third option is to add on the Mobil conversion process and optimize the system for maximum economic return by adding methane and petroleum gas to the list of products. This last option produces an output consisting of 46% substitute pipeline gas, 31% gasoline, 5% petroleum gas, and 18% byproducts. The reduction in thermal efficiency between the first and third options is only about 3.3%.

NOMENCLATURE

A_b	cross-sectional area of bed
a'	interfacial contact area
d_p	particle diameter
g	gravitational acceleration
H	height
k''	ratio of liquid to gas holdups
k_ℓ	liquid-phase mass transfer coefficient
M	total mass
m	mass of solids
P	pressure
$U_{f,g}$	liquid and gas superficial velocities, respectively
V_1	Richardson-Zaki velocity intercept
V_b	bubble rise velocity
We	Weber number
x	partition coefficient

Greek Symbols

ϵ	void fraction
ϱ	density
σ	surface tension

REFERENCES

1. Mukherjee, R. N., P. Bhattachaya, and D. K. Taraphdar, *Fluidization and Its Applications,* H. Angelino, et al. (Eds.), Cepaduci-Editions, Toulouse (1974), p. 372.

2. Begovich, J. J., and J. S. Watson, "Fluidization," in *Proc. 2nd Eng. Found. Conf.,* J. F. Davidson and D. L. Keairns (Eds.), Cambridge Univ. Press, England, (1978), p. 190.

3. Darton, R. C., and D. Harrison, *Fluidization Technology,* D. L. Keairns (Ed.), 1: 399, Hemisphere Pub., NY (1976).

4. Darton, R. C., and D. Harrison, *Inst. Chem. Engrs. Symp. Ser.* (38), paper B1, (London) (1974).

5. Darton, R. C., and D. Harrison, *Chem. Eng. Sci.*, 30: 581 (1975).

6. Bhatia, V. K., and N. Epstein, *Fluidization and Its Applications*, H. Angelino, et al. (Eds.) (Cepaduci Editions, Toulouse) (1976), p 372.

7. Bhatia, V. K., K. A. Evans, and N. Epstein, *Ind. Eng. Chem. Process Design and Development*, 11: 151 (1972).

8. El-Temtamy, S. A., and N. Epstein, *Inst. J. Multiphase Flow*, 4: 19 (1978).

9. El-Temtamy, S. A., Ph.D. Thesis, Cairo University (1974).

10. Lee, J. C., A. J. Sherrard, and P. S. Budkley, *Fluidization and Its Applications*, H. Angelino, et al. (Eds.) Cepaduci Editions, Toulouse (1974), p. 407.

11. Ostegaard, K., and W. Suchozebriski, *4th Europ. Symp. Chem. React. Eng.*, Pergamon Press (1971), p. 21.

12. Dhanuka, V. R., and J. B. Stepanek, "Fluidization," *Proc. 2nd Eng. Found. Conf.* Davidson, J. F. and D. L. Keairns (Eds.), Cambridge Univ. Press, England (1978), p. 179.

13. Dhanuka, V. R., and J. B. Stepanek, "Gas-Liquid Mass Transfer in a Three-Phase Fluidized Bed," *3rd Eng. Found. Conf. on Fluidization*, Henniker, NH (1981).

14. Nishikawa, M., K. Kosaka, and K. Hashimoto, *AIChE J.*, 2: 1,389 (1977).

15. Roszak, J., and R. Gawronski, *Chem. Eng. J.*, 17: 101 (1979).

16. Epstein, N. *Handbook of Fluids in Motion*, N. P. Cheremisinoff and R. Gupta, (Eds.), Ann Arbor Science Publ., Ann Arbor, MI (1983), Ch. 42, pp 1,165–1,182.

17. Mangold, E. D., et al., *Coal Liquefaction and Gasification Technologies*, Ann Arbor Science Publ., Ann Arbor, MI (1982).

18. "EDS Coal Liquefaction Process Development, Phase 111A. Annual Technical Progress Report, January 1–December 31, 1976," FE-2353-9, Exxon Research & Engineering Company, Baytown, TX (1977).

19. Epperly, W. R., and J. W. Taunton, "Development of the Exxon Donor Solvent Coal Liquefaction Process," paper presented at the 85th National Meeting of the American Institute of Chemical Engineers, Philadelphia, PA, (June 7, 1978).

20. Epperly, W. R., and J. W. Taunton, "Exxon Donor Solvent Coal Liquefaction Process Development," paper presented at Coal Dilemma II, American Chemical Society, Colorado Springs, CO, (February 12, 1979).

21. DeVaux, G. R., and B. Dutkiewicz, "H-Coal Commercialization," paper presented at the meeting of the American Institute of Chemical Engineers, (November 1978).

22. "H-Coal Commercial Plant. Part II Technical Proposal to DOE," Ashland Synthetic Fuels Inc. (1978).

23. Kunesh, J. G., et al., "Economics of the H-Coal Process," Report to DOE, Hydrocarbon Research, Inc., Lawrenceville, NJ (1978).

24. Lewis, H. E., et al., "Solvent Refined Coal Process. Quarterly Technical Progress Report, July–September, 1977," FE-2270-27, Catalytic Inc., Wilsonville, AL.

25. Lewis, H. E., et al., "Solvent Refined Coal Process. Operation of Solvent Refined Coal Pilot Plant, Quarterly Technical Progress Report to DOE for April–June 1978," Catalytic Inc., Wilsonville, AL.

26. "Phase II Laboratory Support for H-Coal Project," monthly progress report to DOE No. 14, FE-2547-14, Hydrocarbon Research, Inc., Lawrenceville, NJ (1978).

27. "Phase II Laboratory Support for H-Coal Project," monthly progress report to DOE No. 17, FE-2547-17, Hydrocarbon Research Inc., Lawrenceville, NJ (1978).

28. "Solvent Refined Coal Process. Annual Technical Progress Report to DOE, January-December 1977," Pittsburgh and Midway Coal Mining Co., Shawnee Mission, KS.

29. "SRC-II Demonstration Project, Phase Zero Conceptual Plant Design," Report to DOE, Pittsburgh and Midway Coal Mining Company, Denver, CO (1979).

30. Swabb, L. E., "Liquid Fuels from Coal: From R&D to an Industry," Science 199: 619–622 (1978).

31. Schreiner, M., "Research Guidance Studies to Assess Gasoline from Coal by Methanol-to-Gasoline and Sasol-Type Fischer-Tropsch Technologies, Final Report," FE-2447-13, Mobil Research & Development Corp., Princeton, NJ (1978).

32. Struck, R. T., et al., "Zinc Halide Hydrocracking Process for Distillate Fuels from Coal, Quarterly Technical Progress Report, February 1–April 30, 1978," Conoco Coal Development Company, Research Division, Library, PA (1978).

33. Wise, J. J., and A. J. Silvestri, "Mobil Process Efficiently Converts Methanol to Gasoline," *Oil & Gas J.* (Nov. 1976).

34. Greene, C. R., et al., "Zinc Halide Hydrocracking Process for Distillate Fuels from Coal. Quarterly Technical Progress Report to DOE, August 1–October 31, 1978," Conoco Coal Development Company, Research Division, Library, PA (1978).

35. Lee, W., J. Maziuk, and W. K. Thiemann, "A New Process for Conversion of Coal to Gasoline," paper presented at the 26th DGMK Congress, Berlin, West Germany (October 1978).

36. Meisel, S. L., "Recent Advances in the Production of Fuels and Chemicals over Zeolite Catalysts," paper presented at the Leo Frend Symposium, American Chemical Society, Chicago, IL (August 1977).

37. Meisel, S. L., et al., "Gasoline from Methanol in One Step," *Chemtech* (February 1976).

9

Principles of Fluid Bed Reactor Modelling

CONTENTS

INTRODUCTION, 346

GENERAL CONCEPTS AND DEFINITIONS, 346

Types of Reactions, 348
Diffusion and Exchange Coefficients, 349
Mass and Heat Transfer Kinetics, 351

DIFFUSION INTO POROUS PARTICLES, 355

COMBUSTION OF PARTICLES, 366

FLUID-BED FLOW MODELING, 373

Freely Bubbling Beds, 373
Slugging and Fast Fluidized Beds, 387

PRINCIPLES OF REACTOR DESIGN, 388

NOMENCLATURE, 395

REFERENCES, 397

INTRODUCTION

Reaction kinetics involves the study of the rates and mechanisms by which one chemical species undergoes transformation into another. The rate(s) at which this conversion takes place is normally expressed as the mass (in terms of moles) of a product produced or reactant consumed per unit time. The mechanism(s) is the steps or sequence of individual chemical events whose overall result produces the observed reaction.

Understanding the chemical kinetic mechanism is of great value in extending rate data beyond the original experiments and in generalizing or systematizing the kinetics of reactions. However, in most practical problems, evaluation of reaction mechanisms is a difficult task. Reaction mechanisms are reliably known for only a few systems. Fortunately, postulated theories for mechanisms do exist for a variety of reactions, ranging from simple, gas-phase homogeneous systems to complicated polymerization reactions involving initiation, propagation, and termination steps. This has enabled a fair degree of generalization when attempting to rationalize or explain a particular kinetic reaction. Of principal concern in the design of any reactor is the rate expression, which can only be generalized from a knowledge of the kinetic mechanisms of importance to the specific system.

This chapter discusses principles which form the foundation of modeling reactor systems. The majority of the chapter relates to the complex study of chemical processes in combination with the physical processes of heat and mass transfers. The combination of kinetics with the theories of diffusion, heat transfer, and hydrodynamics provides a series of methods for studying reaction rates, and establishes a scientific basis for designing such processes as combustion and dissolution. The latter part of this chapter describes some of the methodology involved in applying principles to modeling fluid-bed reactor systems.

GENERAL CONCEPTS AND DEFINITIONS

Processes such as combustion and rapid chemical reactions encountered in industrial practice are complex, and analytical treatment requires knowledge of the specific chemistry, fluid dynamics, and heat transfer mechanisms involved. Particularly troublesome to understand and the most often encountered, are reaction systems whereby mixing occurs with nonideal reactions.

The successful design of reactor systems requires understanding chemical kinetics as well as such physical processes as mass and energy transport. These processes, in turn, are strongly dependent upon the hydrodynamics of the system. Hence, the design and operation of equipment for carrying out chemical reactions requires analysis of both physical and chemical processes. The principles governing energy and mass transfers are often as important as those that govern chemical kinetics.

The rate at which one chemical species is transformed into another cannot be predicted with a high level of accuracy. In general, it is a specific quantity which must be evaluated from experiments. Although affected by them, chemical kinetics is not concerned with physical processes but only with the rate of transformation of atoms and molecules from one structural form to another. On the other hand, the rates of physical processes such as heat and mass transport can, in many cases, be estimated from hydrodynamic and reactor geometry considerations.

Very often, when kinetic studies are initiated in industrial research, they are performed in a pilot plant or in pilot-scale equipment, where the true system kinetics are masked by hydrodynamic and/or geometry effects. Hence, to evaluate the chemical kinetics of the system, one must separate the effects of physical processes from the observed data, thus leaving the rate information for the chemical-transformation step alone. The influence of physical steps can be reintroduced for the particular reactor type and operating conditions chosen for the commercial scale. The interrelationship of physical and chemical steps must therefore be considered twice: once in obtaining rates-of-reaction expressions from the available pilot-plant data, and again in applying these expressions to designing the commercial-scale reactor. The interpretation of data is as important as the second step, and entails generally the same type of analysis. There are several terms that require definitions before proceeding to the relevant discussions of this chapter. The first involves a distinction of the types of reactions.

All reactions can be classified into two general groups; namely simple and complex. Simple reactions are those in which rates depend only on the concentrations of the original reactants and do not depend on the concentrations of the reaction products. In contrast, a complex reaction is one where the rate depends on the concentrations of both the reactants and the final products.

The two types of chemical reactions are termed homogeneous and heterogeneous, with the distinction being based on whether the transformations occur in single phase or at an interface, respectively. In the case of a homogeneous chemical reaction, the rate refers to the amount of matter reacting in a unit volume per unit time. That is, it represents the change of the concentration of the substance per unit time. For a heterogeneous reaction, it is the amount of substance reacting on a unit surface area per unit time. For both cases, the reaction rate is a function of the temperature and of the concentrations of the reactants.

The rate constant is a temperature dependent parameter that follows Arrhenius' law:

$$k = ze^{-E/RT} \tag{9-1}$$

where   R = gas constant
         T = absolute temperature
      z, E = constants characterizing the chemical reaction. (z is a pre-exponential factor, and E is the activation energy of the system. The activation energy is the amount of energy required by the reactant molecules to undergo reaction.)

The reaction rate depends on the concentrations of the participating reactants, which can generally be expressed by a power law relation:

$$v_r = kC_A^{n_A} C_B^{n_B} \tag{9-2}$$

where ν is the reaction rate, and C_A, C_B, etc., are the concentrations of the reactants A, B taking part in the reaction. Coefficient k is strictly a function of the temperature and is termed the rate constant. Exponent n refers to the order of the reaction (n_A, n_B refer to the order with respect to reactants A and B, respectively). The overall reaction order is the sum of the individual orders. In the case of gas phase reactions, the overall order is also referred to as the order with respect to the total pressure of the system.

Types of Reactions

The progress of a reaction can be described as either stationary or nonstationary. Defining x as the concentration of the active intermediate, a kinetic expression can be written describing its change with time:

$$\frac{dx}{dt} = n' + fx - gx \tag{9-3}$$

where n' = rate of generation of chains
f = rate of chain branching
g = rate of chain termination

Several solutions to Equation 9-3 are possible depending on the relative magnitudes of the kinetic constants. For example, if g > f, the reaction is stationary and the concentration x of the active intermediate will, with time, tend to the stationary value:

$$x = \frac{n'}{g - f} \tag{9-4}$$

Upon achieving this stationary state, the concentration of the active intermediate will remain constant and the reaction will proceed at the steady rate:

$$\nu = kx \tag{9-5}$$

where k is the rate constant for the chain continuation.

On the other hand, if g < f, then the system is nonstationary, and the solution of Equation 9-3 is of the form:

$$x = \frac{n'}{\phi} (c^{\phi t-1}) \tag{9-6}$$

where $\phi = f - g$, and t is time. As a final example, if g and f both vary, a sharp transition from a stationary to a nonstationary reaction will occur at g = f. This phenomenon is referred to as chain ignition.

A very common type of reaction is autocatalytic, where the rate of the reaction increases with increasing concentration of a product formed in that reaction.

An autocatalytic reaction may be due to an intermediate or a final product. The species which lead to the increase of the rate is known as the active species. Most chemical processes are complex in nature and proceed over active intermediates. A relatively large activation energy is needed for the reactions between two stable molecules, and thus, these reactions are generally slow. Active intermediates react with the original reactants to form the final products. For the reaction over active intermediates to proceed rapidly, it is necessary that these intermediates be regenerated in the course of the reaction. In other words, the reaction between the intermediate and the original reactant must produce not only the stable final product, but also new active intermediates.

In the case of a heterogeneous reaction, the active intermediates play a secondary role compared to the molecules bound to the surface by chemical forces (i.e., chemisorption). In general, the kinetics of a heterogeneous reaction are strongly influenced by the inhomogeneity of the surface. Different portions of the surface are characterized by different heats of adsorption and activation energies. For an ideal surface (i.e., one that is perfectly uniform) the adsorption mechanism can be described by Langmuir's isotherm, which expresses the dependence of the amount g of adsorbed substance on its partial pressure p in the gas phase:

$$g = g_o \frac{p}{p + b} \tag{9-7}$$

where g_o and b are constants that characterize the adsorbent and surface. The idealized Langmuir kinetics imply that the dependence of the rate of reaction on the concentrations of the reactants in the gas phase are of an analogous form.

For a real system, the surface is highly nonuniform, and the dependence of the adsorbed amount of a substance on its partial pressure in the gas phase is better described by the Freundlich isotherm:

$$g = C_p^{1/n} \tag{9-8}$$

where C_p is a constant, and n > 1. The reaction kinetics for this type of adsorption isotherm usually follow a fractional order.

Diffusion and Exchange Coefficients

It is common practice to draw analogies between the mechanism of diffusion and heat transfer, and momentum transfer when describing resistances imposed against fluid motion. In the absence of turbulence, the intensity of all three processes can be characterized by the coefficients of molecular transfer for heat transfer. A thermometric conductivity coefficient, a, can be related to the heat conductivity coefficient, λ, by:

$$a = \frac{\lambda}{c_p \xi} \tag{9-9}$$

where c_p = heat capacity
ξ = density (i.e., the temperature conductivity coefficient is the ratio of the heat conductivity and the heat capacity per unit volume)

For mass transfer, the diffusion coefficient D represents the appropriate exchange coefficient:

$$q = -D\frac{dC}{dx} \tag{9-10}$$

And for the momentum transfer, kinematic viscosity, ν, is the exchange coefficient:

$$\nu = \frac{\mu}{\xi} \tag{9-11}$$

All three coefficients, a, D, and ν have the dimensions of cm²/s.
When a fluid is in turbulent motion, transfer coefficients are expressed in terms of the turbulent exchange coefficient, A. Random turbulent motion of bulk fluids is analogous to the disordered thermal motion of molecules, except that it involves not individual molecules, but small volumes of fluid which keep their individuality for some time. The longitudinal dimensions characterizing turbulent motion are referred to as the scale of the turbulence. From the kinetic theory of gases, the turbulent exchange coefficient can be expressed as:[1]

$$A = \ell u \tag{9-12}$$

where A = turbulent exchange coefficient
ℓ = mixing length
u = mean pulsation velocity

For heat transfer, the ratio of the heat flow, q, and the temperature difference, ΔT, is termed the heat exchange coefficient, α, and is expressed by Newton's law of heat exchange:

$$q = \alpha\Delta T \tag{9-13}$$

In mass exchange in the presence of convection the diffusion velocity constant, β, is analogous to the heat exchange coefficient. It is expressed in terms of the ratio of the diffusion flow, q, and a concentration difference, ΔC:

$$q = \beta\Delta C \tag{9-14}$$

Diffusion flow is expressed in units of moles/cm² s, and concentration in moles/cm² s. Therefore, the diffusion velocity constant is expressed as cm/s. Dimensionally, β does not correspond to α, but rather to $\alpha/c_p\xi$, where c_p is the heat capacity and ξ is the density.

When a boundary exists over which heat or matter exchanges between phases (particularly between a stream of gas or liquid and a solid surface), it is convenient to introduce the concept of an effective film. It can be observed that at some distance from the boundary, both temperature and the concentration are constant, and changes occur only in a layer of thickness, δ, immediately adjacent to the surface. This fictitious layer is referred to as an effective film. Its thickness δ is chosen so that the actual intensity of the transfer is based on the assumption that its mechanism is purely molecular within the film. Consequently:

$$\alpha = \frac{\lambda}{\delta}$$

$$\beta = \frac{D}{\delta} \qquad (9\text{-}15)$$

δ is given as:

$$\delta = \frac{d}{Nu} \qquad (9\text{-}16)$$

Thus, the thickness δ of the effective film appears as an auxiliary magnitude replacing Nusselt's criterion.

When a solid body is immersed in a flowing stream, the fluid exerts a certain force and meets a corresponding resistance. The force acting on the unit surface area of the body is termed the tangential stress, τ. When there is an external flow around a body, the resistance coefficient is given as the ratio of the force acting on unit surface area of the middle section and the velocity push:

$$C = \frac{F}{\delta \frac{\xi V^2}{2}} \qquad (9\text{-}17)$$

where F = total force acting on body
δ = surface area of middle section
V = velocity

In the mechanism of internal friction consisting of momentum transfer, the similitude of diffusion and heat transfer can be extended to frictional resistance. This analogy between heat exchange (and also diffusion) and frictional resistances is known as Reynolds analogy.

Mass and Heat Transfer Kinetics

Heat transport by means of molecular heat conduction is analogous to molecular diffusion and heat transfer by convection in convective diffusion. Heat transfer by radiation has no similar analog in mass transfer. Thus, all theoretical and experimental results obtained in the study of heat transfer can be directly applied to diffusion phenomena, and vice versa. According to Fick's law, the rate of mass related to a unit of outer surface area is:

$$\varrho = -D\frac{dc}{dx} \tag{9-18}$$

D = diffusion coefficient
c = concentration
x = coordinate (normal to the surface)

In contrast to molecular heat conduction and diffusion, where the transfer of heat or of matter is accomplished by the motion of individual molecules, the transfer of heat or of matter due to the motion of the bulk fluid is termed convection. Convection may be free or forced, hence, the fundamental relations of Fourier and Fick must be supplemented by additional terms expressing the transfers by the mass flow. For the latter, designated by ν, Fick's law is expressed as:

$$q = -D\frac{dc}{dx} + \nu_x c_p \tag{9-19A}$$

and Fourier's law is:

$$q = -\lambda\frac{dT}{dx} + c_p \xi \nu_x T \tag{9-19B}$$

where ν_x = component of ν in direction of x coordinate
c_p = heat capacity
ξ = density

Consider the boundary layer to be a flat surface from which the distribution of concentrations in the boundary layer under stationary conditions can be obtained by solving the diffusion equation:

$$\frac{d^2C}{dx^2} = 0 \tag{9-20}$$

using the following boundary conditions: $C = C_p$ when $x = 0$ (at the grain surface), and $C = C_f$ when $x = \delta$ (at the interface of the laminar layer and bulk flow). Upon integration of Equation 9-20, we obtain:

$$C = C_p + \frac{C_f - C_p}{\delta}x \tag{9-21}$$

Substituting Equation 9-21 into Equation 9-18, an expression for the mass flow across the boundary layer is obtained:

$$\varrho = -\frac{D}{\delta}(C_f - C_p) \tag{9-22}$$

The minus sign signifies that $C_f > C_p$ and hence, the transfer of molecules is towards the surface. The ratio D/δ is the mass transfer coefficient or rate constant of diffusion:

$$\beta = \frac{D}{\delta} \qquad (9\text{-}23)$$

The steady-state distribution of concentration in the boundary layer and the flow of mass to the active surface is determined by equation of convective diffusion:

$$w_x \frac{\partial C}{\partial x} + w_y \frac{\partial C}{\partial y} + w_z \frac{\partial C}{\partial z} = D \frac{\partial^2 C}{\partial x^2} \qquad (9\text{-}24)$$

where w_x, w_y, w_z are velocity component vectors and $\partial^2 C/\partial x^2$ is normal to the surface. The other two coordinates are omitted because the mass transfer in those directions is small. The boundary conditions for Equation 9-24 are determined from the fact that the diffusional flow to active surface is equal to the rate of chemical reaction, and at sufficient distance from the surface the concentration is equal to C_f. There are only a few cases where it is possible to obtain an analytical solution to Equation 9-24. More often experimental data can be expressed in terms of the following dimensionless groups:

$$Sh = f(Re, Sc) \qquad (9\text{-}25)$$

where Sh = Sherwood number = $\beta d/D$
       Re = Reynolds number = wd/ν
       Sc = Schmidt number = ν/D

where ν = kinematic viscosity
       w = linear velocity of flow
       d = determining size

For example, the mass transfer coefficient in a fixed bed may be expressed as:

$$\frac{\epsilon}{f} j = \frac{0.30}{Re^{0.35} - 1.90} \qquad (9\text{-}26)$$

where j = $ShSc^{-0.333}Re^{-1}$ = mass transfer factor
       ϵ = bed voidage
       f = form factor (i.e., the ratio of attainable surface of the particle to a sphere surface of the same volume)

The determining linear size in the Reynolds number is the square root of the surface area of the particle's outer surface. Equation 9-26 is valid over the range of:

$$50 < Re < 10{,}000$$

The rate of mass transfer increases with increasing flow velocity. Since the rate of chemical reaction is exponential with respect to temperature, then diffusion is a limiting step which changes sharply the macrokinetic regularities with rising temperature. That is, the mechanisms for both the transfers of heat and mass are the same in a flowing fluid; and Fourier's law corresponds to Fick's law.

$$\varrho_n = \alpha\gamma\frac{dT}{dx} \tag{9-27}$$

where ϱ_n = heat flow through surface 1 to the x-axis
γ = heat capacity of a unit volume of fluid
α = coefficient of thermal diffusivity (conductivity)

Coefficient α has the same dimension as D, and for gases their values are similar (that is, $\alpha\gamma = \lambda$-coefficient of heat conductivity). Heat transfer between the surface of the particle and the surrounding fluid flow can be described by an expression analogous to Equation 9-22.

$$\varrho_n = \alpha'(T_p - T_f) \tag{9-28}$$

where α' is the heat transfer coefficient defined as $\alpha\gamma/\delta$. When $\alpha = D$, from Equation 9-23 and the definition of α', we note that

$$\alpha' = \beta\gamma \tag{9-29}$$

From a practical standpoint, α' can be defined in terms of the dimensionless Nusselt number:

$$Nu = \frac{\alpha'd}{\lambda} = f(Re, Pr) \tag{9-30}$$

where Pr is the Prandtl number ($= \nu/\alpha$).

With porous particles, the exchange of mass and energy between solid and the surrounding flow is even more complex. Inequalities in diffusion rates and reaction products or volume changes occur during chemical reactions that take place within the pore structure. The mass transfer inside the pores of grains plays a critical role in such processes as coal gasification and coal liquefaction. Fick's law is an idealized description of diffusion in broad pores with a standard coefficient of molecular diffusion. For small pores (i.e., pore diameter is less than the average distance of the molecular mean free paths) the Knudsen mechanism is a more appropriate description, and the diffusion coefficient is restated as:

$$D = \frac{1}{3}d_o\left(\frac{8RT}{\pi M}\right)^{0.5} \tag{9-31}$$

where R = universal gas constant
d_o = pore diameter
M = molecular weight

The relationship between the diffusion coefficient and pore diameter is a result of the active role that the pore walls play in the mass transfer process. The Knudsen zones limits are pressure dependent. At low pressures the Knudsen diffusion is manifested only when $d_o < 10^3 \text{Å}$; and with increasing pressure, the limits are moved in the direction of lower pore diameters. Heat transfer inside a porous particle is realized by molecular diffusivity and heat conductivity by the particle itself. It is often possible to consider the porous particle as a uniform substance using effective diffusion and heat conductivity coefficients established from experiments.

DIFFUSION INTO POROUS PARTICLES

Consider a monomolecular irreversible reaction taking place on the surface of a uniform particle without a pore structure. Assume that the entire surface area of the particle is equally exposed to the reagents of the bulk flow. Further assume that the absorption of the substance on the active surface can be described by Henry's law, and hence, the reaction is first order with respect to the concentration of the gas phase, C_p, on the particle surface. For a steady-state process, (i.e., a constant rate of mass transfer to the surface of the particle), the diffusion rate is equivalent to the rate of reaction:

$$\varrho = \beta(C_f - C_p) = \chi C_p \tag{9-32}$$

where χ is the rate constant and is related through

$$C_p = \frac{\beta C_f}{\chi + \beta} \tag{9-33}$$

Substituting Equation 9-33 into 9-32, an expression for the reaction rate retarded by the external diffusion of a reagent is obtained:

$$\varrho = \frac{\chi\beta}{\chi + \beta} C_f \tag{9-34A}$$

or, restating as follows:

$$\chi^* = \frac{\chi\beta}{\chi + \beta} = \frac{1}{\dfrac{1}{\chi} + \dfrac{1}{\beta}} \tag{9-34B}$$

Equation 9-34B defines a first order reaction for the reagent concentration C_f in the bulk flow in terms of an effective rate constant. Note that the inverse of the effective rate constant χ^* is the sum of kinetic and diffusion "resistances" ($1/\chi$ and $1/\beta$). From Equations 9-33 and 9-34B, it follows that $C_p \simeq C_f$ and $\chi \simeq \chi^*$ when $\beta >> \chi$. In this case, the mass transfer of gaseous reagents to the active surface proceeds without restriction, and the rate of the total process is only limited by the rate of chemical reaction.

If $\beta << \chi$, then $\chi^* \simeq \beta$ and the surface concentration C_p approaches zero. In this case, the process rate is limited by diffusion to the active surface, and the mass transfer coefficient, β, depends on the linear velocity of the flow and is almost independent of temperature (i.e., the activation energy is close to zero). Hence, the reaction proceeds in the outer diffusion region. The transfer of the process from kinetic to the outer diffusion region is realized with a rise in temperature and a subsequent slowing down of the motion of gas.

A transition region exists between the kinetic and outer diffusional regions, where β and χ are of the same order of magnitude, and the rate of the total process is determined by kinetic and diffusion factors. In this region the rate of the process is a function of the linear velocity of the flow, which becomes more pronounced as the ratio χ/β increases, and the apparent energy of activation approaches zero. If the reaction order is greater than one, the limits of the diffusion region change with the increasing concentration of the substance in the bulk flow in the direction of lower temperatures. When the reaction order is less than unity, the limits move in the direction of higher temperatures. Upon approaching the diffusion region, the apparent reaction order approaches unity, and $C_p \simeq 0$ in the outer diffusion region. Hence, all reactions must be of first order with respect to the concentration in the bulk flow. The concentration at the particle surface can be expressed as follows:

$$\beta(C_f - C_p) = \chi C_p^{\alpha} \tag{9-35}$$

$$\beta(C_f - C_p) = \frac{\chi C_p}{1 + \beta C_p} \tag{9-36}$$

where β is the adsorption coefficient.

At higher β-values, the surfaces of particles are rapidly covered, and consequently a smaller apparent reaction order with respect to gas surface concentration, C_p, exists.

Assuming that the reaction takes place equally over the entire surface area of the particle,

$$0 = \sum_{i=1}^{S} \nu_i A_i \tag{9-37}$$

where ν_i = molar stoichiometric multiplier or coefficient
A_i = moles of substance i

Assign a negative sign to the stoichiometric coefficients of the initial substances and a positive sign to the reaction products. For inert constituents, assume $\nu_i = 0$. Because the diffusion rates of different constituents vary through the boundary layer, and also a change of volume occurs as a result of the chemical reaction, a density gradient will arise within the boundary layer. This is compensated by a rise of mass flow normal to the grain surface. The directed flow of material is referred to as Stephan flow. When the Stephan flow exists with linear velocity, w, the velocity of transfer of substance i to a flat boundary layer is determined as:

$$\varrho_i = -D\frac{dC_i}{dx} + wC_i \qquad (9\text{-}38)$$

Hence, an additional term characterizing the Stephan flow has been added to Fick's law (Equation 9-18). Note that x is the distance normal from the particle's surface to the bulk flow, and ϱ_i and w are considered positive if they have the same direction of motion (from the particle). In terms of all constituents then:

$$\frac{dC}{dx} = w\sum_{i=1}^{S} \frac{C_i}{D_i} - \sum_{i=1}^{S} \frac{P_i}{D_i} \qquad (9\text{-}39)$$

where $C = \sum_{i=1}^{S} C_i$ = concentration of the reaction mixture.

We note that the flows of substances are proportional to each other since the boundary layer does not reflect hydraulic resistances (that is, P and density, C = P/RT, are equivalent in the boundary layer, and thus, the left-hand side of this expression is zero). Hence, for any pair of substances (A_i, A_j), we note that $\varrho_i = \nu_j/\nu_i\varrho_j$, and Equation 9-39 becomes:

$$0 = w\sum_{i=1}^{S} \frac{C_i}{D_i} - \frac{P_i}{\nu_i}\sum_{i=1}^{S} \frac{\nu_i}{D_i} \qquad (9\text{-}40)$$

Defining the following terms:

$$\sum_{i=1}^{S} \frac{C_i}{D_i} = \frac{C}{D} \qquad (9\text{-}41A)$$

$$\gamma_j = \frac{D}{\nu_j}\sum_{i=1}^{S} \frac{\nu_i}{D_i} \qquad (9\text{-}41B)$$

And from Equation 9-40:

$$w = \frac{\gamma_i}{C}\varrho_j \qquad (9\text{-}42)$$

Equations 9-41B and 9-42 show that the Stephan flow does not exist when the following criterion is met:

$$\sum_{i=1}^{S} \frac{\nu_i}{D_i} = 0 \qquad (9\text{-}43)$$

The flow from the particle surface to the bulk fluid takes place when the diffusional coefficients of all substances are equivalent, which in turn is stipulated by the fact that the reaction takes place at an increasing volume.

Integrating Equation 9-38, taking into account Equation 9-42, gives the distribution of concentrations in the boundary layer:

$$\frac{dC_i}{dx} = \frac{\gamma_i \varrho_i}{CD_i} - \frac{\varrho_i}{D_i} \qquad (9\text{-}44)$$

Integrating over the limits of $x = 0$ to $x = \delta$ (where δ is the boundary layer thickness) gives:

$$\varrho_i = \frac{D_i C}{\delta \gamma_i} \ln \left(\frac{1 - \dfrac{\gamma_i}{C} C_i P}{1 - \dfrac{\gamma_i}{C} C_i P} \right) \qquad (9\text{-}45)$$

For $\gamma = 0$ (no Stephan flow) this expression reduces to Equation 9-22. Stephan flow has a significant influence on the reaction rate. The greater the absolute value of γ is, the less the dissolution of the reaction mixture by inert substances is.

When the reaction proceeds in the transition region, the surface concentration C_{ip} can be evaluated along with the flow of the constituent ϱ_i by substituting the kinetic relationship $\varrho_i (C_{ip})$ in Equation 9-45. In the outer diffusional zone the surface concentration must have at least one of the reactant concentrations close to zero. Because of inequalities in the diffusion rates of reactants through the boundary layer, the other initial constituents may accumulate on the surface even when the reaction is instantaneous. This condition of diffusion stoichiometry occurs when the mass transfer coefficients are equal; and hence, the concentrations of constituents are proportional to their stoichiometric coefficients.

When the mass transfer coefficients differ from each other, this condition may only be fulfilled under a defined composition of the mixture, which is different from the stoichiometric composition. This, however, is a highly unlikely situation. If the reaction takes place according to Equation 9-37, then only for one substance will the surface concentration be close to zero in the diffusion zone. The constituent that is only a small fraction in the reaction mixture will undergo the least diffusion. The reaction rate in this case is equal to the mass transfer to the surface:

$$\varrho_1 = \frac{\beta_1 C}{\gamma_1} \ln \left(1 - \frac{\gamma_1}{C} C_{1h} \right) \simeq B_1 C_{1f} \qquad (9\text{-}46)$$

The remaining constituents present at the active surface will be in abundant concentrations.

The assumption of equal accessibility of surface leads to idealized predictions, which directionally show proper trends for reactions taking place on nonporous particles; however, quantitative measures from such an analysis are of little value. When a fluid flows around an actual catalyst or coal particle, mass transfer conditions vary greatly over its surface. Experimental observations of mass transfer rates taking place when reaction rates are nearly instantaneous provide only average values of the diffusion rate coefficient. Furthermore, equal accessibility is in no way manifested. The influence of unequal accessibility on the process rate may be approximated by assuming that the diffusion boundary layer is immobile and its thickness varies randomly from point to point. Employing the distribution function of the diffusion layer thickness, δ, it is possible to estimate the average value of the effective rate constant, χ^*, by applying Equation 9-34B over the entire particle surface. This type of analysis will lead to an average value of the mass transfer coefficient $\beta = D/\delta$. Unfortunately, evaluations show that only for a first order reaction does the deviation from the principle of equal accessibility lead to the prediction of a decrease of macroscopic process rates. In the case of consecutive reactions, the intermediate products are changed. Thus, for estimating macroscopic reaction rates taking place on unequal surfaces, information on the chemical kinetics and the average mass transfer coefficient alone are insufficient. Instead, the equation of convective diffusion in the boundary layer coupled with proper boundary conditions that take into account the rates of chemical reactions are needed. The solution to this problem for a semi-infinite slab shows that the effective thickness of the boundary layer depends on the fluid physical properties of the flow velocity, and the chemical kinetics on the particle surface. Levich[2] has given the solution to this problem for laminar flow, and approximate solutions for the turbulent and laminar flow cases are given by Rozen.[3] Finding exact solutions to this problem for different geometries and taking into account the heating of reaction mixtures are formidable tasks. Consequently, analyses of diffusion kinetics for the most part rely on the assumption of equal area accessibility, despite evident shortcomings.[4]

With this introduction, we may now address the problem of diffusion into a porous particle. The rate of reaction in a porous solid is composed of the rates on different portions of the surface, characterized by different accessibilities with respect to diffusion. The total reaction rate is a function of the particle shape and the size of the pores. For a finely porous material, the system may be visualized as if the reaction were taking place over the entire volume occupied by the material.

Consider a particle as shown in Figure 9-1, where the internal structure of the solid has a highly developed network of pores. For penetration to the active surface within the particle to occur, the gaseous reagents must diffuse through the pores. If the reaction occurs within the entire mass of the particle, then concentrations and temperature gradients will exist throughout the solid. In an actual situation, the efficiency of the reaction will be lower than when there is equal accessibility to the surface. Two assumptions often invoked are: The porous solid is homogeneous, and the behavior of the gas reagent is analogous to the dissolution of a gas in liquid accompanied by aqueous-phase chemical reaction. As a limiting case, consider the thickness of a porous particle to be infinite. It follows then that the surface of the particle may be viewed as being flat, and hence, it is sufficient to consider diffusion in a direction normal to the surface of the particle. If the diffusing substance enters in an irreversible reaction, then its concentration at any point on the porous particle can be expressed by the solution of diffusion equation:

$$D * \frac{d^2C}{dx^2} = r(C_1 T) \tag{9-47}$$

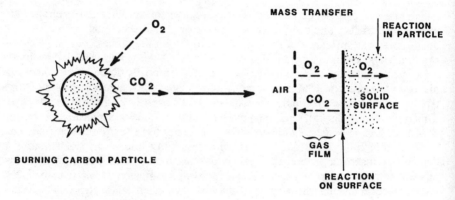

Figure 9-1. Illustration of the mechanisms of diffusion into a porous particle.

where r is the reaction rate related to a unit volume of the particle. The boundary conditions for this problem are as follows:

$$C = C_p \text{ at } x = 0 \text{ (at the surface)}$$

$$C \to 0, \frac{dC}{dx} = 0 \text{ at } x \to \infty \tag{9-48}$$

Integrating Equation 9-47 and applying boundary conditions, (Equation 9-48) gives:

$$\frac{C}{C_p} = \left(1 + \frac{x}{e}\left\{\frac{n - 1}{[2(n + 1)]^{0.5}}\right\}\right)\frac{2}{1 - n} \tag{9-49A}$$

and

$$e = \left(\frac{D^*}{KC_p^{n-1}}\right)^{0.5} \tag{9-49B}$$

where the reaction rate expression has the assumed form of $r = KC^n$. For a first order reaction (n = 1), Equation 9-49A becomes indefinite:

$$\frac{C}{C_p} = \left\{1 + \frac{x}{e}\left[\frac{0}{2(2)^{0.5}}\right]\right\}\frac{2}{0} \tag{9-50}$$

As shown, concentration decreases as the gas travels through the particle for small values of e. For a first-order reaction, the value of e is equal to the distance where the concentration of reagent decreases in e times.

For reaction orders greater than one, the concentration of the reagent never becomes equal to zero, but asymptotically approaches it when x → ∞. Despite this, it is appropriate to denote a final depth of penetration for the reaction inside the particle because at a definite distance from the surface, the concentration of the reagent decreases to an insignificant value. The higher the value of e, the greater the penetration depth. Note from Equation 9-49B that e is a function of the diffusion coefficient; observe that penetration increases with an increase in D*, and decreases with a higher rate constant, K. The increase in the surface concentration, C_p, leads to increases in penetration depth in the particle when n < 1, or decreases when n > 1. Hence, the magnitude of e determines first, the condition of the process and the character of dependence of the reaction rate on observed variables; and second, the validity of the assumptions invoked.

In an actual system such as the combustion of coal particles, there is a distribution of particle sizes. For a certain portion of these particles, the penetration depth of the reaction will be low in comparison to the pore diameter. In this case, we cannot assume the porous particle to be quasi-homogeneous for the large depth of reaction penetration comparable with a characteristic linear size of the particle; that is, the assumption of infinite particle thickness is no longer appropriate. The cases that are appropriate depend on the magnitude of e. If d >> e >> d_o (where d_o is the pore diameter and d the particle size), then the concentration of reagents in the pores is described by Equations 9-49A or 9-50. Inside the particle, the concentration goes to zero. The macroscopic reaction rate related to the unity of outer particle surface, $\varrho*$, is equal to the diffusion flux through a unit of outer surface area of particle:

$$\varrho* = -D*\left(\frac{dc}{dx}\right)_{x=0} = \left(\frac{2}{\alpha+1}D*KC_p^{\alpha+1}\right)^{0.5} \tag{9-51}$$

Equation 9-51 states that the macroscopic reaction rate is approximately equal to the mean geometric reaction and diffusion rates. The effective rate constant according to this expression is $(2D*K/(\alpha+1))^{0.5}$. Since the diffusion coefficient D* is nearly independent of temperature, the apparent activation energy is roughly half of the real energy. The apparent reaction order is equivalent to the mean arithmetic value between the first order reaction and the true order. Specific conditions establish the internal diffusion zone of the reaction. If the reaction takes place in the internal diffusion zone with several initial substances as described by Equation 9-37 and the process is limited by the diffusion of only one reagent, then the order of reaction of this component is approximately the average between the order of the first and true order, and for the remaining components it is half the real order.

A second case of interest is when e >> d. Here the reaction takes place in the internal kinetic zone. The concentrations of components in the total volume of the particle are equal to their surface concentration and the macrokinetics coincide with the true kinetics. The total internal surface of the particle reacts with the gas phase.

A third case worth noting is when e ≃ d_o. Here only a thin layer of the particle near the outer surface reacts with the gaseous reagents. The core of the particle does not undergo reaction, and the gas concentration goes to zero. The macrokinetics coincide with the true kinetics but the amount of the reacting substance is not proportional to the total surface but rather to the outer surface of the particle. Hence, the reaction takes place in the outer kinetic zone.

For all three zones, the concentration on the outer surface of the particle, C_p, is equal to the concentration in the bulk flow, meaning that there is no outer diffusional retardation. This implies a special case where the mass transfer coefficient from the bulk flow to the particle surface, β, must be considerably greater than the value determining the reaction rate inside the particle. The critical value for the internal diffusion zone is $(D*K)^{0.5}$; for the internal kinetic zone it is Ka (where a is the ratio of particle volume to its surface, or hydraulic radius), and for the outer diffusion zone it is the rate constant of the reaction on the particle surface, x. If the value of β is considerably smaller than each of these critical values, then the process is limited by the reagent supply to the particle surface, and the reaction takes place in the outer diffusion zone. In the zone intermediate between the outer diffusion zone and the outer kinetic zone the surface concentration is given by Equations 9-35 and 9-36, from which the macro-rate of the process is determined. The intermediate region between the outer diffusional and the internal kinetic zones has the following form:

$$\frac{d^2C}{dx^2} = \frac{C}{e^2} \tag{9-52}$$

Integrating this expression gives:

$$\frac{C}{C_p} = \frac{Ch\dfrac{a}{e(1 - x/a)}}{Ch(a/e)} \tag{9-53}$$

where the boundary conditions $C = C_p$ at $x = 0$ and $dC/dx = 0$ at $x = a$ have been applied.

The rate of utilization of the internal pore surface can be assessed through the use of an efficiency factor. This parameter is defined as the ratio of the amount of substance reacted in the particle to the amount that might react if the total surface were equally attainable; and correspondingly, the reagent concentration in the entire volume of particle pores would be equal to the concentration on the outer surface of the particle.

For the case of a first-order reaction and considering the active surface to be that of a flat slab of infinite length, having thickness 2a', Equation 9-47 is solved after substituting $r = KC$ and $1 = (D*)^{0.5}/K$:

$$\eta = \frac{\int_v r(C)dv}{r(C_p)V} = \frac{\int_F D* \text{ grad } CdF}{r(C_p)V} \tag{9-54}$$

The numerator's integration must be performed over the entire volume or the total surface of the particle. In the case of monomolecular reaction in the flat slab, the solution is:

$$\eta = \frac{1}{a'C_p} \int_0^{a'} Cdx = \frac{e}{a}Ch\frac{a'}{e} \tag{9-55}$$

This expression states that the rate of utilization of the internal surface is dependent upon the relative value of parameter e and the thickness, a', of the slab. As shown, the efficiency factor decreases with decreasing values of e and becomes zero at e = 0. This limit corresponds to the outer kinetic zone where the internal surface of the particle does not work at all. For e $\to \infty$ (i.e., the transition in the internal kinetic zone) the rate of utilization of the particle surface is equal to unity.

For the monomolecular reaction in a porous spherical particle having radius 3a', the law of concentration changing inside the particle is determined by the solution of the following equation:

$$\frac{d^2C}{dx^2} + \frac{2}{x}\frac{dC}{dx} = \frac{C}{e^2} \tag{9-56A}$$

The appropriate boundary conditions are:

$$C = C_p \text{ at } x = 3a'$$

$$\frac{dC}{dx} = 0 \text{ at } x = 0 \tag{9-56B}$$

Upon integration, we obtain:

$$\frac{C}{C_p} = \frac{3a'}{x} \cdot \frac{Sh\frac{x}{e}}{Sh\frac{3a'}{e}} \tag{9-57}$$

And the rate of utilization of the internal surface of the particle is:

$$\eta = \frac{e}{a'}\left(Ch\frac{3a'}{e} - \frac{e}{3a'}\right) \tag{9-58}$$

The efficiency factor for different geometry solids for a first order reaction scheme as a function of the volume to surface ratio is shown in Figure 9-2. The plots in Figure 9-2 show that the solutions for widely different geometries are quite similar, and hence, Equations 9-55 and 9-58 can be used without incurring significant errors by neglecting the proper particle hydraulic radius. The relationship between the effective diffusion coefficient, D^*, and the particle structure is complex. A comparison between D^* and the real coefficient of molecular diffusion will reveal that $D^* < D$, because for diffusion in a porous particle, not all the surface area is attainable—only that portion that is occupied by pores (i.e., the void fraction ϵ)—and because the path of diffusion in a winding network of pores is longer. The tortuosity

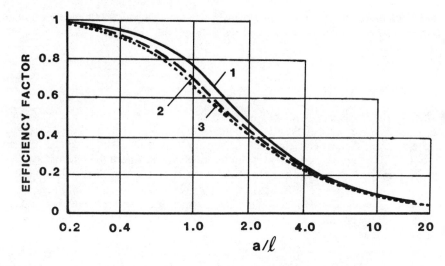

Figure 9-2. Efficiency factor for first order reaction for porous particles of different forms: (1) slab; (2) cylinder; (3) sphere; where a′ is the particle hydraulic radius and ℓ is a characteristic length.

of pore paths can be related to the angle of directions (i.e., from 0° to 90°), over which the probability of diffusion exists. The mean deviation angle is 45° and consequently the length of the path increases by a factor of $2^{0.5}$, according to the shortest distance. Therefore, as a first approximation we may write:

$$D^* = \frac{\epsilon D}{2^{0.5}} \qquad (9\text{-}59)$$

The hydraulic radius, a_o, can be defined in terms of the ratio of pore voidage to the total surface of a unit volume of a particle, ϵ/σ. For round-shaped pores, the hydraulic radius is equal to one fourth the diameter. The reaction rate in the internal diffusion zone as determined from Equation 9-51 is proportional to $\epsilon a_o^{-0.5}$ or $\sigma a_o^{0.5}$. The inverse proportionality of the reaction rate to the square root of the hydraulic pore radius for constant porosity is a result of a reduction in the internal surface of the particle and consequently an effective constant related to a unit volume, k. For the constant internal surface the reaction rate increases proportionally to the square root from the pore hydraulic radius as a result of increasing the effective diffusion coefficient with increasing porosity. The pore expansion for a constant internal surface must, however, be accompanied by a reduction in capillary wall diameters. In small diameter pores molecular diffusion can be described by Knudsen's mechanism. Substituting for the diffusion coefficients D (Equation 9-31) and D* (Equation 9-59) into the reaction-rate expression for the internal diffusion zone (Equation 9-51), we obtain:

$$\varrho \simeq (KD^*)^{0.5} \simeq (\epsilon\sigma d_o)^{0.5} \simeq \epsilon \qquad (9\text{-}60)$$

The transition into the Knudsen region with smaller-size pores (but constant porosity) does not enhance the diffusion process since the increase in internal surface resulting from smaller pores is counterbalanced by the additional resistance to flow in the narrower passages. The reaction penetration into the particle, e, for the Knudsen region is proportional to a_0 and is shown to decrease with narrower-size pores. The pore size distribution is therefore an important factor influencing the macroscopic process rate. The most desirable arrangement of a porous network is one that favors a large number of macropores which permeate the particle. With such an arrangement the internal surface of the particle is large, and relatively wide macropores provide a practically constant concentration of gaseous reagents throughout the entire particle. Note that the total internal diffusion resistance is concentrated in the capillaries. The reaction rate can be obtained by solving Equation 9-47 for the individual microparticles rather than for all the particles. The rate of utilization of the internal surface may be evaluated from Equation 9-58, where a' is the hydraulic radius of a microparticle.

We now direct attention to a homogeneous reaction in which the reactant is supplied by diffusion from another phase, for example, when there is absorption of a gas by a liquid acompanied by a chemical reaction in the liquid.

For porous materials, an effective diffusion coefficient, D', and effective rate constant, K', can be related to the structure of the porous surface. Considering the pores as capillaries that run from the free surface without breaks or intersections throughout the entire thickness of a particle or layer, the pores can then be characterized by a pore diameter, h, the number N of pores per unit surface area, and the labyrinth coefficient x, which is defined as the mean distance along the pores corresponding to unit lengths in the direction normal to the surface

$$x = \frac{d\ell}{dx} \tag{9-61}$$

where ℓ = distance measured along direction of pores
      x = distance measured normal to surface

The surface area of the pores per unit volume of the layer is $xN\Delta h$.
The effective rate of reaction f' (ξ) per unit area of reacting surface can be expressed by:

$$f'(\xi) = xN\Delta hf(\xi) \tag{9-62A}$$

$$k' = xN\Delta hK \tag{9-62B}$$

where k' is the rate constant.
Fick's law of diffusion can be used to obtain the diffusion flow per unit surface area of the free cross-section of pores.

$$q^* = D\frac{dC}{dt} \tag{9-63}$$

To evaluate D', it is necessary to determine the diffusion flow per unit area of the total cross-section of the layer to dC/dx. That is

$$\frac{dC}{d\ell} = \frac{dC}{dx}\frac{dx}{d\ell} = \frac{1}{x}\frac{dC}{d\ell} \tag{9-64}$$

From which the area of the free cross-section of the pores per unit area of the total cross-section of the layer is:

$$\Omega = N\frac{\Delta h^2}{4} \tag{9-65}$$

The diffusion flow q per unit surface area of the total cross-section of the layer can be expressed as follows:

$$q = N\frac{\Delta h^2}{4}q^* = DN\frac{\Delta h^2}{4}\frac{dC}{d\ell}$$

$$= \frac{dN}{x}\frac{\Delta h^2}{4}\frac{dC}{dx}D' = D\frac{N}{x}\frac{\Delta h^2}{4} \tag{9-66}$$

In general, the macroscopic rate of reaction is:

$$\frac{dm}{dt} = \left(\frac{2}{n+1}\theta'k'C^{n+1}\right)^{0.5} \tag{9-67}$$

where n is the reaction order. Upon substituting Equations 9-62B and 9-66 into 9-67, the following expression is derived:

$$\frac{dm}{dt} = \left(\frac{2}{n+1}N^2\frac{\Delta^2 h^3}{4}DkC^{n+1}\right)^{0.5} \tag{9-68}$$

or, taking into account Equation 9-65, we have:

$$\frac{dm}{dt} = \Omega\left(\frac{\delta}{n+1}\frac{Dk}{h}C^{n+1}\right)^{0.5} \tag{9-69}$$

where Ω is dimensionless. This expression shows that the reactivity of the porous material in the range of diffusion in the pores is directly proportional to the porosity, assuming a constant pore diameter. With an increase in pore diameter at constant porosity, the reactivity decreases as the square root of the pore diameter due to the decrease of the total surface area.

COMBUSTION OF PARTICLES

In this section we shall discuss the problem of combustion of single particles. An example of this is the combustion of carbon, which is known to lie in the diffusional range at temperatures above $1100°C-1300°C$. The logarithm of the preexponential factor is a linear function of the activation energy, and the rate constant can be represented by the following empirical formula:

$$k = k_o e \frac{E}{R} \left(\frac{1}{T^*} - \frac{1}{T} \right) \tag{9-70}$$

where k_o = 31.6 cm/s
    T^* = 1240°K for the reaction of carbon with oxygen
    T^* = 1840°K for the reaction of carbon with carbon dioxide

Carbon can be characterized by its activation energy. Strong evidence suggests that the true chemical kinetics of the reaction at the surface follow first order.

Since both concentration and temperature gradients coexist in the same system, both heat transfer and diffusion occur simultaneously. The process then becomes complex because of the effects of thermal diffusion. Heat flow depends not only on the temperature gradient but also on the concentration gradient. Furthermore, the diffusion flow depends not only on the concentration gradient, but also on the temperature gradient.

The laws of diffusion have been derived from the kinetic gas theory by Enskog and Chapman.[4] The final result is the following expression for the law of diffusion in the Maxwell-Stephan form:

$$\bar{u}_1 - \bar{u}_2 = -\frac{P^2}{P_1 P_2} D \left(\frac{1}{P} \text{ grad } P_1 + \frac{k_T}{T} \text{ grad } T \right) \tag{9-71A}$$

The corresponding expression for heat flow is:

$$q = -\lambda (\text{grad } T)_n + \bar{I} \nu_n + J P k_T (\bar{u}_1 - \bar{u}_2) \tag{9-71B}$$

where k_T = thermal diffusion ratio, which is a dimensionless parameter characterizing the given gas pair as its physical constant (k_T is the ratio of the thermal diffusion and the diffusion coefficient)
    $I = C\delta T$ = mean heat content of mixture
    J = thermal equivalent of the work

Equation 9-70 and all expressions for the diffusional flow formulated in this form are valid for binary mixtures only.

For low concentrations of one component of the mixture, k_T is directly proportional to the mole fraction of the substance. The proportionality coefficient is typically in the range of 0.2–0.3 for known gas pairs. With increasing concentration, the growth of k_T with the concentration becomes slower, k_T passes through a maximum and then falls to zero (with decreasing concentration of the second component). Values of k_T increase at larger differences between the molecular weights of the two gases.

The differential equations of heat conductance and diffusion in an immobile medium are as follows:

$$C\delta\frac{\partial T}{\partial t} = \text{div}\left(\lambda \text{ grad } T + JDk_T\frac{P^2}{k_1k_2} \text{ grad } k_1\right) \qquad (9\text{-}72)$$

$$\frac{\partial C_1}{\partial t} = \text{div}\left(\frac{D}{RT} \text{ grad } k_1 + Dk_T\frac{P}{RT^2} \text{ grad } T\right) \qquad (9\text{-}73)$$

If the differences of temperatures and concentrations in the system are small, their dependency on physical properties can be neglected. If the temperature dependence of the diffusion coefficient is neglected, then D/T or D/T^2 is independent of temperature and the differential equations can be expressed as:

$$\frac{\partial T}{\partial t} = a'\Delta T + J\frac{Dk_TP^2}{CS}\text{div}\left(\frac{\text{grad } \beta_1}{\beta_1\beta_2}\right) \qquad (9\text{-}74)$$

$$\frac{\partial C_1}{\partial t} = \frac{D}{RT}\Delta P_1 + \frac{Dk_TP}{RT^2}\Delta T \qquad (9\text{-}75)$$

If temperature or concentration differences are large, the dependence on physical constants must be incorporated into the analysis, and Equations 9-72 and 9-73 become very difficult to handle.

A missing piece of information is the role of hydrodynamics. By considering the transfer of matter related directly to the turbulent motion of a fluid, the study of the kinetics of chemical processes in the diffusional regime can serve as a means for evaluating such hydrodynamic characteristics as velocity distributions, eddies, and the local structure of turbulence.

At large distances from the surface of a particle, the root mean square (rms) of the pulsation velocity u tends to a constant value u_o; from which we may write:

$$u_o = \ell\frac{du}{dy} \qquad (9\text{-}76)$$

where ℓ = mixing length
        y = distance from the surface
        u = mean velocity

The turbulent exchange coefficient plays the role of the kinematic velocity, where $A = \ell u$, and the magnitude $SA = S\ell u$ plays the role of dynamic viscosity. The tangential stress is:

$$\tau = \varrho u^2 \qquad (9\text{-}77)$$

If the curvature of the particle's surface is ignored, the tangential stress τ is independent of the distance y from the surface, and its magnitude can be written in the tangential stress at the surface:

$$\tau_0 = \varrho u_0^2 \tag{9-78}$$

where u_0 is the rms pulsation velocity at a large distance from the surface. Hence

$$u_0 = \left(\frac{\tau_0}{\varrho}\right)^{0.5} = V'\left(\frac{f}{2}\right)^{0.5} \tag{9-79}$$

where f = resistance coefficient
  V' = tangential stress through the velocity.

The thickness of the boundary layer can be written as:

$$\delta = \frac{\nu}{u_0} = \frac{\nu}{V'(f/2)^{0.5}} \tag{9-80}$$

In terms of a dimensionless thickness, L, of the laminar sublayer, the limiting values of the diffusion velocity constant at high Prandtl numbers are:

$$\beta_0 = \frac{Du_0}{L\nu} = \frac{V'}{Pr}\frac{(f/2)^{0.5}}{L}$$

$$M_\infty = \frac{1}{Pr}\frac{(f/2)^{0.5}}{L} \tag{9-81}$$

where M_∞ is the Margoulis criterion.

The transport of heat, matter, and momentum can take place either through molecular or turbulent mechanisms. The intensity of molecular transfer is characterized by the coefficients of diffusion, thermal conductivity, and kinematic viscosity. The expressions for the diffusional flow, heat flow, and the tangential stress are conventionally expressed in terms of the contributions from molecular and turbulent mechanisms:

$$q = (\partial + A)\frac{\partial C}{\partial y} \tag{9-82A}$$

$$q = C\varrho (a + A)\frac{\partial T}{\partial y} \tag{9-82B}$$

$$\tau = \varrho (\nu + A)\frac{\partial u}{\partial y} \tag{9-82C}$$

For the laminar sublayer, the velocity distribution satisfies a relationship of the following form:

$$\frac{dV'}{dy} = \frac{\tau_o}{\mu} \qquad (9\text{-}83)$$

In the core of the flow, dV'/dy is inversely proportional to y, and du/dy can be expressed by:

$$\frac{du}{dy} = \frac{\tau_o}{\mu}\left[1 - f'\left(\frac{\gamma'}{y}\right)\right] \qquad (9\text{-}84)$$

where f' is the transition function. Constant γ' is referred to as the width of the transition zone.

The diffusion flow to the surface of a particle can be evaluated by the usual formulas of the theory of convective diffusion, based on the relative velocity of the flow with respect to the particle.

In the case of combustion, a chemical reaction takes place under conditions of progressive self-acceleration, due to accumulation of heat or of catalyzing active intermediate products. With the former, combustion is termed thermal, and in the latter it is referred to as being diffusional or chain combustion. Thermal combustion reactions occur when reaction rates increase rapidly with rising temperature. Diffusional combustion is observed only in the case of an autocatalytic reaction.

In thermal ignition, a combustible mixture is contained in a reactor vessel, the walls of which are at some temperature T_o. Under proper conditions, the temperature rises to some high value which is close to the theoretical maximum temperature of explosion

$$T_m = T_o + \frac{\phi}{c_p} \qquad (9\text{-}85)$$

where ϕ = thermal effect of the reaction
        c_p = heat capacity of reacting mixture.

The equation of heat conductance with continuously distributed sources of heat is:

$$c_p\varrho\frac{\partial T}{\partial t} = \text{div } \lambda \text{ grad } T + q' \qquad (9\text{-}86)$$

where q' is the density of the sources. The solution to this equation involves specifying a constant wall temperature, from which a temperature distribution in the vessel can be obtained as a function of time.

Application of the stationary theory deals with the stationary equation of heat conductance with continuously distributed heat sources. Its solution yields the stationary temperature distribution in the reacting mixture. The conditions under which such a distribution becomes no longer feasible are the critical conditions of ignition. The stationary equation is:

$$\text{div } \lambda \text{ grad } T = -q' \tag{9-87}$$

Neglecting the temperature dependence of the heat conductivity, we may write:

$$\lambda \Delta T = -q' \tag{9-88}$$

where Δ is the Laplace operator.

The density of the sources of heat q' is the amount of heat evolved by the chemical reaction in a unit volume per unit time. That is, it is the product of the thermal effect and the rate of reaction. Applying the Arrhenius relationship for the density of the heat sources, we obtain:

$$\Delta T = -\frac{\phi}{\lambda} Z e^{-\frac{E}{RT}} \tag{9-89}$$

Equation 9-89 can be integrated using the boundary condition of $T = T_0$ at the wall.

The nonstationary theory involves the use of a thermal balance over the entire reactor vessel, with the assumption of constant, uniform temperature. This assumption is obviously incorrect in the conduction regime, where the temperature gradient is by no means localized at the wall. The amount of heat evolved over the entire volume per unit time by the chemical reaction is:

$$Q = \omega \phi \, Z e^{-\frac{E}{RT}} \tag{9-90}$$

and the amount of heat carried away from the wall is:

$$Q' = \alpha S(T - T_0) \tag{9-91}$$

where ω = vessel volume
S = wall surface area
α = heat exchange coefficient

The difference between these two quantities is the energy required to raise the temperature of the gas to ignition in a unit period of time:

$$Q - Q' = c_p \varrho \omega \frac{dT}{dt} \tag{9-92}$$

where c_p = heat capacity of gaseous mixture
ϱ = density of gaseous mixture (i.e., number of moles per unit volume)

Hence, the thermal balance for the system is:

$$\frac{dT}{dt} = \frac{\phi}{c\varrho} Ze^{-\frac{E}{RT}} - \frac{\alpha S}{c\varrho\omega}(T - T_o) \tag{9-93}$$

Equation 9-93 can be expressed in terms of a dimensionless temperature, θ:

$$\frac{d\theta}{dt} = \frac{\phi}{c\varrho}\frac{E}{RT_o^2} Ze^{-\frac{E}{RT_o}e^\theta} - \frac{\alpha S}{c\varrho\omega}\theta \tag{9-94}$$

For an autocatalytic reaction, the propagation of the flame can be due not only to a transfer of heat from the flame zone to the fresh gas but also to diffusion from the zone of catalytically active reaction products. If the temperature rise in the flame is small (that is, cool flames), the propagation will be entirely due to a diffusion mechanism.

The rate of reaction in this case is given by:

$$\frac{dn}{dt} = f(\eta') \tag{9-95}$$

where η' = relative concentration of the catalytically active product
ϕ = kinetic coefficient (self-acceleration coefficient), which is analogous to the rate constant

The temperature dependence of the reaction rate does not have to be accounted for in this case. Instead, the temperature rise in the flame can be considered to be sufficiently small so as to be neglected (that is, we assume isothermal diffusional flame propagation).

Based on these assumptions, we obtain:

$$D\frac{d^2n}{dx^2} - \omega\frac{dn}{dx} + \phi f(\eta) = 0 \tag{9-96}$$

with the boundary conditions, at $x = -\infty$, $\eta = 0$; at $x = +\infty$, $\eta = 1$ in the case of autocatalysis by final products, and $\eta = 0$ in the case of autocatalysis by intermediate products. The condition of stationary reaction is given by:

$$\frac{\phi D}{\omega^2} = \text{constant} \tag{9-97}$$

and the velocity of stationary flame propagation is:

$$\omega = A(\phi D)^{0.5} \tag{9-98}$$

The value of the constant coefficient A depends on the form of the function $f(\eta')$.

FLUID-BED FLOW MODELING

Freely Bubbling Beds

Thus far we have considered fundamental principles of reaction kinetics, diffusion, and heat and momentum transport. These principles alone, however, are insufficient for describing the mechanisms of a particular reacting system in large-scale equipment. They are a phenomena that must be coupled with the hydrodynamic characteristics of the reactor system in order to design for and predict the overall process behavior. In the case of a fluidized-bed reactor, the principal hydrodynamic characteristics which affect reaction kinetics and the transfers of heat and mass can be related to two areas—the bubble dynamics and the mixing behavior of the fluidized solids.

Wen and Chen[5] have provided an extensive review of the major fluid-bed models available, and a summary of some of their important conclusions are outlined below. To begin, consider a single rising bubble through a bed of fluidized solids as illustrated in Figure 9-3. Three important regimes can be associated with the rising bubble; namely, a wake of solids, which is carried upwards below the bubble void; a shell or cloud of gas surrounding the bubble void; and a small fraction of solid particles entering the bubble void.

The upward solids movement in the bubble wake is counterbalanced by a net downward flow of solids in the emulsion phase, which as Stephans et al.[7] and others[8] have found can entrain some of the gas in the downward direction. The gas velocity in the emulsion phase, U_e, can be expressed as:

$$U_e = (U_{mf}/\epsilon_{mf}) - U_s \qquad (9\text{-}99)$$

where U_s is the absolute velocity of solids in the emulsion phase.

And the solids velocity from a mass balance is:

$$U_s = \frac{U_b \delta f_w}{[1 - (1 + f_w)]} \qquad (9\text{-}100)$$

where f_w = ratio of wake volume to bubble void volume $\simeq 0.33$
$\quad\ \ U_b$ = bubble velocity = $U_{br} + U - U_{mf}$
$\quad\ \ \delta$ = fraction of bed occupied by bubble voids

With very fine particles, gas bubbles rise at a much greater rate than the emulsion gas. The rising bubbles are surrounded by a thin cloud of circulating gas. With large particles, the emulsion gas rises as fast as or faster than bubbles, and the clouds of the bubbles are loosely attached to the gas voids and can even overlap with other clouds and engulf the entire bed. The differences in gas streamlines of the fast and slow bubble regimes are illustrated in Figure 9-4.

At high gas velocities, a bubbling bed transforms into a "turbulent" and "circulating" bed or "fast" fluidized bed. The transitions from bubbling to turbulent and turbulent to fast have been summarized by various investigators.[10,11] Numerous models for describing the bubbling zone in a fluidized bed have been proposed[12-16] and have been classified into three levels by Wen and Chen.[5] A summary of the models and classifications given by Wen and Chen[5] is shown in Tables 9-1 and 9-2.

Horio and Wen[15] have proposed several simple models which fall into the Level I category. Using the notation of Wen and Chen,[5] Figure 9-5 illustrates the models which are either homogeneous (P and M) or two phase (P − P, P − M, C). The material balances for a first order gas-phase reaction following this type of model are as follows:

For the Homogeneous Model:

P Model (plug flow) over incremental bed height,

$$U\frac{dC}{dL} = kC \tag{9-101}$$

M model (complete mixing)

$$U(1 - C_{out}) = kL_{mf}C_{out} \tag{9-102}$$

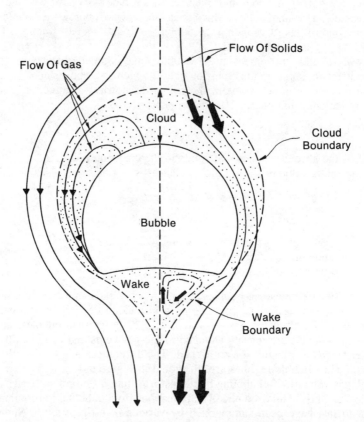

Figure 9-3. A fast two-dimensional bubble and its cloud and wake. (Murray.[6])

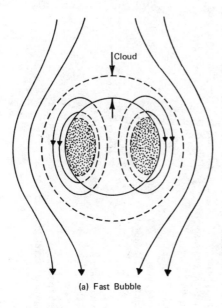

(a) Fast Bubble

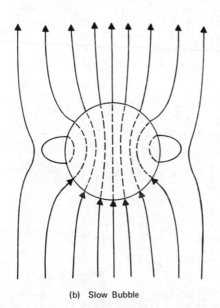

(b)   Slow Bubble

Figure 9-4. Illustration of the differences in gas streamlines between a fast bubble and a slow bubble (Catipovic et al.[9])

Table 9-1
Code for the Classification of Models[5]

Factors	n_1 Way of dividing the phase	n_2 Way of flow assignment	n_3 Cloud volume	n_4 Gas exchange coefficient	n_5 Bubble diameter	n_6 Effect of jet
Values of n_i						
1	3 phases B – C – E	$u_{ob} = u_o - u_{mf}$ $u_{oe} + u_{oc} = u_{mf}$ or $u_{oe} = u_{mf}$	Davidson model $R = \dfrac{\alpha + 2}{\alpha - 1}$ (3-dimensional)	2 interphases Kunii and Levenspiel[24] model	Constant and adjustable	Not considered
2	2 phases B – (C + E)	$u_e = u_{mf}/\epsilon_{mf}$ $u_c = u_b/\epsilon_{mf}$	Murray model $R = \dfrac{\alpha}{\alpha - 1}$	1 interphase Orcutt and Davidson[23] model	Constant $D_{bc} = \begin{cases} D_b \text{ at } L_f/2 \\ \text{or} \\ D_b \text{ at } L_{mf}/2 \end{cases}$	Considered
3	2 phases (B + C) – E	$u_e = u_{mf}/\epsilon_{mf} - u_s$	$R = 1$	1 interphase Partridge and Rowe[28] model	Constant D_{be} from bed expansion data	
4		$u_{ob} = u_o - u_{mf}$ $u_{oc} = 0$ $u_{oe} = 0$		1 interphase Empirical correlation	Varied along the bed axis	
5		$u_{ob} = u_o$ $u_{oc} = 0$ $u_{oe} = 0$				

B = bubble phase L_f = expanded bed height
C = cloud phase L_{mf} = expanded bed height at minimum fluidization
E = emulsion phase

Table 9-2
Classification of Fluidized-Bed Reactor Models[5]

Level	Description	Models	Code ($n_1n_2n_3n_4n_5n_6$)*
I	Parameters are constant along the bed.	Shen and Johnstone[12]	21xxx1
		van Deemter[18]	25xxx1
		Johnstone et al.[19]	31xxx1
	Parameters are not related to the bubble behavior. ($n_3 \sim n_5$ cannot be specified.)	May[20]	21xxx1
		Kobayashi and Arai[21]	31 (or 5) xxx1
		Muchi[22]	31xxx1
II	Parameters are constant along the bed.	Orcutt, Davidson, and Pigford[23]	21x211
		Kunii and Levenspiel[24]	141111
	Parameters are related to the bubble size, which is adjustable. $n_5 = 1 \sim 3$	Fryer and Potter[25]	131111
		—	
III	Parameters are related to the bubble size.	Mamuro and Muchi[26]	21x541
		Toor and Calderbank[27]	311241
		Partridge and Rowe[28]	322341
		Kobayashi, et al.[29]	312541
		Kato and Wen[30]	351441
	Bubble size is varied along the bed axis. $n_5 = 4$	Mori and Muchi[31]	21x541
		Fryer and Potter[25]	21x241
		Mori and Wen[32]	351442

* The definition of the code is given in Table 9-2. Example: 21xxx1 means $n_1 = 2$ (i.e., the bed is divided into two phases, and the cloud phase is included in the emulsion phase); $n_2 = 1$ (i.e., the flow rate in bubble phase is $u_o - u_{mf}$); factors $n_3 \sim n_5$ are not specified (i.e., the parameters are not related to the bubble characteristics); and $n_6 = 1$ (i.e., the effect of jet is not considered).

With two-phase models (Level II models), the excess gas above the minimum fluidization velocity flows through the bed in the form of bubbles.[33] The gas flow-through in the emulsion phase, U_e, (Equation 9-99) may be in either the upward or downward direction. Wen and Chen[5] note that the gas flow-through in the emulsion phase, U_e, can be assumed to be negligible. That is, the exit concentration of the bubble phase is a good approximation of the overall exit concentration from the bed. According to Wen and Chen,[5] this assumption is reasonable for beds with $U_o/U_{mf} \cong 6 \sim 11$. Note, however, that the reaction takes place in both phases, and gas exchange occurs between the phases.

For the bubble phase, the material balance is:

$$\left\{ \begin{array}{c} \text{change in concentration} \\ \times \text{ bubble flow rate} \end{array} \right\} = \left\{ \begin{array}{c} \text{material exchanged} \\ \text{with emulsion} \end{array} \right\} \qquad (9\text{-}103)$$

$$- \left\{ \begin{array}{c} \text{material reacted} \\ \text{in the bubble phase} \end{array} \right\}$$

And for the emulsion phase:

$$\left\{ \begin{array}{c} \text{material exchanged} \\ \text{with bubbles} \end{array} \right\} = \left\{ \begin{array}{c} \text{material reacted in} \\ \text{the emulsion phase} \end{array} \right\} \qquad (9\text{-}104)$$

Table 9-3 summarizes the principal combinations of bubble and emulsion phase models that have been successfully applied to fluid beds. Wen and Chen[5] give some general guidelines as to when to apply each type. Their criteria are based on the type of reactions: slow reactions ($k < 0.5$ s^{-1}; $N_R < 1.0$), intermediate reactions ($0.5 < k < 5.0$s^{-1}; $1 < N_R < 10$), and fast reactions ($k > 5$s^{-1}; $N_r > 10$).

For slow reactions, the predicted conversion is nearly insensitive to N_M or the model used; the reason being that the system is kinetics limited rather than mass transfer limited. Usually a single mixing-train type model (i.e., tanks in series) is used to estimate the lower limit of conversion; however, it is applied on a somewhat arbitrary basis. Little information about the bed hydrodynamics is needed in this approach; however, accurate kinetics data are mandatory. No distinction between bubble and emulsion phases is made.

For intermediate-type reactions, conversion may be limited by chemical kinetics or mass transport between the bubble and emulsion phases. In this case, the combination models for bubble-emulsion phases given in Table 9-3 should be applied. The criteria recommended by Wen and Chen[5] are based on the ratio of the fluidiz-ing-gas velocity to the minimum fluidization velocity. When $U/U_{mf} < 6\text{-}11$, the plug-flow bubble phase/plug-flow emulsion-phase (P-P model) is most appropriate. When $U/U_{mf} > 6\text{-}11$, the plug-flow bubble-phase/mixed-flow emulsion-phase (P-M) model applies. Parameter N_M must be estimated (see notation of Table 9-3) or evaluated from experiments (see data of van Swaaij[10]).

For fast reactions, the conversion again becomes less sensitive to the bubble char-acteristics and mass transfer in the bubbling-bed zone. Conversion in this will be high in the grid region where the gas exchange is rapid and in the freeboard zone

Table 9-3
Summary of Two-Phase Models for Fluidized Beds—Bubbling Zone

Model Description		Material Balance Expression		Notes
Bubble Phase	Emulsion Phase	Bubble Phase	Emulsion Phase	
Plug flow	Plug flow	$\dfrac{dC_b}{d\xi} = N_M(C_e - C_b) - N_R\gamma_s(C_b)$	$N_M(C_e - C_b) = -N_R(1 - \gamma_s)C_e$	
Well mixed	Well mixed	$1 - C_b = N_M(C_b - C_e) + N_R\gamma_s(C_b)$	$N_M(C_e - C_b) = -N_R(1 - \gamma_s)C_e$	Assumes $\gamma_s \to 0$
Plug flow	Well mixed	$\dfrac{dC_b}{d\xi} = N_M(C_e - C_b)$	$N_M(C_e - C_b) = -N_R(1 - \gamma_s)C_e$	
		overall balance— $(1 - C_{out}) = N_R(C_e)$		
Tanks in series	Tanks in series	$C_{bi} - (C_b)_{i-1} = (N_M/n)(C_{ei} - C_{bi})$ $\qquad - (N_R/n)\gamma_s(C_{bi})$	$(N_M/n)(C_{ei} - C_{bi}) =$ $\qquad - (N_R/n)(1 - \gamma_s)C_{ei}$	Approaches bubble-free plug flow model when number of tanks >10. Estimate of appropriate n value is n = L_f/d_b

Nomenclature:

N_R = number of reaction unit = kL_{mf}/U

L_{mf} = fluid bed height at minimum fluidization

N_m = number of transfer units = $F_{be}\delta L_f/U$

δ = volume of bubbles/total bed volume = $(L_f - L_{mf})/L_f$

γ_s = fraction of particles in bubble phase (including cloud) based on total volume of particles

k = first order reaction rate constant

U = superficial gas velocity

L_f = fluidized bed height

C_b, C_e = concentration in bubble phase and emulsion phase, respectively

ξ = dimensionless bed height = L/L_f

d_b = estimated bubble size at mid bed height

where dispersed-phase contact occurs. The P-M model combined with a *grid region model* and a *freeboard model* must therefore be used.

The design of the grid (or gas distributor) is critical with fast reactions since most of the conversion occurs in this lower region of the bed.[34] Hence, the degree of conversion is influenced by grid design parameters. Porous plate distributors, most often used in small-scale equipment, provide increased efficiency compared with perforated plate distributors, which are more typical in large-scale operations.[35] As described in Chapter 4, gas entering the bed through a grid will emerge as pulsating jets which detach to yield formation-size bubbles. For a given free area of grid the jets become shorter and the initial bubbles smaller as the grid orifice size is reduced. In the extreme, a perforated grid plate behaves similar to a porous plate when large numbers of small orifices are used.[32] Thus, the grid region influences the reactor's performance in the following manners: First, if pulsating gas jets exist, they can be expected to provide a zone of very effective gas exchange between the lean and dense phases. Secondly, the influence of the initial bubble size on coalescence and growth of the bubble in the bubbling zone may be profound.

The important parameter in this case is the jet-to-emulsion-gas-exchange coefficient per unit vessel volume, F_{je}. Behie and Kehoe[36] have reported values to lie in the range from about 18 to 4 (s^{-1}), which can be compared with values of δF_{be} (bubble to emulsion coefficient per unit vessel volume) which according to Wen and Chen[5] are typically from 2 to 0.2 (s^{-1}), assuming a value of $\delta = 0.5$. These data suggest that the gas transfer process in the grid region is roughly an order of magnitude faster than that in the bubbling zone of the bed.

Wen and Chen[5] suggest that the extent of the grid region can be assumed to be equal to the jet height, L_J, which can be predicted by the correlation of Wen et al.:[37]

$$\frac{L_J}{d_o} = 1,150 \left\{ \frac{U_J - U_{mfJ}\mu G}{P_G d_p^2 g} \right\} \left(\frac{\varrho_G}{\varrho_s} \right) \left(\frac{d_p}{d_o} \right)^{0.66} \tag{9-105}$$

This has been incorporated into a more sophisticated hydrodynamic model (a modified *bubble assemblage model*) to calculate the height of the first compartment, ΔL_1, which is assumed to be well mixed,[40] thus,

$$\Delta L_1 = L_J + L_c \tag{9-106}$$

where L_c is the critical height above the jets at which the bubble clouds overlap. An extension of the P-M model to account for the enhanced gas exchange in the grid region can also be used.[36] The model, depicted in Figure 9-5B, treats the jets as plug flow in series with the bubble phase, also in plug flow; the emulsion phase is considered well mixed throughout. Using Wen and Chen's[5] notation, the model is designated the $P_J M/P_b M$ model. The material balance equations are identical with the equations for the P-M model except for the definition of the number of mass transfer units; in this case the number of N.T.U. is:

$$\overline{N}_M = N_{Mb} + N_{MJ} \tag{9-107}$$

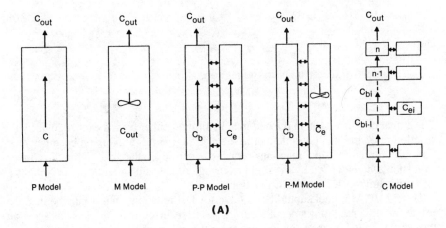

(A)

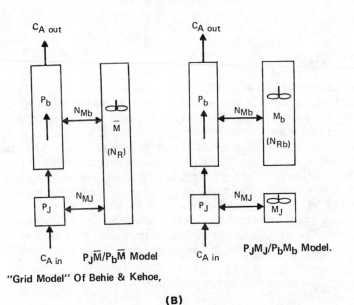

(B)

Figure 9-5. Conceptual fluid-bed models: (A) simple homogeneous and two-phase models—gas phase reaction for the bubbling zone; (B) models for the grid region.

where,

N_{Mb} = mass transfer units in the bubble zone

$\qquad = F_{be} \delta (L_f - L_J) U$ $\qquad\qquad\qquad\qquad\qquad\qquad\qquad$ (9-108)

and

N_{MJ} = mass transfer units in the jet zone

$\qquad = F_{Je} L_J / U$ $\qquad\qquad\qquad\qquad\qquad\qquad\qquad\qquad$ (9-109)

The extent of conversion in the bed may be limited either by gas exchange or by the reaction rate, and it is possible that in the grid region the conversion becomes reaction-rate limited for slow reactions. For fast reactions in the grid region the conversion should be balanced by the rapid exchange of gas and should only become gas-exchange limited for very fast reactions.

The $P_J M / P_b M$ model should be suitable for fast reactions, but it may be inappropriate for slow reactions since it assumes gas transferred from the jets has access to the whole emulsion zone, underestimating the effect of reaction-rate limitation.[5]

Figure 9-5B also shows a model for both fast and slow reactions.[38] This model, designated $P_J M_J / P_b M_b$, assumes the jets are in plug flow and transfer gas to a well-mixed emulsion bounded by the grid region. The P-M grid model is then connected in series with a P-M bubble zone model. N_{MJ}, N_{Mb} are given by Equations 9-105 and 9-106, and

$$N_{RJ} = k L_J / U \qquad\qquad\qquad\qquad (9\text{-}110A)$$

$$N_{Rb} = k(L_{mf} - L_J) / U \qquad\qquad\qquad (9\text{-}110B)$$

Calculations show the significance of the grid region, particularly for fast reactions. Differences between the two models are slight for the fast reactions, but considerable for slow reactions. The $P_J M_J / P_b M_b$ model is recommended for use, although the two models converge for deep beds and low gas rates. Hence, the conversion in the grid region for fast reactions may be predicted by extensions of the P-M model. A more precise analysis awaits suitable correlations for F_{Je} or K_{Je}.

For the reaction in the freeboard region, the discussions of Chapter 5 apply. In particular, an estimate of the extent of the solid-gas reaction in this zone requires information on the solids concentration in the freeboard. This region is most often treated by an axial dispersion-type model, where the axial dispersion coefficient can be estimated from the Peclet number of the gas flow in the freeboard region using the following correlations of Wen and Fan:[39]

$$\left. \begin{aligned} \frac{1}{Pe} &= \frac{1}{Re_p Sc} + \frac{Re_p Sc}{192} \quad (\text{for } Re_p < 2{,}000) \\[2em] \frac{1}{Pe} &= \frac{3 \times 10^7}{Re_p^{2.1}} + \frac{1.35}{Re_p^{0.13}} \quad (\text{for } Re_p \geq 2{,}000) \end{aligned} \right\} \qquad (9\text{-}111)$$

with

$$Re_p = \frac{d_c U \varrho_G}{\mu_G} \qquad (9\text{-}112)$$

$$Pe = \frac{d_c \; U}{E_\delta} \qquad (9\text{-}113)$$

and

$$Sc = \frac{\mu_G}{d_c \; \varrho_G} \qquad (9\text{-}114)$$

The boundary condition used for this case is:

$$C_i(0^-) = C_{io} = C_i(0^+) - \frac{E_\delta}{U}\frac{C_i(0^+)}{dh} \qquad (9\text{-}115)$$

For a first order catalytic reaction, R_i can be represented by the following equation:

$$R_i = -k_{ov}C_i \qquad (9\text{-}116)$$

and for the surface reaction

$$k_{ov} = \frac{1}{\displaystyle\sum_i Y_i \frac{d_{pi}}{6h_{mi}{}^{(1-\epsilon)}} + \frac{1}{k_sS}} \qquad (9\text{-}117)$$

for the volumetric reaction:

$$k_{ov} = \frac{(1 - \epsilon)}{\displaystyle\sum_i Y_i\left(\frac{d_p}{6D'}\right)_i + \frac{1}{k_t}} \qquad (9\text{-}118)$$

Here, D' = gas diffusivity through pores
Y_i = weight fraction of particle size d_{pi} in freeboard
h_{mi} = the mass transfer coefficient across the gas film
k_t = intrinsic reaction rate
S = total surface area

Returning to the bubbling zone of the bed, the more sophisticated models are those that Wen et al.[5] refer to as Level III models. These models attempt to account for variations in bubble size over the height of the fluidized bed. One of the more successful models is the bubble assemblage model,[30,40] which divides the bed into compartments, the height of which is adjusted to the bubble size at that level. The principal features of the model are illustrated in Figure 9-6, and the principal assumptions that form its basis are as follows: First, each of the "η" compartments of the bed consists of a bubble phase and an emulsion phase, and the gas within each

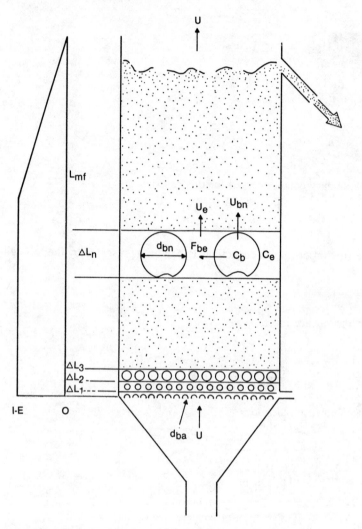

Figure 9-6. Bubble assemblage model (Kato and Wen[30]). See Table 9-5 for parameter relationships.

phase is assumed to be completely mixed. Next, the void space within the emulsion phase is equal to that of the bed at incipient fluidization. The bubble phase is assumed to be composed of spherical bubbles surrounded by spherical clouds. (Davidson[41] provides correlations for predicting bubble size). The voidage is assumed constant from the bottom to a bed height corresponding to L_{mf}, from which it increases linearly to unity at a level corresponding to $L_{mf} + 2 (L_f - L_{mf})$. The gas exchange coefficient, F_{be}, and the bubble size is used. Model predictions are based on solving the mass balance equations around each compartment from the bottom to the top of the bed. For the bubble phase, the mass balance in the nth compartment is:

$$AU[(C_b)_{n-1} - (C_b)_n] = [F'_{be}V_b(C_b - C_e)]_n + (r_bV_c)_n \qquad (9\text{-}119)$$

where F'_{be} = gas exchange coefficient percent volume of bubbles
$\quad\quad\quad r_b$ = reaction rate in cloud per unit volume = kC_b, for first order reaction with respect to gas composition
$\quad V_b, V_c$ = total volume of bubble phase (void and cloud) and bubble clouds in the compartment

Relationships for F'_{be} and V_b, V_c are listed in Table 9-4.
For the emulsion phase, the mass balance is:

$$[F'_{be}V_b(C_b - C_e)]_n = (r_eV_e)_n \qquad (9\text{-}120)$$

where r_e = kC_e, for first order reaction
$\quad\quad V_e$ = volume of emulsion phase (correlation given in Table 9-5)

Bubbling-bed models in general are mildly successful in predicting experimental conversion and selectivity. However, a serious shortcoming with models such as the bubble assemblage model is that they do not account for the gas changing its direction in the bed, and hence, in such situations cannot properly predict concentration profiles.

The reverse flow of gas in the emulsion phase is a result of the downward flow of solids in a certain portion of the emulsion phase. Nguyen et al.[42] and others[7,8,43,44] have recognized the importance of this downard solids movement, noting that it is related to the bubble patterns, and that the gas movement in the particulate (emulsion) phase is related to the solids movement. Nguyen et al.[42] observed from experiments in a two-dimensional bed that the stable bubble pattern in the upper region of the bed leaves a persistent central area relatively bubble free and a pronounced solids downward flow in this area is associated with strong gas backmixing. The reverse flow in the emulsion phase can, however, be introduced in the bubbling-bed model to describe the concentration profile of a fluidized-bed reactor when flow is above a certain critical gas velocity for which this condition prevails (see Wen and Chen,[5] pp. 678–680).

In addition to the gas-flow reversal effect, two additional phenomena can dramatically affect concentration profiles in the bed. First, gas exchange rates near the bottom of the bed could be considerably greater than those found substantially above the grid region. The reason for this is that the bubbles are smaller and move much slower near the distributor. This suggests a need for further experimental studies on bubble characteristics in the region of the bed close to the distributor. Secondly, the concentration profile of the gaseous reactants in the emulsion phase may be significantly affected by the variation in the gas flow rate through the emul-

Table 9-4

Relationships Used in the Bubble Assemblage Model[5]

Parameter	Relationship
Bubble size at given level (L)	$d_b = d_{bm} - (d_{bm} - d_{bo}) \exp [-0.3 \, L'/d_c]$ where $L' = L - L_J$ L_J = jet height
Maximum bubble size	$d_{bm} = 0.652 \, [A(U - U_{mf})]^{0.4}$
Initial bubble size	$d_{bo} = 0.00376 \, (U - U_{mf})^2$ (porous plate) $d_{bo} = 0.347 \, [A(U - U_{mf})/n_d]^{0.4}$ (perforated) where n_d = number of perforations
Bed expansion ratio	$(L_f - L_{mf})/L_{mf} = \delta/(1 - \delta) = (U - U_{mf})/[\phi(g\bar{d}_b)^{0.5}]$ where δ = volume of bubbles/total bed volume
Compartment height	$\Delta L_n = \dfrac{d'_{bn}}{1 + 0.15(d'_{bn} - d_{bm})/d_c}$
Number of bubbles in compartment	$N = 6A(L_f - L_{mf})/[\pi L_f(\Delta L_n)^2]$
$\left[\dfrac{\text{Diameter cloud}}{\text{Diameter bubble}}\right]^3$	$r = (U_{br} + 2U_{mf}/\epsilon_{mf})/(U_{br} - U_{mf}/\epsilon_{mf})$ where $U_{br} = \phi(g\Delta L_n)^{0.5}$ $\geq U_{mf}/\epsilon_{mf}$ with $\phi = \begin{cases} 0.64 \, d_c^{0.4} & d_c \leq 10 \text{ cm} \\ 0.255 \, d_c^{0.4} & 10 \leq d_c \leq 100 \text{ cm} \\ 1.6 \, d_c^{0.4} & d_c \geq 100 \text{ cm} \end{cases}$
Volume of bubble phase (void + cloud)	$V_{bn} = N\pi(\Delta L_n)^3 \, r/6 = V_{bVn}r$ where V_{bVn} = volume of bubble void
Volume of cloud phase	$V_{cn} = N\pi(\Delta L_n)^3 \, (r - 1)/6$
Volume of emulsion phase	$V_{en} = A\Delta L_n - V_{bn}$
Voidage	$1 - \epsilon = L_{mf}(1 - \epsilon_{mf})/L_f, \; L \leq L_{mf}$ $1 - \epsilon = [L_{mf}(1 - \epsilon_{mf})/L_f] - \dfrac{[L_{mf}(1 - \epsilon_{mf})(L - L_{mf})]}{2L_f(L_f - L_{mf})}$ for $L_{mf} \leq L \leq L_{mf} + 2(L_f - L_{mf})$
Gas exchange coefficient	$F'_{be} = F_{be}/r$ and $F_{be} = 11/d_b$

ion phase. In the above discussion it is assumed that this rate equals the true gas low rate through the bubbles, which is not necessarily the case. Both phenomena are not addressed in present bubbling-bed models.

Slugging and Fast Fluidized Beds

Slugging beds are most frequently encountered in small-diameter fluidized beds such as pilot-scale reactors; however, it is conceivable that some commercial-scale gasifiers might approach this condition. Hormand et al.[45] have proposed a model for the case of gas-phase catalyzed reaction in this flow regime. Raghuraman et al.[46] have extended the model to describe the cyclic vibrations characteristic of a steady-state catalytic reactor system.

The model ignores the reaction in the bubble phase, but accounts for the flow through the emulsion phase. Based on the emulsion-phase gas flow being U_{mf} (on a superficial area basis), the following mass balances were developed:

For the flow over the bed's cross-section:

$$U_{mf} \frac{dC_e}{d\xi} + (U - U_{mf}) \frac{dC_b}{d\xi} + N_R C_e = 0 \qquad (9\text{-}121)$$

And for the rising slug of gas:

$$\frac{dC_b}{d\xi} + N_{MS} (C_b - C_e) = 0 \qquad (9\text{-}122)$$

where $N_R = kL_{mf}/U$

N_{MS} = number of gas exchange transfer units in slugging bed = (gas exchange rate per slug volume) $\times$ (L_f/U_s)

A theoretical approximation of the gas exchange process gives:[45]

$$N_{MS} = \frac{L_{mf}}{0.35(gd_c)^{0.5}d_c m} U_{mf} + \frac{16\epsilon_{mf}I}{1 + \epsilon_{mf}} \left(\frac{D}{\pi}\right)^{0.5} \left(\frac{g}{d_c}\right)^{0.25} \qquad (9\text{-}123)$$

where D = gas diffusivity

m = gas slug shape factor given by:

$$m = L_s/d_c - 0.495(L_s/d_c)^{0.5} + 0.061 \qquad (9\text{-}124A)$$

$$L_s/d_c = 0.3 + 3.9(U - U_{mf})/0.35(gd_c)^{0.5} \qquad (9\text{-}124B)$$

Table 9-5
Length Required for Fast Bed Reactors
(Van Swaaij[10])

k Packed Bed (s^{-1})	L (95% Conversion), m; No Mass Transfer Limitation	L (95% Conversion), m; With Mass Transfer Limitation $L_M = 2m$
0.1	500	500
1	50	56
3	17	23
10	5	11
30	1.7	9.8

First order reaction; U = 5 m/s; solids hold-up = 18 volume %; plug flow model

And the expanded bed height is:

$$L_f = L_{mf}\left[1 + \frac{(U - U_{mf})}{0.35(gd_c)^{0.5}}\right] \tag{9-125}$$

Parameter I in Equation 9-123 is the surface integral over the slug surface, which is a function of the ratio of the slug length to diameter ratio (L_s/d_c). Typical values are as follows:

L_s/d_c = 0.3   0.5   1.0   2.0   3.0   4.0   5.0

I = 0.13   0.21   0.31   0.71   0.98   1.24   1.48

At very much higher gas superficial velocities, the bubble structure disappears, and the system becomes a circulating or fast fluidized bed (also called a turbulent fluid bed). Applications of fast fluidization to coal gasification were described in Chapter 7. Simple plug flow models appear best suited for this flow regime. Van Swaaij[10] reports bed height requirements for fast fluidizing beds for different reaction rates. Some of these values are given in Table 9-5.

PRINCIPLES OF REACTOR DESIGN

In developing design criteria for a commercial-scale reactor such as a gasifier, consideration must not only be given to the chemical kinetics but to the flow of reactants and heat transfer with surroundings as well. These factors give rise to temperature and concentration gradients in the bulk of the reactor; but may also lead to the generation of different zones of reaction development in the reactor.

In the previous section, emphasis was placed on coupling the kinetics to hydrodynamic models based on cell-type or mixing tanks in series models. However, our discussions would be incomplete if diffusion-type models were ignored.

The difficulty with these models lies in the fact that they cannot be readily related to the hydrodynamics of the system. In contrast, cell-type models do lend themselves to a physical representation of the macromixing taking place in a fluid bed. Because of their limited applicability, however, discussions here are limited only to the case of a fixed-bed reactor.

In the absence of reactions, the concentration C_i of any component i in the reaction mixture is determined from the solution to the convective diffusion equation:

$$\frac{\partial C_i}{\partial t} = D_i \nabla^2 C_i - \nabla(w_f C_i) \qquad (9\text{-}126)$$

where ∇ is the Laplace operator defined as:

$$\nabla = \frac{\partial}{\partial x} + \frac{\partial}{\partial y} + \frac{\partial}{\partial z}, \quad \nabla^2 = \frac{\partial^2}{\partial x^2} + \frac{\partial^2}{\partial y^2} + \frac{\partial^2}{\partial z^2}$$

In Equation 9-126, w_f is the actual velocity of the gas, and D_i is the diffusion coefficient of component i.

A similar expression can be written for the temperature distribution. The boundary conditions for Equation 9-126 are written with respect to the surface of the solid particles and determined on the basis of equality of diffusion flux of component i on the surface of the particle to the rate of formation of substance i as a result of surface reaction ϱ_i

$$D_i \frac{\partial ci}{\partial n} = \varrho_i (C, T) \qquad (9\text{-}127)$$

where n = direction of external normal
       C = concentration vector

The particle is assumed to be nonporous.

A complete analysis would include the heat condition equation for the solid particles with boundary conditions for heat flux on the surface of particles, as well as boundary conditions for concentration and temperature at the inlet outlet of reactor and its walls. Such a system of equations requires a formidable task for solution, from which diffusion-type models enable a relatively clean approximation method. With this approach, heat and mass transfers can be described by means of an effective thermal conductivity and diffusion coefficient.

A fixed bed consists of a column or layer of solid particles that constitute a network of tortuous flow paths for the gas. The average flow velocity component can be expressed as w/ϵ, where for the purposes of illustration, the flow paths are considered parallel. The transverse component of average velocity is assumed to be zero. In an actual system, the tortuosity of the flow paths causes the flow velocity to be a random function in special coordinates.

If the flow is turbulent, its actual velocity at any point is a random function not only of space but time as well. The influence of molecular diffusion is negligible on the mixing of the flow in the layer of solid particles, hence, averaging over the macrovolume the diffusion member in Equation 9-126 may be neglected. In this case the value of effective diffusion coefficient D is equal for all components of reaction mixture.

It is convenient to define an effective rate of substance formation, e_i, which can be related to a unit volume of the layer. If the reaction proceeds on the surface of the particle then $r_i = \varrho_i \sigma$, where σ is the area of outer surface particle per unit volume of the layer. For a porous particle, $r_i = (1 - \epsilon)r_i^*$, where r_i^* is the effective rate of formation of substance per unit volume of particle. The material balance expression describing the concentration field of substance i in the reactor has the form:

$$D\nabla^2 C_i - \nabla(wC_i) + \zeta_i(C,T) = \frac{\partial C_i}{\partial t} \tag{9-128}$$

where $\nabla(wC_i)$ is referred to as the effective diffusion term.

Fixed-bed reactors allow for little mixing between solid particles. Hence, at a moderate gas flow rate the heat transfer in the layer is controlled almost entirely by the flowing gas. For this regime, the effective coefficient of thermal conductivity is of the same order of magnitude as the effective diffusion coefficient. Experimental observations reveal that the value of the longitudinal effective diffusion coefficient is higher than in transverse direction.

Cell models are actually logical extensions of diffusion models. In the cell model the space among the particles can be represented as a set of cells or tanks with sizes that are comparable to the particle diameter and are connected with each other by narrow channels. The gas can be assumed to be perfectly mixed in each of these cells, which is justified from the viewpoint of turbulence. For sufficiently large ratios of reactor length to particle size, both cell models and diffusion models provide asymptotic solutions. In this case, the effective longitudinal Peclet number ($Pe = w\ell/D$) is equal to $w\ell/d$ in the cell model. (where ℓ is the reactor length and d the particle size). For a cylindrical reactor operating under steady-state conditions the effective concentration and temperature field equations are:

$$D_z \frac{\partial^2 C_I}{\partial z^2} + D_x \left(\frac{\partial^2 C_i}{\partial x^2} + \frac{1}{x} \frac{\partial C_i}{\partial x} \right) - \frac{\partial}{\partial z}(wC_i) + r_i = 0 \tag{9-129}$$

$$\lambda_z \left(\frac{\partial^2 T}{\partial z^2} \right) + \lambda_x \left(\frac{\partial^2 T}{\partial x^2} + \frac{1}{x} \frac{\partial T}{\partial x} \right) - \nu_f \frac{\partial}{\partial z}(wC_i) + r_h = 0 \tag{9-130}$$

where x = coordinate directed along the radius of reactor
$\lambda = \nu_f a$ = effective coefficient of heat conductivity
r_h = effective rate of heat released per unit volume of layer
ν_f = heat capacity per unit volume of layer

The following boundary conditions on the walls of the reactor apply:

$$\frac{\partial C}{\partial x} = 0$$

$$\lambda_x \frac{\partial T}{\partial x} = \alpha(T - T_w) \tag{9-131}$$

where α = heat transfer coefficient through a wall to a heat carrier
T_w = temperature of an outer heat carrier

To simplify the mathematics, the variables in Equations 9-129 and 9-130 are assumed constant over the reactor cross-section, and hence for a tubular reactor, reduce to a set of one-dimensional equations:

$$D_z \frac{\partial^2 C_i}{\partial z^2} - \frac{d}{dz}(w C_i) + r_i = 0 \tag{9-132}$$

$$\lambda_z \frac{\partial^2 T}{\partial z^2} - \nu_f \frac{d}{dz}(wT) - \frac{dH}{dt} - q = 0 \tag{9-133}$$

where r_i = heat released
q = density of heat removal (which is equal to the amount of heat removed per unit volume per unit time)

The value of q is positive in exothermic processes and negative in endothermic processes.

Two limiting cases are conventionally viewed, those of ideal displacement and perfect mixing. Ideal displacement is viewed when $Pe = w\ell/D_z \rightarrow \infty$, and perfect mixing at $Pe = 0$. The first case leads to a system of differential equations of the first order, whereas the second results in a system of algebraic equations. Process development work in reactor design is often aimed at the selection and experimental verification of process models for describing a particular system. This often requires the use of parameter estimation techniques to evaluate the kinetics, macrokinetics, hydrodynamics of the process, and solution of systems of equations that most appropriately model the reactor system.

Bischoff et al.[47] and Levenspiel[48] apply the above concepts to several classical cases such as the design of isothermal and adiabatic reactors. The reader should consult these sources for specific examples. Table 9-6 lists the solutions to several common cases of perfect mix reactors. Table 9-7 also lists integrated forms for various reactions in plug flow reactors.

Table 9-6
Design of Perfect Mixing Reactors

Reaction	Balance Equation	Solution
A → products (zero order)	$C - C_o = -KS$	$C = C_o - KS$
A → products (first order)	$C - C_o = KCS$	$C = \dfrac{C_o}{1 + KS'}$
A → products (second order)	$C - C_o = -KC^2S$	$C = \dfrac{1}{2KS}[(1 + 4KSC_o)^{0.5} - 1]$
$A_1 + A_2 \to$ products	$C_1 - C_{10} = -KC_1(C + c)S$ where $C = C_{20} - C_{10}$	$C = \left(\dfrac{1}{2Ks} + \dfrac{C}{2}\right)\left\{\left[1 + \dfrac{4SC_{10}K}{(1 + KSC)^2}\right]^{0.5} - 1\right\}$
$A_1 \to A_i$ (i = 1, 2, - ... , S − 1) (the same order)	$C_i - C_{io} = K_iC^2$	$\dfrac{C_i - C_{io}}{C_j - C_{jo}} = \dfrac{K_i}{K_j}$
$A_1 \to A_2 - A_3$	$C_1 - C_{10} = (K_1 + K_3)SC_1$ $C_2 - C_{20} = (K_1C_1 - K_2C_2)S$	$C_1 = \dfrac{C_{10}}{1 + (K_1 + K_3)S}$ $C_2 = \dfrac{K_1C_{10}}{(1 + K_2S)[1 + (K_1 + K_3)S]} + \dfrac{C_{20}}{1 + K_2S}$
$A_1 \rightleftarrows A_2$	$C - C_{10} = [-K_1C + K_2(C - c)]S$ where $C = C_{10} + C_{20}$	$\dfrac{C_{10} + K_2C}{1 + (K_i + K_2)S}$

Table 9-7
Integrated Forms of Plug Flow Reactor for Constant Pressure and Temperature Gaseous Reactions

Reaction Order	Kinetics	Rate Expression	Integrated Expression	Comments
0th order homogeneous	$A \xrightarrow{} \cdots$	$-r_A = k$	$\dfrac{k\tau}{C_{A_o}} = X_A = \dfrac{C_{A_o} - C_A}{C_{A_o} + \epsilon_A C_A}$	for any ϵ_A
1st order homogeneous	$A \xrightarrow{} \cdots$	$-r_A = kC_A$	$k\tau = (1 + \epsilon_A)\ln\left(\dfrac{1}{1 - X_A}\right) - \epsilon_A X_A$	for $\epsilon_A \neq 0$
			$k\tau = \ln\left(\dfrac{1}{1 - X_A}\right) = \ln\dfrac{C_{A_o}}{C_A}$	for $\epsilon_A = 0$
1st order reversible	$A \underset{2}{\overset{1}{\rightleftarrows}} R$	$-r_A = k_1 C_A - k_2 C_R$	$k_1\tau = \dfrac{M + rX_{A_e}}{M + r}\left[(1 + \epsilon_A X_{A_e}) \cdot \ln\left(\dfrac{X_{A_e}}{X_{A_e} - X_A}\right) - \epsilon_A X_A\right]$	for $\epsilon_A \neq 0$; X_{A_e} = equilibrium; $M = C_{R_o}/C_{A_o}$
			$k_1\tau = \dfrac{M + rX_{A_e}}{M + r}\ln\left[\dfrac{X_{A_e}}{X_{A_e} - X_A}\right]$	for $\epsilon_A = 0$
			$= \dfrac{M + r(1 - C_A/C_{A_o})}{M + r}\ln\left[\dfrac{C_{A_o} - C_{A_e}}{C_A - C_{A_e}}\right]$	

Table 9-7 (continued)
Integrated Forms of Plug Flow Reactor for Constant Pressure and Temperature Gaseous Reactions

Reaction Order	Kinetics	Rate Expression	Integrated Expression	Comments
2nd order	$\begin{cases} 2A \rightarrow \dots \\ A + B \rightarrow \dots \end{cases}$	$-r_A = kC_A^2$ $-r_A = kC_A C_B;\ C_{B_0} = C_{A_0}$	$k\tau C_{A_0} = 2\epsilon_A(1 + \epsilon_A)\ln(1 - X_A) + \epsilon_A^2 X_A + (\epsilon_A + 1)^2 \dfrac{X_A}{1 - X_A}$	for $\epsilon_A \neq 0$
			$k\tau C_{A_0} = \dfrac{X_A}{1 - X_A} = \dfrac{C_{A_0} - C_A}{C_A}$ or $= \dfrac{1}{C_A} - \dfrac{1}{C_{A_0}} = k\tau$	for $\epsilon_A = 0$.

ϵ_A defined as $\dfrac{V_{X_A = 1} - V_{X_A = 0}}{V_{X_A = 0}}$; where $V = V_0(1 + \epsilon_A X_A)$, volume of reactor.

NOMENCLATURE

A	turbulent exchange coefficient or cross-sectional area
a_0	hydraulic radius
a'	slab thickness
a	ratio of particle volume to its surface
A_i	number of moles of substance i
A	turbulent exchange coefficient
a	thermometric conductivity coefficient
b	characteristic surface constant
C	concentration
c_p	heat capacity
C_p	constant
$C_{A,B}\ldots$	concentration
C_{AF}	gas concentration at top of freeboard region
C_b, C_e	gas concentration in bubble and emulsion, respectively
D', D^*	effective diffusion coefficient
D	diffusion coefficient
d	characteristic dimension
d_0	pore or orifice diameter
d_b, d_{bo}	bubble diameter and initial bubble size, respectively
E	activation energy
E_δ	axial dispersion coefficient
F	force
f'	transition function
f	form factor or resistance coefficient
f_e	fraction of wake solids ejected
f	rate of chain branching
g_0	adsorbent constant
g	rate of chain termination
H_d	solids holdup
h	pore diameter
I	surface integral
$\bar{I}$	mean heat content of mixture
J	thermal equivalent of work
j	mass transfer factor
k_T	thermal diffusion ratio
k'	rate constant
K'	effective rate constant
K	rate constant or mass transfer coefficient
k	rate constant
L	dimensionless thickness
L_{mf}	height of bed at minimum fluidization
L_f	height of fluidized bed
L_c	critical height above jets at which bubble clouds overlap
ℓ	pore dimension or mixing length

M_∞ Margoulis number

m   slug shape factor or mass

M   molecular weight

N_M number of gas mass transfer units

N_R number of transfer units

N_{Rb} number of reaction units in bubbling zone

Nu   Nusselt number

n   number of compartments

n′   rate generation of chains

$n_{A,B}\cdots$ reaction order

Pe   Peclet number

Pr   Prandtl number

p   partial pressure

Q   amount of heat evolved per unit volume and time

q*   diffusion flow per unit surface area of free cross-section of pores

q   exchange coefficient

r   reaction rate per unit volume of particle

Re   Reynolds number

R   universal gas law constant

R_i production rate of species i

r   ratio cloud sphere volume/bubble volume

S   surface area

Sc   Schmidt number

Sh   Sherwood number

T   absolute temperature

t   time or temperature

T   absolute temperature

U_b bubble velocity

U_{br} rise velocity of isolated bubble

U_{cr} critical gas velocity for gas backmixing

U_e gas velocity in the emulsion phase

U_{ob} superficial velocity through bubbles

U_{oc} superficial velocity through clouds

u   velocity

$\bar{u}_i$ energy

V′   tangential stress

V   velocity

V_b volume of bubble phase

w_x, w_y, w_z velocity components along x, y, and z coordinates

x   dimension

x   concentration of active intermediate

Y_i weight fraction of species i

y   ordinate

z   preexponential factor

Greek Symbols

α heat exchange coefficient
α' heat transfer coefficient, see Equation 9-28
β velocity constant or parameter
γ heat capacity per unit volume of fluid
γ' width of transition zone
γ_s fraction of particles in bubble phase
δ volume of bubbles/total bed volume or film thickness
ϵ voidage
η monomolecular reaction rate, i.e., efficiency factor
η' relative concentration of catalytically active product
θ dimensionless temperature
λ thermal conductivity
μ viscosity
ν kinematic viscosity
ν_r reaction rate
ξ ratio of thermal conductivity and heat capacity per unit volume or dimensionless bed height
ϱ rate of mass transfer per unit of outer surface area or molar density
ϱ_n heat flux per unit surface area
σ particle volume
τ stress
ϕ kinetic coefficient
χ rate constant
χ^* effective rate constant
Ω free cross-section of pores per unit area of layer
ω vessel volume

REFERENCES

1. Cheremisinoff, N. P., *Fluid Flow: Pumps, Pipes and Channels,* Ann Arbor Science Pub., Ann Arbor, MI (1981).

2. Levich, V. G., *Physicochemical Hydrodynamics,* Prentice-Hall, Englewood Cliffs, NJ (1962).

3. Rosner, A. M., *Khim. Prom.* (Moscow), (2): 85 (1965).

4. Chapman, S., and T. G. Cowling, *Mathematical Theory of Non-Uniform Gases,* 2nd ed., Cambridge University Press, (1951).

5. Wen, C. Y., and L. H. Chen, "Flow Modelling Concepts of Fluidized Beds," in *Handbook of Fluids in Motion,* N. P. Cheremisinoff and R. Gupta (Eds.), Ann Arbor Science/Butterworth Pub., Ann Arbor, MI (1983).

6. Murray, J. D.; *Chem. Progr. Symp. Ser.*, 62 (62): 71 (1966).

7. Stephens, G. K., R. J. Sinclair, and O. E. Potter; *Powder Technology*, 1: 157 (1967).

8. Kunii, D., K. Yoshida, and I. Hiraki, *Proc. International Symp. on Fluidization*, Netherlands Univ. Press (1967), p. 243.

9. Catipovic, N. M., G. N. Govanovic, and T. J. Fitzgerald, *AIChE J.*, 24: 543 (1978).

10. van Swaaij, W. P. M., *Chemical Reaction Engineering Review*, ACS Symp. Ser., 72: 193 (1978).

11. Staub, F. W., and G. S. Canada, *Fluidization*, Cambridge University Press, (1978), p. 339.

12. Rowe, P. N., *Proc. Second Internat. Symp. on Chem. Reaction Eng.*, A9 (1972).

13. Pyle, D. L., *Adv. Chem. Series,* 109: 106 (1972).

14. Calderbank, P. H., and F. D. Toor; *Fluidization*, J. F. Davidson and D. Harrison (Eds.), Academic Press, London (1971), p. 383.

15. Horio, M., and C. Y. Wen, *AIChE Symp. Series* Vol. 73 (1961), Vol. 9 (1977).

16. Barreteau, D., C. Laguerie, and H. Angelino, *Fluidization*, Cambridge Univ. Press (1978), p. 292.

17. Shen, C. Y., and H. F. Johnstone; *AIChE J.*, 1: 349 (1955).

18. Van Deemter, J. J., *Chem. Eng. Sci.*, 13: 143 (1961).

19. Johnstone, H. F., J. D. Batchelor, and W. Y. Shen; *AIChE J.*, 1: 318 (1955).

20. May, W. G., *Chem. Eng. Prog.*, 55 (12): 49 (1959).

21. Kobayashi, H., and F. Arai, *Chem. Eng. Tokyo*, 29: 885 (1965).

22. Muchi, I., *Memories of the Faculty of Engineering*, Nagoya Univ., 17: 79 (1965).

23. Orcutt, J. C., J. F. Davidson, and R. L. Pigford, *Chem. Eng. Progr. Symp. Ser.*, 58 (38): 1 (1962).

24. Kunii, D., and O. Levenspiel, *Ind. Eng. Chem. Fund.*, 2: 466 (1968).

25. Fryer, C., and O. E. Potter, *Ind. Eng. Chem. Fund.*, 11: 338 (1972).

26. Mamuro, T., and I. Muchi, *J. Ind. Chem. Tokyo*, 68: 126 (1965).

27. Toor, F. D., and P. H. Calderbank, *Proc. Intern. Symp. on Fluidization*, Netherland Univ. Press (1967), p. 373.

28. Partridge, B. A., and P. N. Rowe, *Trans. Inst. Chem. Engrs.*, 44: T349 (1966).

29. Kobayashi, H., et al., *Chem. Eng. Tokyo,* 33: 274 (1969).

30. Kato, K., and C. Y. Wen, *Chem. Eng. Sci.*, 24: 1351 (1969).

31. Mori, S., and I. Muchi; *Chem. Eng. Japan*, 5: 251 (1972).

32. Mori, S., and C. Y. Wen; *AIChE J.*, 21: 109 (1975).

33. Toomey, R. D., and H. F. Johnstone; *Chem. Eng. Prog.*, 48: 220 (1952).

34. Cooke, M. J., et al., "Tripartite Chem. Eng. Conf.," *Symp. on Fluidization*, 1: 14 (1968).

35. Gomezplata, A., and W. W. Shuster, *AIChE J.*, 6: 454 (1960).

36. Behie, L. A., and P. Kehoe, *AIChE J.*, 19 (5): 1,070 (1973).

37. Wen, C. Y., N. R. Deole, and L. H. Chen; "A Study of Jets in a Three-Dimensional Gas Fluidized Bed," *Powder Technology*, in press (1981).

38. Grace, J. R., and H. I. De Lasa; *AIChE J.*, *24*: 364 (1978).

39. Wen, C. Y., and L. T. Fan, *Model for Flow Systems and Chemical Reactors*, Marcel Dekker Inc., NY (1975).

40. Mori, S., and C. Y. Wen; *Fluidization Technology*, 1: 179 (1976).

41. Davidson, J. F., *Trans. Inst. Chem. Eng.*, 39: 230 (1961).

42. Nguyen, H. V., A. B. Whitehead, and O. E. Potter, *AIChE J.*, 23: 913 (1977).

43. Latham, R. L., C. J. Hamilton, and O. E. Potter; *Brit. Chem. Eng.*, 13: 666 (1968).

44. Nguyen, H. V., and O. E. Potter, *Chem. React. Eng.*, Vol. II in Advance in Chemistry Series, 133 (ACS): 290 (1974).

45. Hovmand, S., and J. F. Davidson, *Fluidization*, Academic Press, London (1971), p. 193.

46. Raghuraman, J., and O. E. Potter; *Chemical Reaction Engineering, ACS Symp. Ser.*, 65: 400 (1978).

47. Bischoff, K. B., and G. F. Froment, *Chemical Reactor Analysis and Design*, John Wiley and Sons, Inc., NY (1979).

48. Levenspiel, O., and K. B. Bischoff, *Adv. Chem. Engng.*, Vol. 4, Academic Press, NY (1963).

10

Experimental Methods

CONTENTS

INTRODUCTION, 402

MEASUREMENT OF BUBBLE PHENOMENA, 402

Photographic and X-Ray Techniques, 402
Light Transmission, 404
Piezoelectric Measurement, 407
Gamma-Ray Transmission, 410
Other Nonintrusive Measurement Techniques, 411
Electroresistivity Techniques, 416
Thermal Techniques, 428

MEASUREMENT TECHNIQUES FOR PARTICLE BEHAVIOR, 432

Photographic Techniques (Freeboard Region Studies), 434
Holography, 436
Impact Method, 437
Optical Techniques, 438
Laser-Doppler Anemometry, 442
Time-of-Flight Measurements, 448

MEASUREMENT OF PERFORMANCE PARAMETERS, 456

Temperature and Overall Heat Transfer, 456
Gas Composition, 458

Pressure, 458
Other Parameters, 461

NOMENCLATURE, 461

REFERENCES, 463

INTRODUCTION

This chapter reviews various techniques and instrumentation systems applied in studying and modeling fluidized-bed behavior. Instrumentation systems which are directly employed for monitoring the behavior of commercial fluidized-bed reactors are almost nonexistent, with the exception of conventional sensors that are applied to readily measurable parameters such as solids temperature, exit gas composition, pressure, and overall heat transfer coefficients. More sophisticated techniques have been applied in academic and industrial research laboratories to measure the velocity of solids and gas in the freeboard; freeboard particle size distribution; bubble properties such as size, shape, frequency and rise velocity; apparent bed viscosity and density; local heat and mass transfer coefficients; and solids' behavior in the dense phase. Many of these techniques have not become part of standard plant hardware for monitoring or control partly because of their sensitivity to uncontrolled and harsh environments, such as high temperatures, pressures, humidity, etc.; but also because applications are often too specific to warrant the need for instrument manufacturers to develop packaged systems for the field. Very often, the implementation of a sophisticated instrument package for obtaining localized measurements in a commercial unit is for trouble-shooting purposes or to assist in planning specific design changes. Despite this so-called "thin market" of applications, there is a real need to extend laboratory instrumentation into the field, if for no other reason than to at least understand the true operating characteristics of the reactor, which will ensure or improve future designs.

MEASUREMENT OF BUBBLE PHENOMENA

The position, velocity, and frequency of bubbles in the dense phase of a fluidized bed determine the flow distribution or maldistribution of both solids and gas. Bubbles play the dominant role in establishing the heat transfer characteristics at the reactor walls and the gas-to-solid exchange coefficients. They are of fundamental importance in modeling the reaction kinetics as well as the hydrodynamic behavior of the dense region. The literature describes an overabundance of techniques, invariably for experimental facilities in which the hydrodynamics of the bed is to be characterized. Some of these techniques are relatively simple and can be pieced together from different "off-the-shelf" instrument packages, making them readily adaptable for use in operating units. In addition, many can be integrated with computer facilities for on-line data analysis or storage.

Photographic and X-Ray Techniques

Photographic and visual techniques have most often been used in two-dimensional cold models. Upson and Pyle[1] studied the movement and splitting characteristics of bubbles in a two-dimensional air-fluidized bed. The bed had dimensions of 30 cm × 1.5 cm and was equipped with a porous plastic distributor. Bubble behavior was observed using cine photography at a frame speed of up to 64 frames/s using angled back-illumination. The film was analyzed frame-by-frame on a frame analyzer to determine the frequencies of bubble splitting as a function of bubble size, and also to evaluate the growth rates and wavelengths of the observed disturbances.

The backmixing phenomenon in fluid beds was studied by Fryer and Potter[2] in a two-dimensional bed using this technique. The variation of bubble size with height was determined by filming the surface of the bed for a range of bed heights and gas velocities. At each set of conditions, an eruption diameter was evaluated by estimating the average of two widths at right angles for each of 40 bubbles. Little change in the calculated average after the first 20 bubbles was observed. Data on eruption diameters were used to evaluate various models of backmixing.

Pyle et al.[3] extended their work to a more fundamental study of bubble behavior, again using a two-dimensional bed (128 cm high × 48 cm wide × 1.27 cm broad). Particle movement could be studied using black tracer particles that were colored using an alcohol soluble dye. A small region of the bed was filmed using a high-speed camera at 400 frames/s. Two types of experiments were conducted in this study. First, single artificial bubbles were injected through a solenoid valve. In these tests it was necessary to maintain the gas velocity through the bed just below minimum fluidization conditions to prevent bubble splitting and elongation. In the second type of tests, single bubbles in the freely bubbling bed, far removed from the interface, were filmed. Films were analyzed using a digital motion analyzer.

A final example of the application of this technique is the work of Kunii and co-workers[4] in which the effects of temperature on size and rising velocity of bubbles in a two-dimensional bed were studied. Visual observations of the bubble behavior were made at various temperatures through a transparent window. The bed was equipped with a nichrome wire heater positioned behind the back wall of the bed to maintain it at constant temperature. Pictures of rising bubbles were taken by a 16 mm cine camera, and both the mean size and rising velocity of bubbles were evaluated at a level of 20 cm from the upper surface of the distributor, using 20 independent pictures at a given location. Since the shape of the rising bubbles was distorted, Kunii et al. used the following procedure to evaluate an equivalent bubble diameter:

1. It was assumed that the shape of any bubble observed through the front glass was the central section of a cylindrical bubble.
2. The equivalent bubble size was calculated as the diameter of a sphere that posseses the same volume as the bubble.

The photographic method is a useful technique in laboratory units restricted to cold models and/or low temperatures and pressures. Still photographs have the advantage of being combined with image analysis to evaluate bubble contours and size distributions and to speed up analysis. However, this technique is limited to two-dimensional or flat model beds, where wall effects tremendously distort true bubble characteristics. Although semi-cylindrical columns are a closer approximation of the three-dimensional case, photograph/cine methods still only provide measurements of phenomena at, or very close to, the wall.

The most direct observation of bubble characteristics can be made using x-rays and cine photographic techniques. Rowe and Partridge,[5] Rowe and Matsumo,[6] Rowe,[7] Hager and Tompson,[8] and Judd and Dixon[9] have employed x-rays for measuring bubbles. The principal difficulties in extending these techniques to measurements in commercial units are transmission limitations through thick-walled vessels and poor resolution of bubble planes. By this last point, it is meant that there are difficulties in resolving individual bubble sizes due to the superposition of bubbles at various depths of field. Photographs obtained from beds under profuse bubbling conditions are often distorted by this fact, preventing the determination of a representative statistical bubble size.

Light Transmission

There are two techniques that have been successfully applied in laboratory-scale testing, namely, light scattering and fiber optics. To begin, the local bubble size distribution in a gas fluidized bed is perceived as a probability density function of characteristic size such as the bubble radius. Put et al.[10] related this function to the Maxwell-Boltzmann statistics assumed to be valid for the distribution of the bubble energy taken proportional to its surface area. A weight fraction was introduced in this study to reckon with the geometrical configuration of a light probe used in this study (based on the assumption of spherical bubbles). The experimental detection of bubble size in this study was based on the interaction between a horizontal light beam and the fluidized solids. When the fluidized solids are present within the beam, light is scattered and large attenuation occurs; however, if only gas is present there is no attenuation of the light beam at all.

Figure 10-1 shows a schematic of the equipment used in this study along with the geometrical configuration of the probe. The small light source generated a circular beam of parallel light rays 5 mm wide. The light sensing element was composed of

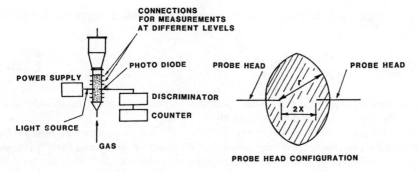

Figure 10-1. Bubble detection system used by Put et al.[10]

a photodiode which faced the light source. This technique provides a local measurement of the number of bubbles passing the probe per unit time (i.e., bubble frequency). This is achieved by simply counting the nonattenuated signal interruptions over a known time interval. Counting is performed using a discriminator and electronic counter. The discriminator level must be predetermined (for example, with the use of an oscilloscope and correlator) so that only the presence of a single bubble bridging the probe opening is detected. By varying the size of the probe opening, several points of the cumulative density function of bubble width, $n(x)$, can be obtained. The function is calculated by accounting for the probability of detecting a certain bubble size in the probe opening:

$$n(x) = \int_{x}^{\infty} D(r,x)\, D(r)\, dr \qquad (10\text{-}1)$$

where $D(r,x)$ is a weight function defined by Put et al.[5]
The derived integral is:

$$n(x) = \frac{2\pi k r^2}{S}\, m\,[1 - \mathrm{erf}(x/2^{0.5} r_m)] \qquad (10\text{-}2)$$

where erf ( ) denotes the error integral.
The weight function, $D(r,x)$, provides the probability that a spherical bubble with radius r is detected by the probe with total opening $2x$. The critical assumption in this technique, therefore, is that bubbles rise randomly and that any location in a column section has an identical probability for any bubble. Figure 10-1 shows that the probe head configuration is taken as small points lying on a horizontal distance $2x$. The weight function $D(r,x)$ can then be taken as being equal to the ratio of the shaded area (i.e., the area of the centers of the bubbles with radius r which can be

detected) and the total area S of the column. The following expression is thus obtained:

$$D(r,x) = \frac{2r^2}{S}\left(\frac{\pi}{2} - \text{arc sin }\frac{x}{r}\right) - \frac{2x}{S}(r^2 - x^2)^{0.5} \tag{10-3}$$

Other investigators that have employed this technique include Yasui and Johanson,[11] Kilkis et al.,[12] and Yoshida et al.[13]

With the introduction of fiber optics bundles, the use of minaturized light probes for localized measurements was adopted in a variety of two-phase flow investigations.[14-17] Ohki et al.[17] used this technique rather successfully in measuring both local particle movement (described later), and bubble characteristics. The components of the electronic system used for measuring bubbles is shown in Figure 10-2. Simultaneous measurement of bubble rise velocity and fraction, frequency, and size of the bubbles in the bed are possible with this setup. Bubbles are detected by the probe (shown in Figure 10-3) based on the light transmission principle as follows: when a bubble wraps around the probe, the light from a stroboscope of flash frequency N_o is transmitted to the light-receiving fiber of the probe, where it is converted to an electric signal via a photomultiplier. The local bubble fraction, ϵ_B, can be computed from the ratio of the photomultiplier's output signal mean frequency and the stroboscope flash frequency, N_o:

$$\epsilon_B = N_c/N_o \tag{10-4}$$

To obtain the mean rising velocity of bubbles, u_B is computed from the output signals of the frequency to voltage (F-V) converters by means of a cross-correlation method. Ohki observed from simultaneous measurements of bubble characteristics and particle movement that the rising velocity of particles is proportional to the local bubble velocity.

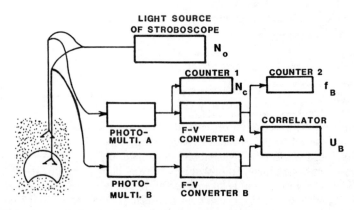

Figure 10-2. Block diagram for bubble characteristics detection using fiber optics probes.[17]

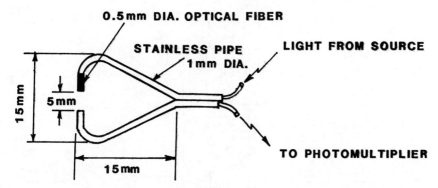

0.5mm DIA. OPTICAL FIBER

STAINLESS PIPE
1mm DIA.

LIGHT FROM SOURCE

15mm

5mm

15mm

TO PHOTOMULTIPLIER

Figure 10-3. Illustration of the details of optical bubble detector used by Ohki et al.[17]

Piezoelectric Measurement

Several investigators[18-22] have employed pressure transducers to infer properties of the bubbling state. The system devised by Taylor et al.[19] is shown in Figure 10-4 in which the study evolved around evaluating the power spectrum of the noise from a pressure transducer. A pressure transducer provides an electrical signal that is proportional to the pressure at the probe tip. Such a signal can be amplified to remove the dc components and spurious high frequency noise. In the system shown in Figure 10-4, the signal is then converted to digital form using an A-D converter, set for sampling at prespecified intervals. The sampling interval is established by a sample frequency generator. A computer was used to generate the power spectrum of a batch of samples from the signal and after conversion to analog form by the D-A converter, the spectrum was displayed on a storage oscilloscope. For tall beds, a specially designed piezoelectric transducer, shown in Figure 10-5 was employed. The transducer was capable of a resolution of 1 mm water gauge with a maximum design of 150 m water gauge. The design consisted of two piezoelectric ceramic discs mounted on each side of an aluminum plate. One plate was exposed to the fluidized-bed pressure while the other was open to the atmosphere. The two elements were connected to the input of a charge amplifier, where the output is proportional to the pressure difference on the elements (in this case, between the frequency limits of 0.01 Hz and 1,000 Hz). The system devised by Taylor et al.[19] provided on-line analysis of the power spectrum. Their analysis scheme on the computer had three major blocks: a controller, a Fast Fourier Transform Algorithm, and an allocator of storage.

The controller block organized a continual sampling of the pressure signal while a spectrum was simultaneously calculated, which controlled the disc-based storage area and displayed the last spectrum. The spectrum was formed using a Decimation in Time Fast Fourier Transform Algorithm followed by a calculation of the modulus of the Fourier coefficients to form the power spectrum. An integer format was

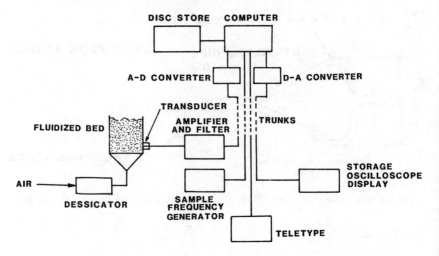

Figure 10-4. Schematic diagram of piezoelectric transducer technique employed by Taylor et al.[19]

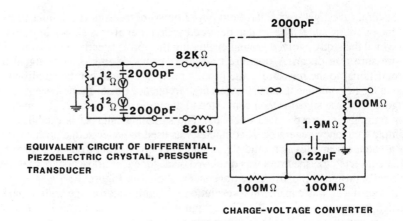

Figure 10-5. Pressure transducer circuit designed by Taylor et al.[19]

necessary since a floating point format would effectively halve the storage capability while increasing computation time. The data was smoothed with a 10% Cosine Bell data window before transformation and the power spectrum smoothed by a three-point weighted moving averaging technique.

Broadhurst and Becker[20] also used spectral analysis of bed pressure fluctuations for interpreting fluid-bed behavior. The technique, in general, is relatively simple to apply and is often used in industrial pilot studies. However, interpretation of the statistical properties of the transducer output signal is not always as straightforward. Figure 10-6 shows typical output signals recorded on an oscillograph from transducers at various heights in a two-ft diameter column, using char particles and air. As shown, the signals clearly show distinct zones of fluidization.

The two most important statistical properties of the pressure fluctuations are the autocorrelation and the frequency spectrum. The first is a measure of the degree of correlation between neighboring values of the pressure fluctuations. The autocorrelation is also used as an intermediate step in the estimation of the spectrum, which measures the distribution of energy with frequency. Broadhurst et al.[20] present various correlations that allow estimation of the peak frequency and the magnitude of the frequency spectrum, from the gas and particle properties and bed dimensions, for fluid beds operating in the slugging regime. They examined the different modes of fluidization ranging from smooth to slugging and observed each to give pressure fluctuations with characteristically different autocorrelation and spectral density functions. For smoothly fluidized beds, the autocorrelation damped quickly to zero, and the spectrum was flat indicating a uniform distribution of energy with frequency.

Figure 10-7 shows the autocorrelation and computed spectrum reported by Broadhurst et al.[20] The advantages of this technique are its simplicity and ability to perform on-line data analysis on a minicomputer. Clearly, the distinctions between slugging and freely bubbling, and bubbling versus nonbubbling are easily made, as shown by the relatively clean output signals of Figure 10-6. However, with the exception of bubble frequency, extension of this technique to measuring bubble size and rise velocity has not been successful. This missing element in the analysis has also limited applications of microwave and ultrasonic-type probes (described later).

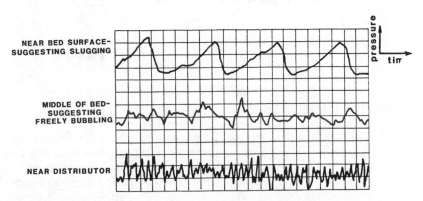

Figure 10-6. Pressure traces obtained at various heights in a three-foot column.

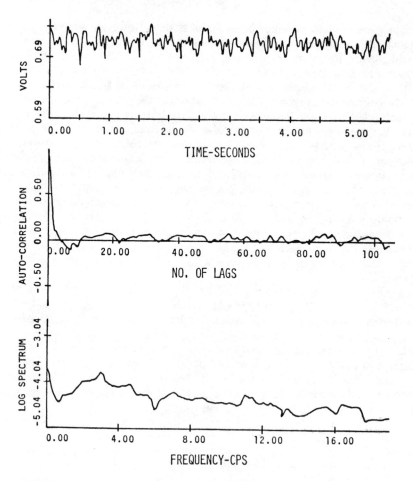

Figure 10-7. Illustration of typical spectral analyses of pressure fluctuations reported by Broadhurst et al.[20]

Gamma-Ray Transmission

Gamma-ray transmission techniques have been used for many years to sense inventories in vessels.[23] In point measurements, the radioactive source in a holder emits a beam of gamma rays across the vessel through its walls to the detector. The detector consists of a Geiger counter that produces an electrical impulse in response to each gamma-photon passing through the tube. These pulses are integrated and transformed into a dc signal proportional to the radiation received at the counter.

In the case of a fluidized bed, the presence of the emulsion over the measuring distance is detected by a drop in the measured gamma ray signal. It is possible to extend this technique for use in large-diameter vessels by locating the source and detector units across a chord.

Common gamma-ray emitting materials used as sources include radium-226 (half life 1,585 years), cobalt-60 (5.2 years) and cesium-137 (33 years).

Gamma rays are electromagnetic and have short wavelengths and high frequency. They are measured in units of radiation intensity in air (millroentgen (mr)). The basis of this detection technique involves an interaction of the radiation with the detection device to produce an ionizing reaction. The degree of ionization can be measured using an appropriate electronic scheme. Two forms of detection are employed, namely, a measurement of the number of interactions of radiation with the detector and measurement of the total effect of the radiation. The former is a counting process in which the energy level of the radiation is ignored, and hence, is best suited for detecting bubble frequency. The second form of measurement is characterized by a mean-radiation level, which can be related to bed voidage. Orcutt and Carpenter[24] successfully applied gamma-ray transmission to detecting the presence of bubbles.

Other Nonintrusive Measurement Techniques

Other techniques that provide the advantage of being noninstrusive measurement methods are laser-anemometry, microwaves, ultrasonic probes, and holography. Among these, only lasers have thus far been applied with success in studying bubble phenomena in fluid beds. Yoshida et al.[25] obtained measurements of the size distributions of bubbles using laser beams. Experimental results showed that the size distribution has a bimodal form that differs from the distribution previously reported.

The use of ultrasonic techniques to detect and measure bubble properties appears to be a reasonable approach. Acoustic Doppler flowmeters have been used for many years in dense slurry-flow applications[23,26] but have also been applied to detecting bubbles in gas-liquid systems.[27-29] The extension to fluidized beds, therefore, seems logical. The Doppler principle for moving targets is illustrated in Figure 10-8. As shown, a target (assume a solid particle) is moving with velocity v between a transmitter in direction θ_t with reference to the target flight and a receiver in direction θ_r. Signals are emitted at time intervals t_o from the transmitter. The target-transmitter and target-receiver distances are L_t, L_r, respectively (at the instant the initial pulse reaches the target). By the time the next pulse reaches the target, the distances change to:

$$L_t + vt_o \cos \theta_t$$

$$L_r + vt_o \cos \theta_r$$

This assumes that $v << c$. The frequency change is directly proportional to the carrier frequency f_o. A single target would eventually be carried out of the system

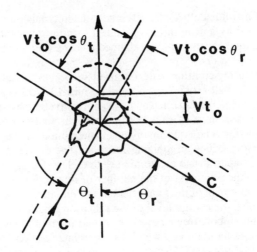

Figure 10-8. Illustration of the principle of the Doppler method.

range and even before that the angles, θ, would change. In slurry flows, the application is straightforward, and the statistical distribution of scatterers remains unchanged. In the case of a fluid bed, large discontinuities exist in the form of bubbles. Hence, at the very least, acoustical Doppler flowmeters should detect differences in signal attenuation from solids versus bubbles. For adequate penetration across a vessel wall the frequency must be reduced as the density and vessel diameter increase. For optimum operation (i.e., for low noise-to-signal ratio) of a Doppler system, the highest frequency feasible should be used. This means that a compromise frequency must be chosen for each application. For slurry flows this frequency range is between $100 \sim 600$ kHz. For very large diameter vessels, it may be necessary to mount both the transmitter and receiver on the same side of the apparatus to achieve a satisfactory signal-to-noise ratio. The advantages of this approach are:

1. It is a nonintrusive measurement technique.
2. A linear relationship between the Doppler shift frequency and flow velocity (or voidage) exists.
3. A direct output of frequency is suitable for telemetry in flow measurements.
4. It is a relatively fast response measurement technique.
5. The electronic circuits for commercial units are relatively simple and require minimal critical adjustment.

In an operating system, a sonic wave is generated and injected into the flow where it is scattered by particles. A second transducer picks up the scattered energy and the signal is amplified and analyzed. These transducers must be designed to survive and operate at process conditions. Hence, the mechanical arrangement requires some consideration. Rapis et al.[26] and Karplus and Raptis[30] describe a wedge configuration for the transducer suitable for adaptation to hot vessel walls. These are designed so that sound waves in the wall propagate in the shear mode, and hence, a simple mode propagation is assured. Some signal strength improvement can be obtained by employing a wall-thickness coincident effect to obtain in-phase propagation after each reflection. That is, the operating frequency is tuned to have a wavelength in the wall equivalent to δ sin a, where δ is the wall thickness and a the propagation angle with the vessel axis. In this case, the transducer images produced by multiple reflections in the vessel wall act as a phased array which has a narrower beam pattern. The output signal will improve at the coincidence frequency.

Schiebe and Killen[27] have applied acoustic techniques for measuring gas bubble size distributions in cavitation research. They employed the acoustic tone burst attenuation technique for measuring the gas bubble size distribution in water, but noted that resolution between size ranges was extremely poor. Yosef et al.[28] used a Doppler velocimeter to obtain the size distribution of gas bubbles in water. Their results indicated a good distribution fit by a log-normal relation. Agrest and Kuznetsov[29] analytically studied the dynamics of bubble size distributions in sound fields, with implications that support this measurement. Clearly, acoustic methods appear well suited for fluid beds, however, they are likely restricted to single-wall vessels. Refractory-lined vessels may introduce special sonic conduction problems that have not been explored in the literature.

Microwaves are another potential candidate for detecting the presence of bubbles. Standard packages are available for level sensing applications[23] and might readily be applied to the fluid-bed case. A system would basically consist of a power supply, pulse modulator, oscillator, and directional antenna. The receiver consists of a directional antenna, a microwave mixer cavity with a barrier diode detector, a high gain, low noise amplifier, a pulse coding network, a voltage comparator circuit, and a relay driver circuit.

These systems operate as follows: In the transmitter, line voltage is converted to a well-regulated and well-filtered 12V dc supply. It is then pulsed randomly at about 1 kHz by the pulse modulator circuit. This circuit is included to permit pulse discrimination circuitry to be used. In addition, pulsing at a 10% duty cycle safely permits peak transmitted power levels 10 times greater than permitted under continuous wave operation. The pulsed dc is fed to a Gunn oscillator in the antenna assembly, where the 12V dc, 1-kHz square wave is converted to a pulsed X-band (10.525 GHz) microwave signal. This signal is radiated by the directional antenna, which is typically a 10-dB gain horn with a beam spread of approximately 40%.

In the receiver, the signal is received by a directional antenna and coupled to a mixer cavity containing a detector diode. The diode converts the low-level microwave signal to a low-level pulsed dc, which is then amplified by an adjustable gain, low noise ac amplifier to a 0-6V dc control signal. This system is interconnected and uses pulse discrimination coding. In these systems the receiver is on only when the transmitter is on, thus the system is immune to false triggering from stray microwave signals from adjacent transmitters or other random sources of microwave interference. The level of the amplified received signal (0-6V dc) is compared with a preset value in a voltage comparator circuit. When the signal level received exceeds the comparator set point, an output signal is initiated, which it processes through time delay circuits to drive the output relay.

Product materials encountered in industry have varying effects on microwave signals. For example, low-level microwaves cannot penetrate metals but are reflected by them. Microwaves are absorbed almost entirely by water and to varying degrees by water-based solutions or products that have a significant moisture content such as grain, wood products, etc.

Transmission losses decrease with increasing dielectric constants and increase with increasing conductivity. For example, air (dielectric constant of 7, conductivity of zero) transmits microwaves with no transmission loss, while sea water (dielectric constant of 55 at X-band, conductivity of 4 mhos/m) provides extreme attenuation of the microwave energy. It is the material's dielectric constant and conductivity that determine whether the material is a good candidate for the use of microwaves in measurement systems.

Microwave devices are being used to measure levels of liquids and solids in tanks, bins, hoppers, and chutes. Nonconductive fiberglass tanks represent minimal losses to X-band microwaves. Sensors are mounted on the outside of the tank, opposite one another. Losses through the tank walls and from air or vapors present above the product are low. In a fluid bed, when a bubble passes the microwave transmitter, the signal drops in attenuation significantly, causing the relay to change state. Metal tanks or hoppers must have "windows" transparent to microwave signals. Sight glasses can be used on storage tanks, compatible with the pressures, temperatures, and chemical properties of the fluidized materials. For metal vessels, windows can be constructed of materials such as high-density polyethylene or other similar substances compatible with the product contained therein. A partial list of materials low in loss (these are potential candidates for windows, as well as detected objects) follows:

Firebrick	Nylon
Fiberglass	Paraffin
Polyethylene	Plexiglass
Polystyrene	Glass (no lead)
PVC powder	Teflon
Lucite	Styrofoam
Lexan	Quartz
Mica	

Vertical or horizontal installation is possible with the mounting point fastened so that it is free from vibrations. The frequencies of transmitter and receiver should be the same. The two units must face each other and be positioned on a common axial line. Slight misalignment is permissible (vertically, a maximum 5% of the distance between transmitter and receiver), but microwave power will be lost. Since the microwave beam is polarized, the receiver and transmitter should not be turned on their longitudinal axis, but at 180° to each other.

If it is impossible to install the microwave units opposite each other, the beams can be deflected by metal reflectors placed vertically to the mounting axis of the transmitter and receiver. The distance between the units is thus reduced by approxi-

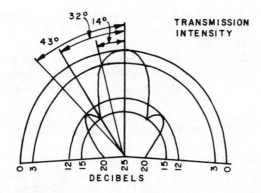

Figure 10-9. Illustration of the lobar propagation of microwaves.

Table 10-1
Attenuation of Microwaves Through Various Materials[23]

Material	Wall Thickness (mm)	Response Distance (m)
PVC	3	10.0
	30	7.5
Polyacryl	15	7.0
Perbunan-rubber	20	2.0
Asbestos	2	6.8
Polyethylene	3	10.0
Glass	8	5.3
	17	2.5
Wood (layered)	16	6.2
	20	5.2
	36	4.0

mately 10% with one reflector, and by approximately 20% with two reflectors. Further reflection on metal parts should, however, be avoided. The distance between transmitter-receiver and the ground or any metal part should amount to at least 15% of the distance between transmitter and receiver. Figure 10-9 shows the lobar propagation curve of the microwave. To detect small bubbles, the distance between the transmitter and receiver should be as short as possible. Materials with low dielectric constants cause slight attenuation, and materials with high dielectric constants produce stronger attenuation. Microwaves are best reflected on metal (refer to Table 10-1 for approximate values).

Application of microwave techniques to detecting bubbles in fluid beds has not been fully demonstrated, and no examples are cited in the literature. However, the approach merits further investigation.

Holography is still another untried technique, but successful applications in measuring drop sizes in immiscible liquids suggest extension to fluid bed studies is possible. This technique is described in the section on solids flow measurements.

Electroresistivity Techniques

These techniques include conductivity, capacitance, inductance, and impedance probes. Some materials, such as coke particles conduct electrical currents rather well, thus allowing electrical resistivity to be used to indicate the presence of bubbles in a fluidized coke bed. Point resistivity measurements were used by Park et al.,[31] Rigby et al.,[32] Burgess and Calderbank,[33] and Calderbank[34] to detect the presence of bubbles in fluidized coke beds. Burgess et al.[33] employed a five-element probe to derive the shape and size of bubbles as well. Resistivity measurements to detect bubbles along with simultaneous transient gas measurements were made by Calderbank[34] to differentiate the compositions of the gas in the emulsion and bubble phases.

Capacitance probes have been employed most often because they work well with nonconducting material. Various probe configurations have been used, ranging from parallel plates to flush mounted plates. Probe configuration is an important consideration with this technique, as different geometries have varying responses. Also, the geometry can alter local flow conditions, and hence, a configuration allowing for minimal disturbance as well as maximum response and sensitivity is needed.

Parallel plate probes typically employ plates that are approximately 10 mm on a side and which are separated from each other by about 10 mm. The capacitance change that occurs when solids (for example, sand), are placed between the plates is of the order of one picofarad. This range allows for capacitance to be measured by simple bridge imbalance techniques. Investigators such as Morse and Ballou[35] Yoshida et al.,[36] and Matsen[37] employed parallel plate probes. Datson[38] modified the parallel plate configuration into parallel rods, which reduced the effect of flow distortion by the probe.

Ormiston et al.,[39] Angelino et al.,[40] Nguyen et al.,[41] Baskakov et al.,[42] and Thiel and Potter[43] employed flush-mounted large-area capacitance probes. These large-area designs are favorable to large capacitance changes and hence, can be detected with conventional bridge circuitry.

Tiny flush-mounted probes along with simultaneous heat transfer measurements were made by Catipovic et al.[44] In this study, the measured capacitance change was on the order of 0.01 picofarads. This design resembles the radio frequency-diode probes developed by Lanneau.[45] Lanneau's probes were originally designed to be very small or pencil-point-type probes. These were later modified by Rooney and Harrison[46] to a multipin probe in order to measure bubble size on a surface. Werther and Molerous[47] and Werther[48] describe in detail, a tiny pencil-point-type probe to measure bubbles with minimal flow disturbances. In Werther's design, variations in the bed's capacitance are detected by a shift in the frequency of an oscillator. This type of circuitry has considerably more sensitivity than a conventional bridge circuit and as such tends to measure the distributed capacitance of the leads along with the capacitance of the probe itself. Fortunately, this can be readily filtered out with an appropriate discriminator system.

Both resistivity and capacitance probes have been extensively tested at Exxon Research and Engineering Co. and combined into a single system briefly described herein. Parallel electrode, flush-mounted probes provide the best design as they can be miniaturized to prevent gross flow disturbances, and response is generally faster than the plate configuration. Geldart and Kelsey[49] report additional findings on probe geometry. By combining capacitance and resistivity bridges in a single unit, the operator can switch the probe to either capacitance or resistivity measurements, depending on the properties of the material in the bed.

Resistivity and capacitance probes can be used to obtain point measurements of complete bubble characteristics, which includes average bubble size, velocity, and frequency. A single probe consisted of two parallel wire electrodes of flush-mounted plates that are excited by a high-frequency signal. When a bubble strikes a single two-electrode probe, an interruption in the electrical signal occurs due to the change in capacitance or resistance of the surrounding media. Figure 10-10 illustrates the measurement principles. In this figure the signal U(t) is shown versus time for the case when a bubble strikes a probe. The bubble generates an electric impulse of duration time, t_B, which is proportional to the pierced length, ℓ, of the bubble.

$$\ell = U_B t_B \qquad (10\text{-}5)$$

where U_B is the rise velocity of the bubble.

By using two probes, A and B, positioned one above the other with a vertical displacement, s, we note that the rising bubble causes a signal interruption, at the lower and then at the higher probe. From the time of the pulse separation, t_s, the rise velocity, U_B, can be computed.

$$U_B = s/t_s \qquad (10\text{-}6)$$

Hence, a single probe enables measurements of the local bubble frequencies (by simply counting the number of electric impulses), and two vertically aligned probes provide measurements of the bubble rise velocity and pierced length of the bubble.

The displacement height s is a critical parameter in the measurements because it is difficult to identify corresponding bubbles in the signals $U_A(t)$ and $U_B(t)$ due to splitting or coalescence of bubbles between probes. If displacement s is too small it is difficult to measure individual pulse separations because small variations in the shape of the leading and trailing edges of the pulses can lead to errors in the magnitude of t_s. The instantaneous rise velocity of a bubble depends on several factors:

1. The rise velocity of an individual bubble is influenced by the proximity and size of neighboring bubbles.

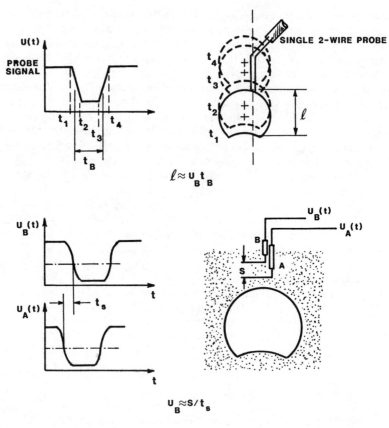

Figure 10-10. Illustration of the measurement principle for rise velocity and pierced length of a single bubble.

2. During the period prior to coalescence, bubbles about to coalesce influence each other's rise velocity.
3. The size and geometry of the probe can alter both the bubble shape and rise velocity.

The optimum separation between two probes is on the order of the radius of the maximum bubble size expected.

The output signal, U(t), of the probe contains information on the bubble phase and on the local porosity variations of the dense phase, as illustrated by the unprocessed signal output in Figure 10-11. The signals due to the bubble pulses and those due to the variations of porosity of the dense phase must be separated. A discriminator circuit can be used to filter out fluctuations in bed porosity. Only that part of the signal U(t) that lies below an adjustable reference value U_D is transmitted undistorted, while for other parts of U(t) the signal is blocked and the output is constant U_D. The discriminator circuit can be designed to produce a signal more suitable for further automatic processing $U''(t)$ in the form of rectangular pulses of a constant height. The duration of such a rectangular pulse is identical to t_B for which the discriminator circuit detects the corresponding pulse. Hence, once U_D is established (by comparing the circuit output to cinegraphic detection of the bubble frequency, say, in a two-dimensional bed for calibration purposes) the output U(t) of the discriminator circuit contains all bubble pulses but no contributions due to the bed porosity fluctuations.

Since instantaneous rise velocities and pierced lengths are virtually stochastic quantities, the measurement of individual bubbles is not meaningful. Instead, the local state of fluidization is best described by mean values as detected at the point of the probe. The bubble mean rise time is measured by means of correlation techniques. The pierced length is affected by two probes, A and B, displaced a distance s in the direction of motion of the structure. These probes provide the electric signals $U'_A(t)$ and $U'_B(t)$ in response to the surroundings. Since it is assumed that all elements move at the same velocity, the two signals are identical except for a constant time displacement. Hence, the mean rise velocity can be estimated by a cross-

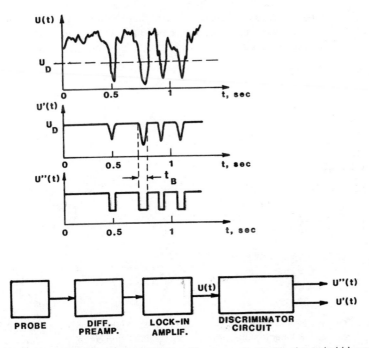

Figure 10-11. Decomposition of the probe signal into components U_2, due to bubbles and U_1, due to dense-phase porosity fluctuation.

correlation of the duration signal times of the two probes and the mean pierced length obtained by an autocorrelation function of the displaced time, t_B. A standard correlator can be used to process these mean values. The specific mathematics of the autocorrelation and cross-correlation functions are described by Werther.[47,48]

Note that the output signal, $U'(t)$, of the discriminator circuit, assuming U_D is properly set, contains all bubbles and is suitable for triggering an electronic counter. The discriminator sends the signal to a counter for a preselected period, T. The counter registers the number n of the bubble pulses within the set period. Hence, for sufficiently large T, the bubble frequency f was directly measured.

The instrumentation setup for the measurements described is shown in Figure 10-12. Two Model 125-A Princeton Applied Research Lock-In Amplifiers are used to both excite the probes and amplify the probe output signals. Two Lock-In Amplifiers are required when probes are synchronized to obtain measurements of the rise velocity. Each Lock-In has a frequency generator which supplies a 10 kHz excitation signal to the probes. A differential preamplifier (diff. preamp.) is used to amplify the probe output signal. The lock-in provides real time comparison of the probe-distorted signal to the reference signal supplied for excitation. Hence, the difference between the probe input and output signals contains information on both bubbles and porosity fluctuations. The portion of the signal containing this information is then sent to the discriminator circuit to separate bubble and porosity information. The processed signal containing information on bubbles only is then sent to the correlator where both cross-correlation of the double-probe signal (rise velocity) and autocorrelation of the single-probe signal (bubble pierced length) can be made. Capability for switching to an electronic counter (for local bubble frequency measurements) and a strip chart recorder (for discriminator/base-level monitoring)

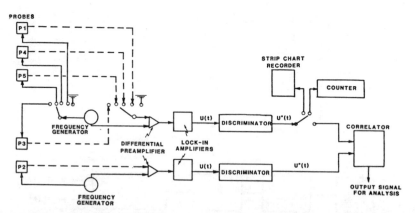

Figure 10-12. Instrumentation set up for measuring mean bubble properties. For simultaneous operation of Probes P2 and P3, the correlator is operated in the cross-correlation mode. Probe P2 operation alone requires auto-correlation mode. Remaining probes provide bubble frequency measurements only.

is included. Each probe has a specially designed dc bridge circuit enabling it to be used either as a capacitance probe or a resistivity probe.

In a fluidized bed, bubbles seldom have regular shapes. In fact, over a period of time, bubbles of considerably different sizes and shapes pass through a given horizontal control volume containing the probe as one of its points.

To obtain a statistically representative mean bubble size an adequate description of the size distribution of the array of bubbles is needed. Because of the irregular shape of bubbles, a measurement of the pierced length in itself does not define bubble size. Werther[45] provides a detailed statistical analysis of the bubble size distribution on the basis of the following model:

A size of distribution defined as: either the cumulative number distribution $N_o(D_h)$ of the horizontal diameters D_h, where $D_{h,min} < D_h < D_{h,max}$; or the cumulative number distribution $Q_o(D_v)$ of the vertical diameters D_v, with $D_{v,min} < D_v < D_{v,max}$.

Because a pierced length lies in the range $0 < \ell < D_{v,max}$, from probability theory:

$$g(\ell)d\ell = \sum_{i=1}^{n} P_{i,1}P_{i,2} \tag{10-7}$$

where 1 and n denote the first and nth size class corresponding to the minimum bubble diameter ($D_{v,min}$) and the maximum bubble diameter ($D_{v,max}$), respectively.

$g(\ell)d\ell$ = probability that a measurement yields a pierced length in the interval (ℓ, $\ell + d\ell$)

$P_{i,1}$ = probability that the struck bubble belongs to the ith class ($D_{v,i}$, $D_{v,i} + \Delta D_{v,i}$).

$P_{i,2}$ = probability that the measured pierced length lies in the interval (ℓ, $\ell + d\ell$) if a bubble in the ith class ($D_{v,i}$, $D_{v,i} + \Delta D_{v,i}$) is struck.

The criterion developed by Werther[48] for deriving the bubble size distribution $Q_o(D_v)$ from a measured distribution of pierced lengths $g(\ell)$ is as follows:

$$Q_o(\ell) = 1 - \left\{ \frac{g(\ell)}{g(D_{v,min})} \right\} \left\{ \frac{D_{v,min}}{\ell} \right\} \quad D_{v,max} < \ell < D_{v,max} \tag{10-8}$$

Where Q_o (ℓ) is the cumulative number density distribution of pierced lengths (cm^{-1}) and $g(\ell)$ is the number density distribution (cm^{-1}). Werther has shown that the distribution $g(\ell)$ is a linear relation passing through the origin, and hence, the lower limit, $D_{r,min}$ of the bubble size distribution can be found. Note that Equation 10-8 shows that only the ratio $g(\ell)/g(D_{v,min})$ is necessary to determine the bubble size distribution. To enable the measurement of the distribution of pulse durations to be automatic, the discriminator circuit is also designed to generate a signal $U'''(t)$ from the signal $U''(t)$, which consists of a series of rectangular pulses of constant

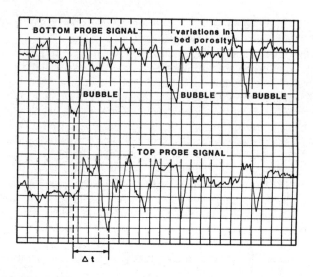

Figure 10-13. Typical oscillograph tracings made by a capacitance probe in a fluidized bed of coal char.

duration but of varying heights. The height of an individual pulse of this last signal is always proportional to the duration of the corresponding bubble pulse.

Because of the uniform duration of pulses, the probability density distribution of the amplitudes of the signal $U'''(t)$, is proportional to the distribution of pulse durations t_g for $U''' > U_o'''$, or more specifically, the bubble pulse durations t_b. A calibration voltage U_e''' must be used to convert the measured signal directly to units of pulse duration t_b. Typical oscillograph tracings of the unprocessed signal from a capacitance probe are shown in Figure 10-13.

Unlike Werther et al. and the system at Exxon, Burgess and Calderbank[55] designed a three-dimensional probe having five channels, to sense the local bubble interface approach angle as well as measure bubble size and velocity. Their system was interfaced with a high-speed digital computer capable of rapid, accurate conversion of analog voltage signals to discrete binary numbers and with software to undertake logical decisions consequent on the spatial orientation of the bubble with respect to the probe axis. The logic selects only those bubbles whose central axes are coincident with the probe axis and calculates their size, shape, and velocity by correction of the resulting nonsquare pulses. It was assumed in deriving the characteristic bubble size distribution function of a dispersion that bubbles rise into the probe in a random fashion and that the measurements are therefore characteristic of unbiased sampling.

The probe arrangement consisted of three symmetrically oriented electrodes around and above the first electrode. Hence, all three electrodes were positioned in a horizontal plane at a specified distance above the central electrode and radially spaced from it. A fifth contact was positioned in the same horizontal plane as the central contact but somewhat distant from it. The arrangement and details of these probes are shown in Figure 10-14.

The probe array was connected so that each contact formed part of an electrical resistivity circuit whereby current flows from an external ac power supply while that contact is resident in the conducting phase and thus develops a voltage across a load resistor, which is measured by the computer in digital form simultaneously for each channel.[33]

The purpose of the fifth electrode (leg 5 in Figure 10-14A) is to measure approximate bubble shapes for those bubbles whose horizontal axes exceed length x_p, as shown in Figure 10-15. The probe array selects bubbles relatively close to their centerlines so the outer electrode 5 measures the vertical distance, L_d, between the bubble leading surface at the centerline and at the radial distance, x_p. It also measures the bubble vertical length at this position, L_o, as follows:

$$L_d = U_B t_5 \qquad (10\text{-}9)$$

and

$$L_o = U_B(t_T + t_c) \qquad (10\text{-}10)$$

The majority of measurements reported by capacitance- and resistance-probe techniques have been made at room temperature. The few experiments that have been made at high temperature reveal that the bubble characteristics are significantly affected by the change of temperature. Mii et al.[50] obtained bubble frequency measurements using a conductivity probe for a bed of graphite particles fluidized by nitrogen in the range of 20°C to 800°C. It was reported that the bubble frequency increased with a rise in temperature. Yoshida et al.[4] noted a decrease in bubble size with an increase in temperature from observations in a two-dimensional bed. Otake et al.,[51] using a capacitance probe to measure bubble sizes during the catalytic cracking of cyclohexane, observed a temperature dependence for both bubble size and frequency. One study opposite to these findings is that of Whittmann et al.,[52] who measured bubble size and rise velocity during the thermal cracking of $NaHCO_3$ of bed temperatures ranging from 65°C to 200°C, and observed no temperature effect on bubble properties.

The capacitance probe does appear to have limitations to high-temperature measurements. The principal restriction is that the probe requires cooling as a whole. Any high-temperature measuring method must be heat-resistant. Yoshida et al.[53] describe an improved technique based on exploitation of the alteration in an electric discharge associated with the probe being in the bubble or emulsion phases. The probe and circuitry are capable of measurements up to about 1000°C. The probe geometry and circuitry are shown in Figure 10-16. The probe's operation is based on the fact that the voltage of dielectric breakdown of dielectric particles is higher in the emulsion phase than in the bubble phase. The probe shown in Figure 10-16 shows two needle-shaped electrodes with their tips facing each other at a gap of several millimeters. An electric discharge is generated across the electrodes when a bubble passes over the gap between probe tips, (that is, the impressed voltage

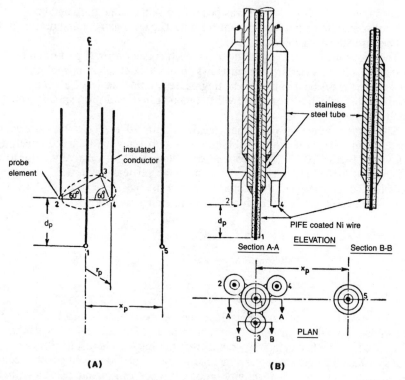

Figure 10-14. Illustration of the bubble measuring arrangement of Burgess et al.:[33] (A) isometric projection of the spacial orientation of the probe contact elements; (B) details of the probe configuration.[33]

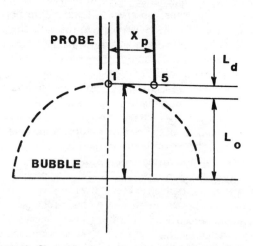

Figure 10-15. Shows five-contact probe measuring bubble shape.[33]

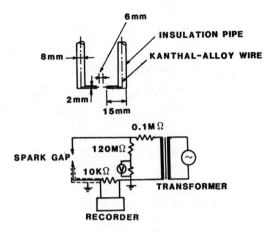

Figure 10-16. Illustration of the probe configuration and circuitry for an electric discharge probe.[53]

across the probe is higher than the breakdown potential when the probe is in the bubble phase). Hence, detection of rapid changes in electric current provides detection of the presence of bubbles. The electrode materials are an important consideration in probe construction as high temperatures can cause oxidation reactions. The probe material used by Yoshida et al. was Kanthal alloy.

Figure 10-17 shows the incipient discharge voltage in the bubble and emulsion phases for quartz sand particles. As shown, the incipient voltage decreases with an increase in bed temperature. The circuitry employs a 50-Hz alternating current. The use of dc causes particles to stick to the electrode surface. Reported voltages range between 5 and 10 kV. With conductive particles such as coal chars, the measuring voltage can be set at the incipient discharge voltage of the bubble phase. In this manner the probe can be employed as a conductivity-type probe. The electric current will then flow only when a cloud of conductive particles passes between the pair of electrodes. A sufficiently low voltage must be employed to prevent electric discharge in the emulsion phase. It should be noted that although the characteristics of the detected signal may vary depending on the conductivity of the solids, the technique described by Yoshida et al. is always suitable provided that there is a difference in the electrical properties between the bubble and emulsion phases. Through the use of dual, double-probe electrodes, complete bubble characteristics (i.e., size, rise velocity, as well as frequency), can be determined, as described earlier.

Two additional types of probes that fall into the category of electroresistivity techniques are inductance and impedance devices. One example of the use of inductance probes is in the work by Cranfield,[54] in which a small probe having a tip that

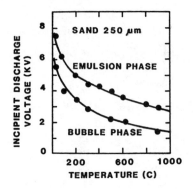

Figure 10-17. Illustration of the relationship between incipient discharge voltage and temperature reported by Yoshida et al.[53]

functions similar to the head on a magnetic tape recorder is used. This type of probe can be used to detect the presence of particles that have ferromagnetic properties. Hence, if the fluidized bed is composed of ferromagnetic solids, the signal at the probe provides an indication of whether the emulsion phase or bubbles are present. The bed does not have to be entirely composed of ferromagnetic particles; instead, it can be seeded with ferromagnetic tracer particles. This approach is useful in studying solids movement and mixing patterns in fluidized beds.

A rather recent development is the impedance probe devised by Linneweber and Blass[55] for obtaining local gas and solids holdup measurements in three-phase fluidized systems. The system employs the double-needle probes described earlier to detect only bubbles and thus obtain the gas holdup. The impedance probe obtains both the solids and gas holdup, and hence, comparison of the two measurements provides the liquid holdup. In the case of three phases, the capacitance or conductivity probe is unaffected by the solids, but rather is influenced by the continuous liquid phase. Figure 10-18 reviews the measuring principle of the needle probes previously described. Note that an electric circuit is completed over the conducting fluid suspension between the needle probe, which is insulated apart from its tip, and an electrode sufficiently large so as not to be affected by gas bubbles. The probe's signal is disturbed when a gas bubble strikes the tip. The time intervals during which the probe tip is surrounded by gas bubbles can be summed to provide the mean value of the gas holdup. As emphasized earlier, this approach only works when the dispersed and continuous phases have significantly different conductivities. If the conductivities of these phases are similar, Linneweber et al. recommend the use of an optical-type probe (Figure 10.18B). In this case, differences in the refractive indices between the dispersed and continuous phases provide an indirect measurement of holdup. The flush-mounted probe configuration and circuitry for the capacitance system described earlier are equally suited for the bubble holdup measurement in the former case.

The impedance technique is based on differences in the dielectric constants and conductivities of the liquid, solids, and gas mediums. The capacity of a plate condenser, for example, is a function of the volume fractions of dispersed phases exposed to the electric field. The actual relationship between impedance and holdup is a function of the size, geometry, and distribution of the dispersed-phase particles. The relationships for the particle system distribution can be mathematically de-

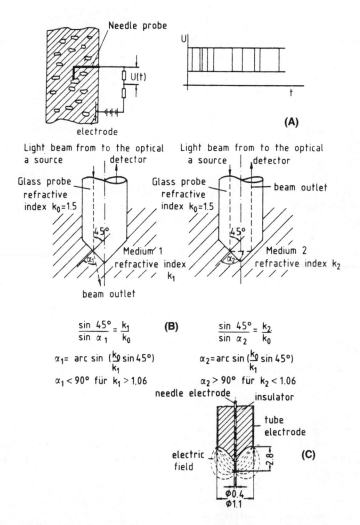

Figure 10-18. Summary of measuring principles behind the double conductivity probes proposed as applied by Lenneweber et al.[55] to measure bubble properties in three phases.

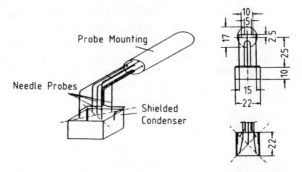

Figure 10-19. Detail of impedance/conductivity probe designed by Lenneweber et al.[55]

scribed by standard models such as the well-known Maxwell distribution. Linneweber et al. have combined the two separate measurement principles into the single-probe configuration shown in Figure 10-19. A relatively large condenser is employed to detect the largest deformable objects, which in a three-phase fluidized bed, such as a bubble column, are bubbles. Hence, the bubbles are treated as small particles compared with the volume of the electric field. Note that the design includes five needle probes to detect the mean values of gas holdup in the electric field of a plate condenser, whose plates are surrounded by Faraday's cave.[55] The resulting signal from the impedence probe is the sum of the gas and solids holdups in the electric field.

Thermal Techniques

Thermal and constant-temperature anemometry techniques have also been applied to indirectly detect bubbles in fluid beds. Wen, et al.[56] constructed a miniature probe composed of a self-heating thermister to sense bubbles. The measurement principle is based on the fact that the probe's heat transfer coefficient in the emulsion phase is significantly greater than in the bubble phase. Consequently, when the probe is in the emulsion phase, its temperature decreases, resulting in an increase in the resistivity of the probe. In Wen's design, the resistivity itself is measured and is used to detect the presence of bubbles.

Other studies[57-59] aimed at examining the heat transfer mechanisms in fluidized beds, describe methods that indirectly sense bubbling conditions. Baskakov et al.[57]

describe a thermoanemometer for directly measuring the instantaneous fluctuations of local heat transfer coefficients. The probe itself consisted of a 5 μm thick platinum foil glued on a surface immersed in the fluid bed. The temperature of the foil was observed to drop abruptly when a packet of cold particles approached the foil, then rose with the heating of particles. The temperature drop continued even further when gas bubbles passed over the foil surface. By simultaneous measurements using a photo-transducer technique, the presence of bubbles was detected. Figure 10-20 shows oscillograph tracings of the simultaneous recording of signals from the photo-transducer and the thermoanemometer, indicating, as in Wen's study, that temperature fluctuations provide a satisfactory approach to bubble detection. Details of the probe configuration employed by Baskakov et al. are also shown in Figure 10-20. Similar techniques are described by Bernis et al.[58] and Goosens and Hellincks.[59]

Table 10-2 summarizes the various techniques described in this section for bubble properties measurements.

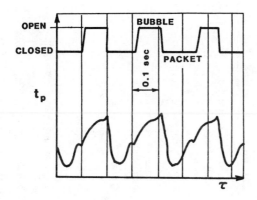

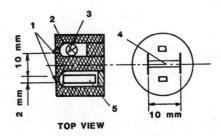

TOP VIEW

Figure 10-20. Illustration of the oscillograph tracings of signals from a phototransducer and thermoanemometer reported by Baskakov et al.[57]

Table 10-2
Summary of Techniques Demonstrated for Measuring Bubble Properties in Fluidized Systems

Technique	Type Measurement		Parameters Measured	System Studied			Computer Interface		Investigators
	Direct	Indirect		Gas/ Liquid	Gas/ Solid	Three- Phase	Used	Appli- cable	(See References)
Acoustic	x		Bubble size distribution/ bubble frequency/rise velocity	x				x	27–30
Capacitance	x		Bubble size (mean) and distribution/bubble frequency/rise velocity/ bubble shape	x	x		x		35–49, 51
Resistivity/ conductivity	x		Same	x	x		x		31–34, 50–53
Inductance	x		Bubble frequency		x			x	54
Impedance	x		Bubble size (mean) and distribution/bubble frequency/rise velocity/ bubble shape			x		x	55
Gamma ray	x		Bubble size/bubble frequency		x			x	24

Table 10-2 (continued)
Summary of Techniques Demonstrated for Measuring Bubble Properties in Fluidized Systems

Technique	Type Measurement		Parameters Measured	System Studied			Computer Interface		Investigators (See References)
	Direct	Indirect		Gas/ Liquid	Gas/ Solid	Three- Phase	Used	Appli- cable	
Laser beams		x	Bubble size/bubble frequency		x			x	25
Light scattering transmission/ photoelectric	x		Bubble size/bubble frequency	x	x		x		10–13
Fiber optics	x		Bubble size/bubble frequency	x	x			x	14–17
Photographic and X-ray	x		Bubble size and distribu- tion/bubble frequency/ rise velocity	x	x				1–9
Piezoelectric/ transducers	x		Bubble frequency/ bubble velocity	x	x		x		18–22
Thermal	x		Bubble frequency		x			x	56–59

MEASUREMENT TECHNIQUES FOR PARTICLE BEHAVIOR

There is considerably less accurate instrumentation for studying solid particle behavior in both the freeboard region and dense bed than there is for studying bubble dynamics. This is surprising since particle dynamics in the freeboard region are critical not only to the overall design of fluid-bed reactors and in specifying particle disengaging/separation equipment, but because of the implications to lean-phase reactions. In the dense, bubbling bed, particle interactions establish the degree of mixedness between particles and gas, and gas and the emulsion.

In Chapter 5, a review of various studies of particle flows in the freeboard region was given. Most of these measurements have been performed on small-scale columns with very narrow particle size distributions. The techniques used to record entrainment and particle size distributions have been relatively simple. One example is that of Page and Harrison,[60] who employed both visual and sampling techniques. In this study, the system was composed of three phases (sand, air, water). Their sampling system is illustrated in Figure 10-21, where the entry to the probe tube was a circular orifice located in the vertical plane. Samples of solids and liquid in the dilute phase were obtained for different sand bed heights and fluidizing velocities, at various radial positions. Bed expansion and bubble size were recorded using photographic techniques. In gas-fluidized systems, standard isokinetic sampling procedures combined with pressure profiles over the column height and/or cinegraphic methods have provided the bulk of the entrainment correlations reviewed in Chapter 5.

In the bed itself, various techniques have been reported to provide direct information on particle interactions and overall solids mixing.[61-72] Rezenbaum et al.[61] describe a simple but clever technique that makes use of an object suspended on a string. The object, immersed in the bed, presumably moves along with the fluidized solids, and the deflection of the string is recorded to reflect particle behavior. Along similar principles, Heertjes et al.[62] used a needle-like probe, in which the stress on the needle provides an indication of the velocity vector of the solids moving past the probe. Oki et al.[64] and more recently, Patrose and Caram[71] employed fiber-optics probes with correlation techniques to evaluate particle velocities moving across the face of the probe. Marsheck et al.[63] employed a double-thermister probe to record solids movement in the bed. In this set-up, the solids were heated by one thermister, and the temperature of the solids was detected by a second thermister. This technique provides a measurement of the solid's velocity component in the direction of the thermisters.

Three additional techniques have been widely employed for solids movement measurements in the dense region; these are radio transmitter, radioactive tracer, and magnetic tracer techniques. In the radio transmitter method, a tiny radio transmitter is located in a tracer particle (called a radio pill). The behavior of a typical particle can be studied by positioning receivers at various circumferencial and vertical positions along the bed.[65]

May,[66] Kondukov,[67] and others[68,69,72] have employed radioactive tracer particles. In these studies the tracer particles are introduced at one point in the bed and monitored by Geiger counters at various locations within and outside the column. When

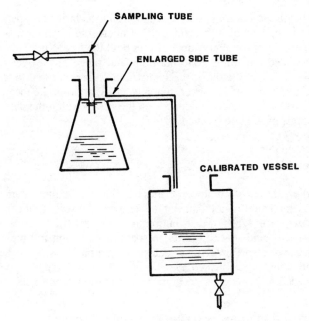

SAMPLING TUBE

ENLARGED SIDE TUBE

CALIBRATED VESSEL

Figure 10-21. Sampling-probe apparatus of Page et al.[60]

radioactive particles having a short half-life are employed, it is not necessary to remove the tracer from the bed before initiating the next experiment. Lehtola and Kuoppamaki[72] recently applied this technique to studying the mixing efficiency of continuous industrial-type mixers.

There are other techniques that are well adapted to cold model studies. An example is the introduction of colored solid particles into a fluidized bed followed by slumping and sampling to evaluate how solids disperse. This technique can be combined with high-speed cinegraphic methods to obtain dynamic evaluation of mixing studies. One problem with this approach is if the study concerns a particular solid material, the choice of tracer may pose a problem. Two alternatives are to coat the actual material with a paint or dye, and to coat a sample with salt. In the salt tracer method, samples can be withdrawn from the bed at various locations and analyzed for local salt concentration by standard wet titration methods or the use of a salinity meter.

In addition to these methods, there are a variety of instruments that are available for studying particle dynamics, but which have not been extensively applied to fluid-bed studies. These techniques have had a proven track record as reliable measurement methods in dilute two-phase systems such as immiscible liquids and gas-liquid. A review of the operating principles along with guidelines for applying them to fluid-bed studies with particular emphasis on studying the freeboard region, follows.

Before we begin these discussions, it is important to clarify the specific parameters of interest in such studies. It is not only of interest to learn more about mixing patterns and particle movement/trajectories in both the freeboard and dense region of the bed, but also the solids concentrations and range of particle sizes. In the freeboard, knowledge of the particle size distribution is important to transport and reaction-yield mechanisms. However, in many cases, appropriate mean values will suffice. The particular mean size depends on the use to which the data is to be applied. In general, means are defined as:

$$d_{pq} = \left[\frac{\int x d^p dd}{\int x d^q dd} \right]_{x \to \infty}^{1/(p-q)} \tag{10-11}$$

As noted earlier, the most common of these definitions is the volume to surface area, d_{32} (i.e., the Sauter mean diameter). The type of distribution can also be important. The two main types of distribution are temporal (i.e., varies with time at one point in space), and spacial (varies in space at one point in time).

The magnitude of effort involved in determining a mean particle size from individual measurements is established by the required sample size. Large samples are sometimes needed to provide an accurate representation of the mean population.

Photographic Techniques (Freeboard Region Studies)

Small, fast-moving particles are difficult to photograph, unless careful consideration is given to proper illumination and the photography required. In addition, the interpretation of the images produced must be carefully considered for accurate results.

Effects to consider in applying this technique are the illumination-intensity/particle-size/velocity relationships and the angular variation of scattered light. The required illumination is governed by the particle size and velocity. A fundamental axiom from geometrical optics shows that the light scattered from a small sphere in the size range of $10-10^3$ μm is:

$$I = I_o F(\theta) d^2 \tag{10-12}$$

where I_o = incident illumination
$F(\theta)$ = function dependent on the direction of observation with respect to that of illumination
d = particle size

Exposure time is defined as the time required for a particle to travel a small fraction of its own diameter. The exposure is defined as the total amount of light covering any portion of the photographic plate. The exposure for the portion of the plate onto which the image of a particle is focused is:

$$E = (I_o F(\theta) d^2) \left(\frac{K_E d}{V_p} \right) = \frac{K_E I_o F(\theta) d^3}{V_p} \tag{10-13}$$

where K_E = fraction of diameter particle permitted to move during photography
V_p = particle velocity

The value of E must be set to a prescribed level to provide sufficient light for producing a visible image on the developed plate. This value is dependent on the incident light intensity, which in turn depends on particle size and velocity; i.e.:

$$I_o \propto d_p^{-3}$$

$$\left. \begin{array}{c} \\ \\ \\ \\ \end{array} \right\} \qquad \qquad (10\text{-}14)$$

$$I_o \propto V_p$$

From the theories of Fraunhofer diffraction and Mie scattering, $F(\theta)$ increases with incident angle θ (θ is the angle included between the illuminating and observing light paths; and this angle tends to $0°$). It follows that the illumination is also a function of particle size and velocity, and the illumination should be set as close to $0°$ to the observing direction as possible. At exactly $0°$, the shadows of particles in flow will also be recorded.

For contrast purposes, back illumination can be used in which recorded particles will appear as black dots or dark dashes on a bright background. Kirkman et al.[73] give guidelines for photographing droplet sprays using this technique.

To extract information on the direction of motion and velocity of particles, a double exposure technique outlined in the literature for studying sprays can be used.[74,75] This involves using double flash exposures, where measurements are taken from the start of one streak to the start of the next. Multiple flashes can be provided by a stroboscopic light source. Note however, that these units do not always provide sufficient illumination intensity and/or a fast enough rate of interruption. To compensate for this, McCreath et al.[74] describe a double flash system, where the first spark focuses at the point of origin of the second spark by means of a lens system. A further lens focuses them both onto the camera shutter with a small region of the flow. A technique described by Finlay and Welsh[75] employs two flash units arranged such that their directions of illumination are perpendicular to each other, and one of these units faces the particle. A half-silvered mirror is positioned at the intersection of the light paths and at $45°$ to each other as shown in Figure 10-22.

If the particle flow is composed of very small solids, magnification of the photographic stage may be necessary. This usually requires small image distances which can pose difficulties experimentally. Large magnifications are generally achieved using small depths of field. Hence, particles that fall outside small elements on either side of the plane of focus appear blurred. The limits of the depth of field are usually defined with respect to the smallest diffuse image of a point that is indistinguishable from a point. Several criteria exist that relate the depth of field to various relevant parameters, such as aperture size, magnification, and focal length.

A small depth of field, however, does mask some information on the particle behavior. For example, it is undesirable for obtaining the spacial distribution of particles. When using large depths of field, the magnification error caused by the differ-

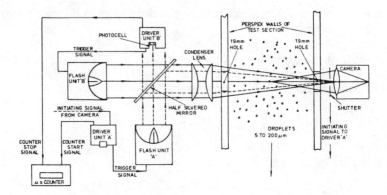

Figure 10-22. Illustration of the double flash technique employed by Finlay and Welsh.[75]

ent particle paths and sizes can be significant. There are several methods for overcoming this problem, such as stereoscopy and simultaneous observation of several neighboring planes. When these methods are used with a small depth of field, exact image distances can be detected.[77-79] Azzopardi[80] provides an overview of these alternative techniques.

Simmons[81] and Dix et al.[82] have replaced the photographic plate by photo detector arrays. The photo-detector signals can be sorted in a minicomputer. In Dix's setup, a focusing system is used that allows one to distinguish between particles in focus, particles nearly in focus, and particles completely out of focus. This provides information on the longitudinal positions of particles. Outputs from the detector arrays are electronically formatted and punched onto tape for subsequent computer analysis. The analysis reveals information along three coordinates plus time.

Holography

Photographic and cinegraphic techniques only provide a record of events in two dimensions. Holograms, on the other hand, freeze three-dimensional scenes. This is accomplished by the interference pattern formed by the light scattered by the particle and light which is unaffected by the particle. The principle behind forming a hologram is illustrated in Figure 10-23. As shown, a beam of coherent light is split into two parts and illuminates the particle. The light is reflected by the particle onto a photographic plate on which the hologram is to be produced and arrives at the same instant as a reference beam that is deflected around the particle unchanged in phase. A phase difference between the two beams causes interference from which the recorded hologram is composed of zones of high and low intensity. To examine the hologram, reconstruction is needed, which is effected by illuminating the hologram with the reference beam from the same direction as during the recording experiment. The hologram itself serves as a diffraction barrier or screen for the reference beam, thus producing a wave pattern. The end result is a three-dimensional picture of the original particle.

The principal advantages of holography are that there is little restriction on the depth of field and that a uniform magnification of particles separated longitudinally can be achieved when the reconstructed hologram is projected.

As a rule of thumb, the depth of field should be 100 d^2/λ, where d is the particle size and λ the wavelength of the illumination used.[80]

In order to ensure that the particles appear as stationary objects, movement during the formation of the hologram should be restricted to 10% of the fringe spacing. Pulsed ruby lasers are capable of producing an exposure of approximately 30 ms. This essentially renders motionless particles moving with velocities in the upper range of 100 ms^{-1}. Holography has not been applied to fluid-bed studies but would appear to be a worthwhile approach to studying both bubble dynamics and particle behavior in both the dense and freeboard regions.

Impact Method

The use of cascade samplers or impactors is standard in stack testing procedures, and isokinetic sampling of the freeboard region is practiced. Cascade samplers are devices containing a series of carefully designed nozzles and baffles. Particles of different sizes are directed into chambers where they are captured on appropriate filter plates or perforated slides designed to remove certain-size classes of solids. Samples on each plate can then be analyzed either by weight methods or particle count using microscopy or image analysis. Ultrafines can be analyzed using a Coul-

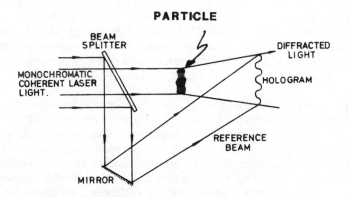

Figure 10-23. Illustration of the production of holograms.

ter counter. There are several sources of error associated with this technique, a major one being that particles tend to agglomerate under conditions of condensation/ evaporation. Recommended sampling procedures are given in Reference 83.

Optical Techniques

These techniques have already been described for bubble characteristic studies; however, a review of principles is worthwhile before extending these techniques to examining particle behavior, particularly in the freeboard.

The amount of light scattered by a particle is a function of the intensity of the illuminating radiation, the diameter and refractive index of particles, the wavelength and polarization of light, and the direction of observation relative to that of illumination. Mie[84] formalized the theory of scattering on the basis of electromagnetic theory, and reviews of the principles are given by van de Hulst[85] and Kirker.[86] The theory shows that the scattering caused by a spherical object varies in an oscillatory manner with the angle of observation.

The specific pattern depends on the particle's relative refractive index and a dimensionless particle size defined as $\pi d/\lambda$ (see Blau et al.[87] for details). For single spherical particles larger or smaller than the wavelength of light, limiting but simpler theories apply. For particles smaller than the wavelength of light, the principles of geometric optics apply. That is, the angular distribution of scattered intensity can be used for sizing particles as can variations in polarization or color. The limiting range is for particles less than 1 μm in size.[86] For our range of interest, the theory of Raleigh applies, where the intensity of the light scattered at a given angle is directly proportional to the diameter raised to the square power.

With multiparticle flows it is generally assumed that the scattering by an array of particles is indistinguishable and as such, the scattering functions for an isolated particle apply. The sum of the intensity scattered by individual particles is thus taken as the cumulative effect. On this basis, it is further assumed that there is no rescattering of scattered light. However, these assumptions are only justified for a sufficiently dilute system. A plot of the scattering coefficient, K, is shown in Figure 10-24. As shown, the total amount of light scattered only departs from the square law dependence at very small particle sizes. Below 1 μm in size the function is monotonically increasing, and between 1 and 10 μm, the function is shown to be oscillated. At d > 10 μm, K is independent of particle size. It can be concluded that a method based on total light scattered is feasible only for particles smaller than 1 μm.

Limiting present discussions to single particles, common practice is to use a narrow parallel beam of illumination along with a similar observation beam. This allows a small probe volume to be established that will thus minimize the opportunity of a coincidence. A discriminator circuit is required in order to reject any signal arising from the coincidence of two particles (a coincidence which thus produces a doublet pulse). To avoid detecting a particle that is only partially within the probe measuring volume, an annular beam of light of a different color can be used to form a ring around the volume. Through the use of beam splitters and filters, the signals

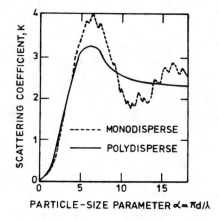

PARTICLE-SIZE PARAMETER $\alpha = \pi d/\lambda$

Figure 10-24. Plot of the scattering coefficient.

from each color could be separately monitored. Using appropriate circuitry, particles only partially in the detection volume could be identified as they would give a simultaneous signal in each color, and hence would be removed during the data analysis or acquisition stages. The techniques used for scattering from single particles are described in References 87 through 91.

Now consider a cluster of particles, each having the same diameter and shape. The additivity rule can be applied to the scatter from the monosized group of particles. To evaluate the particle size from this summing, the concentration must be known. The same principle can be applied to a distribution of particle sizes, where the scatter is summed with respect to a weighted average, with the fraction of each size present in the sample. For particles in the size range of 10 to 1,000 μm, the forward direction must be used to attain a sufficiently sensitive intensity variation to different particle sizes.

A number of studies have used light scattering techniques to obtain droplet-size distributions in gas-liquid flows.[92-97] Dobbins et al.[92] studied the small angle forward scatter for a polydispersion fitted by an upper limit log normal distribution. This particular study revealed the scattered light distribution to be relatively insensitive to parameters that characterize the particle size distribution, and hence, the method could be restricted to obtaining only the Sauter mean diameter. Deich et al.[93,94] and Chin et al.[95] observed the opposite; that is, the size/light distribution was found to be sensitive for the approach used for particle size determination.

Regardless of the specific method employed, there are some obstacles to overcome during experiments. One problem is light that is diffracted at a fixed angle from particles located at different distances from the detector arrives at different areas of the detector, thus causing extraneous or confusing signals. Azzopardi[80] describes a solution to this by positioning a lens between the object and the detector so that the latter is at the focal plane of the lens. In this manner, the lens serves as a

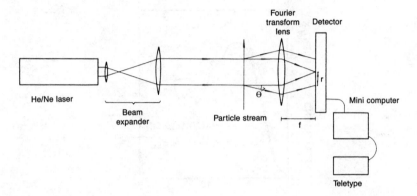

Figure 10-25. Illustration of diffraction equipment and optical geometry for Fourier transform lens.[80]

Fourier transformer, where the light diffracted by particles in any given direction is collected at a single point, irrespective of the particle's position. Figure 10-25 shows the diffraction system and optical geometry of a Fourier transform lens. The displacement of a point from the optical axis will only depend on the focal length of the lens and the angle at which light is diffracted (i.e., $r = \theta f$; r is the displacement from the optical axis, f is the len's focal length, and θ is the angle of the diffracted beam). By traversing the detector across the focal plane, the light diffracted at different angles can then be detected.

The angular distribution of diffracted light varies according to the Airy function:

$$I \propto \left[\frac{2J_1(\alpha \sin \theta)}{\alpha \sin \theta} \right]^2 \frac{1}{2} (1 + \cos^2 \theta) \tag{10-15A}$$

and for small angles:

$$I \propto \left[\frac{2J_1(\alpha\theta)}{\alpha\theta} \right]^2 \tag{10-15B}$$

where α = dimensionless particle size ($= \pi d/\lambda$)
  J_1 = first order Bessel function of the first kind
  I = illumination

The Airy function is shown plotted in Figure 10-26 for the distribution of light diffracted by an opaque disc. This poses a very practical problem in that the range of intensities to be detected drops off sharply, thus requiring a detector having a very large range. Chin et al.[95] have proposed the use of photographic plates and a microdensitometer as one solution. Density is a linear function of log intensity at a large range of intensity and hence, can be compressed into a small density range.

An alternative method is that of Cornillault,[96] who employed a screen having vari-ous-size apertures for a photodetector. In this approach, as the detector moves from the optical axis it is covered by a screen having an aperature of increasing size. Annular ring detectors described in References 97 and 98 perform a similar func-tion to the variable area screen. These latter arrangements are used in conjunction with a Fourier transform lens.

A backscattering device for measuring mass flux data is described by Shafner et al.[99] The measurement depends on the light scattered per unit volume of particle. The system employs a large probe volume in which the total light backscattered from all the particles within this volume is collected.

The optical systems described thus far are reasonably sophisticated, and yet mea-surement interpretation is still subject to some question. A relatively simple ap-proach that could be adapted to commercial units, provided viewing ports are per-missible, is based on the principle of light obscuration. As a particle flows across a light beam, the amount of light that emerges from the control volume along the irradiation direction diminishes. The diminution of light can be described by:

$$I_{out} = I_{in} - (I_{scA} + I_{ABs}) \tag{10-16}$$

where I_{scA} = amount of light scattered in directions other than the irradiation direction
I_{ABs} = amount of light absorbed by the particle

For large, single particles, the last two terms are indistinguishable and considered as one group, which is proportional to the projected area of the particle or that por-tion of it in the control volume. Various techniques based on this principle are de-scribed in the literature (see References 100–105). The general approach involves the use of a light beam having a rectangular cross-section with the particle moving across the longer side. The area involved in this case is proportional to d^2 when d is

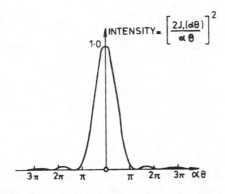

Figure 10-26. Plot of Airy function using Equation 10-15B.

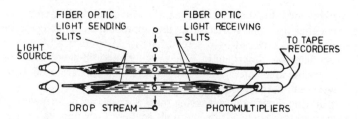

Figure 10-27. Setup for particle detection using light obscuration principle.[100]

smaller than the beam width (i.e., the shorter side). If the particle is larger than the width, then the linear relationship turns out to be a good approximation.[80] Fiber optics probes can be used in this approach, where a rectangular beam is produced by illuminating one end of the fiber bundle while the other end is splayed out flat and a reverse fiber bundle is used for recording the observation. The technique used by Ritter et al.[100] is illustrated in Figure 10-27. By employing two such detectors, one below the other, complete information on particle dynamics can be obtained (i.e., diameter, flow velocity, and frequency or concentration).

Laser-Doppler Anemometry

In principle, a laser-Doppler anemometer uses the frequency information contained in light scattered by particles that pass through a fringe or interference pattern to determine velocities. Since the intensity of light depends on the particle size, a number of studies have been aimed at both examining the influence of size on velocity measurements, as well as in obtaining particle size information (see References 106 through 112 for examples).

Several theories have been postulated to provide a working relationship between the signal visibility (i.e., the ratio of ac to dc components in the burst of scattered light), and the ratio of particle size to fringe spacing. Fistrom et al.[108] provide one relationship from geometric optics. Hong and Jones[110] and others[113-115] provide more rigorous calculation approaches. One difficulty with this technique is that the observation angle and solid collection angle must be carefully chosen to optimize the signal strength. The limited range of drop sizes for which the visibility is an unambiguous function (fringe spacing constant) is a disadvantage of the method. According to Farmer's relationship, a necessary condition to avoid ambiguity is:

$$\frac{d_{max}}{\lambda*} < 1.22\pi \qquad (10\text{-}17)$$

This means that a relatively large probe volume is required as at least 10 fringes are usually required to produce a usable signal. Another disadvantage is that particles that do not pass through the center of the probe volume yield Doppler bursts that are different from those from the center of the probe volume.[106] Thus the method will be difficult to use in the presence of "off center" particles; however, careful focusing of the cross beams and the observing optics can minimize the problem to an extent. It is this problem that makes a discriminator module in the output circuitry, necessary. The addition of a gate photomultiplier at 90° to the input light beams permits the selection of those particles passing through the center of the probe volume (see Ungut et al.[116]). The coincidence of two particles within the probe volume can give a spurious signal.

In these cases, it is the spacing between two particles that becomes the controlling variable. The method described by Ungut et al.[116] requires only one measurement detector at a fixed position. It is the Doppler burst which is the measured signal and hence, allows extraction of information on both velocity and size on a particle by particle basis.

Durst et al.[109] have conducted extensive tests to assess the suitability of different illumination/detection arrangements. One of their configurations that employs two photodetectors is illustrated in Figure 10-28. When a particle travels through the detection volume, the outputs of the photodetectors are Doppler bursts that are out of phase with one another. The phase difference is dependent on the particle size, and decreases with decreasing size. Various other configurations and techniques using laser anemometry principles are described by Chigier et al.,[117] Yule et al.,[118] and Wigley.[119] All of these systems have some limitations, a principal one being saturation of the measurements when applied to high number density particle systems.

Particle sizing interferometric techniques have greatly extended the range of particle number density over which measurements can be made and are commercially available as packaged systems.[120] Again, these systems have the advantage of being insensitive to the absolute intensity of scattered light and light absorbed by the particle and of providing information on both size and velocity, simultaneously.

As noted earlier, light scattered by spherical particles of diameters much larger than the wavelength of the incident light can be described by geometrical optics theory. From van de Hulst,[85] when $\alpha > 10$ (where $\alpha = \pi d/\lambda$), the scattered elec-

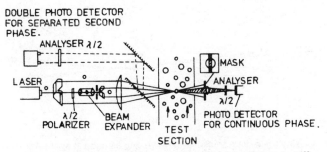

Figure 10-28. Laser-Doppler scheme posed by Durst et al.[109]

tromagnetic radiation can be described using theories of diffraction, refraction, and reflection. One half of the scattered light is due to diffraction and is concentrated in the forward direction about the laser beams, while the other is due to refraction and reflection and is scattered in all directions about the particle. With the appropriate selection of off-axis angles for the size and index of refraction of the particles to be measured, the diffracted light can be removed from consideration.

Bachalo et al.[120] describe a technique for sizing spherical particles based on the measurement of the relative phase shift that occurs when two light waves pass through the particles on different paths. Figure 10-29A illustrates the principle in which two rays (which are normal to the waves) pass through a droplet and arrive at a common point on the plane of detection. The interference pattern of the scattered light can be measured and related to the particle size. The optical arrangement used in the analysis is shown in Figure 10-29B. By measuring the visibility or amplitude modulation of the interference pattern formed by the scattered light and collected over a finite collecting aperture, information to size the droplets is obtained.

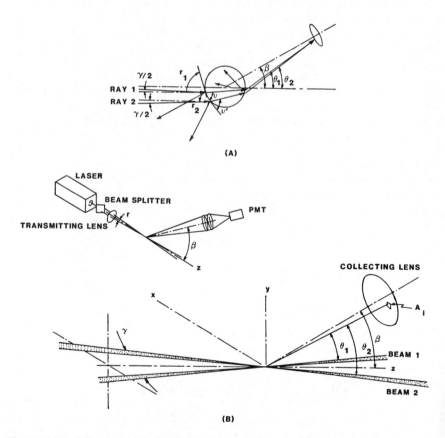

Figure 10-29. (A) Ray trace diagram illustrating the angles used in light scattering analysis; (B) illustration of the interferometer setup described by Bachalo et al.[120]

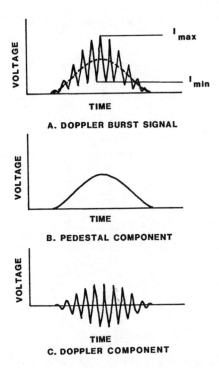

Figure 10-30. Illustration of the Doppler burst signal and the Doppler and pedestal components.

The intensity of the light scattered by a droplet located at the intersection of two laser beams is:

$$I = \frac{1}{n} \left\{ |E_{s1}|^2 + |E_{s2}|^2 + 2|E_{s1}| \; |E_{s2}| \cos \sigma \right\} \tag{10-18}$$

where $|E_s|$ = magnitude of complex field function
$\quad\quad \sigma$ = phase angle between the scattered fields E_{s1} and E_{s2}
$\quad\quad n$ = wave impedance

The visibility which is the ratio of the ac or Doppler component of the signal to the dc or pedestal component by Bachalo et al.[120] is:

$$\tilde{v} = 2 \left| \frac{\int_{Alens} \int |E_{s1}| \; |E_{s2}| \cos \sigma \; dA}{\int_{Alens} \int (|E_{s1}|^2 + |E_{s2}|^2) \; dA} \right| \tag{10-19}$$

The Doppler burst signal and its components are shown in Figure 10-30.

INTERFERENCE FRINGE PATTERN

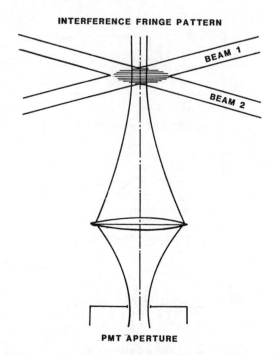

PMT APERTURE

Figure 10-31. Illustration of the 90° light scatter detection scheme.

Information on the size of the droplet is contained in the phase shift of the light waves passing through the spherical droplet. Two plane waves incident on the droplet, one from each beam, pass through the droplet at angles that differ by the beam intersection angle. The waves scattered from each beam arrive at the detection plane with a phase difference that forms the interface pattern. Relationships describing the phase shift of the light waves passing through the droplet (or reflected from it) assume that the particles are spherical.

In general, detecting reflected light is not as sensitive for sizing droplets as refracted light, but in the case of a fluid bed, where we are dealing with solid particles, it is the one possible option.

There are angles at which the light reflected and refracted by particles is of the same order of magnitude but will be out of phase. Light collection at these angles should be avoided in order to prevent ambiguity in the measurements.

In very dense particle flows, a 90° scatter detection mode is used. The light scattered by the particles in this case, is dominated by reflection. Figure 10-31 shows the schematic of the measurement region for this case. The 90° cone of light collection intersecting the focused laser beams forms an extremely small measurement volume. The focused beam diameters can be as small as 50 μm and the aperture on the photomultiplier is set to admit the image of the beam.

Particles crossing the probe volume will scatter light in proportion to their size; however, the pedestal component of the signal will grow with the size of the particle while the Doppler modulation grows as the product of the pedestal and the visibility.[120] This product is zero when the diameter is very small, reaches a maximum for intermediate size particles, and decreases to zero again for larger particles.

The magnitude of the pedestal and the Doppler component thus establishes the size of the sampling volume. Particles with a large magnitude of the Doppler component will therefore be detected over a larger volume than those with a smaller modulated signal.

The system described by Bachalo et al.[120] will count the number of particles in each size range. Because the probability of detecting particles that produce a small modulated signal (have a small sampling volume) is smaller than the probability of detecting particles with a large modulated signal, the system displays a biased histogram of particle size versus the number of particles. To counterbalance this biasing, the detectable cross-sectional area of each particle size must be known. The number of particles detected at a given size range will then be divided by the normalized cross-sectional area to obtain the correct distribution.

The light source is provided by a 15 mW helium-neon laser. Several optical configurations are required to provide the probe diameters and interference fringe spacings appropriate to the size ranges to be measured. With the combination of the collimating beam expander and transmitting lens that can be inserted or removed from the optical path, a large range of probe diameters is attainable.

The transmitting system can be fitted with Bragg cell-frequency shifting to control the relative-frequency bandwidth and to resolve any flow direction ambiguity.

The collected scattered light is focused by a second lens onto an aperature on the photomultiplier tube. The size of the aperture is variable to accommodate the particular probe diameter being used and still remains small enough to block light scattered from outside of the probe volume. The optical configuration for the system is shown in Figure 10-32.

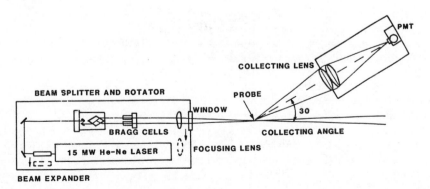

Figure 10-32. Optical configuration for interferometer system described by Bachalo et al.[120]

Time-of-Flight Measurements

Essentially all the optical techniques described for studying single particle dynamics in the freeboard can be extended to measure transit times between two measurement points, and from a measure of residence times within one probe volume, particle sizes can be obtained. Recall from the discussions on instrumentation for studying bubble dynamics, the relationship between velocity, residence time, and particle size is:

$$V = \frac{d + \ell}{t_R} \qquad (10\text{-}20)$$

where V = particle velocity
 ℓ = characteristic width of probe volume
 t_R = residence time
 d = particle diameter or cord length

Distance ℓ must obviously be minimized otherwise it will obscure the indication of d. It should also be minimized to prevent coincidence.

These techniques appear well developed, and there are a number of successful examples in the literature. By miniaturizing the optical probe used for studying bubble rise velocity, Oki et al.[121] record the transit time between two pairs of fiber optics transmitters/receivers as illustrated in Figure 10-33. From the time of flight between the pairs, the velocity can be obtained, and then from the residence time within the vision of one pair the diameter is computed as given by Equation 10-20. The time of flight (i.e., transit time) depends on several factors: velocity and particle size, and also on the distance between the particle and the probe (z), and the eccentricity of the particle from the probe centerline (y). These last two factors call for the use of three observation fibers surrounding a transmitter to provide sufficient information on transit and residence times to enable calculation of diameters for any y and z coordinates. Again, correlation techniques can be used to evaluate a

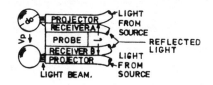

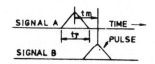

Figure 10-33. Illustration of the time-of-flight technique used by Ohki et al.[121]

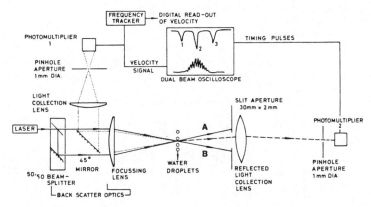

Figure 10-34. Illustration of the laser anemometer system described by Wigley.[119]

mean particle size. A distribution of sizes can also be obtained by computing the size of each particle and sorting. This approach will also provide a distribution of particle velocity. An inherent assumption with this approach is that particle motion is unidirectional.

Another example is the work of Lading[122] who employed two parallel beams a short distance apart in the flow direction and detected the obscuration of the beams. Correlation techniques were employed to evaluate mean velocities and a method for obtaining the particle size versus particle velocity spectrum was given.

Techniques described earlier (in particular, that of Ritter et al.[100] and Lafrance et al.[101]), can be extended to provide time-of-flight measurements. These can be arranged to detect transit times between beams, which will thus yield velocities; and particle sizes are computed from residence times within one beam. Color edging techniques described earlier can be used to eliminate particles not totally in the beam for cases where a particle chord and not a diameter is measured.

Wigley[119] devised an elaborate time-of-flight measurement technique using forward and backscatter signals from a laser anemometry system shown in Figure 10-34. The system provides a probe volume having a small dimension in the transverse direction of the particles. By means of a backscatter signal, the velocity is measured in the usual manner. In the forward direction, when a particle enters the probe volume of beam A, it is reflected at the glancing angle through the slit into the photomultiplier. As the same particle leaves the probe volume, the event reoccurs at beam B, but at a displaced time. The two separate events produce photomultiplier signals that detect the start and finish of the time of the residence. The slit aperture is set so as to ensure that signals are only generated by particles passing through the center of the probe volume. In applying Equation 10-20, ℓ is considered negligible, and the relevant particle size is thus obtained from the measured velocity and residence times. Wigley[119] applied the technique to studying droplet sprays and found it to be a suitable method for particle sizes in the range of 100—1,000 μm.

A summary of the techniques described in this section is given in Table 10-3.

(text continued on page 456)

Table 10-3
Summary of Particle Dynamics Measurement Techniques

General Basis of Method	Detailed Basis of Method	Number of Mass Flux Data	Single Particles Counted	Distribution of Mean	Type of Distribution	Size Range μm	Disadvantages/ Difficulties in Use	Advantages
Photographic	Photography	Number and mass flux	Yes	Distribution	Spatial	5 → mm	1. Errors in data abstraction 2. Data abstraction tedious 3. Subjective judgement involved in selection of 'in-focus' drops 4. Very high quality photographs needed for automatic or semi-automatic data abstraction 5. Depth of field problems often considered	1. Very simple equipment required 2. Non disturbing to some flow fields (if unenclosed)
	Photography related methods	Number and mass flux	Yes	Distribution	Spatial/ temporal			
	Holography	Number and mass flux	Yes	Distribution	Spatial	2 → mm	1. Same as for photography 2. Requires more equipment than photography	1. Freeze 3-D scenes which can be analyzed at leisure 2. No depth of field problems

Table 10-3 (continued)
Summary of Particle Dynamics Measurement Techniques

General Basis of Method	Detailed Basis of Method	Number of Mass Flux Data	Single Particles Counted	Distribution of Mean	Type of Distribution	Size Range μm	Disadvantages/ Difficulties in Use	Advantages
Impact	Sample slides	Number and mass flux	Yes	Distribution	Temporal	5–500	1. Disturbs flow field 2. Small drops by-pass slides	1. Counting can be effected at leisure
	Cascade impactors	Number (mass flux only Cascade/Slide methods)	Yes	Distribution	Temporal	0.5–20	1. Drops deposit on sampling tube walls 2. Sampling probe head disturbs flow field	
Electrical	Resistance/capacitance Bridge completion	Mass flux Number and mass flux	No Yes	Mean Distribution	Temporal	100–2,000 10–5,000	1. Probe in flow 2. Data abstraction method very weak	
	Charge removal	Number and mass flux	Yes	Distribution	Temporal	100–5,000	1. Probe in flow 2. Charge density not uniform over probe 3. Controversy over signal/drop size relation	

Table 10-3 (continued)
Summary of Particle Dynamics Measurement Techniques

General Basis of Method	Detailed Basis of Method	Number of Mass Flux Data	Single Particles Counted	Distribution of Mean	Type of Distribution	Size Range μm	Disadvantages/ Difficulties in Use	Advantages
Optical	Scattering by single particle at one angle	Number and mass flux	Yes	Distribution	Temporal	500–2,000	1. Problems of coincidence and edge effects 2. Uses absolute intensity measurement	
	Scattering by single particle-ratio methods	Number and mass flux	Yes	Distribution	Temporal	<1	1. Method insensitive above 1 μm	
	Multiple particle scattering—diffraction	—	No	Distribution	Spatial/ temporal	2–1,000		1. Sensitive in changes in mean width of distribution
	Obscuration	Number and mass flux	Yes	Distribution	Spatial/ temporal	50–1,000	1. Uses absolute intensity measurements 2. Not space specific	1. Signal/diameter relation linear for large particles
	Obscuration—detector counting	Number and mass flux	Yes	Distribution	Spatial/ temporal	10–100	1. Not space specific	1. Does not use absolute intensity measurements
	Turbidity	—	No	Mean	—		1. Most suitable for very small particles	1. Only measures d_{32}

Table 10-3 (continued)
Summary of Particle Dynamics Measurement Techniques

General Basis of Method	Detailed Basis of Method	Number of Mass Flux Data	Single Particles Counted	Distribution of Mean	Type of Distribution	Size Range μm	Disadvantages/ Difficulties in Use	Advantages
Optical	Laser doppler—visibility	Number and mass flux	Yes	Distribution	Temporal	<10	1. Ambiguity of fringe spacing 2. Simple relationships only exist for limited conditions, e.g. forward scatter 3. Analysis and relationships very complex in backscatter	1. Also provides velocity
	Laser doppler—variable fringe spacing	Number and mass flux	Yes	Distribution	Temporal	Not known	1. Variable fringe spacing difficult to produce 2. Point of equivalent size difficult to determine	
	Laser doppler—phase lag	Number and mass flux	Yes	Distribution	Temporal	Not known	1. Very small phase differences to be measured	1. Also provides velocity

Table 10-3 (continued)
Summary of Particle Dynamics Measurement Techniques

General Basis of Method	Detailed Basis of Method	Number of Mass Flux Data	Single Particles Counted	Distribution of Mean	Type of Distribution	Size Range μm	Disadvantages/ Difficulties in Use	Advantages
	Laser doppler—envelope modulation	Number and mass flux	Yes	Distribution	Temporal	Not known	1. Expected modulations not seen in experiments	
	Sampling followed by optical analysis	Number and mass flux	Yes	Distribution		1–80	1. Sampling disturbs flow structure	
	Fibers	Number and mass flux	Yes	Distribution	Temporal	100–400	1. Probe in flow stream 2. Slow removal of particles in dense sprays 3. Data abstraction method incomplete 4. Lower limit set by noise	
Time of Residence	Fibers	Number and mass flux	Yes	Distribution	Temporal	200–1,000	1. Probe in flow 2. Distance of particles from probe and from probe center line important but not allowed for (can be overcome)	1. Also provides velocities

Table 10-3 (continued)
Summary of Particle Dynamics Measurement Techniques

General Basis of Method	Detailed Basis of Method	Number of Mass Flux Data	Single Particles Counted	Distribution of Mean	Type of Distribution	Size Range μm	Disadvantages/ Difficulties in Use	Advantages
	Laser anemometer	Number and mass flux	Yes	Distribution	Temporal	100–1,000	1. Needs good access	1. Also provides velocities 2. Can identify non-spherical particles
	Scanning beam	Number and mass flux	Yes	Distribution	Temporal	10–1,000	1. Limited to flow through narrow cell 2. Measures chord length 3. Not space specific	
	Beam interrupt	Number and mass flux	Yes	Distribution	Spatial/ temporal		1. Not space specific 2. Coincidence and edge effects 3. Can measure chord	
	Needle contact	Number and mass flux	Yes	Distribution	Temporal		1. Most suitable for bubbles 2. Problems due to drop deformation/ breakup on first needle	1. Also provides velocities

MEASUREMENT OF PERFORMANCE PARAMETERS

At the start of this chapter it was noted that few instrumentation systems have been extensively applied to studying fluid-bed behavior, despite the fact that a large number of experimental techniques devised for two-phase flow systems in general exist. The role of instrumentation in commercial-size units is almost nonexistent with the exception of the most standard techniques to provide basic measurements on gross performance parameters. These performance parameters are readily measurable variables, such as solids temperature, exit gas composition, bed pressure and overall density, and overall heat transfer coefficients. Direct measurement of mass transfer is not practiced, although one study (Ziegler and Brazelton[123]) is worth noting. This was a fundamental investigation that attempted to measure the mass transfer between a particle and the gas in the bed. The particle used was porous and was saturated with a fluid that would evaporate in the bed. Measurements of the particle's surface temperature during the constant-rate drying period provided an estimate of the mass transfer coefficient. There is certainly greater need for techniques to obtain this type of direct measurement. The general philosophy, however, is that a good understanding of the system hydrodynamics will provide a more rigorous basis for estimating both heat and mass exchange coefficients.

In this last section only a compilation of pertinent literature pertaining to the measurement of bed performance parameters is given. Techniques used for the most part are standard and relatively straightforward.

Temperature and Overall Heat Transfer

Thermography techniques for fluidized beds are well developed, with the simplest approach being to simply insert thermocouples directly into the fluidized solids. The sensible heat of the solids actually serves as a tracer whereby the study of solids motion is possible via heating particles in one region of the bed and measuring the temperature of the particles in another portion of the bed. Thiel and Potter[124] describe a rapid-response temperature probe for this purpose.

Another standard approach is optical pyrometry, provided the solids temperatures are sufficiently high to be incandescent. Examples of this technique are given by Juveland et al.[125] and Makhorin et al.[126] In the latter case, the study used an infrared sensitive photographic film to evaluate temperature distributions in the bed.

The measurement of gas temperatures (as bubbles) is a more difficult problem since the gas phase has a much lower heat capacity than the solids. Consequently, the gas reaches the same temperature as the solids very rapidly. There are, however, exceptions, as in the cases of large gas bubbles or highly exothermic reactions. Under these conditions, the bubble phase can have a measurably different temperature than the solids or emulsion phase. At very high temperatures, the radiation from solids can introduce a source of error to the measurements, thus requiring special precautions. One approach is to withdraw a sample of the gas through a tube at a relatively high velocity with a miniature thermocouple positioned in the sampling line. The sampling tube is designed to shield the thermocouple from the radiation effects of the solids, and the high velocity helps to improve the gas-to-thermocouple heat transfer. Details of this approach are given by Juveland, et al.[125] and Shakhova et al.[127]

Industrial-scale systems are often well equipped with temperature measuring devices to allow reasonable approximations of heat transfer coefficients. Again, this is conventional technology; however, special techniques have been devised in laboratory-scale studies to obtain more detailed information on hydrodynamic behavior and bed performance. A number of the literature-reported studies have been aimed at developing design-oriented correlations for heat transfer coefficients describing the exchange between the fluidized bed and heat exchanger tubes. Examples of studies of steady-state local measurements are Botterill et al,[128] Patel and Simpson,[129] and Canada et al.[130] Overall heat transfer from a tube to a fluidized bed was studied by Botterill et al.,[128] Xavier and Davidson[131] and Andeen et al.[132] Steady-state-to-wall heat transfer measurements were made by Hoebnik et al.[133] Other steady-state measurements concerning bed-to-heat exchange-fin arrangements are reported by Genetti and co-workers.[134,135]

Transient heat transfer studies are just as prevalent in the open literature and perhaps more meaningful in that they provide distinction between the contributions due to the emulsion and bubble phases. Obviously, these are local measurements; that is, they are obtained in volumes that are inherently smaller than the bubbles themselves. There are a variety of probes described in the literature for this purpose, most of which are designed to monitor the local fluctuations in the heat transfer coefficient. Many of these are sensitive to loading; i.e., the temperature of the probe changes noticeably when the heat transfer coefficient varies. (The probe's temperature drops for an increase in the heat transfer coefficient; and the probe temperature rises when the coefficient drops such as when a bubble flows by and causes a drop in the coefficient.) In this manner, the solids in the emulsion phase that first contact the probe are overheated, and the solids which flow past the probe thereafter are underheated. Heat transfer coefficients evaluated in this manner should not be expected to agree with those reported between a bed and an isothermal body. A summary of the various heat transfer studies reported for both steady-state and transient conditions is given in Table 10-4. The types of probes used in these studies (see, for example, Gardon[145,146]) are capable of measurements at fairly high temperatures and sense a significant temperature differential between the bed and probe surface. These designs are particularly well suited for industrial applications. One novel approach is that of Barker,[140] which consists of a small sphere allowed to move about in the bed and which transmits a radio signal indicating its surface temperature. By means of a radio decay process, heat is generated at a constant rate from within the sphere, and thus the surface temperature provides an indication of the heat transfer coefficient.

Other novel techniques that are possibly applicable to commercial units are described by Bernis[147] and Catipovic et al.[44] In the former case, a miniaturized hot-film constant-temperature-type probe was immersed in the Capitovic's system which was composed of multiple hot-film transducers flush mounted onto the surface of a heat exchanger tube. The approach of using constant temperature probes is appealing because it not only provides an accurate measure of the local heat transfer coefficient, but also makes it feasible to maintain the same temperature at the probe as the immediate surroundings. In addition, these types of probes generally have a faster response to temperature fluctuations. The principles behind this approach are based on standard constant-temperature, hot-wire/film anemometry (see Reference 148 for an introduction to anemometry principles). The sensor itself (wire or a flush-mounted film) essentially forms one arm of a standard Wheatstone bridge. The sensor is maintained at a constant temperature by the power (i.e., current and voltage drop across the sensor); however if the temperature of the probe's surface is changed (caused by convective cooling when a bubble flows by or conduction as a cool patch of solids moves across the surface) a servo-amplifier in the electronic circuit induces an instantaneous surge in power to bring the probe back up to temperature. It is this change in power that is directly proportional to the instantaneous heat transfer coefficient.

Gas Composition

A number of studies have been aimed at studying gas compositions in both the dense bed and the freeboard zone, using both steady state and transient-type measurements. Pertinent literature is summarized in Table 10-4.

Measurement of this parameter during steady-state is relatively straightforward; generally relying on an appropriate sampling technique in which a sample of the gas is withdrawn through a sampling line and analyzed external to the bed. Generally, a filter is fitted to the tip of the sampling probe to prevent particles from being drawn into the sampling line.

For transient-type measurements, several techniques have been devised. Chavarie et al.[157-159] describe an in situ method in which an ultraviolet detector is used for measuring the ozone concentration in bubbles. Several investigators[163-165] arranged a gas sampling probe that was synchronized with the injection of bubbles; consequently, the gas composition in the bubbles alone could be measured.

Other approaches have combined bubble detection devices with the sampling probe for studies in the bed (see Fitzgerald,[70] Calderbank et al.,[34] and Rietema et al.[166] for example).

Perhaps the most common technique and one often favored in pilot-plant studies is the injection of a slug of tracer gas through the bottom of the bed. Continuous sampling at the discharge of the column provides information on the overall residence time of the gas. From that point, a variety of techniques can be used to evaluate compositions; examples are a mass spectrometer,[162] flame ionization detectors,[170] thermal conductivity cells.[171]

Pressure

Pressure-drop detection is perhaps the most straightforward measurement that can be made in operating fluid beds. There are few restrictions, and measurements can be made under the most severe conditions. Pressure-sensing devices, such

Table 10-4
Summary of Fluid Bed Performance Parameters Studied

Mechanism Studied	Conditions	System of Interest	Investigators
Heat transfer (local coefficients)	Steady state	Exchange between fluidized bed and heat exchange tubes	Botterill et al.[128] (1970), Patel and Simpson[129] (1977), Canada and McLaughlin[130] (1978)
		Bed to heat exchange fins	Bartel et al.[136] (1971), Genetti et al.[134] (1971), Priebe and Genetti[135] (1977)
		Between bed and various immersed objects	Sampson[137] (1973), Kobayashi et al.[138] (1970)
Heat transfer (overall coefficients)	Steady state	From tube to fluidized bed	Botterill[128] (1970), Andeen et al.[132] (1978)
		Bed to wall heat transfer	Hoebink et al.[133] (1978)
Heat transfer (local fluctuations)	Transient	Heat exchange within bed	Mickley et al.[139] (1961), Wen et al.[56] (1978), Barker[140] (1967), Khan et al.[141] (1978), Selzer and Thompson[142] (1977), Agrawal and Ziegler[143] (1970), Tout and Clift[144] (1973), Gardon[145] (1953), Gardon and Baskakov[146] (1973)
		Heat transfer from small constant temperature surfaces	Bernis et al.[147] (1976), Catipovic et al.[44] (1978)
Gas composition	Steady state	Composition within the bed	Gabor and Mecham[149] (1964), Yoshida et al.[4] (1969), Behie et al.[150] (1976), Fryer and Potter[151] (1976), Hsiung and Thodos[152] (1975), Gibbs and Hedley[153] (1978), Nguyen et al.[154] (1977)
		Composition within freeboard region	Lange[155] (1972), Bartock et al.[151] (1972)

Table 10-4 (continued)
Summary of Fluid Bed Performance Parameters Studied

Mechanism Studied	Conditions	System of Interest	Investigators
Gas composition	Transient	Composition within the bed	Chavarie and Grace[157-159] (1975–1976), Drinkenberg and Rietema[160-161] (1972–1973), Goedecke and Shugurl[162] (1973), Rowe et al.[163] (1971), Rowe[164] (1974), Cankurt and Yerushalmi[165] (1978), Fitzgerald[70] (1967), Calderbank et al.[34] (1976), Rietema and Hoebink[166] (1976)
		Overall exit concentration—from bed and freeboard	Gilliland and Mason[167] (1952), Perry and Gibbs[168] (1971), Zalewsky and Hanesiam[169] (1973), Goedecke and Shugurl[162] (1973), Yates and Constans[170] (1973), Bohle and Van Swaay[171] (1978)
Quality of fluidization	Transient	Pressure fluctuations over bed height	Lirag and Littman[172] (1971), Baird and Klein[173] (1973), Kilkis et al.[7] (1973), Taylor et al.[174] (1973), Verloop and Heertjes[175] (1974), Boeyens and Geldart[176] (1974), Kang et al.[177] (1967), Littman et al.[178] (1970)
Gas velocity	Steady state	Gas velocity in freeboard region and gas jets in the fluidized bed	Donadono and Masamilla[179] (1978)
		Gas velocity inside rising bubbles	Nguyen et al.[180] (1975), Filla et al.[181] (1976), McGraw[182] (1977)
Bed viscosity	Steady state	Solids fluidity/ quality of fluidization	Ashwin et al.[183] (1960), Hagyard and Sacerdote[184] (1966), Lehman et al.[185] (1973), Finnerty et al.[186] (1969)

as transducers, used in industrial-scale systems are generally equipped with a back-purge arrangement that utilizes a constant flow of inert gas to prevent particles and/or corrosive fluids from entering lines and contacting the sensors. The most common measurement is a time-averaged pressure drop, which provides a good indication of the bed expansion and hence, overall bed density. Recall that when the bed is fluidized, the pressure drop is approximately equal to the hydrostatic head of bed material. For a bed of constant cross-section, the pressure drop is then equal to the weight of solid material in the bed divided by the bed's equivalent cross-sectional area.

In laboratory-scale tests, standard transducers have been extended to obtaining transient-type measurements of pressure fluctuations. As noted previously, the frequency of pressure fluctuations is approximately equal to the rate of eruption of bubbles at the bed's surface. The magnitude of these pressure fluctuations is comparable to the hydrostatic head displaced by a bubble. Hence, dynamic pressure measurements contain information on the bed hydrodynamics. The most common application has been to sense the bubbling state; however, an arrangement of multiple transducers located along the vertical of a column can provide additional information, such as the bubble rise velocity. Arrays of transducers used in this manner are described by various investigators.[178-179] Table 10-4 lists various investigators that relied principally on pressure measurements to infer information about the hydrodynamics.

Other Parameters

Other parameters which have been studied under laboratory conditions are the gas velocity in the freeboard region and bubble phase, and the effective viscosity of the fluidized bed (refer to Table 10-4). Conventional techniques have been used to measure the overall gas velocity through a fluidized bed, such as orifice and venturi meters, Pitot tubes and hot-wire anemometry. Gas circulation and velocity in bubbles have been examined by several investigators.[181-183]

The effective bed viscosity has already been described in Chapter 3. Interest in this parameter has been more academic, although it is an operational characteristic of a fluidized bed. Techniques used for evaluating the rheological state of liquids have been applied directly to fluidized solids. Considerable variations in values reported on effective viscosities exist, with no clear explanations for these discrepancies.

NOMENCLATURE

a	propagation angle
d	particle size
d_{32}	Sauter mean diameter
$D(r,x)$	weight fraction

$D_{V,B}$ bubble size or diameter
E_s scattered field
$|E_s|$ magnitude of complex field function
f lens focal length
f_o signal frequency
$F(\theta)$ function of observation direction
$g(\ell)$ probability that measure pierced length lies between ℓ and $\ell + \Delta\ell$
I illumination
I_o incident illumination
J_1 first order Bessel function
K scattering coefficient
K_E fraction of particle size moving during photography
ℓ bubble pierced length
L_d measured vertical pierced bubble length
L_r, L_t target and transmitter distances from receiver, respectively
n wave impedance
$n(x)$ cumulative density function
N_c output signal mean frequency
N_o flash frequency
$P_{i,j}$ probability function
r bubble radius
r displacement of bubble radius
S area
s displacement
t_B duration time of interrupted signal
t_R residence time
t_s pulse generation time
T,t time
u_B bubble rise velocity
$U(t)$ electrical signal (time dependent)
V_p particle velocity
$\tilde{V}$ visibility parameter defined by Equation 10-19
x weight or number fraction
x_p dimension

Greek Symbols

α dimensionless particle size
δ wall thickness
ϵ_B local bubble frequency
θ_r, θ_t angle of signal receiving and transmitting, respectively
λ wavelength of illumination
σ phase angle

REFERENCES

1. Upson, P. C., and D. L. Pyle, *International Congress on Fluidization and Its Applications,* Toulouse, France (1973).

2. Fryer, C., and O. E. Potter, *International Congress on Fluidization and Its Applications,* Toulouse, France (1973).

3. Martin-Gautier, A. L. F., and D. L. Pyle, "The Fluid Mechanics of Single Bubbles," in *Fluidization Technology,* Vol. 1, D. L. Keairns (Ed.), Hemisphere Pub. Corp., Washington (1976).

4. Yoshida, K., S. Fugii, and D. Kunii, "Characteristics of Fluidized Beds at High Temperatures," in *Fluidization Technology,* Vol. 1, D. L. Keairns (Ed.), Hemisphere Pub. Corp., Washington, (1976).

5. Rowe, P., and B. Partridge, *Trans. Inst. Chem. Engrs.,* 43: T157 (1967).

6. Rowe, P., and R. Matsumo, *Chem. Eng. Sci.,* 26: 923 (1971).

7. Rowe, P. N., *Fluidization,* Academic Press, NY (1971).

8. Hager, W. R., and W. J. Thompson, *AIChE Symp. Series, 128,* 69: 68, (1973).

9. Judd, M., and P. Dixon, *AIChE Symp. Series, 176,* 74: 38, (1978).

10. Put, M., A. Francesconi, and W. Goossens, *International Congress on Fluidization and Its Applications,* Toulouse, France (1973).

11. Yasui, G., and L. N. Johanson, *AIChE J.,* 4: 446 (1958).

12. Kilkis, B., F. M. DeGeyter, and J. J. Ginoux, *International Congress on Fluidization and Its Applications,* Toulouse, France (1973).

13. Yoshida, K., et al., *Fluidization,* Vol. 13, Cambridge Univ. Press, London (1978).

14. Lockett, M. J., and A. A. Safekourdi, "Light Transmission Through Bubble Swarms," *AIChE J.,* 23 (3): 395–398 (1977).

15. Cheremisinoff, N. P., "An Experimental Investigation of Pressure Drop and Heat Transfer in Two-Phase (Gas-Liquid) Flows," Ph.D. Thesis, Clarkson College of Technology, Potsdam, NY (1977).

16. Coulaloglou, C. A., and L. L. Tavlarides, *AIChE J.,* 22 (2): 289–297 (March 1976).

17. Ohki, K., and T. Shirai, "Particle Velocity in Fluidized Beds," in *Fluidization Technology,* Vol. 1, Cambridge University Press, London (1978).

18. Gerald, C. F., *Chem. Eng. Prog.,* 47: 199 (1951).

19. Taylor, P. A., M. M. Lorenz, and M. R. Sweet, in *International Congress on Fluidization and Its Applications,* Toulouse, France (1973).

20. Broadhurst, T. E., and H. A. Becker, in *Fluidization Technology,* Vol. 1, Cambridge University Press, London (1978).

21. Kang, W. K., J. P. Sutherland, and G. L. Osberg, *I&EC Fund.,* 6: 499 (1967).

22. Littman, H., and G. A. J. Homolka, *Chem. Engr. Progr. Symp. Series, 105,* 66: 37 (1970).

23. Cheremisinoff, N. P., *Process Level Instrumentation and Control,* Marcel Dekker, Inc., New York (1981).

24. Orcutt, J. C., and B. H. Carpenter, *Chem. Eng. Sci.,* 26: 1,049 (1971).

25. Yoshida, K., et al. *Proc. of Eng. Found. Conf.,* 2nd, Trinity College, Cambridge, England, Cambridge Univ. Press (Apr. 2-6, 1978).

26. Raptis, A. C., H. B. Karplus, and W. W. Managan, *Fossil Energy—I&C Briefs,* 1 (1): U.S. Dept. of Energy (March 1980).

27. Schiebe, F. R., and J. M. Killen, Minn. Univ., St. Anthony Falls Hydraul. Lab., Proj. Report 120 (May 1971).

28. Yosef, B., et al. *J. Appl. Phys.,* 46 (2): 738-740 (Feb. 1975).

29. Agrest, E. M., and G. N. Kuznetsov, *Sov. Phys. Acoust.,* 20 (2): 213-216 (Nov.-Dec. 1974).

30. Karplus, H. B., and A. C. Raptis, ANL-FE-49622-TMO6 (1979).

31. Park, W. H., et al. *Chem. Eng. Sci.,* 24 (1969).

32. Rigby, G. R., et al., *Chem. Eng. Sci.,* 25: 1,729 (1970).

33. Burgess, J. M., and P. H. Calderbank, *Chem. Eng. Sci.,* 30: 1,511 (1975).

34. Calderbank, P. H., J. Pereira, and J. M. Burgess, *Fluidization Technology,* Vol. I, McGraw-Hill Pub., NY (1976).

35. Morse, R. D., and C. O. Ballou, *Chem. Eng. Prog.,* 47: 99 (1951).

36. Yoshida, K., T. Ueno, and D. Kunii, *Chem. Eng. Sci.,* 29: 77 (1974).

37. Matsen, J. M., *AIChE Symp. Series, 128,* 69: 31 (1973).

38. Datson, M., *AIChE J.,* 5: 169 (1959).

39. Ormiston, R. M., F. R. G. Mitchell, and J. F. Davidson, *Trans. Inst. Chem. Engrs.,* 43: T209 (1965).

40. Angelino, H., C. Charzat, and R. Williams, *Chem. Eng. Sci.,* 19: 289 (1964).

41. Nguyen, X. T., L. S. Leung, and R. H. Weiland, *Chem. Eng. Sci.,* 30: 1,187 (1975).

42. Baskakov, A. P., et al., *Int'l. Congress on Fluidization and Its Applications,* Toulouse, France (1973).

43. Thiel, W. J., and O. E. Potter, *I&EC Fund.,* 16: 242 (1977).

44. Catipovic, N. M., et al., "Heat Transfer to Horizontal Tubes in Fluidized Beds," EPRI Report, Palo Alto, CA (1979).

45. Lanneau, K. P., *Trans., Inst. Chem. Engrs.,* 38: 125 (1960).

46. Rooney, N. M., and D. Harrison, *Fluidization Technology,* Vol. II, McGraw-Hill Pub., NY (1976).

47. Werther, J., and O. Molerous, *Int. J. Multiphase Flow 1,* (1973), p. 103.

48. Werther, J., *Fluidization Technology*, Vol. I, McGraw-Hill Pub., NY (1976).

49. Geldart, D., and J. R. Kelsey, *Powder Technology*, 6: 45–50 (1972).

50. Mii, T., K. Yoshida, and D. Kunii, *J. Chem. Eng. Japan*, 6: 196 (1973).

51. Otake, T., et al., *J. Chem. Eng. Japan*, 8: 388 (1975).

52. Whittmann, K., et al., *Fluidization*, J. F. Davidson (Ed.), Cambridge Univ. Press (1978).

53. Yoshida, K., J. Sakane, and F. Shimizu, *Ind. Eng. Chem. Fund.*, 21: 83–85 (1982).

54. Cranfield, R. R., *Chem. Eng. Sci.*, 27: 239 (1972).

55. Linneweber, K. W., and E. Blass, *Germ. Chem. Engr.*, 6: 28–33 (1983).

56. Wen, C. Y., et al., *Fluidization*, Cambridge Univ. Press (1978), p. 32.

57. Baskakov, A. P., et al., *Int'l. Congress on Fluidization and Its Applications*, Toulouse, France (1973).

58. Bernis, A., et al., *Int'l. Congress on Fluidization and Its Applications*, Toulouse, France (1973).

59. Goosens, W. R. A., and L. Hellincks, *Intl. Congress on Fluidization and Its Applications*, Toulouse, France (1973).

60. Page, R. E., and D. Harrison, *Intl. Congress on Fluidization and Its Applications*, Toulouse, France (1973).

61. Rezenbaum, R. B., O. M. Todes, and L. N. Fainshtein, *J. of Engr. Phys.*, 25 (4): 1,216 (1975).

62. Heertjes, P. M., J. Verloop, and R. Willems, *Powder Technology*, 4: 38 (1970/71).

63. Marsheck, R. M., and A. Gomezplata, *AIChE J.*, 11: 167 (1965).

64. Okhi, K., W. P. Walawender, and L. T. Fan, *Powder Technology*, 18: 171 (1977).

65. Merry, J. M. D., and J. F. Davidson, *Trans. Inst. Chem. Engr.* (1973).

66. May, W. G., *Chem. Eng. Prog.*, 55: 49 (1959).

67. Kondukov, N. B., *Intl. Chem. Engr.*, 4: 43 (1964).

68. Blickel, T., O. Borlai, and L. Hodany, *Intl. Congress on Fluidization and Its Applications*, Toulouse, France (1973).

69. Haines, A. K., and R. P. King, and E. T. Woodburn, *AIChE J.*, 18: 591 (1972).

70. Fitzgerald, T. J., *Systems and Process Control*, CEP Technical Manual, 30 (1967).

71. Patrose, B., and H. S. Caram, *AIChE J.*, 28 (4): 604–609 (July 1982).

72. Lehtola, S., and R. Kuoppamaki, *Chem. Eng. Sci.*, 37 (2): 185–191 (1982).

73. Kirkman, G. A., and C. J. Ryley, "The Use of Laser Photography for Measuring the Diameters of Entrained Droplets in Two-Phase Flow," Liverpool Univ., Dept. Mech. Engng., Report (1969).

74. McCreath, C. G., M. F. Roett, and N. A. Chigier, *J. Phys. E. Sci. Instrum.*, 5: 60 (1972).

75. Findlay, I. C., and M. Welsh, *J. Photographic Sci.*, 16: 70 (1968).

76. Cox, A., *Photographic Optics*, Focal Press, London (1966).

77. Reddy, K. V. S., M. C. van Wijk, and D. C. T. Pei, *Can. J. Chem. Engng.* 47: 85 (1969).

78. Whalley, P. B., et al., UKAEA Report, AERE-R-8787 (1977).

79. Dombrowski, N., and J. A. Weston, *J. Photographic Sci.*, 14: 215 (1966).

80. Azzopardi, B. J., *Intl. J. Heat & Mass Transfer*, 22: 1,245–1,279, (Sept. 1979).

81. Simmons, H. C., and H. H. Gaag, U.S. Patent 3609043 (1971).

82. Dix, M. J., H. Sawistowski, and L. R. T. Tyley, Proc. 11th Inst. Congress High Speed Photography; P. J. Rolls (Ed.), Chapman and Hall Pub., London (1975).

83. Cheremisinoff, P. N., and R. Young, *Pollution Engineering Practice Handbook*, Ann Arbor Science Pub., Ann Arbor, MI (1974).

84. Mie, G., *Annln. Physik*, 25: 377 (1908).

85. van de Hulst, H. C., *Light Scattering by Small Particles*, Wiley, New York (1957).

86. Kirker, M., *The Scattering of Light and Other Electromagnetic Radiation*, Academic Press, NY (1969).

87. Blau, H. H., D. J. McCleese, and D. Watson, *Appl. Optics*, 9: 2,522 (1970).

88. Landa, I., and E. S. Tebay, *I.E.E.E., Trans. Instrum. Measurements*, 21: 516 (1972).

89. Keller, A., *Trans. A.S.M.E., J. Basic Engng.*, 94: 917 (1972).

90. Mason, B. J., and R. Ramanadham, *Q.J.R. Meteorol. Soc.*, 79: 490 (1953).

91. Shofner, F. M., et al., Fifth Annual Industrial Air Pollution Control Conference, Knoxville, TN (1975).

92. Dobbins, R. A., L. Crocco, and I. Glassman, *Am. Inst. Aeronaut. Astronaut. J.*, 1: 1,982 (1963).

93. Deich, M. E., G. A. Saltanov, and A. V. Kurshakov, *Thermal Engng.*, 18: 127 (1971).

94. Deich, M. E., G. W. Tsiklauri, and V. K. Shanin, *High Temp.*, 16: 102 (1972).

95. Chin, J. H., C. M. Sliepcevich, and M. Tri-us, *J. Phys. Chem.*, Ithaca, 5: 841 (1955).

96. Cornillault, J., *Appl. Optics 11*, (1972), p. 265.

97. Switherbank, J., et al., *Prog. Astronaut. Aeronaut.*, 53: 421 (1976).

98. McSweeney, A., and W. Rivers, *Appl. Optics*, 11: 2,101 (1972).

99. Shafner, F. M., G. Kreikebaum, and H. W. Schmitt, 68th Air Pollution Control Association Meeting, Boston (1975).

100. Ritter, R. C., N. R. Zinner, and A. M. Sterling, *Phys. Med. Biol.*, 19: 161 (1974).

101. Lafrance, P., et al. *Physics Fluids*, 17: 1,469 (1974).

102. Schleusener, S. A., and A. A. Reed, *Rev. Scient. Instrum.*, 38: 1,152 (1967).

103. Schleusener, S. A., *Powder Technology*, 1: 364 (1968).

104. Shuster, B. G., and R. Knollenberg, *Appl. Optics*, 11: 1,515 (1972).

105. Rhodes, C. A., et al., *Powder Technol.* 14: 203 (1976).

106. Farmer, W. M., *Appl. Optics*, 11: 2,603 (1972).

107. Farmer, W. M., *Appl. Optics*, 13: 610 (1974).

108. Fistrom, R. M., et al., *Faraday Symp. Chem. Soc.*, 7: 183 (1973).

109. Durst, F., and M. Zare, *U. Karlsruhe*, SFB-80/TM63 (1975).

110. Hong, N. S., and A. R. Jones, *J. Phys. D: Appl. Phys.*, 9: 1,839 (1976).

111. Jones, A. R., *J. Phys. D: Appl. Phys.*, 6: 417 (1973).

112. Jones, A. R., *J. Phys. D: Appl. Phys.*, 7: 1,369 (1974).

113. Robards, D. W., *Appl. Optics*, 16: 1,861 (1977).

114. Adrian, R. J., and K. L. Orloff, *Appl. Optics*, 16: 677 (1977).

115. Chu, W. P., and D. M. Robinson, *Appl. Optics*, 16: 619 (1977).

116. Ungut, A., et al., A.I.A.A. 16th Aerospace Sciences Meeting, Huntsville, AL (1978).

117. Chigier, N. A., and A. J. Yule, Conf. on Physical Chemistry and Hydrodynamics, Oxford (1977).

118. Yule, A. J., et al., *J. Energy*, 1: 220 (1977).

119. Wigley, G. UKAEA Report, AERE-R-8771 (1977).

120. Bachalo, W. D., C. F. Hess, and C. A. Hartwell, Winter Annual Meeting of ASME, NY (Dec. 2–7, 1979).

121. Oki, K., T. Akehata, and T. Shirai, *Powder Technology*, 11: 51 (1975).

122. Lading, L., Third Biennial Symposium on Turbulence in Liquids, U. Missouri-Rolla, Missouri (1973).

123. Ziegler, E. N., and W. T. Brazelton, *I&EC Fund.*, 3: 94 (1964).

124. Thiel, W. J., and O. E. Potter, *AIChE J.*, 24: 561 (1978).

125. Juveland, A. C., H. P. Deinken, and J. E. Dougherty, *I&EC Fund.*, 3: 329 (1964).

126. Makhorin, K. E., V. S. Pikshov, and G. P. Kuchin, *Fluidization*, Cambridge Univ. Press (1978), p. 93.

127. Shakhova, N. A., and G. N. Lastovtseva, *J. of Engr. Phys.*, 25 (4): 1,201 (1975).

128. Botterill, J. S. M., R. Chandrasekhar, and M. van der Kolk, *Chem. Eng. Prog. Symp Series, 105,* 66: 61 (1970).

129. Patel, R. D., and J. M. Simpson, *Chem. Eng. Sci.,* 32: 67 (1977).

130. Canada, S., and M. McLaughlin, *AIChE Symp. Series, 176,* 74: 27 (1978).

131. Xavier, A. M., and J. F. Davidson, *Fluidization,* Cambridge Univ. Press, (1978), p. 333.

132. Andeen, B. R., L. R. Glicksman, and R. Bowman, *Fluidization,* Cambridge Univ. Press, (1978), p. 345.

133. Hoebnik, J. H., and K. Rietema, *Fluidization,* Cambridge Univ. Press, (1978), p. 327.

134. Genetti, W. E., R. A. Schmall and E. S. Grimmett, *AIChE Symp. Series, 116,* 67: 90 (1971).

135. Priebe, S. J., and W. E. Genetti, *AIChE Symp. Series, 161,* 73: 39 (1977).

136. Bartel, W. H., W. E. Genetti, and E. S. Grimmett, *AIChE Symp. Series, 116,* 67: 87 (1971).

137. Sampson, T., *Intl. Congr. on Fluidization and Its Applications,* Toulouse, France (1973).

138. Kobayashi, M., D. Ramaswami, and W. T. Brazelton, *Chem. Eng. Prog. Symp. Series 105,* 66: 58 (1970).

139. Mickley, H. S., D. S. Fairbanks, and R. D. Hawthorne, *Chem. Eng. Prog. Symp. Series, 32,* Vol. 51 (1961).

140. Barker, J., *I&EC Fund.,* 6: 139 (1967).

141. Khan, A. R., J. F. Richardson, and K. J. Shakiri, *Fluidization,* Cambridge Univ. Press, (1978), p. 351.

142. Selzer, V. W., and W. J. Thompson, *AIChE Symp. Series, 161,* 73: 29 (1977).

143. Agrawal, S., and E. N. Ziegler, *Chem. Eng. Prog. Symp. Series, 105,* 66: 68 (1970).

144. Tout, J., and R. Clift, *AIChE Symp. Series, 128,* 69: 78 (1973).

145. Gardon, R. *Trans. ASME: J. of Heat Transfer,* 82: 396 (1960).

146. Gardon, R. *Review Sci. Inst.,* 24: 366 (1953).

147. Bernis, A., et al., *Fluidization Technology,* Vol. I, McGraw-Hill, NY (1976).

148. Cheremisinoff, N. P., *Fluid Flow: Pumps, Pipes and Channels,* Ann Arbor Science Pub., Ann Arbor, MI (1981).

149. Garbor, J. D., and W. J. Mecham, *I&EC Fund.,* 3: 60 (1964).

150. Behie, L. A., M. A. Bergougnon, and C. G. J. Baker, *Fluidization Technology,* Vol. I, McGraw-Hill, NY (1976).

151. Fryer, C. and D. E. Potter, *AIChE J.,* 22: 38 (1976).

152. Hsiung, T. H., and G. Thodos, *Chem. Eng. Sci.*, 32: 581 (1977).
153. Gibbs, B. M., and A. B. Hedley, *Fluidization*, Cambridge Univ. Press (1978), p. 235.
154. Nguyen, H. V., A. B. Whitehead, and O. E. Potter, *AIChE J.*, 6: 913 (1977).
155. Lange, H., *AIChE Symp. Series, 126*, 26: 17 (1972).
156. Bartock, W., et al., *AIChE Symp. Series, 126*, 68: 30 (1972).
157. Chavarie, C., and J. R. Grace, *Chem. Engr. Sci.*, 31: 741 (1976).
158. Chavarie, C., and J. R. Grace, *Fluidization Technology*, Vol. I, McGraw-Hill, NY (1976).
159. Chavarie, C., and J. R. Grace, *I&EC Fund.*, 14: 79, (1975).
160. Drinkenberg, A. A. H., and K. Rietema, *Chem. Eng. Sci.*, 28: 359 (1973).
161. Drinkenberg, A. A. H., and K. Rietema, *Chem. Eng. Sci.*, 27: 1,765 (1972).
162. Goedecke, R., and K. Schugurl, *Fluidization Technology*, Vol. I, McGraw-Hill Book Co., NY (1976).
163. Rowe, P. N., T. J. Evans, and J. C. Middleton, *Chem. Eng. Sci.*, 29: 1,943 (1971).
164. Evans, T. J., and P. N. Rowe, *Chem. Eng. Sci.*, 29: 294 (1974).
165. Cankurt, N. T., and J. Yerushalmi, *Fluidization*, Cambridge Univ. Press, (1978), p. 387.
166. Rietema, K., and J. Hoebnik, *Fluidization Technology*, Vol. I, McGraw-Hill Book Co., NY (1976).
167. Gilliland, E. R., and E. A. Mason, *I&EC Fund.*, 44: 218 (1952).
168. Perry, M. G., and B. M. Gibbs, *AIChE Symp. Series, 116*, Vol 67 (1971).
169. Zalewsky, W. C., and D. Hanesian, *AIChE Symp. Series, 128*, 69: 58 (1973).
170. Yates, J. G., and J. A. P. Constans, *Chem. Eng. Sci.*, 28: 1,341 (1973).
171. Bohle, W., and W. P. M. van Swaay, *Fluidization*, Cambridge Univ. Press, (1978), p. 167.
172. Lirag, R., and H. Littman, *AIChE Symp. Series, 116*, 67: 11 (1971).
173. Baird, M. H. I., and A. J. Klein, *Chem. Eng. Sci.*, 28: 1,039 (1973).
174. Taylor, P. A., M. H. Lorenz, and M. R. Sweet, *Int. Congr. on Fluidization and Its Applications*, Toulouse, France (1973).
175. Verloop, J., and D. M. Heertjes, *Chem. Eng. Sci.*, 29: 1,035 (1974).
176. Boeyens, J., and D. Geldart, *Chem. Eng. Sci.*, 29: 255 (1974).
177. Kang, W. K., J. P. Sutherland, and G. L. Osberg, *I&EC Fund.*, 6: 499 (1967).
178. Littman, H., and G. A. J. Homolka, *Chem. Eng. Prog. Symp. Series, 105*, 66: 37 (1970).
179. Donadono, S., and L. Masamilla, *Fluidization*, Cambridge Univ. Press (1978), p. 375.

180. Nyugen, H. V., L. S. Leung, and R. H. Weiland, *Chem. Eng. Sci.*, 30: 1,187 (1975).

181. Filla, M., et al., *Chem. Eng. Sci.*, 31: 359 (1976).

182. McGraw, D. R., *Chem. Eng. Sci.*, 32: 11 (1977).

183. Ashwin, B. S., et al., *J. Sci. Instr.*, 37: 480 (1960).

184. Hagyard, T., and A. M. Sacerdote, *UEC Fund.*, 5: 500 (1966).

185. Lehman, H., H. Ritzmann, and K. Schugerl, *Intl. Congr. on Fluidization and Its Applications*, Toulouse, France (1973).

186. Finnerty, R. G., et al., *I&EC Fund.*, 8: 271 (1969).

11

Vertical Flow of Particulate Solids in Standpipes and Risers

By C. S. Teo and L. S. Leung
Department of Chemical Engineering
University of Queensland, St. Lucia, Australia

CONTENTS

INTRODUCTION, 472

GENERAL THEORIES FOR THE UPFLOW AND DOWNFLOW OF SOLIDS, 472

Flow Regimes, 474
Fluidized Flow Modes, 475
Nonfluidized Flow, 477
Summary of Flow Regimes, 478

QUANTITATIVE DEMARCATION BETWEEN FLOW REGIMES, 479

Demarcation between Fluidized and Nonfluidized Flows, 479
Demarcation within the Fluidized Mode—Type I and Type II, 481
Demarcation within the Nonfluidized Mode in Standpipes: Tranpacflo and Pacflo, 485

DRIFT FLUX MODEL AND KWAUK'S MODEL FOR GENERALIZED TWO-PHASE FLOW, 485

Drift Flux Model, 485
Kwauk's Model, 487

EQUATIONS PERTAINING TO EACH FLOW REGIME, 488

Nonfluidized Flow, 488
Fluidized Flow, 489

VERTICAL DOWNFLOW OF SOLIDS IN STANDPIPES, 490

Coexistence of Flow Regimes and Pressure Profile, 491
Coexistence of Flow Regimes at Constant Superficial Fluid Velocity, 491
Coexistence of Flow Modes with Variation in Superficial Velocity, 495
Effect of Gas Compression and Aeration, 498
Stability of Standpipe Flow, 500

VERTICAL PNEUMATIC CONVEYING IN RISER FLOW, 509

Choking versus Nonchoking System, 512
Choking System, 519
Nonchoking System, 524
Prediction of Pressure Drop, Solids Holdup, and Solid Velocity for Lean-Phase Mode, 526
Prediction of Pressure Drop, Solids Holdup and Solid Velocity for Dense-Phase Mode, 529
Particle Segregation in Vertical Pneumatic Transport, 530
Design Philosophies, 532

NOMENCLATURE, 533

REFERENCES, 535

INTRODUCTION

This chapter is concerned with the flow of particulate solids up a riser tube, down a standpipe, and through a constriction such as a valve. From the analogy between upflow and downflow, different types of flow behavior are quantitatively defined. Equations for demarcation between flow modes, for the stability of each flow mode, and for the description of the pressure gradient, voidage, and velocities in each flow mode are presented. The aim of this chapter is to summarize published materials on the subject in a manner useful to the design and operating engineer.

GENERAL THEORIES FOR THE UPFLOW AND DOWNFLOW OF SOLIDS

Solids can be transported up or down an inclined or vertical pipe. Such a pipe, with solids traveling downwards cocurrently or countercurrently to a fluid, is referred to as a standpipe. A pipe in which solids are lifted upwards by a fluid is known as a riser. Standpipes and risers together often form part of a solid circulatory loop. The solid flow rate may be controlled by means of a slide valve affixed to the bottom end of the standpipe or by other means.

Figure 11-1 depicts a typical fluid-bed hydrocarbon catalytic cracking plant consisting of a reactor and a regenerator interconnected through standpipes and risers. Catalyst from the regenerator descends through a standpipe and slide valve by gravity, is picked up and conveyed pneumatically up a riser into the reactor, and returns to the regenerator via a second standpipe and a second riser. The main function of a standpipe is often to provide a "head of solids" so that solids from a point at lower pressure can be transferred to a point at higher pressure. Thus P_3 (Figure 11-1) at the bottom end of the regenerator standpipe below the slide valve is usually higher than P_1 at the upper end; while P_2 immediately upstream of the slide valve is higher than P_3, giving for normal operation $P_2 > P_3 > P_1$. The regenerator standpipe also acts as a seal separating the hydrocarbon feed to the reactor from the fluidizing air in the regenerator. The separation is achieved by maintaining a positive $P_2 - P_3$

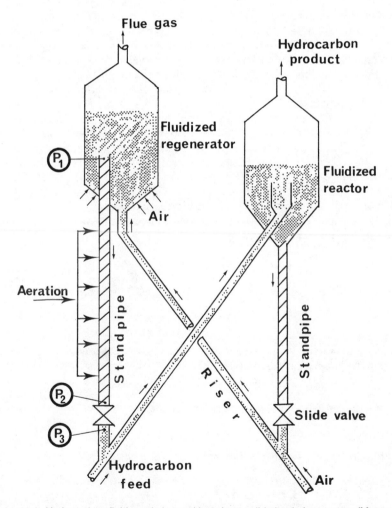

Figure 11-1. Hydrocarbon-fluid catalytic cracking-plant, solid-circulation system (Matsen[1]).

thus preventing any hydrocarbon from flowing upwards through the regenerator standpipe to the regenerator.

Standpipes and risers can be found in many other reaction systems including the Fischer-Tropsch, coal gasification, and coal liquefaction processes. A number of such processes have been described by Zenz and Othmer,[2] Kunii,[3] and in Chapters 6 through 8.

Flow Regimes

When the flow of a fluid upwards through a packed bed of granular solids is gradually increased, the solids remain stationary, as a packed bed initially, until the minimum fluidization velocity is reached. At the minimum fluidization velocity, U_{mf}, the particles are said to be fluidized and the voidage at the point is defined as ϵ_{mf}, the voidage at minimum fluidization. The average slip velocity, U_{sl}, defined as the average fluid velocity minus the average solid velocity, is given by U_{mf}/ϵ_{mf} at minimum fluidization since the average solid velocity in this case is zero. At $U_{sl} < (U_{mf}/\epsilon_{mf})$, the bed of particles is in the packed state, while at $U_{sl} \geq (U_{mf}/\epsilon_{mf})$, the particles are fluidized.

Lapidus and Elgin,[4] Mertes and Rhodes,[5] Kwauk,[6] Matsen,[1] and others have shown that at a given slip velocity, the behavior of a fluidized bed is similar to that of a vertical flow of the same fluid-particle system. Thus, in a standpipe or a riser, when $U_{sl} \geq (U_{mf}/\epsilon_{mf})$, the particles in the standpipe/riser will be fluidized. Similarly, the voidage in the vertical flowing system will be the same as that in the stationary fluidized bed at the same slip velocity. This analogy forms the backbone of the analyses of solids flow in vertical standpipes and risers.

Taking all velocities as positive in the upwards direction, the average slip velocity in the standpipe or riser is given by

$$U_{sl} = V_f - V_s \tag{11-1a}$$

$$= U_f/\epsilon - U_s/(1 - \epsilon) \tag{11-1b}$$

This definition of slip velocity does not make any assumptions about the nature or flow pattern of the suspension in the pipe. For downflow of solids in a standpipe, U_{sl} can be positive or negative. In a stationary fluidized bed and in a riser, U_{sl} is generally positive. From the analogy between a fluidized bed and a flowing system, we can define the two general flow regimes:

1. Fluidized solid flow, in which particles are in suspension:

$$U_{sl} \geq (U_{mf}/\epsilon_{mf}) \tag{11-2a}$$

$$\text{and } \epsilon \geq \epsilon_{mf} \tag{11-2b}$$

2. Nonfluidized solid flow, in which particles move en bloc with little relative motion:

$$U_{sl} < (U_{mf}/\epsilon_{mf}) \tag{11-3a}$$

$$\text{and } \epsilon < \epsilon_{mf} \tag{11-3b}$$

Nonfluidized flow has been referred to as moving-bed flow, packed-bed flow and slip-stick flow. We shall discuss further subdivisions within the fluidized regime and the nonfluidized regime.

Fluidized Flow Modes

Within the fluidized mode in standpipes, Kojabashian[7] was the first to recognize that further subdivision is useful. By assuming a linear relationship between U_{sl} and ϵ, he suggested that $(\partial P/\partial \epsilon)_{w_s,w_f} = 0$ may be useful in demarcating two types of fluidized flow regimes. Leung and Jones,[8,9] by showing that $(\partial P/\partial \epsilon)_{w_s,w_f} = 0$ of Kojabashian is equivalent to $(\partial U_f/\partial \epsilon)_{U_s} = 0$, suggested the following criterion for demarcation:

Type I fluidized flow defined by:

$$(\partial U_f/\partial \epsilon)_{U_s} < 0 \tag{11-4}$$

and

$$U_{sl} \geqslant (U_{mf}/\epsilon_{mf}) \tag{11-2a}$$

Type II fluidized flow defined by

$$(\partial U_f/\partial \epsilon)_{U_s} > 0 \tag{11-5}$$

$$U_{sl} \geqslant (U_{mf}/\epsilon_{mf}) \tag{11-2a}$$

This classification of Leung and Jones does not depend on the assumption of Kojabashian of a linear relationship between U_{sl} and ϵ used in his derivation.

Another method of arriving at the classification given by Equations 11-4 and 11-5 is to consider the direction of the continuity wave (or porosity wave) in a two-phase system. The continuity wave velocity, V_w, is expressed by Slis et al.[10] and Wallis:[11]

$$V_w = [\partial U_f/\partial \epsilon]_{(U_s+U_f)} \tag{11-6}$$

By assuming that for a given gas-solid system a unique function exists between voidage and slip velocity (Lapidus and Elgin;[4] Matsen[1]), the following equation can readily be derived (Jones[12]):

$$V_w \equiv [\partial U_f/\partial \epsilon]_{(U_s+U_f)} = (1 - \epsilon)(\partial U_f/\partial \epsilon)_{U_s} \tag{11-7}$$

As 1-ϵ is positive, V_w and $(\partial U_f/\partial\epsilon)_{U_s}$ have the same sign and the demarcation represented by Equations 11-4 and 11-5 is equivalent to

$$V_w < 0 \quad \text{for Type I fluidized flow} \tag{11-8}$$

$$V_w > 0 \quad \text{for Type II fluidized flow} \tag{11-9}$$

The use of the direction of the continuity wave to demarcate flow regimes and to predict flow stability was first suggested by Staub.[13] He proposed that $(\partial U_f/\partial\epsilon)_{U_s}$ represents the velocity of a "continuity wave" of the system and suggested the terms "more dilute" and "more dense" to describe systems in which $(\partial U_f/\partial\epsilon)_{U_s}$ is less than or greater than zero. Such a definition is identical to the defined criterion for demarcation between Type I and Type II flow. The use of "more dilute" and "more dense" to describe Type I and Type II fluidized flow should be avoided as it will be shown later that the type of fluidized flow is not defined by voidage alone. At the transition point

$$(\partial U_f/\partial\epsilon)_{U_s} = 0 \tag{11-10a}$$

or

$$V_w = 0 \tag{11-10b}$$

Equation 11-10a shows that perturbation of voidage will lead to instability. Thus operation at the transition point is unstable and this instability is generally known as "flooding." Lapidus and Elgin[4] define flooding by

$$\left[\partial U_f/\partial(1 - \epsilon)\right]_{U_s} = 0 \tag{11-11}$$

while Mertes and Rhodes[5] define flooding by

$$(\partial U_s/\partial\epsilon)_{U_f} = 0 \tag{11-12}$$

It can be shown that all three criteria, Equations 11-10, 11-11, and 11-12 for flooding are equivalent.

In vertical upflow, an increase in the fluid velocity at the same solid flux will always result in an increase in voidage, i.e., $(\partial U_f/\partial\epsilon)_{U_s} > 0$. Thus fluidized upflow is always Type II fluidized flow.

There is no need to distinguish between Type I and Type II fluidized flow in a riser.

Nonfluidized Flow

For nonfluidized solid flow in standpipes, Kojabashian[7] proposed further subdivision into *transition packed-bed flow*, in which voidage increases with slip-velocity; and *packed-bed flow*, in which voidage is equal to that of a closely compacted bed, ϵ_p, independent of slip-velocity. He suggested that transition packed-bed flow occurs within the range of slip velocity, U_{sl}, from

$$0 < U_{sl} < (U_{mf}/\epsilon_{mf}) \tag{11-13a}$$

Knowlton et al.[14,15] suggested the use of a linear relationship between voidage and slip velocity for transitional packed-bed flow as follows:

$$\epsilon = \epsilon_p + (\epsilon_{mf} - \epsilon_p)U_{sl}/(U_{mf}/\epsilon_{mf}) \tag{11-14}$$

In transitional packed-bed flow, termed as Tranpacflo (Leung and Jones[16]), the solid is partially supported by fluid drag.

In packed-bed flow in standpipes the fluid moves faster downwards than the solid thus creating a negative slip velocity. The solids are compacted by fluid drag and tend to arrange themselves to the voidage of a vibrated packed bed. Thus packed-bed flow can be quantitiatively defined by

$$U_{sl} < 0 \tag{11-15}$$

and $$\epsilon = \epsilon_p \tag{11-16}$$

The acronym Pacflo has been suggested for packed-bed flow (Leung and Jones[16]).

In an upflow of particles in a riser, nonfluidized flow is not common. It can only occur either when the solid is propelled upwards by some mechanical means or by fluid drag with high positive slip velocity in the presence of a constriction at the downstream end of the riser (Leung et al.,[17] Aoki et al.,[18] Vogel and Marcus[19]). The constriction can be in the form of an orifice or pipe bend (Figure 11-2). The particles are in a compact state (with voidage similar to ϵ_p) due to the presence of the constriction. Leung et al.[17] have classified two types of nonfluidized upflow, viz.:

1. *Unconstrained packed-bed flow* in which the solid is propelled by some mechanical means with slip velocity less than U_{mf}/ϵ_{mf} and voidage less than ϵ_{mf}.
2. *Constrained packed-bed flow* with a constriction downstream in which voidage is below ϵ_{mf} and often close to ϵ_p and with positive slip velocity that can be significantly higher than U_{mf}/ϵ_{mf}.

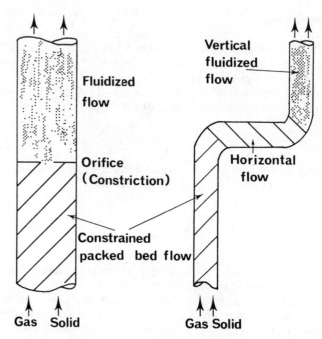

Figure 11-2. Constrained packed-bed flow.

Summary of Flow Regimes

For flow in standpipes we can summarize the following four flow modes:

1. Type I fluidized flow

$$U_{sl} \geq (U_{mf}/\epsilon_{mf}) \qquad\qquad (11\text{-}2a)$$

$$(\partial U_f/\partial \epsilon)_{U_s} < 0 \qquad\qquad (11\text{-}4)$$

or $V_w < 0$ (continuity wave downwards) \qquad (11-8)

2. Type II fluidized flow

$$U_{sl} \geq (U_{mf}/\epsilon_{mf}) \qquad\qquad (11\text{-}2a)$$

$$(\partial U_f/\partial \epsilon)_{U_s} > 0 \qquad\qquad (11\text{-}5)$$

or $V_w > 0$ (continuity wave upwards) \qquad (11-9)

3. Transition packed bed flow

$$0 < U_{sl} < (U_{mf}/\epsilon_{mf})$$ (11-13a)

$$\epsilon_p < \epsilon < \epsilon_{mf}$$ (11-13b)

$$\epsilon = \epsilon_p + (\epsilon_{mf} - \epsilon_p)U_{sl}/(U_{mf}/\epsilon_{mf})$$ (11-14)

4. Packed-bed flow

$$U_{sl} < 0$$ (11-15)

$$\epsilon = \epsilon_p$$ (11-16)

For flow of solids in a riser, we have

1. Fluidized flow (Type II fluidized flow)

$$U_{sl} \geq U_{mf}/\epsilon_{mf}$$ (11-2a)

$$\epsilon \geq \epsilon_{mf}$$ (11-2b)

2. Unconstrained packed-bed flow with no constraint downstream

$$U_{sl} < (U_{mf}/\epsilon_{mf})$$ (11-3a)

$$\epsilon < \epsilon_{mf}$$ (11-3b)

3. Constrained packed-bed flow with a constraint downstream

$$U_{sl} >> (U_{mf}/\epsilon_{mf})$$ (11-2a)

$$\epsilon = \epsilon_p$$ (11-16)

QUANTITATIVE DEMARCATION BETWEEN FLOW REGIMES

Demarcation between Fluidized and Nonfluidized Flows

Demarcation between fluidized and nonfluidized flows (unconstrained) is readily obtained from their definitions, i.e.

for fluidized flow: $U_{sl} \geq U_{mf}/\epsilon_{mf}$ (11-2a)

for nonfluidized flow: $U_{sl} < U_{mf}/\epsilon_{mf}$ (11-3a)

The deciphering of flow modes in an operating system is straightforward for up-flow but complex in downflow. For solid upflow, nonfluidized flow is uncommon and is readily identified by the presence of mechanical propulsion (in the unconstrained case) and by the very high pressure drop (in the constrained case). Deciphering of the flow mode in the downflow of solids, however, is not straightforward. Later it will be shown that specification of U_s and U_f does not determine the specific flow pattern as either fluidized flow or nonfluidized flow is possible at certain given sets of U_s and U_f. A knowledge of voidage in the tube is often necessary to ascertain the flow pattern in a standpipe. While voidage can be directly measured by γ-ray adsorption techniques, this does not form part of the standard instrumentation of the industrial standpipe or riser. Information on pressure profiles is more often available. Typical pressure profiles for different flow patterns in standpipe flow are given in Figure 11-3. Figure 11-3a shows the unique pressure profile for nonfluidized flow with a negative slip velocity. In this case, the flow pattern in the standpipe can be inferred from a knowledge of the pressure profile only. The pressure profile depicted in Figure 11-3b can refer to fluidized flow or nonfluidized flow with a positive pressure gradient (Tranpacflo). The pressure profile in Figure 11-3c may represent dilute-phase fluidized flow (with little change in pressure along the tube) or nonfluidized flow with zero or low slip velocity. Some guidelines for deciphering flow modes in an industrial standpipe have been discussed by Leung and Wilson.[20]

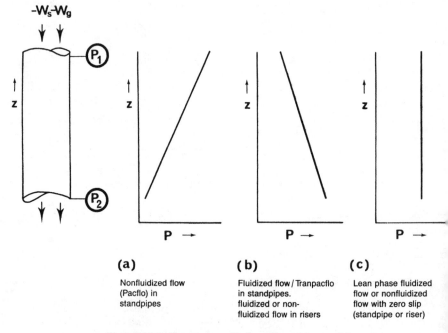

Figure 11-3. Pressure profile for different types of flow.

Demarcation within the Fluidized Mode—Type I and Type II

As noted earlier, all fluidized upflow is of Type II. Thus demarcation between Type I and Type II fluidized flow is only relevant to downflow of solids. From Equations 11-4 and 11-5, the demarcation between the two types of flow is given by

$$(\partial U_f / \partial \epsilon)_{U_s} = 0 \qquad\qquad (11\text{-}10a)$$

For a given fluid-solid system, there is a unique relationship between slip velocity and voidage. This relationship can be obtained experimentally by measuring the fluidization characteristics of the system, or from published correlations such as those due to Richardson and Zaki[21] for a particulate system or to Matsen[1] for a bubbling system. For a particular alumina-cracking catalyst, air fluidizing experiments give a relationship (Leung and Jones[8]):

$$U_{sl} = 8.4\epsilon^2 - 6.66\epsilon + 1.36 \qquad\qquad (11\text{-}17)$$

for $\epsilon_{mf} < \epsilon < 0.75$

From Equations 11-10a and 11-17 and the definition of slip velocity in Equation (11-1), the following quantitative demarcation between Type I and Type II fluidized flow for the alumina catalyst is obtained:

$$(1 - \epsilon)^2 (25.2\epsilon^2 - 13.3\epsilon + 1.36) < - (W_s / \varrho_s) \text{ Type I} \qquad (11\text{-}18a)$$

$$> - (W_s / \varrho_s) \text{ Type II} \qquad (11\text{-}18b)$$

A quantitative flow regime diagram for the catalyst from Equation 11-18 is given in Figure 11-4. The figure shows that voidage by itself does not define the flow regime and Type I and Type II can occur over the entire range of voidage from ϵ_{mf} to 1. A quantitative flow regime diagram similar to Figure 11-4 can be constructed for any fluid-solid system provided an experimental slip-velocity-voidage relationship of the system is available.

Simple batch fluidization tests will yield this expression.

In the absence of any experimental slip-velocity-voidage relationship, for a liquid-solid system, the Richardson-Zaki equation,

$$U_{sl} = U_t \epsilon^{(n-1)} \qquad\qquad (11\text{-}19)$$

can be used. From Equation 11-10a and 11-19, the following demarcation equation can readily be obtained:

$$-n(1 - \epsilon)^2 \epsilon^{(n-1)} > U'_s \quad \text{Type I fluidized flow} \qquad (11\text{-}20a)$$

$$-n(1 - \epsilon)^2 \epsilon^{(n-1)} < U'_s \quad \text{Type II fluidized flow} \qquad (11\text{-}20b)$$

The demarcation can also be obtained from the generalized fluidization chart of Kwauk[6] in Figure 11-5, which has a remarkable similarity to Leung and Jones quantitative flow regime diagram (Figure 11-4). Kwauk's flow chart has an obvious advantage of including one more parameter, i.e. U_f', which allows one to generalize fluidization theories embracing countercurrent, cocurrent, cogravity, and countergravity fluid-solid flows. In more recent work, Kwauk[22] demonstrated the feasibility of obtaining similar charts for gas-solid systems. Although the correlation used for gas-solid systems needs further refinement, the chart computed has revealed the important characteristics obtained experimentally. A direct comparison of Figure 11-4 and Figure 11-5 in the cocurrent cogravity flow shows that Type II fluidized flow occurs at a narrow range of U_s. Also, for a particular voidage, solid velocity in Type I flow will be higher in magnitude than that in Type II flow.

In the case of a bubbling gas-solid fluidized system in a standpipe, the flowing bubbling-bed expansion equation of Matsen et al.[23] may be used:

$$U_{sl} = \frac{U_B(\epsilon - \epsilon_{mf}) + U_{mf}(1 - \epsilon)}{\epsilon(1 - \epsilon)} \tag{11-21}$$

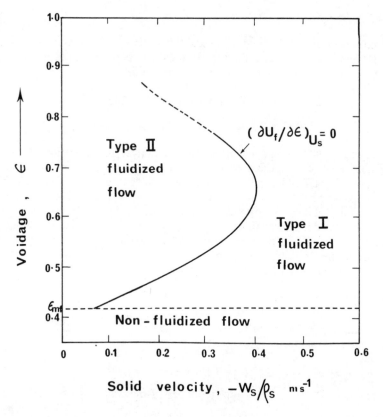

Figure 11-4. Quantitative flow regime diagram for an alumina catalyst (after Leung and Jones[8]).

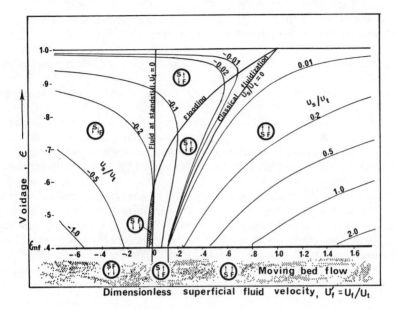

Figure 11-5. Constant-n chart for generalized fluidization (Kwauk[6]).

From Equations 11-1 and 11-21, we can write

$$U_f = \left[(1 - \epsilon_{mf})/(1 - \epsilon)\right]\left[U_B + W_s/\varrho_s(1 - \epsilon_{mf})\right]$$

$$+ U_{mf} - U_B - \frac{W_s}{\varrho_s} \qquad (11\text{-}22)$$

U_B in Equation 11-22 refers to the typical rate of rise of a single bubble in a quiescent gas-solid fluidized bed. For a small diameter standpipe or riser, U_B can be taken as the velocity of rise of a single slug given by the equation of Davidson and Harrison,[24] i.e.

$$U_B = 0.35(gD)^{0.5} \qquad (11\text{-}23)$$

From Equations 11-10a and 11-22, assuming a constant U_B with respect to slip velocity, we obtain

$$-W_s > U_B \varrho_s(1 - \epsilon_{mf}) \quad \text{for Type I fluidized flow} \qquad (11\text{-}24a)$$

$$-W_s < U_B \varrho_s(1 - \epsilon_{mf}) \quad \text{for Type II fluidized flow} \qquad (11\text{-}24b)$$

Equation 11-24 suggests that within the fluidized mode the flow mode is dependent only on the mass flux of solids. Such a flow regime diagram is shown by the straight line ABD in Figure 11-6. The demarcation line ABD, however, is an over-simplification based on two erroneous assumptions:

1. U_B is constant and independent of slip velocity over the whole range of slip velocity.
2. The expansion equation is applicable at a voidage close to 1 when bubbles are expected to be absent.

At a low slip velocity close to and slightly higher than U_{mf}/ϵ_{mf}, any bubbles, if they are present in the standpipe, might not have reached their "typical" size. Thus U_B in Equation 11-23 is dependent on slip velocity (i.e., a function of voidage) particularly at a voidage close to ϵ_{mf}.

At a voidage close to 1 (greater than about 0.85), bubbly flow breaks down and will be replaced by "streaming flow" with clusters of particles flowing down in "streamers" as described by Judd and Dixon.[25] The bubbly flow slip-velocity-voidage relationship (Equation 11-21) will not be applicable. Thus a more realistic flow demarcation line may be represented by MBCE in Figure 11-6.

A flow diagram such as that shown in Figure 11-5 or Figure 11-6 will be useful in the quantitative prediction of flow regime within the fluidized mode.

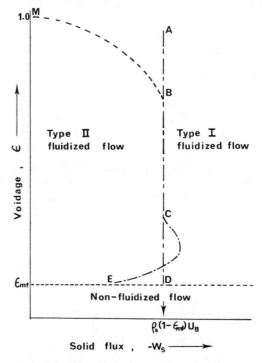

Figure 11-6. Flow regime diagram with Matsen's expansion equation (line ABD) and with modified expansion equations (line MBCE).

Demarcation within the Nonfluidized Mode in Standpipes: Tranpacflo and Pacflo

In the case of solids upflow, the demarcation between unconstrained and constrained nonfluidized flow was described earlier. In this subsection we shall confine the discussion to solids downflow. The demarcation between Tranpacflo (in which ϵ is affected by the slip velocity) and Pacflo (in which ϵ is a constant) in standpipes is defined (Kojabashian[7]) by the magnitude of the slip velocity, i.e.

$$(U_{mf}/\epsilon_{mf}) > U_{sl} > 0 \quad \text{for Tranpacflo} \tag{11-13a}$$

$$U_{sl} < 0 \quad \text{for Pacflo} \tag{11-15}$$

Knowlton et al.[15] used the same criteria and suggested the following linear relationship between voidage and slip velocity in the Tranpacflo regime:

$$\epsilon = \epsilon_p + (\epsilon_{mf} - \epsilon_p) U_{sl}/(U_{mf}/\epsilon_{mf}) \tag{11-14}$$

where ϵ_p is the voidage of a vibrated packed bed. In the Pacflo regime they suggested that voidage would be ϵ_p.

It should be pointed out that the importance of gas-solid characteristics has not been considered in deriving Equation 11-14. The range of $\epsilon_{mf} - \epsilon_p$ will not be the same for different gas-solid systems. Both the validity of Equation 11-14 and the range of $\epsilon_{mf} - \epsilon_p$ can readily be confirmed in a laboratory.

DRIFT FLUX MODEL AND KWAUK'S MODEL FOR GENERALIZED TWO-PHASE FLOW

In previous sections, the parameter of slip velocity is used to describe the analogy between suspension downflow, suspension upflow, and stationary fluidization. Two other related parameters have been used, that is, the drift flux (Wallis[11]) and the superficial slip velocity (Kwauk[6]). Both models are now briefly described.

Drift Flux Model

Wallis[6] defined this model, j_{fs}, as the volumetric flux of fluid relative to a surface moving at the volumetric average velocity, giving

$$j_{fs} = U_f(1 - \epsilon) - U_s\epsilon \tag{11-25a}$$

or

$$j_{fs} = U_{sl}\,\epsilon(1 - \epsilon) \tag{11-25b}$$

Since U_{sl} is a unique function of voidage for a given fluid-solid system, it follows from Equation 11-25b that j_{fs} is also a unique function of voidage. For a system following the Richardson-Zaki equation of expansion (Equation 11-19), Equation 11-25b becomes:

$$j_{fs} = U_t \epsilon^n (1 - \epsilon) \tag{11-26}$$

A typical plot of j_{fs}/U_t versus ϵ is given in Figure 11-7. The broken line below ϵ_{mf} indicates nonfluidized flow. For a given set of U_s' and U_f', j_{fs}' and ϵ are related by the linear equation (11-25a), representing a line joining $\epsilon = 0$, $j_{fs}' = U_f'$ and $\epsilon = 1$, $j_{fs}' = -U_s'$. For cocurrent downflow, both U_s and U_f are negative and Equation 11-25a is represented by the line MM'. This line may intersect the drift flux curve at two points: A for fluidized solid flow, B for nonfluidized flow. This suggests that cocurrent downflow, either fluidized or nonfluidized flow, is possible for a fixed set of U_s and U_f values. For cocurrent upflow, Equation 11-25a is represented by line LL' intersecting the drift flux curve at only one point for a particular set of U_s and U_f: either at point C_1 for U_s and U_{f1} giving rise to nonfluidized flow ($\epsilon < \epsilon_{mf}$), or at point C_2 for U_s and U_{f2} giving rise to fluidized flow ($\epsilon > \epsilon_{mf}$). Thus for a

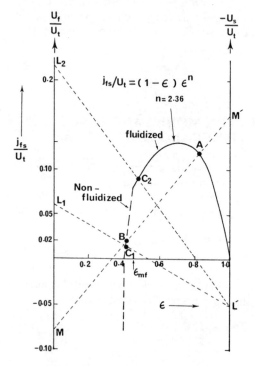

Figure 11-7. Wallis[11] drift-flux plot.

given set of U_f and U_s, only one flow mode in the riser is possible. Similarly, possible flow regimes for countercurrent flows can be identified from the drift-flux plot.

The drift-flux plot is useful for describing voidage for a given solid system for different fluid and solid velocities, irrespective of cocurrent or countercurrent flow.

Kwauk's Model[6]

In previous sections, the actual slip velocity, U_{sl}, was used to describe the analogy between standpipe and riser flows to that of the stationary fluidized bed. In a stationary fluidized bed, the solid velocity is zero, and the slip velocity is given by

$$U_{sl} = U_{fB}/\epsilon \qquad (11\text{-}27)$$

where B refers to a stationary fluidized bed.

While in the standpipe and riser, the slip velocity is given by

$$U_{sl} = U_f/\epsilon - U_s/(1 - \epsilon) \qquad (11\text{-}1)$$

Both Equations 11-27 and 11-1 are analogous for any set of U_{sl} and ϵ, resulting in

$$U_{fB} = U_f - U_s\left(\frac{\epsilon}{1 - \epsilon}\right) \qquad (11\text{-}28a)$$

$$U_{fB} = \epsilon U_{sl} \qquad (11\text{-}28b)$$

ϵU_{sl} is defined as the superficial slip velocity in the standpipe or riser.

From fluidization experiments, general correlations may be based on the superficial fluid velocity, U_{fB}, which is analogous to the superficial slip velocity in a standpipe and riser. Kwauk[6] used the superficial velocity analogy approach. For a fluidized system following the Richardson-Zaki expansion equation (11-19):

$$U_{fB} = U_t\epsilon^n \qquad (11\text{-}29)$$

Combining Equations 11-28 and 11-29 and dividing through by U_t yields

$$\epsilon^n = U_f' - U_s'\left(\frac{\epsilon}{1 - \epsilon}\right) \qquad (11\text{-}30a)$$

$$\epsilon^n = \epsilon U_{sl}' \qquad (11\text{-}30b)$$

ϵ^n is related to j_{fs}' by a factor of $1-\epsilon$ as in Equation 11-26. By plotting ϵ^n against ϵ, Kwauk[6] obtained a superficial slip-velocity plot similar to the drift-flux plot, but magnified by the factor $(1-\epsilon)^{-1}$. He then showed U_f' and U_s' as two parallel vertical lines with signs opposite to each other, exactly identical to those shown in Figure 11-7 for the drift-flux plot. Thus solutions to Equation 11-30a were obtained by drawing straight lines joining sets of U_s' and U_f' to intersect the superficial slip velocity-voidage curve. The method is similar to that for using the drift-flux plot described earlier.

Another useful general diagram due to Kwauk[6] is the constant-n chart as depicted in Figure 11-5. For a given fluid-solid system, the Richardson-Zaki exponent, n, is a constant. Equation 11-30a can be solved by plotting U_f' versus ϵ for various constant values of U_s'. In Figure 11-5 the line for $U_s' = 0$ corresponds to a stationary fluidized bed, with solid upflow to the right of the line and solid downflow to the left of the line. For solid downflow, the chart shows that a line at a constant U_f' may intercept a constant U_s' line at two points, one fluidized, the other nonfluidized, or both fluidized, indicating multiple solutions of the Richardson-Zaki equation in the range of voidages from ϵ_p to 1. However, in the case of solid upflow, a constant U_f' line can intercept a constant U_s' line at only one point, either fluidized or nonfluidized, arriving at the same conclusion as from the drift-flux plot.

The possibility of cocurrent downflow in either the fluidized mode or the nonfluidized mode at a given set of mass fluxes of solid and fluid (W_s and W_f) has been confirmed in an analysis by Leung and Wilson.[20] Such a possibility illustrates the usefulness of the Wallis drift-flux plot or Kwauk's superficial slip-velocity plot and generalized fluidization chart.

EQUATIONS PERTAINING TO EACH FLOW REGIME

Nonfluidized Flow

Two one-dimensional equations are available for describing the fluid pressure gradient and normal stress acting on the solid in steady nonfluidized flow. Yoon and Kunii[26] showed that pressure gradients can be written in terms of slip velocity via the modified Ergun[27] equation giving:

$$-\frac{dP}{dz} = K_1 U_{sl} + K_2 U_{sl} | U_{sl} |$$ (11-31)

where $K_1 = 150\mu(1-\epsilon)^2/(\phi d_v \epsilon)^2$ (11-32)

$K_2 = 1.75\ \varrho_f(1-\epsilon)/\phi d_v \epsilon$ (11-33)

where ϕ = sphericity

$= \dfrac{\text{surface area of sphere with same volume as particle}}{\text{surface area of particle}}$

$= \pi d_v^2/S$ (11-34)

d_v = volume equivalent particle diameter

$= 1/\Sigma(x_i/d_i)$ for mixed sized particles (11-35)

The calculation of pressure gradient from Equation 11-31 is sensitive to the voidage. In standpipe flow with negative slip velocity, $\epsilon = \epsilon_p$ should be used. For a positive slip velocity in standpipes, the voidage can be calculated from Equation 11-14:

$$\epsilon = \epsilon_p + (\epsilon_{mf} - \epsilon_p)U_{sl}/(U_{mf}/\epsilon_{mf}) \tag{11-14}$$

In riser flow, the slip velocity is often positive for nonfluidized flow. The assumption of $\epsilon = \epsilon_p$ is generally valid when there is a constriction downstream as in constrained packed-bed flow.

It is often worthwhile to carry out simple laboratory measurements for flow through a packed bed to obtain constants K_1 and K_2 in Equation 11-31 experimentally. Extrapolation to account for appropriate values of ϱ_f and μ under operating conditions are required.

A second equation pertaining to nonfluidized flow can be obtained by a momentum balance, giving (see Spink and Nedderman,[28] Grossman[29]):

$$d\bar{\sigma}_z/dz + dP/dz + 4\tau_w/D + \varrho_s(1 - \epsilon)g$$
$$+ \varrho_f\epsilon g + V_s(1 - \epsilon)\varrho_s dV_s/dz + V_f\epsilon\varrho_f dV_f/dz = 0 \tag{11-36}$$

For fully developed flow, Equation 11-36 becomes

$$d\bar{\sigma}_z/dz + dP/dz + 4\tau_w/D + \varrho_s(1 - \epsilon)g + \varrho_f\epsilon g = 0 \tag{11-37}$$

The normal stress profile can be obtained by integrating Equation 11-37 once dP/dz is calculated from Equation 11-31. The wall shear stress can be estimated by

$$\tau_w = \mu_w\sigma_r \tag{11-38}$$

and

$$\sigma_r = \bar{\sigma}_z(1 - \sin \delta)/(1 + \sin \delta) \tag{11-39}$$

for a Coulombic solid.

In the previous analysis the mean normal stress $\bar{\sigma}_z$ is taken to be the same as the normal stress near the wall. In a more rigorous analysis, $\bar{\sigma}_z$ in Equation 11-39 should be replaced by σ_z near the wall (Walters[30]).

Fluidized Flow

In fluidized flow, solids are no longer in contact; $\bar{\sigma}_z$ in Equation 11-36 is zero giving:

$$dP/dz + 4\tau_w/D + \varrho_s(1 - \epsilon)g + \varrho_f\epsilon g + W_s dV_s/dz + W_f dV_f/dz = 0 \tag{11-40}$$

For a gas-solid system, neglecting the gas inertia and momentum terms, Equation 11-40 can then be integrated between two points to give

$$-\left[P\right]_{P_0}^{P_z} = P_0 - P_z = \int_0^z \varrho_s(1 - \epsilon)g\,dz + \left[W_s^2/\varrho_s(1 - \epsilon)\right]_0^z$$

$$+ 4\int_0^z (\tau_w/D)dz \tag{11-41}$$

and

$$\tau_w = \tfrac{1}{2}\varrho_s(1 - \epsilon)V_s^2 f_s + \tfrac{1}{2}\varrho_f \epsilon V_f^2 f_f$$

$$= \tfrac{1}{2}f_s W_s^2/[\varrho_s(1 - \epsilon)] + \tfrac{1}{2}f_f W_f^2/(\varrho_f \epsilon) \tag{11-42}$$

From Equations 11-41 and 11-42 we obtain:

$$\Delta P = P_0 - P_z = \int_0^z \varrho_s(1 - \epsilon)g\,dz + \left[W_s^2/\varrho_s(1 - \epsilon)\right]_0^z$$

$$+ \int_0^z \left\{2f_s W_s^2/[\varrho_s(1 - \epsilon)D]\right\}dz$$

$$+ \int_0^z \left[2f_f W_f^2/(\varrho_f \epsilon D)\right]dz \tag{11-43}$$

Knowledge of the voidage profiles is required to solve Equation 11-43 numerically as shown by Ginestra et al.[31,32] for solid downflow and by Yang[33] for solid upflow. For fully developed dense or bubbly flow, ϵ may be obtained from equations such as Equations 11-17 or 11-22. Estimation of the wall friction factors will be discussed in subsequent sections.

VERTICAL DOWNFLOW OF SOLIDS IN STANDPIPES

In a solid-transfer system, problems in solids circulation can often be traced to the standpipes. Erratic circulation, sudden loss of solid flow and rapid change in pressure are some of the common problems encountered (Matsen,[34] Dries[35]). The complexity of standpipe flow is caused by

1. The large number of possible flow regimes that can occur in a pipe.
2. The variation of characteristics of each flow regime.
3. The transition of one flow regime to another at critical conditions.
4. The possibility of coexistence of more than one flow regime in the pipe.
5. The interactive effects of the characteristics of flow through a pipe and a slide valve.

6. The large number of parameters such as particle size distribution, slide valve opening, terminal pressure, aeration gas rate, etc. that can affect flow stability.

The aim of this section is to summarize the published analyses of standpipe flow in a manner useful for design and operation.

Coexistence of Flow Regimes and Pressure Profile

Earlier the different possible flow regimes in a standpipe were described. In this section the coexistence of more than one flow mode in the same standpipe will be discussed. There are two broad categories of coexistence in a standpipe:

1. Coexistence caused by change in superficial fluid velocity in the standpipe; such change can be caused by the introduction of aeration fluid into the pipe, by change in pipe diameter, or by the compressibility of the fluid.
2. Coexistence with no change in superficial fluid or solid velocity throughout the tube.

Coexistence of Flow Regimes at Constant Superficial Fluid Velocity

The coexistence of flow regimes at a constant superficial fluid velocity can be demonstrated in a liquid-solid standpipe (Leung[36]) and can be deduced from a drift-flux plot as depicted in Figure 11-8. The curve in Figure 11-8 represents a plot of drift flux j'_{fs} versus voidage ϵ for a solid-fluid system with $\epsilon_{mf} = 0.45$, $\epsilon_p = 0.40$, and $n = 2.36$. Between voidages of 0.40 and 0.45, the system is not fluidized and the drift flux versus voidage is represented by a broken line. For a fixed set of U_f and U_s, j_{fs} is a linear function of ϵ as represented by the continuity equation (Equation 11-25a).

$$j_{fs} = U_f(1 - \epsilon) - U_s\epsilon \qquad (11\text{-}25a)$$

Line M_1M_1' represents the continuity equation for a given set of U_f and U_s. The intersections of M_1M_1' with the drift-flux curve (points A and B) represent possible operating conditions for the particular fluid-solid systems at the specified set of U_f and U_s. Points A and B represent two fluidized-flow operating points. It can readily be shown that,

$$\text{at A,} \quad \left(\frac{\partial U_f}{\partial \epsilon}\right)_{U_s} < 0 \qquad \text{(Type I fluidized flow)}$$

and

$$\text{at B,} \quad \left(\frac{\partial U_f}{\partial \epsilon}\right)_{U_s} > 0 \qquad \text{(Type II fluidized flow)}$$

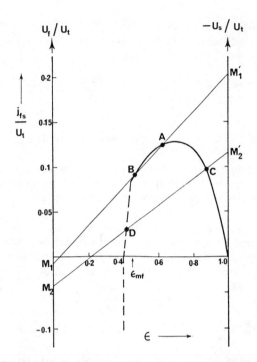

Figure 11-8. Coexistence of flow regimes in standpipes.

Thus at the set of U_f and U_s considered, two modes of fluidized flow can occur, and should they occur in the same tube, we have coexistence of two fluidized modes.

For a different set of U_f and U_s, represented by $M_2 M_2'$, the intersections C and D in Figure 11-8 represent Type I fluidized flow (at C) and nonfluidized flow (at D). Thus to summarize we have:

1. Type I fluidized flow with relatively high voidage (dilute phase, point A) on top of Type II fluidized flow with low voidage (dense phase, point B).
2. Type I fluidized flow (point C) on top of nonfluidized flow (point D).

Leung and Jones[16] further subdivided the latter category depending on the voidage in the fluidized section to give

2a. Type I fluidized flow (dilute phase with voidage close to 1) with nonfluidized flow.
2b. Type I fluidized flow (dense phase with voidage close to ϵ_{mf}) with nonfluidized flow.

In the nonfluidized-flow section we can have either Tranpacflo (if the slip velocity is positive) or Pacflo (if the slip velocity is negative).

For this category of coexistence (constant superficial fluid velocity), Staub[13] suggested that a coexistence is only stable if the continuity waves on either side of the interface propagate towards the interface. The velocity of a continuity wave is given by Equations 11-6 and 11-7, i.e.

$$V_w = (1 - \epsilon) (\partial U_f / \partial \epsilon)_{U_s} \tag{11-7}$$

$$V_w < 0 \quad \text{for Type I fluidized flow, continuity waves} \tag{11-8}$$
$$\text{propagate downwards}$$

$$V_w > 0 \quad \text{for Type II fluidized flow, continuity waves} \tag{11-9}$$
$$\text{propagate upwards}$$

Thus in accordance with Staub, it is stable to have Type I fluidized flow on top of Type II fluidized flow but not vice versa. A pictorial representation of the three possible modes of coexistence and the corresponding pressure profiles are given in Figures 11-9, 11-10 and 11-11.

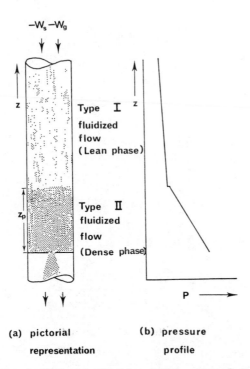

Figure 11-9. Coexistence of Type I fluidized flow at high voidage (lean phase) and Type II fluidized flow at low voidage (dense phase), showing pressure profile (after Judd and Rowe[37]).

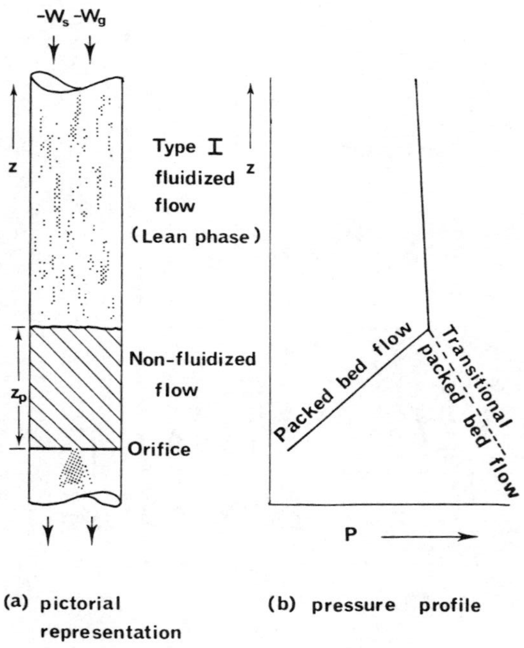

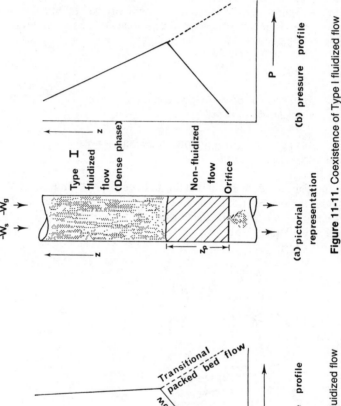

Figure 11-11. Coexistence of Type I fluidized flow (dense phase) with nonfluidized flow, showing pressure profile (after Leung and Wilson[20]).

Figure 11-10. Coexistence of Type I fluidized flow (lean phase) on top of nonfluidized flow, showing pressure profile (after Kunii and Levenspiel[38]).

Coexistence of Flow Modes with Variation in Superficial Velocity

Change in superficial gas velocity in a standpipe can be introduced by gas compression (particularly in a tall pipe) and by the injection of aeration gas into a standpipe. While the general effects of gas compression and aeration on standpipe operation will be considered later, their specific effects on coexistence of flow modes are considered in the immediate discussions.

Coexistence of Flow Modes Caused By Gas Compression

The effect of gas compression depends on whether the pressure gradient is negative (pressure increasing in the downwards direction) or positive (pressure decreasing in the downwards direction). In fluidized flow, the pressure gradient is generally negative and the superficial gas velocity increases (i.e., is less negative) in the downwards direction for cocurrent flow as a result of gas compression. In Type I fluidized flow, since

$$(\partial U_g/\partial \epsilon)_{U_s} < 0 \tag{11-44}$$

we have $(\partial \epsilon/\partial z)_{U_s} > 0$

and for Type II fluidized flow

$$(\partial U_g/\partial \epsilon)_{U_s} > 0 \tag{11-45}$$

and $(\partial \epsilon/\partial z)_{U_s} < 0$

Thus in Type I fluidized flow, the effect of gas compression would cause a decrease in voidage down the standpipe. If the pipe is long enough, the voidage would eventually decrease to a value of ϵ_{mf} causing a transition to Tranpacflo.

Further compression reduces the voidage down the pipe until it reaches a constant value of ϵ_p (where dP/dz is zero as the slip velocity will also be zero and no further gas compression would occur). The voidage and pressure profile of such a system is depicted in Figure 11-12. The pressure and mixture density profiles presented by Dries[39] for 0.86 m diameter and 21 m long standpipe in a hydrocarbon catalytic cracking plant are very similar to those shown in Figure 11-12.

Coexistence of Flow Modes Caused By Introduction of Aeration Gas

While a change in pressure along a standpipe may cause a gradual change in the superficial gas velocity, the injection of aeration gas into a standpipe introduces a stepwise change in the gas velocity. The effect of this stepwise change on the flow mode in a standpipe is important as this is often a major cause of malfunction in industrial standpipes. In the extreme case, Dries[35,39] showed that the injection of aeration gas could result in the formation of a "pseudobridge" above the injection point. Here the roof is supported by the permeation of gas through it as well as from

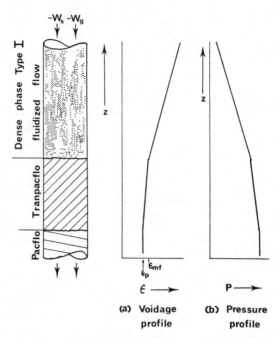

(a) Voidage
profile

(b) Pressure
profile

Figure 11-12. Effect of gas compression on cocurrent Type I fluidized flow in a tall standpipe showing: (a) possible voidage profile; (b) corresponding pressure profile.

wall friction. Such a bridging phenomenon is not restricted to small diameter standpipes. Dries observed the formation of a pseudobridge in a standpipe of 0.11 m diameter and suggested that flow instabilities in a 0.2 m diameter cyclone dipleg and an 0.86 m diameter 21 m long industrial standpipe are caused by the formation of such pseudobridges. The region below the bridge can be either fluidized or non-fluidized according to Dries.

A general theoretical treatment of the effect of aeration on flow mode had been presented by Ginestra et al.[31,32] They considered a standpipe system with a conical hopper at its upper end and an orifice at its lower end as shown in Figure 11-13. By numerically integrating the one-dimensional momentum and continuity equations, they showed that eight different types of coexistence of flow patterns were predicted depending on terminal pressure, openings of the orifice, aeration gas rate, and number and location of aeration point (Figure 11-13). The results of their analysis are presented in a "performance diagram" relating discharge rate of solid materials to the overall pressure rise, orifice opening, and aeration rate. Such a performance diagram is given in Figure 11-14, from which the stability of any steady state can be deduced (Rangachari and Jackson[40]). Experimental verification of their analysis will be necessary before such diagrams can be used with confidence in design.

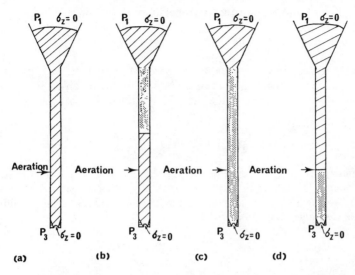

Figure 11-13. Different types of flow coexistence predicted from analysis of Ginestra et al.[31,32]

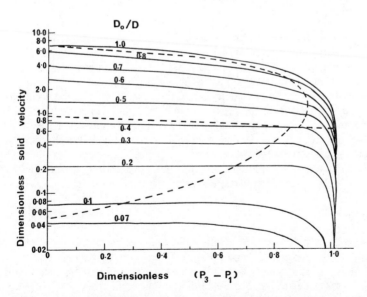

Figure 11-14. Standpipe performance diagram for the analysis of Ginestra et al.,[32] plot of dimensionless solid velocity versus dimensionless $P_3 - P_1$ for various orifice diameter/pipe diameter. Broken lines indicate changes in flow pattern. P_3 and P_1 indicated in Figure 11-13.

Effect of Gas Compression and Aeration

Gas Compression

For nonfluidized flow, the quantitative effect of gas compression as a result of pressure change in a standpipe can be assessed with the modified Ergun equation (Equation 11-31), by expressing the gas velocity in terms of gas mass flux and gas pressure.

$$-dP/dz = K_1 U_{sl} + K_2 U_{sl} |U_{sl}| \tag{11-31}$$

For fluidized flow, the voidage profile is obtained by solving for P and ϵ simultaneously down a standpipe in fluidized flow. This can be done by differentiating Equation 11-43 with respect to z and combining the resultant equation with a suitable expansion equation (Do et al.[41]).

Aeration

Mal-operation of industrial standpipes can often be traced to the misuse of aeration gas (see Dries[35] and Reference 42). It is important to distinguish two functions of aeration gas, i.e., the aeration required to counteract gas compression and aeration in excess of that required to counteract gas compression. The two effects of aeration will be discussed separately in the following sections.

Aeration for counteracting gas compression. In a tall standpipe, the effect of the gas compression is minimized in practice by the introduction of aeration into the standpipe at regular intervals along the pipe. Matsen[34] suggested that the optimal rate of aeration gas should be that just sufficient to counteract compression to maintain the same superficial gas velocity along the pipe. For fluidized solid flow, for instance, the amount of aeration required can be calculated provided the solid circulation rate and the slip-velocity-voidage relationship are known. Dries[39] observed that the operation of a 0.86 m diameter 21 m long standpipe in the fluidized mode is in support of Matsen's suggestion. In dense-phase fluidized flow the following equation can be applied to estimate the approximate aeration gas required to counteract the effects of gas compression over a length of standpipe.

$$-W_{ga} = -W_g(\varrho_{g1} - \varrho_{gz})/\varrho_{gz} \tag{11-46}$$

where W_{ga} = mass flow of aeration gas per unit cross-section of standpipe
ϱ_{g1}, P_1 = gas density and pressure at position 1, respectively
ϱ_{gz}, P_z = gas density and pressure at z above position 1, respectively, as defined in Figure 11-15.

Generally in design calculations for fluidized flow, the solid flux W_s is specified. Voidage ϵ in the standpipe is kept close to ϵ_{mf} to maximize pressure buildup in the

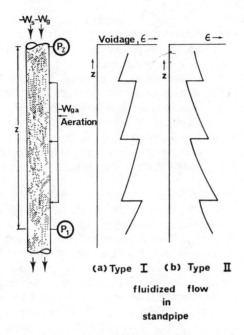

(a) Type **I**   (b) Type **II**

fluidized   flow
in
standpipe

Figure 11-15. Effect of multiple aeration injection on voidage profile for Type I and Type II fluidized flow.

downwards direction. The gas entrainment rate W_g in Equation 11-46 is calculated from W_s, ϵ and an expansion equation such as Equation 11-22:

$$U_g = [(1 - \epsilon_{mf})/(1 - \epsilon)] [U_B + W_s/\varrho_s(1 - \epsilon_{mf})] \\ + U_{mf} - U_B - W_s/\varrho_s \qquad (11\text{-}22)$$

W_{ga} in Equation 11-46 is the total aeration gas rate to be injected into a section z of pipe. As shown in Figure 11-15, the aeration gas should be spread over a number of injection points to give a more uniform voidage profile along the tube. While there is no published guideline for spacing between aeration points, the spacing should be sufficiently close together such that transition to packed-bed flow (as discussed earlier) would not develop as a result of compression. Figure 11-15 also indicates the difference in the voidage profile with aeration for Type I and Type II fluidized flow.

Often the nature of the aeration gas injected is different from the gas entrained down a standpipe. In a catalytic-cracker regenerator standpipe, for instance, steam is injected into the standpipe, containing a mixture of catalyst and air. The change in molecular weight of the gas mixture will have to be accounted for in the calculations in Equation 11-46.

Aeration in excess of counteracting gas compression. The effect of aeration gas in excess of that required to counteract gas compression is complex and depends on (1) the geometry of the system, (2) the properties of the gas-solid-tube system, and (3) the operating flow modes in the standpipe.

If the aeration gas travels downwards in the same direction as solids and entrained gas, increase in the aeration rate $-W_{ga}$ at a point results in a decrease in the gas entrainment rate $-W_g$ above the aeration point. Note $-W_g$ is positive downwards. Thus for nonfluidized flow, a reduction of $-W_g$ will increase the slip velocity and result in an increase in the pressure gradient $-dP/dz$ (see Knowlton and Hirsan,[14] Leung et al.[43]). Further increase in $-W_{ga}$ may increase the slip velocity above the aeration point to a point at which the particles become fluidized or when flow becomes unstable.

For fluidized flow in a standpipe, an increase in $-W_{ga}$ once again results in a decrease in $-W_g$ above the aeration point. However, this may lead to a decrease or increase in slip velocity depending on whether the flow mode above the aeration point is Type I fluidized flow or Type II fluidized flow. For Type II fluidized flow $(\partial U_g/\partial \epsilon)_{U_s} > 0$ and an increase in $-W_{ga}$ (i.e. decrease in $-U_g$), an increase in voidage is observed. For Type I fluidized flow, however, $(\partial U_g/\partial \epsilon)_{U_s} < 0$, and an increase in $-W_{ga}$ will result in a decrease in voidage above the aeration point. Thus in the latter case further increases in aeration rate $-W_{ga}$ will eventually lead to the voidage decreasing to the critical value of ϵ_{mf} where fluidized flow is no longer possible (Leung,[44] Leung and White[45]). A stepwise change in the behavior in the standpipe can be expected to occur at the critical aeration rate. The introduction of aeration gas is often the source of operating problems in industrial standpipe. For Type I fluidized flow for instance, gas compression would reduce the voidage down the standpipe as discussed earlier. As the standpipe often operates close to ϵ_{mf}, there is a tendency of Type I flow defluidizing to nonfluidized flow as a result of gas compression. The standard means to counteract gas compression is to introduce aeration gas. Hence, if aeration gas is introduced in excess, the excess aeration gas will lead to transition to nonfluidized flow and flow instability . This sensitive behavior to gas compression and aeration of Type I fluidized flow is often the underlying problem of many standpipe operations. Thus, adjustment of the aeration rate can cause flow instability as well as the formation of a pseudobridge in the standpipe (Dries[35]).

An example of the dramatic effect of the aeration rate on standpipe operation can also be seen by the analysis of Ginestra et al.[32] A number of possible flow patterns in a standpipe is possible depending on aeration rate and location of aeration point. Figure 11-13 represents the system studied by Ginestra et al.[32] and some of the flow modes predicted by their analysis.

Stability of Standpipe Flow

The question of stability of standpipe flow can be discussed from a number of approaches. It is important to recognize that a given flow system may be analyzed to be stable from one viewpoint but unstable from another viewpoint. Stability in standpipe flow is discussed in terms of the following:

1. Microscopic or hydrodynamic stability of downflow of a *uniform* suspension
2. Macroscopic instability as a result of flooding represented by

$$(\partial U_f / \partial \epsilon)_{U_s} = 0 \qquad (11\text{-}10a)$$

3. Macroscopic instability from the viewpoint of direction of propagation of continuity wave
4. Macroscopic instability in systems from the viewpoint of a Ledinegg-type[46] supply-demand analysis
5. Multiple steady states and bifurcation-type instability
6. Oscillatory steady state as represented by slip-stick flow
7. Stability analysis of Rangachari and Jackson[40]

Stability of Uniform Suspension Flow

The problem of stability of a uniform suspension flowing vertically downwards is analogous to the problem of stability of a uniform stationary fluidized bed. The latter question had been studied by a number of workers and had been reviewed by Jackson.[47] A common approach is to apply a linear perturbation technique to a quiescent steady state of uniform voidage (Jackson,[48,49] Pigford and Baron,[50] Murray,[51] Anderson and Jackson[52]). Such analyses predict that the state of uniform gas-solid fluidization is inherently unstable as a result of voidage waves propagating with increasing amplitude with respect to time and direction of fluid flow. The instability is reflected in practice by the presence of bubbles in a fluidized bed. By comparing the rate of growth of the voidage wave of different systems, it is possible to rank the degree of "aggregativeness" of the various fluidized beds. The most important parameters in the order of ranking are the density ratio (ϱ_s / ϱ_g) and particle diameter d. Systems with large ϱ_s / ϱ_g and large d tend to be more "aggregative." The ranking resulting from the analyses is consistent with observations that some gas-solid systems are "more aggregative" or "less particulate" than others. One practical criterion of the degree of aggregativeness is the ratio of U_{mb} / U_{mf}. U_{mb} is the fluidization velocity at which bubbling initiates. For less aggregative gas-solid systems, $U_{mb} / U_{mf} > 1$. Thus apparently uniform fluidization can occur within the range of fluidization velocity between U_{mf} and U_{mb}. Geldart[53] Type A gas-solid systems behave in this manner. For systems with high "degrees of instability" predicted by the analyses, the observed ratio of U_{mb} / U_{mf} is equal to 1.

Tsutsui and Miyauchi[54] studied the effect of fines and size distribution on the fluidity of particles with surface-to-volume mean diameter from 43 to 169 μm and below 44 μm fines ranging from 0.3 to 32%. They concluded that for systems with the same surface-to-volume mean diameter, good fluidity was exhibited by systems with wide size ranges and with high percentages of fines. This conclusion is in support of the empirical observation that the presence of fines may improve operation in a standpipe by reducing the "aggregativeness" of the particles.

The stability analysis for uniform fluidization can be extended to an upflowing suspension with similar results (see Yousfi and Gau,[55] Grace and Tuot[56]). Grace and Tuot extended Jackson's analysis to show that the cocurrent upflow of a uniform gas-solid suspension is also unstable. In a similar analysis, Jones[12] considered the downflow of a uniform suspension in a standpipe. The result of his analysis confirms that the downflow of a uniform gas-solid suspension is likewise unstable. In practice this is manifested by the presence of bubbles in dense-phase fluidized downflow (Judd,[57] Matsen[1,34]) or the presence of streamers and clusters for lean-phase downflow. It is likely however that a gas-solid system that exhibits high U_{mb}/U_{mf} in fluidization may flow down a standpipe as a homogeneous fluidized mixture within a small range of slip velocity around that at minimum fluidization, and as in bubbling flow at high slip velocity. For systems with U_{mb}/U_{mf} equal to 1, bubbling flow is expected to occur at all slip velocities greater than that at minimum fluidization.

Flooding Instability

One limit of operation in countercurrent flow and in cocurrent downflow is known as "flooding." Flooding occurs when an unsteady-flow solution to the continuity and momentum equations arises due to a change in the superficial velocity of one phase while the other is fixed (Wallis[11]). Lapidus and Elgin[4] had defined the flooding locus mathematically by $[\partial U_f/\partial(1 - \epsilon)]_{U_s} = 0$. Mertes and Rhodes[5] referred to flooding by $(\partial U_s/\partial \epsilon)_{U_f} = 0$. These reconcile with the demarcation between Type I and Type II fluidized flow of

$$(\partial U_f/\partial \epsilon)_{U_s} = 0 \tag{11-10a}$$

The loci of U_s and U_f at which flooding occurs can be obtained in a drift-flux plot from straight lines tangential to the drift-flux curve (Wallis[11]). Thus U_{f1} and U_{s1}; U_{f2} and U_{s2} in Figure 11-16 represent sets of flooding gas and solid superficial velocities for the system. Alternatively the flooding locus can be derived analytically for a system in which the slip-velocity-voidage relation is known. For a system following the Richardson-Zaki equation[21]

$$(U_{sl}/U_t) = \epsilon^{(n-1)} \tag{11-19}$$

the following locus for flooding can readily be obtained from Equations 11-1, 11-10a and 11-19:

$$-U_{sF} = nU_t\epsilon^{(n-1)}(1 - \epsilon)^2 \tag{11-47}$$

For gas-solid systems with the presence of bubbles an expansion equation such as Equation 11-22 due to Matsen[1] is more realistic than the Richardson-Zaki equation:

$$U_g = [(1 - \epsilon_{mf})/(1 - \epsilon)] [U_B + U_s/(1 - \epsilon_{mf})] - U_B + U_{mf} - U_s \tag{11-22}$$

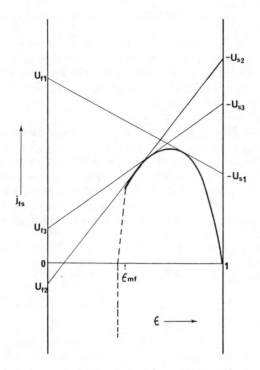

Figure 11-16. Flooding loci from Wallis[11] drift-flux plot. Loci represented by U_{f1}, U_{s1}; U_{f2}, U_{s2}; U_{f3}, U_{s3}, ...

If we assume that the characteristic bubble velocity U_B for a particular gas-solid system is a constant, the flooding locus can be obtained from Equations 11-10a and 11-22 to give

$$-U_s/(1 - \epsilon_{mf}) = U_B \qquad (11\text{-}48)$$

The actual solid velocity is $-U_s/(1 - \epsilon)$ and is in most practical cases, close to $-U_s/(1 - \epsilon_{mf})$. Equation 11-48 indicates that the flooding instability occurs when the actual solid velocity is approximately equal to U_B, the characteristic velocity of rise of a single bubble in the gas solid system.

It is interesting to note that Matsen[1] reported instability in an industrial standpipe when the solid velocity is equal to the bubble rise velocity, U_B. Thus, according to Matsen, a bubble will be held stationary in the pipe; coalescence of bubbles will occur until a large bubble fills a significant length of a standpipe. From Equation 11-48 we can see that such a phenomenon may be the actual mechanism leading to the flooding instability of a bubbly flow system.

Stability from Continuity (Kinematic) Wave Direction Consideration

Continuity waves are a quasi-steady-state phenomenon in which one steady-state value (e.g. voidage at a point in a standpipe) propagates into another one, and there are no dynamic effects of inertia or momentum. The "continuity wave" is often described as the "kinematic wave" (Lighthill and Whitham[58]) and has been described as the "voidage or porosity wave" in relation to a fluidized bed (Slis et al.[10]).

Consider the steady flow of a fluidized mixture down a standpipe. If a stepwise change in gas velocity is made, a new steady-state voidage will eventually take over the whole standpipe. During the transient period, a continuity wave is formed propagating with a finite velocity (V_w) from a region of one voidage to a region of the second voidage. Referring to Figure 11-17, the continuity wave velocity can be derived by considering the movement of gas and solids across the control volume aa and bb (Wallis[11]). Relative to the wave front, as much gas is approaching as is departing. Therefore

$$(-U_g) - \epsilon(-V_w) = (-U_g) + \delta(-U_g) - (\epsilon + \delta\epsilon)(-V_w) \qquad (11\text{-}49)$$

Note that the total flux in the tube $U_g + U_s$ is a constant with respect to z and to time after the step change. Thus Equation 11-49 becomes

$$V_w = [\partial U_g / \partial \epsilon]_{(U_g + U_s)} \qquad (11\text{-}6)$$

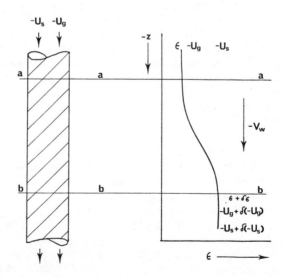

Figure 11-17. Propagation of a continuity wave (after Wallis[11]).

Similarly we can consider the continuity of the solid phase to obtain

$$V_w = [\partial U_s / \partial (1 - \epsilon)]_{(U_g + U_s)} \tag{11-50}$$

It can be readily be shown (Wallis[11]) that the V_w obtained from Equations 11-6 and 11-50 are the same. The sign of V_w determines the direction of the propagation. In the present nomenclature, a negative V_w refers to a downwards wave and vice versa.

Staub[13] defined a "continuity wave velocity" for the gas phase as $(\partial U_g / \partial \epsilon)_{U_s}$ and a continuity wave velocity for the solid phase as $[(\partial U_s / \partial (1 - \epsilon)]_{U_s}$, which are different from that of the conventional definition given by Equations 11-6 and 11-50. For any gas-solid system in which a unique function exists between voidage and slip velocity it can be shown (Jones et al.[59]) that

$$[\partial U_g / \partial \epsilon]_{(U_s + U_g)} = (1 - \epsilon) (\partial U_g / \partial \epsilon)_{U_s} \tag{11-7}$$

Since $1-\epsilon$ in Equation 11-7 is always positive, the continuity velocity defined by Staub[13] has the same sign as V_w. Staub[13] suggested that the direction of his continuity waves (and thus the sign of V_w) could be used to predict if a fluidized-flow regime is stable. According to Staub[13] "an operating point will be stable provided that the phase flow is controlled from the top when the continuity waves propagate downwards and provided that the phase flow is controlled from the bottom when the continuity waves propagate upwards." As $(\partial U_g / \partial \epsilon)_{U_s}$ is our criterion for demarcation of Type I and Type II flow, Staub's criterion can be restated as follows for fluidized standpipe flow:

Type I flow $[(\partial U_g / \partial \epsilon)_{U_s} < 0]$ stable if controlled from the top
Type II flow $[(\partial U_g / \partial \epsilon)_{U_s} > 0]$ stable if controlled from the bottom

Staub's postulate has yet to be tested experimentally. There is also some uncertainty as to what constitutes a control in practice (Jones et al.[59]). In a system such as that shown in Figure 11-18, neither the gas nor the solid flow rate can be directly controlled. Thus it is not clear whether such a system is top controlled or bottom controlled. Further work in this field is necessary.

Another outcome from the continuity wave direction postulate of Staub relates to the coexistence of two fluidized modes. According to Wallis[11] and Staub[13] a stable interface can only occur when the continuity wave on both sides of the interface propagates towards it. Thus a stable coexistence of the two fluidized modes can only occur if Type I flow is on top of Type II flow. This would imply from Staub's postulate that the system is top controlled (for Type I flow to occur) and bottom controlled (for Type II flow to occur) *at the same time!*

Ledinegg Supply-Demand Analysis of Flow Stability

The stability analysis of Ledinegg[46] for gas-liquid flow in vertical boiler tubes is analogous to the simple analysis of stability of a flow reactor. Here a system of

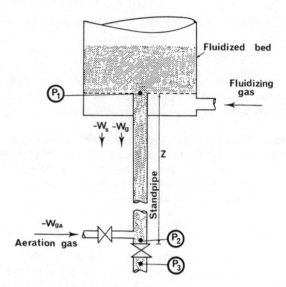

Figure 11-18. Standpipe system in which P_1, P_3, valve opening, and aeration rate are independent parameters.

equations for a particular operation is reduced to two—a supply equation and a demand equation. Solutions of the equations are represented by points of intersection of the two curves representing the two equations. The stability of a particular operating point can be assessed by a simple perturbation argument. The application of such an analysis to standpipe flow has been presented by Do[60] and by Jones et al.[59] Both analyses consider a standpipe system represented by Figure 11-18.

For this system the independent parameters are P_1, P_3, the degree of valve opening A/A_o, and the aeration gas rate U_{ga}. The dependent variables are solid and gas entrainment rates, U_s and U_g, voidage profile, and P_2. For steady-state operations we can write four algebraic equations to describe the system for fluidized flow:

1. Overall momentum equation for standpipe, Equation 11-43
2. Slip-velocity-voidage expansion for standpipe, such as Richardson-Zaki type equation (Equation 11-19)
3. Two orifice equations, such as the modified Jones and Davidson equation (Equation 11-51) and modified Ergun equation (Equation 11-52)

$$-W_s' = C_{DV}(\pi/4) (D_o - Kd)^2 (2\varrho_{mf}\Delta P_o)^{0.5} \tag{11-51}$$

$$-\Delta P_o = K_3 U_{sl} + K_4 U_{sl}|U_{sl}| \tag{11-52}$$

Presenting the equations in terms of slip velocity/voidage the Richardson-Zaki equation is termed the demand equation—the amount of slip velocity demanded by a system for a voidage ϵ to be maintained. The other three equations are combined in the form of slip velocity versus ϵ to give the supply equation—representing the slip velocity supplied by the system at a given voidage. The two equations are represented graphically in Figure 11-19, showing two intersection points, A and B. Intersection A can be shown to represent an unstable stationary point by a simple perturbation analysis. Referring to Figure 11-19, if voidage is perturbed from ϵ_A to $\epsilon_A + \delta\epsilon$, a slip velocity of $U_{slA} + \delta U_{sl}$ is generated by the system (the supply equation). This slip velocity can support a higher voidage (point D in Figure 11-19) and the voidage will keep on increasing until the second stationary point at B is reached. By a similar analysis it can be shown that operation at point B is stable and perturbation of voidage will be damped.

Jones et al.[59] and later Jones[12] analyzed the same system and showed that stable fluidized operation is predicted at high voidage close to 1 and for a narrow range of voidage close to ϵ_{mf}. The result of the analysis is consistent with the observation of Judd and Rowe[37] that ". . . powders in a gas flow system can only exist at certain concentrations, a fairly narrow range around packed bed values and a wider range corresponding to lean phase transport values extending to zero . . . ."

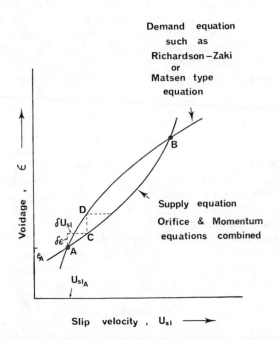

Figure 11-19. Stability consideration from supply-demand analysis (after Do[60]): Demand equation—fluidization expansion equation such as the Richardson-Zaki or Matsen equation; Supply equation—orifice and standpipe momentum equations combined; A—Unstable stationary point; B—Stable stationary point.

Multiple Steady State and Bifurcation-Type Instability

There are at least two types of situations in which multiple steady states could occur. In one, gas and solid flow rates are fixed. For a given set of gas and solid flow rates there may be more than one solution to the continuity and momentum equations. An example of this is represented by two intersections in the drift-flux plot given in Figure 11-7. The stability of the stationary points as represented by the two intersection points has been described earlier and will not be further discussed here.

The second type of multiple steady states refers to multiple solutions to the equations for a given standpipe system in which the gas and solid rates are not the same at the various stationary points. For a system represented by Figure 11-18, for instance, at a given set of operating conditions, there may be multiple solutions to the equations. This could lead to the possibilities of multiple steady states and one or more such steady states may satisfy the stability criterion described earlier. In the case of two stable flow states for a given set of operating variables, the steady state attained by the system depends on the history of the system. Such hysteresis effects had been observed in industrial operation and in the laboratory (Leung and Jones,[8] Jones[12]).

In some standpipe systems, change in an operating parameter at a critical point can result in a stepwise change in the system. An example of this is the variation of the aeration gas rate into a standpipe. Often there is a critical aeration rate at which a change in flow regime in the standpipe may occur. Thus, at the critical aeration rate a dramatic change in voidage and pressure profile and gas and solid recirculation rates may occur. Similar bifurcation-type changes can also be triggered by a variation in the valve opening and other independent parameters of the system.

Oscillatory Steady State

Perhaps one of the least well understood modes of standpipe flow is the so-called slip-stick flow. In this mode, solids travel in stop-start oscillatory motion down a pipe with a frequency of oscillation in the range of approximately 0.1 to 1Hz. Two possible explanations have been presented for this type of flow. The first asserts that it is due to solids arching or bridging in the pipe and then the inertia of downflowing particles hitting the arch from above causing it to break down. The process then repeats itself leading to the observed periodic behavior. The second line of reasoning suggests that this stop-start flow may be controlled cycling between nonfluidized flow and fluidized flow. Further work is required here.

A Linearized Stability Analysis of Rangachari and Jackson[40]

Ginestra et al.[31,32] analyzed the steady-state behavior of a system in which a vertical standpipe was fed from a conical mass-flow hopper at the top and controlled by an orifice at the bottom as shown in Figure 11-13. The results of their one-dimensional theory were presented as performance charts in which solid velocity was plotted against the pressure rise across the complete system, with the size of the control orifice as a parameter (Figure 11-14). The effects of aeration and particle sizes had also been analyzed.

In a follow-up paper, Rangachari and Jackson[40] presented a stability analysis on the simplest case of an unaerated standpipe without restriction at the bottom. The flow pattern now is simplified, as the pipe is always filled with a suspension of solids in gas. The results of their analysis revealed that all states belonging to arcs of the performance curve with positive slope, i.e. $d(P_3 - P_1)/d(-U_s) > 0$, were unstable, while all states belonging to arcs with negative slope were stable.

They extended this stability analysis to consider the effects of orifice openings and the aeration of the pipe. To simplify the analysis, the possibility of a packed bed above the aeration point was excluded. The flow in the orifice region was deemed to achieve steady state instantaneously at all times. Even with the assumption made, the secular equation obtained was complex and numerical solution was required. The results of the numerical solution had confirmed that the stability criterion was the same. If this result is generally true, then the stability criterion is very simple, i.e.

$$d(P_3 - P_1)/d(-U_s) > 0 \quad \text{(unstable)} \quad (11\text{-}53a)$$

$$d(P_3 - P_1)/d(-U_s) < 0 \quad \text{(stable)} \quad (11\text{-}53b)$$

This simple criterion permits the stability of a steady state to be deduced directly from the performance chart for their system. Experimental follow-up of this analysis will be of much significance.

It can be seen from previous subsections that quantitative description of some aspects of standpipe flow is available. The entire picture is far from clear, and the stage has not been reached when industrial downpipes can be designed with complete confidence. Some practical guidelines for design are available in the literature (see Matsen[34] and Reference 42). These guidelines are not comprehensive and were often based on data from actual operation rather than from theoretical analysis. A number of theoretical analyses in standpipe design is also available (Ginestra et al.,[31,32] Leung,[44] Leung et al.,[43] Leung and Jones,[8] Jones,[12] Eleftheriades and Judd,[61] Chen et al.,[62-64] Do et al.,[60] and Knowlton et al.[15,65]). The usefulness of these analyses is uncertain as the validity of some of the assumptions used in these analyses has yet to be verified.

VERTICAL PNEUMATIC CONVEYING IN RISER FLOW

In vertical upflow as a suspension, $(\partial \epsilon / \partial U_f)_{U_s}$ is generally positive. Thus upflow as a suspension will always be Type II fluidized flow. A different criterion for classification of flow modes in upflow of solids in a vertical tube is available. Zenz[66] described the characteristics of vertical upflow in terms of a pressure gradient versus gas velocity plot (Figure 11-20) with solid flow rate as a third parameter.

Line AB in Figure 11-20 refers to zero solid flow in the pipe and a family of curves of increasing solid flow rates are also presented in the figure. Referring to a

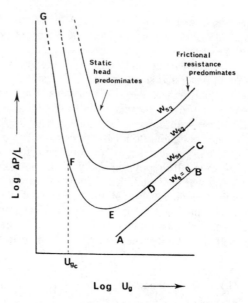

Figure 11-20. Flow characteristics in vertical pneumatic conveying.

fixed solid flow rate of W_{s1}, at a high gas velocity (say, point C), the solid volumetric concentration is low (well below 1%) and the particles are apparently uniformly dispersed. This is known as lean-phase or dilute-phase flow. When the gas velocity is reduced at the same solid flow rate W_{s1}, solid concentration in the pipe increases and wall frictional loss decreases.

The pressure gradient in fully developed vertical conveying is made up of two components, i.e., a wall frictional loss component and a gravitational component. As the gas velocity is reduced, frictional loss decreases while the gravitational component increases as a result of an increase in solid concentration. Along CD the decrease in frictional loss is significantly higher than the increase in the gravitational component. Thus the overall pressure gradient decreases with a decrease in gas velocity along CD. As the gas velocity is further reduced, the gravitational component becomes more significant and the curve goes through a minimum at E. Further decrease in gas flow rate will lead to an increase in pressure gradient along EF as the solid concentration is higher and the gravitational component becomes predominant. Along FG, the pressure gradient increases rapidly and the solid concentration is much higher; the flow mode here is then defined as dense-phase flow. The solid particles are no longer uniformly dispersed. Two types of dense-phase flow are possible depending on the characteristics of the gas-solid-tube system. In one, defined as slugging dense-phase conveying, particles are conveyed upwards by "slugs" or "bubbles." In the other, defined as dense-phase conveying without slugging, clusters of particles appear and solids are conveyed upwards with considerable internal solid circulation.

For the slugging conveying system, the transition from lean-phase flow to slugging conveying is a sharp one (point F in Figure 11-20), and this transition is known as "choking." For nonslugging dense-phase conveying, the transition between lean-phase and dense-phase conveying is diffuse. The flow chart in Figure 11-21 shows the two possible classes of behavior as the gas velocity is reduced from a high value at the same solid flow rate. In general, fine particles in large tubes tend towards nonslugging dense-phase flow, while choking is observed with coarse particles in small tubes. As shown in Figure 11-21 when the gas velocity is further reduced in the nonslugging dense-phase mode, slugging or bubbling dense-phase conveying occurs, although this transition from the nonslugging to the slugging/bubbling mode is also diffuse. Further reduction in the gas flow rate at the same solid flow rate will eventually result in transition from suspension flow to nonfluidized packed-bed flow as shown in Figure 11-21.

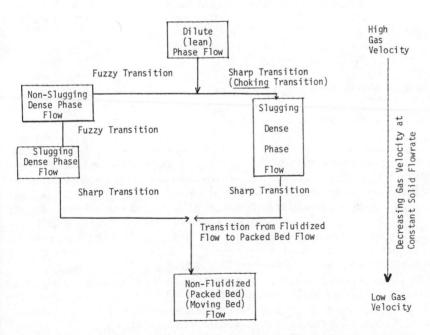

Figure 11-21. Possible flow patterns in vertical pneumatic conveying showing two types of systems: the choking-type system (right hand branch) and the nonchoking-type system (left hand branch).

A system that follows that left hand branch of the chart in Figure 11-21 is defined as a *nonchoking-type system* while one that follows the right hand branch as a *choking-type system*.

In practice vertical pneumatic conveying is generally carried out in the dilute-phase regime and much of the published work on vertical pneumatic conveying has been restricted to this regime. For operation in the dilute-phase regime it is desirable to operate at as low an air flow rate as possible from energy requirements, pipe erosion, and particle attrition considerations. Dense-phase flow is less often used because of the erratic nature of the flow, the pressure fluctuations, high pressure drops, and pipe line vibration. In a solid-riser reactor, however (in which the vertical pneumatic conveying tube acts as a gas-solid reactor), dense-phase flow is sometimes preferred to give a high solid concentration in the tube. Moving-bed flow is generally to be avoided because of very high pressure drop and the problem of blockage.

In the design of a vertical pneumatic conveying system, it is important to be able to predict the flow behavior of a particular gas-solid system, the transition velocities for various flow patterns, and the pressure drop for each flow regime. These questions will be taken up in this section. Another design parameter of interest is particle-segregation in conveying, when particles of a mixed size or mixed properties are conveyed. In this case the *in situ* composition of particles in the tube may be significantly different from the composition of particles entering or leaving the conveyor. The question of particle-segregation is important when a riser is used as a reactor.

Choking Versus Nonchoking System

The Choking Phenomenon

The phenomenon of choking in vertical pneumatic conveying had been described in detail by Zenz and Othmer.[2] At a high gas velocity particles are carried up the riser tube as an apparently evenly dispersed suspension in the so-called lean-phase mode. If the air velocity is reduced gradually at the same mass flow rate of solid, the *in situ* solid concentration increases. A point will be reached when the uniformly dispersed suspension becomes unstable. The entire suspension collapses, and particles are then transported up the riser in slugging flow at a higher average solid concentration. The point of choking is the transition point from upflow of solids as a thin suspension (i.e. lean-phase flow) to slugging flow (i.e. slugging dense-phase flow). The gas velocity at the choking point is the choking velocity at the particular solid flow rate (U_{gc} in Figure 11-20). Similarly the choking transition can also be approached from the slugging dense-phase mode by gradually increasing the air velocity until transition to lean-phase conveying occurs.

It should be stressed that the choking transition is not the same as the transition or instability resulting from interaction between the characteristics of the blower and of the pneumatic conveying system. With blowers characterized by reducing volumetric delivery at increasing delivery pressure, the transition from lean-phase flow to dense-phase flow regimes may be triggered off by a sudden increase in solid concentration or flow rate or a sudden reduction of gas flow rate. Figure 11-22 represents pressure drop versus gas flow-rate characteristics for a conveying system at different solid flow rates (full lines) and the characteristics of the blower in the conveying system (broken line). For a fixed solid flow rate, W_{s1}, the figure shows two possible operating points at A and B. It can be shown that operating point B is inherently unstable. Perturbation of the local gas flow rate, for instance, will result in instability from a sensitivity analysis. A small reduction in the gas flow rate at B would result in an increase in the pressure drop, resulting in a further decrease in the gas flow rate and the eventual blockage of the tube. Such instability should not be confused with the "choking" transition and has been described by Leung et al.[67] and by Doig.[68]

Bandrowski et al.[69-71] described another form of instability for a given blower-conveying system at a point when the blower characteristics curve intercepts the conveying system characteristic curve tangentially at a point such as M in Figure 11-23. Perturbation from the operating point M will result in blockage in the tube. Such an operating point was defined by Bandrowski et al. as "choking." In this case the choking velocity is dependent not only on the characteristics of the gas-solid-tube system but also on that of the blower/compressor. To avoid confusion it is perhaps more appropriate to define an operating point M as the "blockage" point rather than the "choking" point.

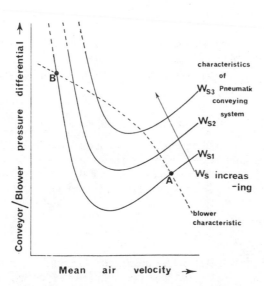

Figure 11-22. Operational instability between blower and conveyor (Doig[68]).

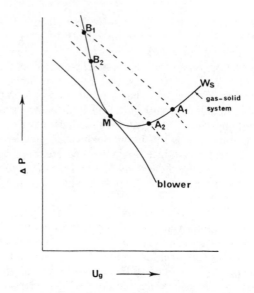

Figure 11-23. Various operating points from the interaction of the characteristics of blower and gas-solid system.

Choking Versus Nonchoking

A number of conflicting analyses on predicting whether a system would exhibit the choking phenomenon is available in literature (Yousfi and Gau,[55] Yang,[72] Smith,[73-74] Matsen,[75]). A discussion and comparison of their analyses will be given here.

Analysis of Yousfi and Gau[55]

In an analysis similar to that proposed by Molerus[76] for fluidization, Yousfi and Gau considered the stability of a uniform suspension of particles subject to a sinusoidal perturbation of gas velocity. They suggested that choking would occur if the uniform suspension of particles is unstable. Their analysis leads to

$$U_t^2/gd \equiv Fr_d > 140 \tag{11-54}$$

for choking to occur.

Systems with Fr_d less than 140 are not expected to exhibit the choking phenomenon. Yousfi and Gau claimed that their prediction was supported by their own experimental results on 20 μm and 55 μm catalysts which did not choke in accordance with predictions from Equation 11-54.

The analysis of Yousfi and Gau has two serious deficiencies, i.e., the assumption that drag forces are not affected by change in voidage, and wall effects are not accounted for. As the analysis is for an unbounded fluid with no wall effects, it cannot predict whether pipe diameter will cause a system to choke. In practice, tube diameter is an important parameter; a gas-solid system may exhibit choking in a small tube but not in a large tube.

Analysis of Yang[72]

Yang considered the stability of slugging conveying (as against the stability of a uniform suspension). Following an argument put forward by Harrison et al.[77] and de Kock[78] that a bubble in a fluidized bed became unstable when its velocity was the same as the terminal velocity of a single particle, Yang postulated that slugging conveying became unstable when the slug velocity, U_B, relative to the dense-phase solids, was greater than U_t.

For a slug, its velocity is given by (Davidson and Harrison[24]):

$$U_B = 0.35(gD)^{0.5} \qquad (11\text{-}23)$$

Thus, Yang's criterion becomes:

$$0.35(gD)^{0.5} > U_t \text{ for no slugging (i.e. no choking) to occur}$$

$$\text{or} \quad U_t^2/gD \equiv Fr_D > 0.12 \text{ for choking to occur} \qquad (11\text{-}55)$$

In Yang's analysis the key parameter is the Froude number based on tube diameter, compared with a Froude number based on particle diameter in the analysis of Yousfi and Gau. Comparison of the two criteria is given in Figure 11-24. It can be seen that both the criteria appear to represent the published data well. A lot more experimental work is needed in the second and fourth quadrants of Figure 11-24 to critically compare the two criteria.

Analysis of Smith[73,74]

Using an earlier analysis of Slis et al.[10] on the velocity of propagation of a continuity or porosity wave, Smith showed that the wave velocity in vertical pneumatic conveying relative to the solid velocity was the same as that for a fluidized bed. For a system following the Richardson-Zaki expansion equation 11-19, the wave velocity can be shown to be given by

$$V_W = U_t \epsilon^n (1 - \epsilon)/\epsilon \qquad (11\text{-}56)$$

where V_w = velocity of continuity or porosity wave

$$\equiv (\partial U_g/\partial \epsilon)_{(U_s + U_g)} \qquad (11\text{-}6)$$

The exponential n in Equations 11-56 and 11-19 is a function of the particle Reynolds number and d/D (see Richardson and Zaki[21]).

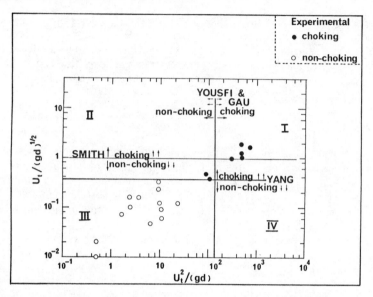

Figure 11-24. Comparison of experimental observations with predictions on demarcation between choking and nonchoking systems (after Yang[72]).

In vertical pneumatic conveying Smith suggested arbitrarily an effective bubble diameter in a riser tube, giving a corresponding bubble rise velocity of

$$U_B = 0.41(gD)^{0.5} \tag{11-57}$$

As it is inconceivable that a bubble can travel faster than the continuity wave, Smith postulated that for a bubble to be stable (i.e. for choking to occur)

$$V_w > U_B \tag{11-58}$$

Equations 11-56, 11-57, and 11-58 can be combined to yield

$$U_t \epsilon^{n-1} n(1 - \epsilon)/(gD)^{0.5} > 0.41 \tag{11-59}$$

for choking to occur.

Equation 11-59 cannot, however, be used directly for the prediction of demarcation between choking and nonchoking as ϵ is unknown. Taking the limiting case for a maximum value of $[\epsilon^{(n-1)}(1 - \epsilon)]$ in Equation 11-59 we have:

$$U_t n\{[(n - 1)/n]^{n-1} - [(n - 1)/n]^n\}/(gD)^{0.5} > 0.41 \tag{11-60}$$

The range of n is from about 2.4 to 4.6 (Richardson and Zaki[21]). For n = 2.4 we have

$$U_t^2/gD > 0.59 \text{ for choking to occur} \tag{11-61}$$

For n = 4.6 we have

$$U_t^2/gD > 0.95 \text{ for choking to occur} \tag{11-62}$$

Equations 11-61 and 11-62 are similar in form to Yang's criterion given by Equation 11-55 although the bases of the analyses of Smith and of Yang are entirely different. Examination of the data in Figure 11-24 suggests that Yang's equation is more consistent with observed results.

Analysis of Matsen[75]

All conventional slip-velocity-voidage relationships, such as the Richardson-Zaki equation or the bubbly bed expansion equation, predict that voidage increases monotonically with slip velocity. Matsen[75] suggested that at voidage close to 1, the reverse trend occurs as a result of clusters formation. He suggested the following relationship for voidage close to 1:

$$(U_{Sl}/U_t) = 10.8(1 - \epsilon)^{0.293} \tag{11-63}$$

For a system following a relationship such as Equation 11-63 it can be shown that for a given U_g, there is a maximum value of U_s corresponding to $(\partial U_s/\partial \epsilon)_{U_g} = 0$. This is represented by curve ABCD in Figure 11-25. Matsen suggested that to the right of ABCD in Figure 11-25, operation in the dilute-phase regime occurs following an equation such as 11-63. To the left of ABCD dense-phase flow occurs following a conventional expansion relationship such as the Richardson-Zaki equation or the bubbly bed expansion equation (Equation 11-21). ABCD thus represents the transition from dilute-phase flow to dense-phase flow and was suggested by Matsen as the choking transition. Figure 11-26 is a plot similar to Figure 11-25, with constant voidage lines superimposed for the dilute-phase regime and the dense phase required.

Consider the gradual reduction of gas flow rate at a constant solid rate from one operating point in the dilute-phase regime (along FBE in Figure 11-26). The voidage will decrease gradually until the limiting operating point for the dilute-phase regime is reached at B. Further reduction of gas flow rate will result in a stepwise reduction in voidage and a change to the dense-phase regime. This transition, described as choking by Matsen[75] occurs with a stepwise change in voidage. At higher solid flow rates, such as along NCM, choking will occur with a smaller stepwise change in voidage. Finally at a critical solid flow rate the transition from lean-phase regime to dense-phase regime (PDQ in Figure 11-26) will occur without any stepwise change in voidage. Without the stepwise change, it is impossible to discuss that a transition (i.e. choking) has in fact occurred. Thus according to Matsen[75] a gas-solid-tube system can exhibit the choking phenomena at a low solid ve-

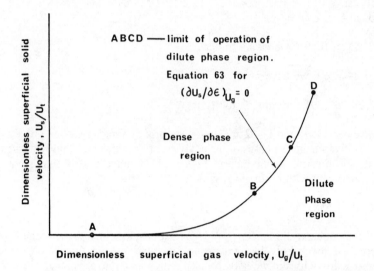

Figure 11-25. Gas-solids upflow (after Matsen[75]).

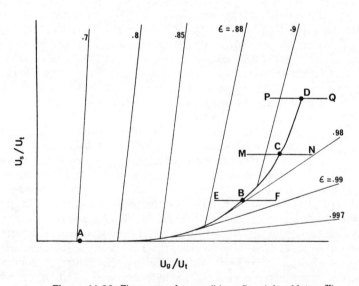

Figure 11-26. Flow map of gas-solids upflow (after Matsen[75]).

locity but not at a higher solid velocity. All systems would exhibit a choking transition provided the solid velocity is low enough (the velocity may have to be negative for choking to occur for some systems). Matsen's analysis is consistent with observations that the magnitude of the stepwise change in voidage at choking does vary with solid flow rate. His postulate, however, is contrary to the theories of previous workers (Yousfi and Gau,[55] Yang,[72] and Smith,[73,74]) that a given gas-solid-tube system either will exhibit choking or will not exhibit choking. Further work on understanding the phenomenon of choking is needed.

In summary, three criteria are available in the literature for predicting whether choking would occur in a system. The theoretical bases of the three theories are entirely different. Of the three predictions, Yang's[72] analysis, appears to be more consistent with experimental results. The experimental evidence, however, is far from conclusive. The recent analysis of Matsen[75] suggested that whether a system exhibits choking is dependent on the solid flow rate. This conclusion is contrary to the assumptions made in the three previous analyses. Much further work is required to clarify the mechanism of choking.

Choking System

Prediction of Choking Velocity

The choking gas velocity, U_{gc}, is the superficial gas velocity for a certain solid flow rate at which choking occurs, and the voidage at choking, ϵ_c, refers to the voidage at the onset of choking on the dilute-phase side of the stepwise transition. For systems that exhibit the choking phenomenon, prediction of the choking velocity is important as it sets the minimum gas velocity for operation in the lean-phase mode. In pneumatic conveying it is usually desirable to operate at as low an air flow rate as possible from energy requirements, pipe erosion, and particle attrition considerations. In lean-phase conveying, the minimum conveying velocity is set by the choking velocity in vertical conveying, by the analogous "saltation" velocity in horizontal conveying or by conditions to ensure self cleaning after shut down. This section is confined to the prediction of choking velocity in vertical pneumatic conveying.

Although the mechanism of choking is not properly understood, a large number of empirical equations are available in literature for estimating choking velocity. These had been reviewed by Doig and Roper[79] and more recently Punwani et al.[80] In particular Punwani et al. compared the various correlations by means of the root mean square relative deviation (RMSRD) defined as

$$\left([1/(N-1)] \sum_{i=1}^{i=N} \left\{ \left[(U_{gc})_{calculated} - (U_{gc})_{measured} \right] / (U_{gc})_{measured} \right\}^2 \right)^{0.5} \qquad (11\text{-}64)$$

where N is the number of experimental observations compared. Only three correlations have a RMSRD of less than 50% when compared with experimental observations. These will be discussed here.

Equation of Leung et al.[67] (RMSRD = 39%)

Leung et al. derived the following equation for calculating choking velocity by (1) assuming that the relative velocity between solid and gas was equal to U_t at choking and (2) using an average value of 0.97 as the choking voidage:

$$U_{gc} = 32.3U_s + 0.97 U_t \tag{11-65}$$

For mixed particle system they suggested that Equation 11-65 could be written in the form of

$$U_s x_{if} = 0.03 x_{it}(U_{gc}/0.97 - U_{ti}) \tag{11-66}$$

and

$$\Sigma x_{if} = \Sigma x_{if} = 1 \tag{11-67}$$

where x_{if} = volume fraction of particles in feed with free-fall velocity U_{ti}
x_{it} = volume fraction of particles in tube with free-fall velocity U_{ti}

Equations 11-66 and 11-67 permit estimation of the choking velocity for mixed-size particles. One major drawback of the equation of Leung et al. is that it does not account for the effect of tube size in choking.

Equations of Yang[81] (RMSRD = 44%)

Yang assumed that at choking the solid-wall friction factor f_s was a constant at 0.01 and that the relative velocity between gas and solid was equal to U_t. From a force balance on the solids assuming:

$$C_{D\epsilon} = C_{D\infty}\epsilon^{-4.7} \tag{11-68}$$

he derived a set of two equations, which could be solved simultaneously to obtain the choking velocity and the choking voidage:

$$2gD(\epsilon_c^{-4.7} - 1)/(U_{gc} - U_t)^2 = 0.01 \tag{11-69}$$

$$U_s = (U_{gc} - U_t) (1 - \epsilon_c) \tag{11-70}$$

Predictions from Yang's equations are in good agreement with published data in literature. For particles of mixed size, U_t in Equations 11-69 and 11-70 may be replaced by a mean terminal velocity as follows:

$$\overline{U}_t = \Sigma x_{if} U_{ti} \tag{11-71}$$

where x_{if} = volume fraction of particles in feed with terminal velocity U_{ti}. It is not possible to assess the applicability of the extended equation for mixed-size particles as insufficient experimental data are available. Note, U_{gc} rather than V_{gc} is used in Equations 11-69 and 11-70 for convenience as an approximation, as voidage at choking is close to unity. More recently Yang[82] suggested that a value of solid friction factor f_s equal to 0.04 (instead of 0.01) at choking gives a better correlation of published experimental results. Thus Equation 11-69 becomes

$$2gD(\epsilon_c^{-4.7} - 1)/(U_{gc} - U_t)^2 = 0.04 \tag{11-72}$$

It is claimed that Equations 11-72 and 11-70 give a better correlation of published results and are recommended for predicting the choking velocity.

Equations of Punwani et al.[80] (RMSRD = 25%)

Punwani et al. questioned the constant solid-friction-factor assumption of Yang and obtained an empirical relation for variation of the friction factor at choking with gas density based on the high pressure results of Knowlton and Bachovchin.[83,84] They then modified the Yang equation to allow for this variation to give the following equation for predicting choking voidage and choking velocity:

$$2gD(\epsilon_c^{-4.7} - 1)/(U_{gc} - U_t)^2 = 0.074 \, \varrho_f^{0.77} \; (\varrho_f \text{ in } lb/ft^{-3}) \tag{11-73}$$

and

$$U_s = (U_{gc} - U_t) (1 - \epsilon_c) \tag{11-70}$$

In a recent paper Yang[82] suggested that Equation 11-73 should be replaced by

$$\frac{2gD(\epsilon^{-4.7} - 1)}{(U_{gc} - U_t)^2} = 6.81 \times 10^5 \left(\frac{\varrho_g}{\varrho_s}\right)^{2.2} \tag{11-74}$$

which gives better correlation of published results. Equations 11-74 and 11-70 can be combined to yield the choking gas velocity and choking voidage.

For mixed-size particles, Punwani et al. suggested that Equation 11-70 can be replaced by

$$U_s x_{if} = (1 - \epsilon_c) x_{it} (U_{gc} - U_{ti}) \tag{11-75}$$

and

$$\Sigma x_{it} = \Sigma x_{if} = 1 \tag{11-67}$$

Selection of Choking-Velocity Correlations

In summary a large number of empirical correlations is available in literature. Yang's latest equation (11-74) is perhaps the most reliable and is recommended for adoption. Comparisons between predictions and experimental observation suggest that the choking velocity can be predicted to within ±50%. Thus a safety factor of 1.5 should be applied to the calculated choking velocity in setting the minimum transport velocity in vertical pneumatic conveying in the lean-phase flow mode. It should be cautioned, however, that all the experimental results have been obtained in tubes smaller than 80 mm diameter with a significant amount of results obtained in tubes smaller than 40 mm diameter. The applicability of these empirical equations to large tubes is uncertain. Further, the results on mixed-size particles are meager. The reliability of the two correlations for mixed-size particles is therefore unknown. Finally the effect of proximity of pipe-bends on choking velocity in a vertical tube has yet to be studied systematically. There is a need for more theoretical work aimed at understanding the phenomenon of choking and more experimental work aimed at extending the range of applicability of the empirical equations.

Transition from Dense-Phase Conveying to Packed-Bed Conveying

The equation for predicting the transition from dense-phase fluidized flow to packed-bed flow may be derived by equating the slip velocity at vertical pneumatic conveying with the slip velocity at minimum fluidization (Leung et al[17]). At this transition the voidage in the riser tube is equal to the voidage at minimum fluidization, ϵ_{mf}, giving

$$U_g/\epsilon_{mf} - W_s/[\varrho_s(1 - \epsilon_{mf})] = U_{mf}/\epsilon_{mf} \qquad (11\text{-}76)$$

Equation 11-76 relates the gas and solid velocities at the transition from fluidized-solid flow to packed-bed flow. Taking an average voidage of 0.45 for ϵ_{mf}, Equation 11-76 can be simplified to the following dimensionless form for predicting this transition:

$$0.55\ U_g'' - 0.45\ U_s'' = 0.55 \qquad (11\text{-}77)$$

where $U_g'' = U_g/U_{mf}$
$\quad\quad\ \ U_g'' = W_s/(\varrho_s U_{mf})$

A Quantitative Flow Regime Diagram

In pneumatic conveying it is often useful to express the solid-to-gas loading ratio R_L as a parameter. Equation 11-77 for transition from fluidized-bed flow to packed-bed flow can be written as

$$R_L = 1.22(\varrho_s/\varrho_g)[1 - (U_{mf}/U_t)/(U_g/U_t)] \tag{11-78}$$

As the ratio of U_t/U_{mf} is a function of the Archimedes number [$Ar = \varrho_g (\varrho_s - \varrho_g)gd^3/\mu^2$], we can write $U_t/U_{mf} = f(Ar)$ and

$$R_L = 1.22(\varrho_s/\varrho_g)[1 - 1/U_g'f(Ar)] \tag{11-79}$$

where $U_g' = U_g/U_t$ (11-80)

For the lean-phase to dense-phase flow (i.e. choking) transition, Equations 11-70 and 11-72 can be written as:

$$R_L = 1 - [0.02 F_r(U_g' - 1)^2 + 1]^{-0.213}(1 - 1/U_g')(\varrho_s/\varrho_g) \tag{11-81}$$

The relationship between U_t and U_{mf} can be written as (Bourgeois and Grenier[85]):

For $10^2 < Ar < 4 \times 10^4$

$$U_t/U_{mf} = 135.7 - 45.0 \log Ar + 4.1 (\log Ar)^2 \tag{11-82a}$$

For $4 \times 10^4 < Ar < 8 \times 10^6$

$$U_t/U_{mf} = 26.6 - 2.3 \log Ar \tag{11-82b}$$

For $8 \times 10^6 < Ar$

$$U_t/U_{mf} = 10.8 \tag{11-82c}$$

Equations 11-79 and 11-81 can be used for the construction of a quantitative flow-regime diagram (Leung et al,[86] Leung[87]) as presented in Figure 11-27 for a sand-air system. The diagram is useful in defining the range of loading ratio for a given flow pattern. The maximum loading ratio possible for lean-phase flow and dense-phase slugging can also be obtained from the diagram. Constant-solid flux lines have been included in Figure 11-27. For a given solid flux, the diagram can be used in specifying the operating gas flow rate. For a solid flux of 500 kgm^{-2}s^{-1} shown in Figure 11-27, the minimum gas velocity required to attain lean-phase flow is represented by point M in the figure. An appropriate safety factor of 1.5, say, may be applied to the gas flow rate.

The existence of a maximum loading-ratio limit for slugging dense-phase flow for a given system as shown in Figure 11-27 had also been pointed out by Dixon,[88]

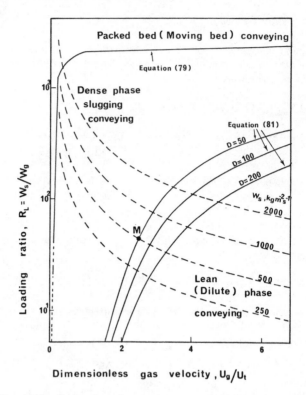

Figure 11-27. Quantitative flow regime diagram for vertical pneumatic conveying. (Data used in calculation: U_{mf} = 0.24 ms^{-1}, U_t = 3.4 ms^{-1}, ϱ_s = 2,500 kgm^{-3}, ϱ_g = 1.38 kgm^{-3} with three tube diameters.)

who showed how the maximum ratio varies quantitatively with powder properties, conveying air pressure, and solid mass flux.

Nonchoking System

Earlier, equations for predicting whether a system will exhibit the "choking transition" were presented. In general, fine particles in large diameter tubes tend not to choke. This section pertains to nonchoking systems. In a nonchoking system, the four possible flow patterns as the gas velocity is reduced at a fixed solid flow rate are given in Figure 11-21 as

1. Dilute (lean)-phase flow
2. Nonslugging dense-phase flow

3. Slugging dense-phase flow
4. Packed-bed flow.

The transition from lean-phase flow to nonslugging dense-phase flow is diffuse. When gas velocity is reduced at a given solid rate in the lean-phase mode, solid concentration increases in the tube. No equation has been published for predicting the demarcation of this diffuse transition. The recent work of Matsen[75] may be useful in developing such an equation. If we define the transition as the point of change over from one type of expansion equation (11-63) to another type of expansion equation (11-21), the two equations could be solved simultaneously to obtain the voidage for change over. From this voidage the transition gas velocity can be calculated for a given solid flow rate. Experimental verification of such an analysis will be extremely difficult as the onset of nonslugging dense-phase flow is difficult to observe.

The phenomenon of nonslugging dense-phase conveying is analogous to the "turbulent regime" of fluidization reported by Kehoe and Davidson.[89] They observed, as the velocity of gas flow through a fluidized bed of fine powder was raised, the breakdown of the slugging regime into "a state of continuous coalescence—virtually a channeling state with tongues of fluid darting in zig-zag fashion through the bed." The bed has the appearance of turbulence and is known as the turbulent regime. The turbulent regime of fluidization refers to zero transport of solid. If solid is introduced into the bottom of the fluidized bed and withdrawn from the top, as in pneumatic conveying, we have the recirculating fluidized bed operating in the turbulent regime. This recirculating fluidized bed has been termed "fast fluidization" (Yerushalmi et al.[90,91]) and has commercial applications as a chemical reactor (Reh[92]).

The "nonslugging dense-phase mode" defined here is similar to the so-called fast fluidization. Thus the behavior of nonslugging dense-phase mode may be deduced from the meager recent studies on fast fluidization (Yerushalmi et al,[90,91] Reh,[92] Yerushalmi and Cancurt,[93] Cancurt and Yerushalmi,[94] Li and Kwauk[95]). While little generalized quantitative information is available, the following characteristics of nonslugging dense-phase flow can be established:

1. Pressure gradient in the tube decreases rapidly with increase in gas velocity at a constant solid flow rate.
2. Pressure gradient increases with solid rate at a given gas velocity.
3. Slip velocities are high and can be an order of magnitude above the free-fall velocity. There is some evidence that the higher the gas velocity, the higher the slip velocity.
4. Solid volumetric concentration as high as 25% has been observed before slugging flow sets in.
5. The transition from lean-phase flow to nonslugging dense-phase conveying is diffuse.
6. The transition from nonslugging dense-phase conveying to bubbling (or slugging) dense-phase conveying is also diffuse.
7. At low gas velocity within this regime, it is possible to have solid downflow near the wall of the pipe although the net solid flow is upwards. This gives

rise to the possibility of "negative wall friction," i.e. the frictional pressure drop is negative.

Thus to summarize for nonchoking systems, quantitative prediction of the two transition velocities from lean-phase flow to nonslugging dense-phase flow and from nonslugging dense-phase flow to slugging (bubbling) dense-phase flow is not possible. Finally the transition from slugging dense-phase flow to packed-bed flow in this nonchoking system is identical to that of the choking system. Equation 11-77 can therefore be used to predict this transition.

Prediction of Pressure Drop, Solids Holdup, and Solid Velocity for Lean-Phase Mode

Formulation of Equations

In theory, a set of four unsteady-state differential equations, viz., two continuity equations and two momentum equations, can be written to describe V_s, V_g, ϵ, and P in gas-solid flow in a pipe (Hinze[96]). In practice, however, the formulation of these equations is controversial and their solution is complex (Gidaspow and Solbrig[97]). Consider the simple case of a one-dimensional steady-state model for vertical gas-solid flow of a uniform suspension. The three non-controversial equations are

$$\text{gas continuity: } \frac{d}{dz}(\epsilon \varrho_g V_g) = 0 \tag{11-83}$$

$$\text{solid continuity: } \frac{d}{dz}[(1 - \epsilon)\varrho_s V_s] = 0 \tag{11-84}$$

$$\text{mixture momentum: } -\frac{dP}{dz} = (1 - \epsilon)\varrho_s V_s \frac{dV_s}{dz} + \epsilon \varrho_g V_g \frac{dV_g}{dz}$$

$$+ [\varrho_s(1 - \epsilon) + \varrho_g\epsilon]g + F_w \tag{11-40}$$

F_w in Equation 11-40 represents the pressure gradient caused by friction between the gas-solid mixture and the wall (not merely between the gas and the wall as stated by Arastoopour and Gidaspow[98]). F_W is related to the mixture wall shear stress, τ_w, and for a circular pipe

$$F_w = 4\tau_w/D \tag{11-85}$$

The form of the fourth equation, the solid momentum equation, is controversial. Arastoopour and Gidaspow[98] compared the following four forms of the solid momentum equations:

Fluid phase pressure drop model, Soo[99]:

$$\varrho_s V_s \frac{dV_s}{dz} = F_s - \varrho_s g \tag{11-86a}$$

Pressure drop in solid and fluid phases annular flow model, Nakamura and Capes[100]:

$$\varrho_s V_s \frac{dV_s}{dz} = F_s - \varrho_s g - (dP/dz) \qquad (11\text{-}86b)$$

Partial pressure drop in both phases model, Deich et al.[101]:

$$\varrho_s V_s \frac{dV_s}{dz} = F_s - \varrho_s g - (dP/dz) + \frac{p}{(1 - \epsilon)} \frac{d\epsilon}{dz} \qquad (11\text{-}86c)$$

Relative velocity model, Gidaspow[102]:

$$-\frac{\varrho_s}{2} \frac{d}{dz} (V_g - V_s)^2 = F_s - \varrho_s g \qquad (11\text{-}86d)$$

F_s = drag force on unit volume of particle

In their comparison they showed that results from Equation 11-86c are not consistent with observed experimental trends; Equations 11-86a and 11-86b give similar results as the contribution of dP/dz is small compared with $\varrho_s g$. Arastoopour and Gidaspow[98] claimed good agreement between predictions from their relative velocity model (using Equation 11-86d) with the published results of Zenz[66] and of Hariu and Molstad[103]. The relative velocity model is derived from the principles of nonequilibrium thermodynamics by assuming that the internal energy of a particle is a function of the relative velocity between gas and particle. In their calculation Arastoopour and Gidaspow[98] neglected frictional loss between particle and wall. They assumed that F_w was related directly to the Fanning friction factor f_g for gas flow by

$$F_w = \frac{f_g \varrho_g V_g^2}{2D} \qquad (11\text{-}87)$$

For these reasons the validity of their comparison is doubtful and it is not possible to ascertain, at this stage, if the relative-velocity model is superior to other conventional equations for predicting pressure drop, solid velocity, and holdup. In the following subsection, comparison will be made on various conventional equations.

Predictions from Published Correlations

For the calculation of pressure gradient, Equation 11-40 can be rewritten in the following form:

$$-(dP/dz) = [\varrho_s(1 - \epsilon) + \varrho_g \epsilon]g + W_g(dV_g/dz) + W_s(dV_s/dz) + 4\tau_w/D \qquad (11\text{-}40)$$

The right hand side of Equation 11-40 represents the three components of the pressure gradient, viz., gravity, acceleration, and wall friction. Wall friction is generally considered to be made up of two additive components, one for the gas and one for the solids, i.e.:

$$-\left(\frac{dP}{dz}\right)_f = 4\tau_w D = \frac{2f_g\varrho_g V_g^2\epsilon}{D} + \frac{2f_s(1 - \epsilon)\varrho_s V_s^2}{D} \tag{11-88}$$

where f_s, f_g are solid and gas friction factors respectively. f_g is often assumed to be the same as the Fanning friction factor; and as voidage is close to 1, $(V_g^2\epsilon)$ in Equation 11-88 can be replaced by U_g^2. Churchill[104] proposed the following correlation for f_g.

$$f_g = 2[8/Re_g)^{12} + 1/(A + B)^{1.5}]^{1/12} \tag{11-89a}$$

$$\text{where} \quad A = (2.457 \ln \{1/[(7/Re_g)^{0.9} + 0.27 \, e/D]\})^{16} \tag{11-89b}$$

$$\text{and} \quad B = (37,530/Re_g)^{16} \tag{11-89c}$$

$$e = \text{effective roughness}$$

A large number of correlations for predicting pressure gradient in vertical pneumatic conveying is available in the literature. Modi et al.[105] listed 20 such correlations and suggested that the following correlations of Konno and Saito[106] and of Yang[107] gave reasonable agreement with published results on the pneumatic conveying of coal:

Correlation of Konno and Saito for fully developed flow

$$U_g - V_s = U_t \tag{11-90}$$

$$\text{and} \quad f_s = 0.0285/[V_s/(gD)^{0.5}] \tag{11-91}$$

The correlation of Yang for fully developed flow is:

$$V_s = V_g - U_t\{[1 + 2f_s V_s^2/(gD)]\epsilon^{4.7}\}^{0.5} \tag{11-92}$$

$$f_s = 0.0032 [(1 - \epsilon)/\epsilon^3] [(1 - \epsilon)Re_t/Re_p]^{-0.979} \text{ for } V_g/U_t > 1.5 \tag{11-93a}$$

$$f_s = 0.010 [(1 - \epsilon)/\epsilon^3] [(1 - \epsilon)Re_t/Re_p]^{-1.021} \text{ for } V_g/U_t < 1.5 \tag{11-93b}$$

$$\text{where} \quad Re_t = \varrho_g U_t d/\mu \tag{11-94}$$

$$Re_p = \varrho_g(V_g - V_s)d/\mu \tag{11-95}$$

The above correlations are written for fully developed flow. Similarly equations can be written in the accelerating flow regime. In their correlation for solid-wall friction factor, neither Konno and Saito nor Yang took into account the important parameter of the coefficient of friction between particle and wall. This serious omission throws doubt on whether their correlations may be extrapolated with confidence. The contribution of the particle-wall coefficient of friction to frictional-pressure drop has been considered by a number of workers (Barth,[108,109] Krotzsch[110]). Recently Scott[111] proposed the following correlation including the coefficient of friction between particle and wall, β:

$$f_s = \beta g D / [2V_s(U_g - U_t\beta^{0.5})] \tag{11-96}$$

The validity of Equation 11-96 and other correlations including β is yet unknown as information on β is often not available for evaluation of the correlations.

In summary many correlations are available for predicting pressure drop and solid velocity in dilute phase conveying. All such correlations are empirical in nature based on published experimental results. There is considerable doubt whether the correlations may be extrapolated with confidence, if at all.

Prediction of Pressure Drop, Solids Holdup, and Solid Velocity for Dense-Phase Mode

While a large number of correlations is available for lean-phase mode operations, few equations are available for predicting operations in the dense-phase mode (both slugging dense-phase mode and nonslugging dense-phase mode). In the dense mode, homogeneity of the mixture can no longer be assumed and the one-dimensional model as described by Equations 11-83, 11-84, 11-40, and 11-86 will no longer be applicable.

For slugging dense-phase flow, it has been suggested (Matsen[1]) that equations applicable for a slugging fluidized bed can be extended to slugging conveying by assuming that at the same slip velocity the voidage in the system is similar. Thus for dense-phase slugging conveying we can write (Matsen[1]):

$$\frac{1 - \epsilon}{1 - \epsilon_{mf}} = \frac{[U_s/(1 - \epsilon_{mf}) + U_B]}{[U_g + U_s + U_B - U_{mf}]} \tag{11-22}$$

U_B in Equation 11-22 refers to the velocity of rise of a single slug and for an axisymmetric slug

$$U_B = 0.35(gD)^{0.5} \tag{11-23}$$

For some gas-solid systems (particularly for Geldart[53] Type B and D solids), half-nose slugs are formed (rather than the full nose, axisymmetric slug) and the appropriate equation for U_B is (Kehoe and Davidson[89])

$$U_B = 0.35(2gD)^{0.5} \tag{11-97}$$

Equation 11-22 permits the calculation of voidage and hence the gravity component of the overall pressure gradient in slugging conveying. The wall-friction component is sometimes negligible in slugging conveying as it is often small compared with the gravity component.

For nonslugging dense-phase flow, the experimental results of Yerushalmi and Cankurt[93] and Yerushalmi et al.[91] provide a qualitative guide for the estimation of the pressure gradient. They suggested that the system can be modeled by assuming that particles travel upwards in spherical clusters. A method was proposed for estimating the diameter of these clusters, and the system is then assumed to be equivalent to the conveying of a uniform suspension of "clusters" of density equal to the bulk density of the clusters. A method was proposed for quantitative estimation of pressure drop based on the model and their experimental results. The applicability of this method, however, to other gas-solid systems, has yet to be tested.

A more plausible model for nonslugging dense-phase flow is the annular flow model of Nakamura and Capes.[100] In the model particle flow is divided into two regions: the core with particles upflow and the annulus with particle downflow. Gas velocity, solid velocity, and voidage in the two regions are different. As solids-flow is downwards near the wall, the annular flow model predicts negative wall friction as had been reported by Van Swaaij et al.[112] The model thus describes approximately the physical situation in nonslugging dense-phase flow in which particle recirculation is observed. In their model, Nakamura and Capes[100] presented two sets of momentum equations, one for flow in the annulus and the other for the core. The equations contained many unknowns, e.g., voidage in the two regions, mass flow of solid and gas in the two regions, size of the core, shear stress across the core-annulus interface, as well as the wall shear stress. By neglecting the shear stress across the core-annulus interface and by assuming that flow in the riser is such that the pressure drop is minimized, equations were derived that were shown to give qualitative agreement with observations. Recent support of the model is available from the experimental results of Bandrowski et al.[69] Further experimental support for the model will be useful to establish it on a firmer basis.

A third model for predicting nonslugging dense-phase flow was recently presented by Arastoopour and Gidaspow.[98,113,114] Using their relative velocity model (Equations 11-83, 11-84, 11-40, 11-86d) and the assumption that particles form together in "clumps" of the same density as the particles, they showed that by adjusting the clump size the calculated pressure drop could be made to agree with the observed results of Knowlton and Bachovchin[84] in the accelerating region and with the results of Yerushalmi and Squires[115] for fast fluidization. As yet it is not possible to predict a priori the appropriate "clump" size to permit quantitative prediction. Nor does their model account for solid backflow.

In summary an equation is available for estimating pressure gradient in slugging dense-phase flow but no reliable equations are available for estimating pressure gradient in nonslugging dense-phase flow. Much further work will be required.

Particle Segregation in Vertical Pneumatic Transport

When mixed-size or mixed-property particles are transported pneumatically, the *in situ* composition of the mixture in the pipe can often be significantly different from that of the feed or delivered mixture. This difference arises as a result of differences in velocity of particles of different size and properties. An estimate of the *in situ* composition (or the degree of segregation) is often important in relation to pressure drop estimation and more importantly in relation to riser reactors design (where the riser tube serves as a chemical reactor).

Segregation in vertical pneumatic conveying has been studied by a number of workers (Leung et al,[67] Nakamura and Capes,[116] Muschelknautz,[117] Hair and Smith,[118] Yang,[119] and reviewed by Yang[119]). At very high gas velocity, the degree of segregation is negligible. Segregation becomes progressively more pronounced as the gas velocity is reduced. While little information is available to predict segregation in dense-phase pneumatic conveying some equations are available for predicting segregation in lean-phase flow. The equations of Yang[119] will be reported here as they can deal with multicomponent systems and appear to agree with observation. The analyses of Muschelknautz[117] and of Nakamura and Capes[116] are more fundamental and complex but are restricted to binary systems.

Equations for Predicting Segregation

Segregation in a pneumatic conveying tube is caused by the nonuniformity in particle velocities for particles of different sizes and properties. A simple model is to assume that the slip velocity of each class of particle is equal to its free-fall velocity, i.e.:

$$V_g - V_{si} = U_{ti} \qquad (11\text{-}98)$$

The continuity equation for component i is given by

$$W_s X_i = Y_i V_{si}(1 - \epsilon)\varrho_{si} \qquad (11\text{-}99)$$

where X_i = mass fraction of component i in the feed mixture
Y_i = *in situ* volume fraction of i in the pipe

From Equations 11-98 and 11-99 the *in situ* composition in the tube and the degree of segregation can be calculated (Leung et al.[67]).

The segregation tendency calculated from this simple model is greater than that observed in practice, especially at low gas velocity. Equation 11-99 does not take into consideration the interaction between particles and the effect of wall friction. Both these factors are taken into consideration in Yang's model. Allowing for voidage and wall effects, solid velocity is given by Yang[119]:

$$V_{si} = V_g - U'_{ti}[(1 + 2f_s V_{si}^2/gD)\epsilon^{4.7}]^{0.5} \qquad (11\text{-}100)$$

f_s in Equation 11-100 is a weighted average solid friction factor. U'_{ti} in the equation is a modified terminal velocity of particle i to include the effects of "interactions between different components." Methods for calculating f_s and U'_{ti} were suggested by Yang. They can be used in conjunction with Equations 11-99 and 11-100 to calculate the *in situ* concentration in the tube and hence the degree of segregation. Good agreement between predictions and observed segregation of binary mixture was claimed by Yang. No multicomponent mixture segregation measurement has been reported in the literature and the validity of Yang's equations for multicomponent systems has yet to be verified.

Design Philosophies

The design of a pneumatic conveying system for conveying a given material at a given rate from one point to another involves the specification of:

1. Route of the pipe.
2. Type of conveying system to be used (e.g., vacuum or positive pressure; low pressure, medium pressure, or high pressure; closed loop or open loop).
3. Details of individual components (feeding and discharge mechanism, valves, cyclones, types of bends, materials of construction . . .).
4. Flow pattern in the tube (lean phase, dense phase, or moving bed).
5. Pipe size.
6. The air flow rate.
7. The overall pressure drop.
8. The air blower/compressor.

Generally, design of pneumatic conveying systems is based on rules of thumb, previous operating experience, and proprietary know-how of specialist companies. In this section we shall discuss the quantitative aspects of design, covering the selection of flow pattern, pipe diameter, air flow rate, and pressure drop. Other aspects of design are considered in the next chapter.

General Design Procedures (After Bandrowski[71])

A number of workers have discussed quantitative design of pneumatic conveying (Rose and Duckworth,[120] Kunii and Levenspiel,[38] Leung and Wiles,[121] and Bandrowski[71]). A summary of the procedure recommended by Bandrowski[71] follows:

1. The characteristics of the solid to be tranported and the rate of transportation are specified.
2. Select the operation flow mode. Generally, dilute-phase flow is selected unless there are compelling reasons why dense-phase flow is preferable.
3. Assume a conveying pipe diameter, D.
4. Determine the conveying characteristics from published correlations for the particular solid flow.

   $$\Delta P_t = f(U_g)$$

   where ΔP_t = pressure drop in conveying system including losses in valves, bends, and fittings.

5. Determine the point of minimum pressure drop on the characteristic curve obtained in Step 4; i.e., ΔP_{tmin} and U_{gmin}.

6. Check that $\Delta P_{t_{min}} < \Delta P^*$ where ΔP^* is the maximum pressure drop allowed in the pneumatic conveying system including losses in valves, bends, and fittings.
7. Select a blower with characteristics that match the system characteristics without giving rise to flow instability.
8. Repeat Steps 4–7 for a different diameter.
9. From the sets of pipe diameters, blowers, and operating gas velocity, select the optimum combination for minimum overall cost.

Where the pneumatic conveying system is used as a reactor or heat transfer device, other considerations will become important. In a given reactor, for instance, it might be necessary to design the operating conditions to give a specific residence time of the solids in the gas. Such a consideration will dictate the design of the system.

Additional recommended readings are References 122 through 183.

NOMENCLATURE

A	cross-sectional area of pipe
A_o	cross-sectional area of orifice or slide valve
Ar	Archimedes number, $\varrho_g(\varrho_s - \varrho_g)gd^3/\mu^2$
$C_{D\epsilon}$	drag coefficient at voidage $= \epsilon$
$C_{D\infty}$	drag coefficient at $\epsilon = 1$
C_{DV}	valves coefficient defined in Equation 11-52
D	tube diameter
d	diameter of a spherical particle
d_s	specific surface area diameter
d_v	volume equivalent particles diameter
D_o	orifice diameter
f	wall friction factor
f_g	Fanning friction factor
f_f	fluid friction factor
f_s	solid friction factor
F_s	drag force on unit volume of particle
F_w	pressure gradient caused by wall friction, $- (dP/dz)_f$
Fr_d	Froude number, U_t^2/gd
Fr_D	Froude number, U_t^2/gD
g	acceleration due to gravity
j_{fs}	drift flux defined in Equation 11-25
j'_{fs}	j_{fs}/U_t
k	orifice correction factor defined in Equation 11-52
K_1	parameter defined in Equation 11-32
K_2	parameter defined in Equation 11-33
K_3	$[150\mu(1 - \epsilon_{mf})^2] [D_o(A/A_o)]/(4\phi d_v\epsilon_{mf})^2$
K_4	$1.75 \, \varrho_g(1 - \epsilon_{mf})D_o(A/A_o)^2/(24\phi d_v\epsilon_{mf})$
n	exponent in Richardson-Zaki equation (11-19)

N   number of experimental observations

P   pressure

P_1, P_2, P_3 pressure at locations defined in Figures 11-1 and 11-18

ΔP pressure drop

ΔP_o pressure drop across orifice, $P_2 - P_3$

R_L loading ratio, W_s/W_g

RMSRD   root mean square relative deviation

Re_g Reynolds number based on superficial velocity $\varrho_g U_g d/\mu$

S   surface area of a particle

U_B velocity of a single bubble in a fluidized bed or slug velocity relative to dense phase solids, always positive

U_f superficial fluid velocity, positive upwards

U_f' U_f/U_t

U_g superficial gas velocity (positive upwards)

U_g' U_g/U_t

U_g'' U_g/U_{mf}

U_{ga} aeration gas rate expressed as superficial velocity in standpipe

U_{gc} choking velocity

U_{mb} minimum fluidization velocity at which bubbling occurs

U_{mf} minimum fluidization velocity (always positive)

U_{sl} slip velocity defined by Equation 11-1, positive upwards.

U_s superficial solid velocity, positive upwards

U_s' U_s/U_t

U_s'' U_s/U_{mf}

U_{SF} flooding solid velocity

U_t free-fall velocity of a single particle

U_{ti} free-fall velocity of component i in mixture

$\bar{U}_t$ mean terminal velocity, ΣX_{fi}, U_{ti}

U_{ti}' modified terminal velocity of particle i including effects of interactions between different components

V_f actual fluid velocity, U_f/ϵ

V_g actual gas velocity, U_g/ϵ

V_s actual solid velocity, $U_s/(1 - \epsilon)$

V_w velocity of continuity wave defined by Equation 11-6 positive upwards

W_f mass flux of fluid, $U_f \varrho_f$

W_{ga} aeration rate expressed as mass flux of gas

W_s solid flux, $U_s \varrho_s$

W_s' solid mass flow rate, $W_s A$

X_i weight fraction of particles with diameter d_i

X_{if} volume fraction of particles in feed with free-fall velocity U_{ti}

X_{it} volume fraction of particles in tube with free-fall velocity U_{ti}

Y_i *in situ* volume fraction of component i in pipe

Z   length coordinate, positive upwards

Z' Z/D

Z_p length of dense-phase section as defined in Figures 11-9 through 11-11

Greek Symbols

β coefficient of friction between particle and wall
δ internal angle of friction
ϵ voidage
ϵ_c voidage at choking
ϵ_{mf} voidage at minimum fluidization
ϵ_p voidage of vibrated packed bed
μ fluid viscosity
μ_w coefficient of friction between solid particles and tube wall
ϱ_B bulk density, $\varrho_s(1 - \epsilon)$
ϱ_f fluid density
ϱ_g gas density
ϱ_{mf} bulk density at minimum fluidization $\varrho_s(1 - \epsilon_{mf})$
ϱ_s solid density
σ_r normal stress in radial direction
$\bar{\sigma}_z$ mean normal stress in vertical direction
τ_w wall shear stress due to gas-solid mixture
ϕ sphericity defined by Equation 11-34

REFERENCES

1. Matsen, J. M., *Powder Technology*, 7: 93–96 (1973).

2. Zenz, F. A., and D. F. Othmer, *Fluidization and Fluid Particle Systems*, Reinhold Publishing, NY (1960).

3. Kunii, D., *Chem. Eng. Sci.*, 35: 1,887–1,911 (1980).

4. Lapidus, L., and J. C. Elgin, *AIChE J.*, 3: 63–68 (1957).

5. Mertes, T. S., and H. B. Rhodes, *Chem. Eng. Prog.*, 51: 429–432, 517–522 (1955).

6. Kwauk, Mooson, *Scientia Sinica*, 12: 587–612 (1963).

7. Kojabashian, C., Ph.D. Thesis, Massachusetts Institute of Technology (1958).

8. Leung, L. S., and P. J. Jones, *Proc. International Fluidization Conference*, J. F. Davidson, and D. L. Keairns, (Eds.) Cambridge University Press (1978), pp. 116–121.

9. Leung, L. S., and P. J. Jones, *Powder Technology*, 20: 145–160 (1978).

10. Slis, P. L., Th. W. Willemsee, and H. Kramers, *App. Sci. Research*, A8: 209–219 (1959).

11. Wallis, G. B., *One Dimensional Two-Phase Flow*, McGraw-Hill Book Company, NY (1969), p. 93.

12. Jones, P. J., Ph.D. Thesis, University of Queensland (1981).

13. Staub, F. W., *Powder Technology*, 26: 147–159 (1980).

14. Knowlton, T. M., and I. Hirsan, *Hydrocarbon Processing*, 57: 149–156 (1978).

15. Knowlton, T. M., I. Hirsan, and L. S. Leung, in *Fluidization*, J. F. Davidson, D. L. Keairns, (Eds.) Cambridge University Press, Cambridge (1978), pp. 128–131.

16. Leung, L. S., and P. J. Jones, *Gas-Solid Downflow in Standpipes* in *Multiphase Science and Technology Series,* Hemisphere Publishing Corp., London (1980).

17. Leung, L. S., R. J. Wiles, and D. J. Nicklin, *Trans., Inst. Chem. Engrs.,* 47: T271–278 (1969).

18. Aoki, R., et al., *Journal of the Research Association of Powder Technology,* Japan 10 (9) (1973).

19. Vogel, R., and R. D. Marcus, *Pneumotransport* 5: 1–24, H. S. Stephens, and C. A. Stapleton, (Eds.) BHRA Fluid Engineering, Cranfield (1980).

20. Leung, L. S., and L. A. Wilson, *Powder Technology,* 7: 343–349 (1973).

21. Richardson, J. F., and W. N. Zaki, *Trans. Inst. Chem. Engrs.,* 32: 35–53 (1954).

22. Kwauk, Mooson, *Proc. Chemeca 80,* Melbourne, 98–108 (1980).

23. Matsen, J. M., S. Hovmand, and J. F. Davidson, *Chem. Eng. Sci.,* 24: 1,743–1,754 (1969).

24. Davidson, J. F. and D. Harrison, *Fluidized Particles,* Cambridge University Press, Cambridge (1963).

25. Judd, M. R., and P. D. Dixon, "The Flow of Fine Dense Solids Down a Vertical Standpipe," paper presented at AIChE Annual Conference, Chicago, (December 1976).

26. Yoon, S. M., and D. Kunii, *Ind. Eng. Chem. Process Design and Development,* 9: 559–566 (1970).

27. Ergun, S., *Chem. Eng. Progr.,* 48 (2): 89–94 (1952).

28. Spink, C. D., and R. M. Nedderman, *Powder Technology,* 21: 245–261 (1978).

29. Grossman, G., *AIChE J.,* 21 (4): 720–730 (1975).

30. Walters, J. K., *Chem. Eng. Sci.,* 28: 13–21 (1973).

31. Ginestra, J. C., S. Rangachari, and R. Jackson, *Powder Technology,* 27: 69–84 (1980).

32. Ginestra, J. C., S. Rangachari, and R. Jackson, in *Fluidization* ed. J. R. Grace, and J. M. Matsen, (Eds.) Plenum Publishing Corp., NY (1980), pp. 477–484.

33. Yang, W. C., *Ind. Eng. Chem. Fund.,* 12: 349–352 (1973).

34. Matsen, J. M., in *Fluidization Technology,* Vol. II, D. L. Keairns, et al. (Eds.), Hemisphere Publishing, Washington (1976), pp. 135–153.

35. Dries, H.W.A., *Proc. Powder Europa 80, IPI* (1980).

36. Leung, L. S., in *Fluidization Technology*, Vol. II, D. L. Keairns, et al. (Eds.), Hemisphere Publishing, Washington (1976), pp. 125–134.

37. Judd, M. R., and D. N. Rowe, in *Fluidization*, J. F. Davidson, and D. L. Keairns, (Eds.) Cambridge University Press (1978), pp. 110–115.

38. Kunii, D., and O. Levenspiel, *Fluidization Engineering*, John Wiley, New York (1969), pp. 13–63.

39. Dries, H. W. A., in *Fluidization*, J. R. Grace, and J. M. Matsen, (Eds.) Plenum Press, NY (1980), pp. 493–500.

40. Rangachari, S., and R. Jackson, *The Stability of Steady States in a One-Dimensional Model of Standpipe Flow*, to be published (1981).

41. Do, D. D., et al., *Proc. Particle Technology*, Nuremberg, H. Brauer, and O. Molerus, (Eds.) D23–46 (1977).

42. "Refining Operations Updated", *Hydrocarbon Processing*, (March 1980), pp. 55–56.

43. Leung, L. S., P. J. Jones, and T. M. Knowlton, *Powder Technology*, 19: 7–15 (1978).

44. Leung, L. S., *Powder Technology*, 16: 1–6 (1977).

45. Leung, L. S., and E. T. White, *Chem. Engr. in Aust;* 2: 1–4 (1977).

46. Ledinegg, M., *Die Warme*, 61: 891–898 (1938).

47. Jackson, R., *Chem. Eng. Progress Symp. Ser. X.*, 66 (105): 3–13 (1970).

48. Jackson, R., *Trans. Inst. Chem. Engrs.*, 41: 1–12 (1963).

49. Jackson, R., *Trans. Inst. Chem. Engrs.*, 41: 13–18 (1963).

50. Pigford, R. L., and T. Baron, *Ind. Eng. Chem. Fund.*, 4: 81–86 (1965).

51. Murray, J. D., *J. Fluid Mech.*, 21: 465–478; 22: 57–69 (1965).

52. Anderson, T. B., and R. Jackson, *Ind. Eng. Chem. Fund.*, 6: 478–484 (1967).

53. Geldart, D., *Powder Technology*, 7: 285–292 (1973).

54. Tsutsui, T., and T. Miyauchi, *Int. Chem. Eng.*, 20 (3): 386–393 (1980).

55. Yousfi, Y., and G. Gau, *Chem. Eng. Sci.*, 29: 1,939–1,954 (1974).

56. Grace, J. R. and J. Tuot, *Trans. Inst. Chem. Engrs.*, 57: T49–T54 (1979).

57. Judd, M. R., *Proc. Particle Technology*, Nuremberg, H. Brauer, and O. Molerus, (Eds.) 3: Di18–21 (1977).

58. Lighthill, M. J. and G. B. Whitham, *Proc. Royal Soc.*, 229A: 281–295 (1955).

59. Jones, P. J., C. S. Teo, and L. S. Leung, in *Fluidization*, J. R. Grace, and J. M. Matsen, (Eds.) Plenum Press, NY (1980), pp. 469–476.

60. Do, D. D., B. E. Thesis, University of Queensland (1976).

61. Eleftheriades, C. M. and M. R. Judd, *Powder Technology* 21: 217–225 (1978).

62. Chen, T. Y., W. P. Walawender, and L. T. Fan, *AIChE J.*, 26 (1): 24–30 (1980).

63. Chen, T. Y., W. P. Walawender, and L. T. Fan, *Handbook of Fluids in Motion*, N. P. Cheremisinoff and R. Gupta (Eds.) Ann Arbor Science, Ann Arbor, MI (1983), Ch. 27, pp. 691–714.

64. Chen, T. Y., W. P. Walawender, and L. T. Fan, *AIChE J.*, 26 (1): 31–36 (1980).

65. Knowlton, T. M., et al., "Void Gas Stripping in Standpipes", AIChE Annual Meeting, San Francisco (1979).

66. Zenz, F. A., *Ind. Eng. Chem.*, 41: 2,801-2,806 (1949).

67. Leung, L. S., R. J. Wiles, and D. J. Nicklin, *Ind. Eng. Chem. Process Design and Development*, 10: 183–189 (1971).

68. Doig, I. D., *The South African Mechanical Engr*, 25: 395–397 (1975).

69. Bandrowski, J., et al., *Inz. Chem.* 7: 243–253, 499–517 (1977).

70. Bandrowski, J., et al., *Inz. Chem.*, 8: 779–795 (1978).

71. Bandrowski, J. and G. Kaczmarzyk, *Powder Technology*, 28: 25–33 (1981).

72. Yang, W. C., *Proceedings of Pneumotransport 3*, BHRA Fluid Engineering, E5–49 to E5–55. (1976).

73. Smith, T. N., *Proc. of Chemeca 77*, Inst. Chem. Engrs. in Australia, (1977), pp. 328–332.

74. Smith, T. N. *Chem. Eng. Sci.*, 33: 745–749 (1978).

75. Matsen, J. M., *Powder Technology*, 32: 21–33 (1982).

76. Molerus, O., *Chem. Eng. Techn.*, 39: 341–348 (1967).

77. Harrison, D., J. F. Davidson, and J. W. de Kock, *Trans. Inst. Chem. Engrs.*, 39: 202–212 (1961).

78. de Kock, J. W., Ph.D. Thesis, University of Cambridge (1961).

79. Doig, I. D., and G. H. Roper, *Aust. Chem. Engng*, 4(4): 9–19 (1963).

80. Punwani, D. V., M. V. Modi, and P. B. Tarman, *Proc. Int. Powder and Bulk Solids Handling and Processing Conference,* Powder Advisory Centre, Chicago (1976).

81. Yang, W. C., *AIChE. J.* 21: 1,013–1,015 (1975).

82. Yang, W. C., "Criteria for Choking in Vertical Pneumatic Conveying Lines" to be published. (1982).

83. Knowlton, T. M. and D. M. Bachovchin, "The Determination of Gas-Solids Pressure Drop and Choking Velocity as a Function of Gas Density in a Vertical Pneumatic Conveying Line", paper presented at the Int. Conf. on Fluidization, Pacific Grove, California, June (1975).

84. Knowlton, T. M. and D. M. Bachovchin, in *Fluidization Technology*, Vol. 2, D. L. Keairns, et al., (Eds.) Hemisphere Publishing Corporation, Washington (1976), pp. 253–282.

85. Bourgeois, P. and P. Grenier, *Can. J. Chem. Engng.*, 46: 325–338 (1968).

86. Leung, L. S., R. J. Wiles, and D. J. Nicklin, *Proceedings of Pneumotransport 1*, BHRA Fluid Engineering, B93-104 (1972).

87. Leung, L. S., *Powder Technology*, 25: 185–190 (1980).

88. Dixon, G., "The Impact of Powder Properties on Dense Phase Flow," paper presented at Int. Conf. on Pneumatic Conveying, Powder Advisory Centre, London (1979).

89. Kehoe, P. W. K. and J. F. Davidson, *Inst. Chem. Engrs.* (London) Symp. Series, 33: 97–116 (1971).

90. Yerushalmi, J., D. H. Turner, and A. M. Squires, *Ind. Eng. Chem. Process Design and Development*, 15: 47–53 (1976).

91. Yerushalmi, J., et al., *Chem. Eng. Prog. Symp. Series*, 176: 1 (1978).

92. Reh, L., *Chem. Eng. Prog.*, 67 (2): 58–63 (1971).

93. Yerushalmi, J., and N. T. Cankurt, *Powder Technology*, 24: 187 (1979).

94. Cankurt, N. T., and J. Yerushalmi, in *Fluidization*, J. F. Davidson, and D. L. Keairns, (Eds.) Cambridge University Press, Cambridge (1978), pp. 387–393.

95. Li, Youchou and Mooson Kwauk, in *Fluidization*, J. R. Grace, and J. M. Matsen, (Eds.) Plenum Press, New York (1980), pp. 537–544.

96. Hinze, J . O., *Appl. Sci. Res.*, Section A, 11:33-43 (1962).

97. Gidaspow, D. and C. W. Solbrig, "Transient Two-phase Flow Models in Energy Production," AIChE 81st National Meeting April, 11 (1976).

98. Arastoopour, H. and D. Gidaspow, *Ind. Eng. Chem. Fund.*, 18: 123 (1979).

99. Soo, S. L., *Fluid Dynamics of Multiphase Systems*, Blaisdell Publishing Co., Waltham, Mass. (1967), p. 279.

100. Nakamura, K. and C. E. Capes, *Can. J. Chem. Eng.*, 51: 39–46 (1973).

101. Deich, M. E., et al., *High Temperature* 12 (2): 299 (1974); (translation of *Teplofiz Vys. Temp.*) 12 (2): 344, (1974).

102. Gidaspow, D., in *Two Phase Transport and Reactor Safety*, S. Kakal and T. N. Veziroglu, I: 283–298, Hemisphere Publishing Corp., Washington (1978).

103. Hariu, O. H., and M. C. Molstad, *Ind. Eng. Chem.* 41: 1,148–1,160 (1949).

104. Churchill, S. W., *Chemical Engineer*, 91–92, (Nov. 7 1977).

105. Modi, M. V., A. T. Talwalker, and D. V. Punwani, *Proc. Int. Powder and Bulk Solids Handling and Processing Conference*, Powder Advisory Centre, Chicago (1978).

106. Konno, H., and S. Saito, *J. Chem. Eng. Japan*, 31: 211–217 (1967).

107. Yang, W. C., *Proc. Int. Powder and Bulk Solids Handling and Processing Conference*, Powder Advisory Centre, Chicago (1977).

108. Barth, V., *Chem. Eng. Tech.*, 20 (1): 29–32 (1954).

109. Barth, V., *Chem. Eng. Tech.*, 30: 171–180 (1958).

110. Krotzsch, P., *Chem. Eng. Tech.*, 44: 1,354–1,360 (1972).

111. Scott, A. M., *Proc. 4th Int. Powder Technology and Bulk Solids Conference 10*, Powder Advisory Conference, Harrogate, London (1977).

112. Van Swaiij, W. P. M., C. Buurman, and W. C. Van Breugel, *Chem. Eng. Sci.*, 25: 1,818–1,820 (1970).

113. Arastoopour, H., and D. Gidaspow, Second Multiphase Flow and Heat Transfer Symposium Workshop, 16–18 April, Miami Beach, Florida (1979).

114. Arastoopour, H., and D. Gidaspow, *Powder Technology*, 22: 77–87 (1979).

115. Yerushalmi, J., and A. M. Squires, *AIChE Symp. Ser.*, 73 (161): 44–50 (1977).

116. Nakamura, K. and C. E. Capes, in *Fluidization Technology*, Vol. 2, D. L. Keairns, et al., (Eds.) Hemisphere Publishing Corp., Washington (1976), pp. 159–184.

117. Muschelknautz, E., *Ver. Deut. Ing. Forschungsheft*, 476: 32–35 (1959).

118. Hair, A. R. and K. L. Smith, *Mech. Chem. Eng. Trans.*, Inst. of Engrs. Australia, MC8, 1: 19–23 (1972).

119. Yang, W. C., *Proc. of Pneumotransport 4*, BHRA Fluid Engineering, B21-31 (1978).

120. Rose, H. E., and R. A. Duckworth, *The Engineer*, 227. (1969).

121. Leung, L. S. and R. J. Wiles, *Ind. Eng. Chem. Process Design and Development*, 15: 552–558 (1976).

122. Leung, L. S., and C. S. Teo, *Chem. Eng. Sci.*, 38(1):115–119 (1983).

123. Altiner, H. K., and J. F. Davidson, in *Fluidization*, J. R. Grace, and J. M. Matsen, (Eds.) Plenum Press, NY (1980), pp. 461–468.

124. Bachovchin, D. M., et al., "Solids Transport Between Adjacent CAFB Fluidized Beds," Report No. EPA-600/7-79-021, United States Environmental Protection Agency (1979).

125. Beverloo, W. A., H. A. Leniger, and J. van de Velde, *Chem. Eng. Sci.*, 15: 260–266 (1961).

126. Boothryod, R. G., *Trans. Inst. Chem. Engrs.*, 44: 306–372 (1966).

127. Brown, R. L., and J. C. Richards, *Trans. Inst. Chem. Engrs.*, 37: 108–119 (1959).

128. Brown, R. L. and J. C. Richards, *Trans. Inst. Chem. Engrs.*, 38: 243 (1960).

129. Brown, R. L. and J. C. Richards, *Rhelogica Acta*, 4: 153 (1965).

130. Bulsara, P. U., F. A. Zenz, and R. A. Eckert, *Ind. Eng. Chem. Process Design and Development*, 3 (4): 348–355 (1964).

131. Burkett, R. J., et al., *Chem. Eng. Sci.* 26: 405–412 (1971).

132. Callcott, T. G., *Proc. Aust. Inst. of Mining and Metallurgy*, Newscastle Conference, 177–186 (1959).

133. Capes, C. E., *Can. J. Chem. Eng.*, 49: 182–186 (1971).

134. Capes, C. E., and K. Nakamura, *Can J. Chem. Engng.*, 51: 31–38 (1973).

135. Carleton, A. J., *Powder Technology,* 6: 91–96 (1972).

136. Davidson, J. F., and R. M. Nedderman, *Trans. Inst. Chem. Engrs.,* 51: 29–35 (1973).

137. Dixon, G., *Int. J. Multiphase Flow,* 2: 465–470 (1975).

138. Dixon, P. D. "The Flow of Fine Powders Down Vertical Standpipes" M.Sc. Thesis, University of Natal, South Africa (1977).

139. Fowler, R. T., and J. R. Glastonbury, *Chem. Eng. Sci.,* 10: 150–156 (1959).

140. Franklin, F. C., and L. N. Johanson, *Chem. Eng. Sci.,* 4: 119–129 (1955).

141. Hinkle, B. L., Ph.D. Thesis, Georgia Institute of Technology (1953).

142. Holland, J., et al. *Trans. Inst. Chem. Engrs.,* 47: T154–159 (1969).

143. Holtkamp, W. C. A., F. T. Kelly, and T. Shingles, *Chemistry South Africa,* (March 1977), pp. 44–46.

144. Ishida, M. and T. Shirai, *J. Chem. Eng. Japan,* 8: 477–481 (1975).

145. Jahnig, C. E., D. L. Campbell, and H. Z. Martin, in *Fluidization,* J. R. Grace and J. M. Matsen, (Eds.) Plenum Press, NY (1980), pp. 3–24.

146. Jones, D. R. M. and J. F. Davidson, *Rheologica Acta,* 4: 180–186 (1965).

147. Jones, P. J. and L. S. Leung, *Proc. 5th National Chem. Engng. Conf.,* Inst. of Chem. Engrs. in Aust., Canberra, 322–327 (1977).

148. de Jong, J. A. H., *Powder Technology,* 3: 279–286 (1980).

149. de Jong, J. A. H., *Powder Technology,* 12: 197–200 (1975).

150. de Jong, J. A. H. and Q.E.J.J.M, Hoelen, *Powder Technology,* 12: 201–208 (1975).

151. Keairns, D. L., et al., "Evaluation of the Fluid-Bed Combustion Process," Vol. II, EPA-650/2-73-0486 (1973).

152. Keneman, F. E., *Izv Akav,* Nauk SSSR, Otd. Tekhn, Nauk Mekham in Mashinostr, 2: 70–75 (1960).

153. Ketchum, M. S., "The Design of Walls, Bins, and Grain Elevators;" 3rd Ed. McGraw Hill, NY (1919), p. 323.

154. Kurz, H. P. and H. Rumpf, *Powder Technology,* 11: 147–154 (1975).

155. Kwauk, Mooson, in *Proceedings 1st Iranian Congress of Chemical Engineering,* P. Davallo, et al., (Eds.) 2: 539, Elsevier Pub. Co., Amsterdam (1974).

156. LaNauze, R. D., and J. F. Davidson, in *Fluidization Technology,* D. L. Keairns, et al., (Eds.) 2: 113, Hemisphere Publishing, Washington (1976).

157. Mason, J. S., and R. G. Boothroyd, Pneumotransport 1, BHRA Fluid Engineering, C1-1 to C1-16 (1971).

158. Massimilla, L., V. Betta, and C. Della Rocca, *AIChE J,* 7: 502–508 (1961).

159. Massimilla, L:, and G. Volpicelli, *AIChE J.,* 9:139–141 (1963).

160. Matsen, J. M., "Entrainment Research: Achievements and Opportunities," in N.S.F. Workshop on Fluidization, H. Littman (Ed.) (1979).

161. McDougall, I. R., and A. C. Evans, *Trans. Inst. Chem. Engrs.*, 44: T15-24 (1966).

162. McDougall, I. R., and G. H. Knowles, *Trans. Inst. Chem. Engrs.*, 47: T73-79 (1969).

163. Nedderman, R. M., and U. Tuzun, *Powder Technology*, 22: 243-253 (1978).

164. Papazoglou, C. S., and D. L. Pyle, *Powder Technology*, 4: 9-18 (1970).

165. Rausch, J. M., Ph.D. Thesis, Princeton University (1948).

166. Resnick, W., et al., *Ind. Eng. Chem. Fundamentals* 5(3): 392-397 (1966).

167. Sandy, C. W., J. T. Daubert, and J. H. Jones, *Chem. Eng. Prog. Symp. Ser.*, 66(105): 133-142 (1970).

168. Savage, S. B., *Brit. J. Appl. Phys.*, 16: 1,185 (1965).

169. Savage, S. B., *Inst. J. Mech. Sci.*, 9: 651-659 (1967).

170. Shook, C. A., A. J. Carleton, and R. J. Flain, *Trans. Inst. Chem. Engrs.*, 48: T173-175 (1970).

171. Smith, J. C. and U. S. Hattiahgadi, *Chem. Eng. Commun.*, 6: 105-115 (1980).

172. Soo, S. L., *AIChE J.*, 7: 384-391 (1961).

173. Stemerding, S., J. H. de Groot, G. M. J. Kuypers, *Proc. Fluidization Symposium Society of Chemical Industries*, London (1963).

174. Tanaka, I., N. Yoshihara, and H. Shinohara, *Kagaku Kogaku Ronbunshu*, 4: 238-241 (1978).

175. Tanaka, I., N. Yoshihara, and H. Shinohara, *Kagaku Kogaku Ronbunshu*, 4: 317-319 (1978).

176. Trees, J., *Trans. Inst. Chem. Engrs.*, 40: 286-296 (1962).

177. Walker, D. M., *Chem. Eng. Sci.*, 21: 975-997 (1966).

178. Wen, C. Y. and H. P. Simons, *AIChE J.* 5: 263-268 (1959).

179. Wen, C. Y. and A. F. Galli, in *Fluidization*, J. F. Davidson, and D. Harrison, (Eds.) Academic Press, NY (1971), pp. 677-709.

180. Williams, J. C., *Chem. Eng. Sci.*, 32: 247 (1977).

181. Zenz, F. A., *Fluidization Technology*, Vol. II, D. L. Keairns, et al., (Eds.) Hemisphere Publishing, Washington (1976), pp. 239-252.

182. Yuasa, Y. and H. Kuno, *Powder Technology*, 6: 97-104 (1972).

183. Engh, T. A., *J. Engs. Ind. Trans. ASME*, 91: 335,341 (1969).

12

Considerations in Pneumatic Transport

CONTENTS

INTRODUCTION, 543

REGIMES OF FLOW, 545

CHOKING AND PRESSURE DROP, 548
Dilute-Phase Flows, 548
Flow Through Bends and Elbows, 552
Dense-Phase Conveying (Vertical Systems), 554

COMMERCIAL TECHNIQUES FOR PNEUMATIC CONVEYING, 555

NOMENCLATURE, 558

REFERENCES, 570

INTRODUCTION

This chapter discusses additional considerations of solids conveying in transfer lines and risers, solids conveying by gas flows as practiced in fluidized-bed operations and in transfering solids into and between reactor vessels, bins, hoppers, etc.

Gas-solids transfer systems are generally designed as either dilute or dense phase. Dilute-phase systems are normally low pressure and characteristically handle low solids loadings having high gas velocities. These systems have comparatively lower pressure losses per unit length of conveying line in comparison to dense-phase designs. In contrast, dense-phase systems operate with higher pressure losses and with characteristically high solids loadings. Due to these high loadings, such systems are operated at low gas velocities to minimize solids degradation and line erosion.

Technology in this area has evolved considerably over the past five decades, and today well-developed design criteria are available but for limited cases. Solids flows, particularly at high solids concentration and in large lift lines are unpredictable, and much of the design and scale-up basis are empirical. By way of review, consider momentarily a single particle introduced to a flowing gas stream. In a vertical flow orientation (i.e., gas flowing upward), the gravitational force will cause the particle to fall in the downward direction. The difference between the gas and solids velocity is referred to as "slip," and the magnitude of slip establishes the solid particle's velocity, the flow regime, and ultimately the pressure drop due to solids holdup and frictional effects.

The velocity of a single particle flowing up a vertical line, u_{so} is often defined as the difference between the gas superficial velocity, v, and the particle's "terminal settling velocity," U_{to}.

$$U_{so} = V - U_{to} \tag{12-1}$$

Recall that for a single particle, the terminal settling velocity is defined by Stoke's law for particle Reynolds numbers less than about 0.4:

$$U_{to} = \frac{d_p^2(\varrho_p - \varrho_g)g}{18\mu} \tag{12-2}$$

At higher Reynolds numbers, the "intermediate law" and "Newton's laws" are used to estimate the single particle terminal velocity.

$$\text{Intermediate law: } U_{to} = \frac{4}{225}\left[\frac{(\varrho_p - \varrho_g)^2g^2}{\varrho_g}\right]^{0.333}d_p \; ; 0.4 < Re_p < 500 \tag{12-3}$$

$$\text{Newton's law: } U_{to} = \left[\frac{3.1(\varrho_p - \varrho_g)gd_p}{\varrho_g}\right]^{0.5} \; ; 500 < Re_p < 200,000 \tag{12-4}$$

In Chapter 1 a procedure was given to evaluate single-particle settling velocities without applying a trial-and-error procedure to Equations 12-2 through 12-4.

In a horizontal line orientation, the important particle velocity is the *saltation velocity*. This is defined as the minimum velocity which will prevent solids deposition on the floor of the line. Zenz[1] experimentally evaluated single particle saltation velocities for a wide variety of spherical and angular-shaped materials. The minimum velocity required to transport a particle without saltation and without obviously rolling or bouncing on the bottom of the line, was correlated with a particle drag coefficient, C_D. In this method, a plot of $(Re_pC_D)^{0.333}$ versus $(C_DRe_p^2)^{0.333}$ is prepared (it is basically a log plot of the single particle saltation velocity, V_{so}, divided by a system dependent constant versus the particle size divided by another system dependent constant). The resultant curves reveal a minimum that shows that for very fine solids, smaller particles can require a higher velocity to prevent saltation than larger particles. One explanation for this is that smaller particles become trapped in an inviscid boundary layer at the wall of the pipe, thus preventing reentrainment. In contrast, larger particles are more readily resuspended since they exceed the size of the boundary layer and are subject to higher velocity gradients, even at the same line superficial velocities.

The term *pickup velocity* is closely related to the saltation velocity. The pickup velocity is the fluid velocity required to resuspend a particle initially at rest on the bottom of a line. The forces that act on a single particle initially at rest on a surface are lift, drag, friction, and gravity. By defining each of these forces, the fluid velocity at which a particle will roll, slide, or become suspended can be theoretically determined. This approach was developed and experimentally verified by Halow[2] for materials having a wide range of physical and chemical characteristics. Materials as diverse as Rice Krispies™ and lead shot were used in these studies, and Rossetti[3] summarizes these findings graphically. The particle pickup velocity can be determined from the plots summarized by Rossetti from information on line size and physical properties of the solids and gas.

Analyses of single-particle behavior in flowing gas streams is useful for obtaining a qualitative understanding of the dynamic forces at play, but in practice are only useful when designing for very dilute suspension flows. When particle concentrations are substantial, interactions between particles result in an additional complex mechanism that establishes the aerodynamic properties of solids bulk transport.

REGIMES OF FLOW

Several flow regimes are observable in both dilute- and dense-phase conveying systems. The transition from one regime to another depends on the line orientation, particle and gas properties, and gas velocity, as well as the particle loading concentration. The various regimes are illustrated in Figure 12-1. In dilute-phase vertical transport, when gas velocities are sufficiently high, both phases flow uniformly up the pipe. In this mode, the frictional pressure drop is significant. At lower gas velocities the solids near the walls of the line decelerate, and eventually have no net vertical movement. These particles appear to swirl, float, and oscillate near the wall. The solids rate is maintained by flow through the central core of the line, and essentially all of the solids pressure drop is due to the head of solids in the pipe. At even lower gas velocities, the solids in the vicinity of the wall actually move downward while the solids rate is maintained by the upward flow of material in the central region of the pipe. The total pressure drop due to solids can be less than that from the head of solids in the line in this annular-type flow mode. In general, this dilute-phase flow regime is unstable and small variations in the gas velocity can

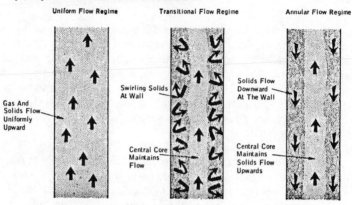

Decreasing Gas Velocity

A. VERTICAL DILUTE PHASE CONVEYING

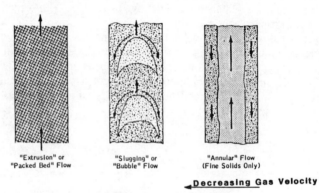

Decreasing Gas Velocity

B. VERTICAL DENSE PHASE CONVEYING

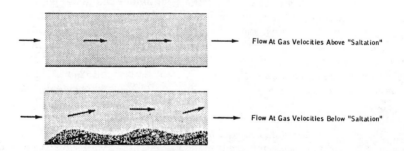

C. HORIZONTAL DILUTE PHASE CONVEYING

Figure 12-1. Illustration of flow regimes observed in dilute-phase vertical and horizontal conveying and dense-phase vertical conveying.

result in large differences in pressure drop. Rossetti[3] notes that coarse particles are unable to make the transition to annular flow. These particles tend to exhibit a dense-phase-type of slugging flow instead of annular flow. Slugging flow results in significantly higher pressure losses which eventually lead to choked flow conditions (i.e., limited pressure drop is available for conveying).

Different flow regimes are observed in horizontal line orientations in dilute-phase transport (Figure 12-1). In particular, two distinct regimes exist at gas velocities above and below the saltation velocity. At gas velocities above saltation, the solids flow appears dispersed and greatly resembles the uniform flow regime observed in vertical flows. That is, solids are suspended and move along with the gas, and for the most part are uniformly distributed across the line. In this regime the pressure drop increases with increasing gas velocity. At lower gas velocities, however, the carrying capacity of the line is eventually exceeded and solids begin to deposit onto the floor (the gas velocity at which deposition occurs is referred to as the saltation velocity). At velocities below the saltation velocity the pressure drop increases with decreasing velocity due to the increased solids deposition. With large particles, saltation phenomena quickly results in a significant rise in pressure drop. For fine solids the deposition occurs slowly and nonuniformly down the length of the line, consequently, the overall pressure drop increases more slowly but is erratic. This is due to the unstable nature of the nonuniformly sized and distributed deposits that roll down the pipe much like dunes in a desert.[3] These dunes form and travel the length of the pipe slamming into elbows, bends, fittings, or valves at the end of the transfer line.

Vertical dense-phase conveying is most commonly employed in standpipes and risers in petroleum and petrochemical plant operations. The various dense-phase flow modes that occur in vertical lines are also shown in Figure 12-1. In addition to the annular-flow regime, previously described for fine particles, slugging and "extrusion" or "packed bed" flow are observed.

In slugging or bubble flow, gas bubbles act as pistons between slugs of solids to transport the solids. This is similar to the action observed in a slugging fluidized bed. The size of the bubbles in the line is controlled and determined by the line size. As the superficial gas velocity is decreased further, transport occurs in the "extruded" or "packed bed" mode. The solids tend to move slowly through the line with a density close to the bulk density of the material. There is essentially no relative motion between the particles (as in a packed bed), and the solids behavior is analogous to that of deformable material being extruded through a pipe.

Dense-phase conveying in a horizontal orientation typically appears in either the extruded mode or in the form of a series of short plugs separated by pockets of conveying gas. Systems are designed in this mode of operation by minimizing the size of the plugs while maintaining operability. The purpose of this is to reduce the required pressure level for conveying since the pressure required to transfer a solid plug in a line is proportional to the square of the length of the plug. It is therefore necessary to allow the pressure to be transmitted throughout the particle mass while reducing the plug length of the solids conveyed. The means by which these plugs are generated forces a distinction between horizontal and vertical dense-phase systems. Most horizontal dense-phase systems employ high pressure gas to form the desired plugs or to transmit the pressure throughout the solids being forced through the line. This gas may issue from an aeration or fluidization device that aids the solids feeding, from a small perforated internal tube running the length of the pipe, or from external bypass pipes for gas only. Horizontal dense-phase conveying systems also differ in feed hopper designs. The principal differences in feed hopper design are whether the solids are fluidized or aerated by an external gas supply; whether the hopper is pressurized; and whether the solids are discharged internally from a fluidized bed or forced from the hopper into an external conveying line. The specific system depends on the characteristics of the solids being conveyed. Further discussions are given later in this chapter.

CHOKING AND PRESSURE DROP

Dilute-Phase Flows

Choking conditions and pressure drop are reasonably well understood from a scale-up point of view for small lines handling dilute flows. The state-of-the-art design is perhaps slightly better for vertical systems.

For vertical systems, Yang[4] provides criteria for evaluating whether choking will occur based on a dimensionless Froude number group defined as $u_{to}/(gD)^{0.5}$. The criterion given to avoid choking is that a critical Froude value of 0.35 be exceeded. Leung et al.[5] notes that choking occurs when the voidage in the transport line, ϵ_c, is approximately 0.97. Yang[6] proposes that the gas velocity and voidage at choking can be estimated assuming a solids friction factor of 0.01 at choking conditions. The point at which choking occurs can then be determined by solving the following equations for ϵ_c and the gas velocity at choking, v_c.

$$U_o = (V_c - U_{to})(1 - \epsilon_c) \tag{12-5}$$

$$(\epsilon_c^{-4.7} - 1) = \frac{0.1(V_c - U_{to})^2}{2g_cD} \tag{12-6}$$

where u_o is the superficial solids velocity defined as the ratio of the mass flux, G_s, to the particle density, ϱ_p. It should be emphasized that these are approximate correlations and hence, conveying systems are normally designed for the higher gas velocities where both solids and gas move uniformly up the pipe.

In the absence of particle-particle interactions, (i.e., single-particle or very dilute flows), the solids velocity in vertical lines can be approximated as the difference between the superficial gas velocity and the particle terminal settling velocity. This simplified approach can lead to erroneous predictions at higher solids loadings. When fine particles are introduced to a flowing gas stream, they tend to agglomerate or cluster.[7] Also, coarse particles may have an effective terminal velocity that is actually less than calculated.[8] Rossetti[3] presents a correlation that gives an effective particulate size applicable to pneumatic transport. This effective cluster diameter can be correlated with the terminal settling velocity of the single particle, and the relationship is presented in Figure 12-2. By specifying an effective cluster diameter, Figure 12-2 can be used to obtain an effective terminal velocity, u_{et}, for the solids. The following expression can be used to estimate the effective terminal velocity for uniform particle flows. The relationship is based on the solution of the momentum equations for the gas and the solids using the Richardson-Zaki relation for evaluat-

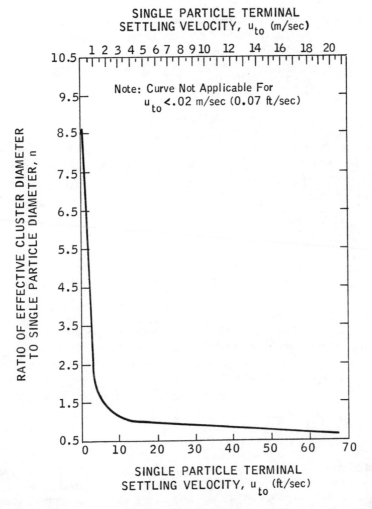

Figure 12-2. Plot of effective cluster diameter to single-particle-diameter ratio as function of single-particle terminal velocity, given by Rossetti.[3]

ing interparticle forces and approximating the solids friction factor as a constant divided by the solids velocity, as suggested by Nakamura et al.[9]

$$U_s = \frac{V - U_{et}\left(1 - \dfrac{\Delta P_g}{2\varrho_p H}\dfrac{g_c}{g}\right)}{1 + \dfrac{CU_{et}}{4gD}}$$ (12-7)

Where ΔP_g = single-phase gas frictional pressure drop per unit height of line
D = diameter of the line
C = system constant

For metal lines Rossetti[3] recommends a C value of 0.20 m/s (0.66 ft/s).

For fully developed flows, the total pressure drop per unit length of vertical line can be estimated as follows:

$$\frac{\Delta P_v}{H} = \frac{f_g \varrho_g V^2}{2g_c D} + \left(\frac{\Delta P_f}{H}\right)_s + \frac{G_s}{U_s}\left(\frac{g}{g_c}\right)$$ (12-8)

Each of the terms in Equation 12-8 has significance. The first term on the RHS is the gas frictional pressure drop based on the Darcy friction factor (i.e., 4 × Fanning friction factor), the second term is the friction losses due to the solids and the last RHS term denotes the solids head, where G_s is the superficial solids mass flow rate. The total frictional pressure drop due to the solids, $(\Delta P_f/H)_s$, can be expressed in terms of the solids velocity:

$$\left(\frac{\Delta P_f}{H}\right)_s = f_s\left[\frac{\varrho_0 U_s^2}{2g_c D}\right]$$ (12-9)

where f_s = solids friction factor
ϱ_0 = pseudo density (i.e., the dispersed phase density $= G_s/u_s$)

For uniform solids flow, Capes et al.,[8] Rossetti,[3] and others[10,11] have observed the solids friction factor, f_s, to be nearly inversely proportional to the solids velocity. Rossetti[3] has proposed a correction factor for correlating the frictional pressure drop, which is presented graphically in Figure 12-3. The relationship in Figure 12-3 is a plot of the ratio of experimentally determined frictional-to-total-solids pressure drop versus the dimensionless group CU_s/gD, where C is defined as the system's frictional correction coefficient; applied in the following manner:

$$\left(\frac{\Delta P_f}{H}\right)_s + \frac{G_s}{U_s}\left(\frac{g}{g_c}\right) = \frac{CU_s \varrho_0}{2g_c D} + \varrho_0\left(\frac{g}{g_c}\right)$$ (12-10)

The dashed curve in Figure 12-3 is based on the inverse U_s assumption for the solids friction factor, whereas, the solid curve is based on measured values. This shows the inverse solids velocity assumption to be a reasonable approximation for the uniform solids flow regime. Rossetti[3] notes that large deviations from the theoretical predictions occur in the annular flow region for $CU_s/gD < 1$ and recom-

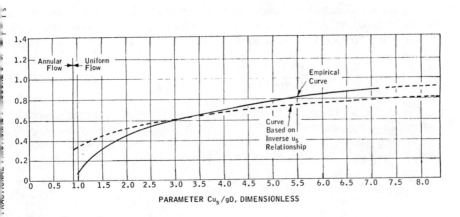

Figure 12-3. Plot of ratio of frictional to total solids pressure drops versus dimensionless correction term described by Rossetti.[3]

mends that pneumatic conveying systems for coarse particulates should not be designed for $CU_s/gD < 1$ because of the potential for operating in a slugging-flow regime with sharply higher pressure drops that could choke the line. Precautions are needed in operating fine particle systems at conditions where $CU/gD < 1$. In this regime small changes in the gas flow rate can result in significant variations in the actual pressure drop.

In the horizontal flow orientation, the saltation velocity is the critical design criterion. As a rule-of-thumb, these systems should be designed to operate at gas velocities that exceed the saltation velocity by 10% to 15%. This tends to minimize solids deposition, at the same time lowering horsepower requirements, erosion, and solids attrition.

The saltation velocity, V_s, is a linear function of the solids mass flux and depends on the particle and gas properties and the solids size distribution. Rossetti[3] reports the following relationship for V_s:

$$V_s = V_{so}\left(1 + \frac{G_s}{k\varrho_p}\right)\tag{12-11}$$

where V_{so} is an effective single particle saltation velocity and $G_s/k\varrho_p$ relates the effect of solids flux on the saltation velocity. A reasonable approximation for the effective single-particle saltation velocity is the pickup velocity as described by Halow[2] and in Figure 12-2.

Parameter k in Equation 12-11 is a mass flux factor that attempts to account for the effect of particle size distribution. It has been found to be a strong function of the spread (i.e., standard deviation) of the particle size distribution.

Since for a horizontal orientation, there are no head losses due to solids in the line, the overall equilibrium pressure drop per unit length is simply the sum of the gas and solids frictional pressure drop contributions.

$$\left(\frac{\Delta P}{L}\right)_H = \frac{f_g \varrho_g V^2}{2g_c D} + \left(\frac{\Delta P_f}{L}\right)_{SH} \tag{12-12}$$

At gas velocities in excess of the saltation velocity, the flow resembles vertical uniform flow regimes, and as such, the solids friction factor is approximately inversely proportional to the solids velocity. This means that the solids frictional pressure drop per unit length of horizontal pipe can be expressed as:

$$\left(\frac{\Delta P_f}{L}\right)_{SH} = \frac{C_H G_S}{2g_c D} \tag{12-13}$$

at gas velocities above the saltation velocity.

At superficial gas velocities below the saltation velocity, the available flow area is established by the solids flowing and/or deposited along the floor of the line. The gas above the deposited layer flows at the saltation velocity; however, some of the gas tends to percolate through the deposited solids layer causing it to expand or fluidize. Hence, it is appropriate to refer to an effective line diameter. Rossetti[3] has correlated this effective diameter in terms of the calculated diameter of the open line, D_C, where D_C is the equivalent calculated diameter of the unblocked area assuming that there is no gas within the deposited solids.

$$D_c = \left(\frac{VD^2}{V_{so}} - 4\,\frac{W_s}{k\varrho_p}\right)^{0.5} \tag{12-14}$$

W_s is the solids mass flow rate. The relationship between D_e and D_c is shown graphically in Figure 12-4, and the pressure drop at gas velocities below saltation can be estimated from the following relationship, again provided from Rossetti's studies:

$$\left(\frac{\Delta P}{L}\right)_H = \frac{\xi \varrho_g V_{so}^2 (1 + \phi)^2}{2g_c D_e} + \frac{2C_H W_s}{\pi g_c D_e^3} \tag{12-15}$$

where $\xi = 0.0056 + 0.5\left(\frac{\varrho_g V(D/D_e)^2 D_e}{\mu}\right)^{-0.32}$

$\phi = 4W_s/\pi k\varrho_p D_e^2$

Flow-Through Bends and Elbows

Dilute solids-phase flows through bends and elbows involve complex interactions between particles. The pressure losses associated with elbows are the sum of two

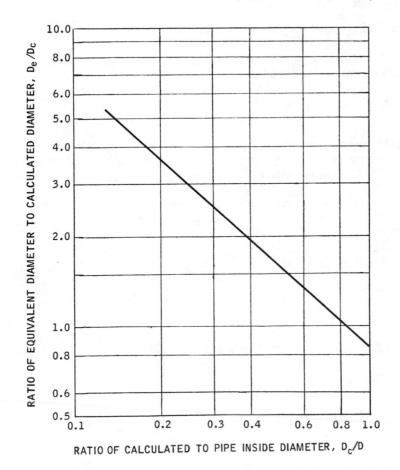

Figure 12-4. Illustration of the relationship between D_e/D_c versus D_c/D as given by Rossetti.[3]

components: the pressure drop across the elbow itself and losses due to solids recirculation in the downstream piping.

$$\Delta P_e = (k_g + k_{el}\eta)\frac{\varrho_g V^2}{2g_c} \tag{12-16}$$

k_g and k_{el} are friction coefficients that account for the gas phase and the contributions due to the elbow and resultant downstream losses, respectively. Parameter η is the solids loading defined as the mass ratio of solids to gas flows. Correlations for k_g and k_{el} are reported by Rossetti.[3] An average value for k_g is 0.35, and k_{el} is a function of the particle terminal settling velocity.

Dense-Phase Conveying (Vertical Systems)

For vertical systems, Leung and Wiles[12] give the following criterion for estimating the gas velocity for transition to packed-bed flow:

$$0.55 \, V_{mf} = 0.55V - 0.45U_o \tag{12-17}$$

For the annular flow regime, Nakamura et al.[9] derived expressions that describe the average voidage and that translate into pressure drop predictions. A drawback with this model is that it contains several empirical coefficients which may be system-dependent.

The slugging-bed flow regime has been modeled by Matsen[13] using bubble theory. In this approach, the voidage, ϵ, for a slugging system is described by the following relation:

$$(1-\epsilon)/(1-\epsilon_{mf}) = [U_b + W_s/(\varrho_p(1-\epsilon_{mf})])/(V + U_b - V_{mf} + W_s/\varrho_p) \tag{12-18}$$

where ϵ_{mf} = voidage at minimum fluidization
       U_b = bubble rise velocity

For slugging beds, the rise velocity can be approximated by:

$$U_b = 0.35(gD)^{0.5} \tag{12-19}$$

Since the solid's movement in slugging flow is relatively low, pressure losses can be estimated simply from the head (i.e., frictional losses are ignored):

$$\Delta P_v = \varrho_p(1 - \epsilon) \, H \left(\frac{g}{g_c}\right) \tag{12-20}$$

For vertical extrusion or packed-bed flow, Leung et al.[12] have proposed a modified Ergun-type equation to estimate pressure losses:

$$\frac{\Delta P d_p \epsilon^3}{H\varrho \, [(V - U_o)\epsilon]^2 \, (1 - \epsilon)} = 150/Re_{sl} + 1.75 \tag{12-21}$$

where Re_{sl} is the particle Reynolds number defined in terms of the slip velocity

$$Re_{sl} = \frac{\varrho_g(V - U_o)d_p}{\mu} \left(\frac{\epsilon}{1 - \epsilon}\right) \tag{12-22}$$

Voidage, ϵ, is normally taken to be at minimum fluidization conditions.

COMMERCIAL TECHNIQUES FOR PNEUMATIC CONVEYING

The majority of application-oriented descriptions concerning pneumatic conveying have revolved around petroleum applications thus far. However, both dense-and dilute-phase conveying are widely practiced throughout the chemical and allied industries as well. Many of these applications are aimed at bulk transport and unloading; weighing, batching, and delivery; and conveying materials from storage areas. Dense-phase transport in horizontal orientations is attractive in high pressure transfers between process vessels and for fines disposal transfers. Examples of such applications are transferring granulated plastics, glass, cement, powdered chemicals, ceramics, food, minerals, and ores. Commercially packaged systems are available for these applications. Design and scale-up procedures are for the most part empirical, and often, vendor testing is mandatory to ensure that dense-phase conveying can be achieved for a particular system.

Three distinct methods of low-velocity conveying most often employed are:

1. Conventional dilute-phase conveying for powders and granules
2. Dense-phase, low-velocity conveying for powders
3. Dense-phase, low-velocity conveying for granulates

Table 12-1 summarizes typical operating ranges recommended by one vendor for each method.

Each conveying method offers certain advantages with respect to the material handled and the intended service. For example, the conventional dilute-phase conveying method has low initial cost, is flexible with respect to product changes, and negative pressure applications are possible. Dense-phase conveying methods well-suited to handling abrasive materials generally have lower power requirements and require small gas volumes for conveying.

The various techniques for conveying materials in horizontal lines are illustrated in Figure 12-5. The dilute conveying approach (Figure 12-5) is normally used for products that have a low air permeability and a high air-retention capability and utilize a method of splitting a material plug into short, conveyable lengths. In position 1 Figure 12-5A, a plug of the material in the line is not split up; in position 2, a bypass arrangement is used to break up the plug without the use of additional gas.

Materials tend to dam and pack in conveying lines, at velocities of 600 to 3,000 fpm, causing long plugs of material to form. For such products the conveying air must bypass the plug to a point where the resistance of the plug is less than the air pressure, thereby splitting the plug into lengths that are readily conveyable (Figure 12-5B). Note that these slugs are formed over the entire length of the system and that no secondary or booster air is required. In the first method, velocity increases are a result of the air expansion.

In Figure 12.5B, at point A where a plug forms, air immediately bypasses, going up into the secondary pipe and moving along where the resistance of the plug is less than the force of the air. At point B, it begins to fluidize the material again. This action causes the leading edge of the plug to be sliced off, section by section (points C, D, etc.), working in a backward fashion until the plug disappears.

Table 12-1

Typical Operating Ranges for the Three Types of Dilute-Phase (Horizontal) Conveying Methods

Method	Trade Name	Flow Pattern	Air Velocity	Material-to-Air Ratio	Operating Pressure
Dilute-phase conveying	Fluidlift		3,000 to 7,000 FPM	10 to 20	Up to 15 psig
Dense-phase, low-velocity powder conveying	Fluidstat		600 to 3,000 FPM	20 to 150	8 to 90 psig
Dense-phase, low-velocity granulates conveying	Takt-Schub		400 to 1,200 FPM	20 to 150	8 to 90 psig

Courtesy of Buhler-Miag, Inc., Minneapolis, MN.

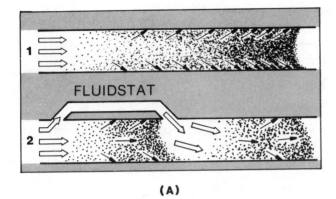

(A)

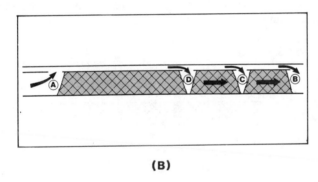

(B)

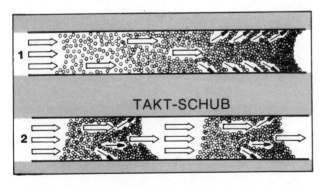

(C)

Figure 12-5. Illustration of the working principles of low-velocity pneumatic conveying methods. (Courtesy of Buhler-Miag, Inc., Minneapolis, MN.)

The conveying arrangement for granulates that have a high air permeability and a low air-retention capability, utilizes a method of alternately feeding material at the feed point which are maintained throughout the length of the system without the aid of bypass or booster lines (Figure 12-5C). The pressure drop when conveying in this method is considerably less than when conveying a single plug that is the same length as the total of the short plugs. This is illustrated by Figure 12-6, whereby through the intermediate feeding of the product, the conveying pressure is reduced from P_{E1} to P_{E2}.

The air permeability and air retention capabilities of materials are important considerations in the conveying systems described. Normally, the particle size distribution of the product is an indication of its air permeability and air retention capabilities.

In the dilute conveying approach, an ideal product would be a powder with a broad particle size distribution, whereas with the latter, the ideal product would be a granulate with all particles of the same size. Although this represents the ideal for each system, the application range is broader and the operating parameters can be adjusted for products with less than ideal particle size distribution. Figure 12-7 shows one manufacturer's criteria of particle size for the application of conveying.

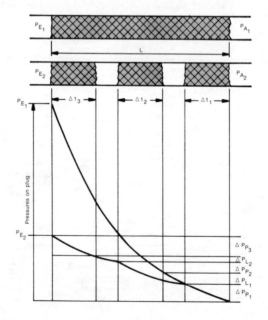

Figure 12-6. Through intermediate feeding of the product, the conveying pressure is reduced from P_{E1} to P_{E2}. (Courtesy of Buhler-Miag, Inc., Minneapolis, MN.)

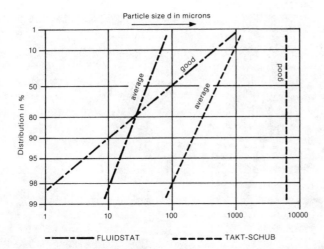

Particle size d in microns

—————— FLUIDSTAT   —————— TAKT-SCHUB

ᵧure 12-7. General criteria of particle size for the application of conveying systems. (Cour-
ᵧy of Buhler-Miag, Inc., Minneapolis, MN.)

Various solids feeding methods are employed with these systems. For low capacities and relatively short conveying distances, and when handling compatible products, it is possible to use a conventional airlock/feeder at the system inlet. This
feeding method requires a relatively low system-operating pressure and therefore is
limited in its application. However, when possible, the airlock provides a relatively
inexpensive feeding device, while providing a continuous conveying process. For
design parameters that require higher operating pressures, a pressure vessel is used
at the system inlet, which can be either a single or double arrangement. The single
vessel is used in systems that do not require continuous conveying or when handling
distinct batches, whereas the double vessel arrangement is used when continuous
conveying is necessary.

Typical installations are shown in Figures 12-8 through 12-10. Figure 12-8
shows a dense-phase, low-velocity powder handling system. This arrangement permits product weighing as the material is conveyed. The system is batch operated
and has relatively low maintenance requirements. Figure 12-9 shows a product conveying system where the material is transferred in small individual plugs. Finally,
Figure 12-10 shows a conveying pipeline arrangement employing drum diverters
and isolation valves.

All low-velocity pneumatic conveying systems display a characteristic pressure-
velocity curve for a given solids throughput rate. Figure 12-11 shows the principal
features. Curve L represents air friction, as determined by the air flowing through
the pipeline. As noted earlier, air friction increases approximately proportional to
the square of velocity.

Figure 12-8. A batch-weighing/material-transport system. (Courtesy of Buhler-Miag, Inc., Minneapolis, MN.)

Figure 12-9. A "solid slug" transport system (trade name TAKT-SCHUB). (Courtesy of Buhler-Miag, Inc., Minneapolis MN.)

Figure 12-10. Typical conveying pipelines employing drum diverters and isolation valves. (Courtesy of Buhler-Miag, Inc., Minneapolis, MN.)

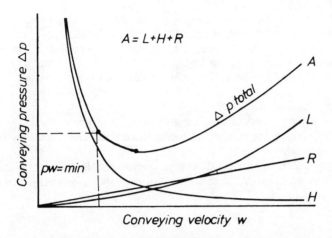

Figure 12-11. Illustration of the characteristic pressure-drop velocity curve for a constant solids-throughput rate: L—air friction; R—wall friction of solids; H—air-to-solids ratio, damming forces; A—total pressure losses. (Courtesy of Buhler-Miag, Inc., Minneapolis, MN.)

Line R represents the friction of the solids against the wall. The material is slowed down by the wall and has to be continuously reaccelerated; it increases approximately at a linear ratio to velocity.

Curve H is the air-to-solids ratio, denoting damming forces (produced when material becomes plugged in the pipe). With decreasing velocity the air-to-solids ratio in the conveying pipe increases (at constant material throughputs) and thus also, the pressure drop producing a characteristic hyperbolic curve.

Curve A is the sum of all the individual pressure drops. The exact course of the characteristic curve A, representing the sum of the individual curves, depends on the type of material being conveyed and on the conveying methods. The basic pattern, however, is an asymmetric, parabolic function that is applicable to any pneumatic conveying system.

The latest pneumatic conveying technology distinguishes between four conveying methods of commercial significance. Proper selection depends on the properties of the material to be conveyed:

1. Dilute-phase conveying
2. Dense-phase conveying
3. High-density, slug-phase conveying
4. High-density, pulse-phase conveying

The first two are conventional conveying methods, whereas the latter two are low-velocity conveying methods that have been introduced on the market over the last decade.

Figure 12-12 shows the basic phase patterns in the conveying pipe, and lists the approximate corresponding values for air and solids velocities, air-to-solids ratios, and specific pressure losses. Figure 12-13 provides information on the operating ranges of these four conveying methods.

The advantages of dilute-phase and dense-phase conveying include:

- Relatively inexpensive systems
- Virtually any pneumatically conveyable material can be carried
- Dependable conveying is in most cases ensured even when switching from one product to another
- These systems are always good in cases where operating hours are limited and energy is no concern, or where no low-velocity system is better suited due to a specific advantage.

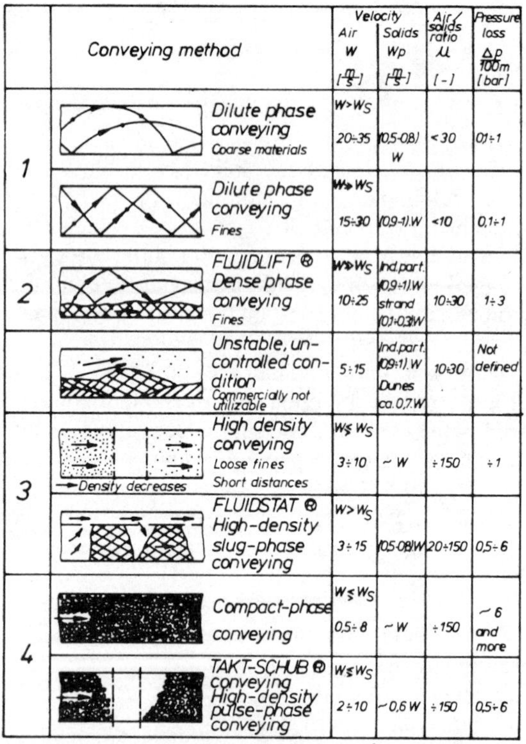

	Conveying method	Velocity Air W $[\frac{m}{s}]$	Velocity Solids Wp $[\frac{m}{s}]$	Air/solids ratio μ $[-]$	Pressure loss Δp/100m $[bar]$
1	Dilute phase conveying — Coarse materials	W>Ws, 20÷35	(0.5-0.8)W	<30	0.1÷1
	Dilute phase conveying — Fines	W»Ws, 15÷30	(0.9-1)W	<10	0.1÷1
2	FLUIDLIFT ® Dense phase conveying — Fines	W»Ws, 10÷25	Ind.part. (0.9÷1)W / strand (0.1-0.3)W	10÷30	1÷3
	Unstable, un-controlled con-dition — Commercially not utilizable	5÷15	Ind.part. (0.9÷1)W / Dunes ca.0.7W	10÷30	Not defined
3	High density conveying — Loose fines, Short distances, Density decreases	Ws≤Ws, 3÷10	~ W	÷150	÷1
	FLUIDSTAT ® High-density slug-phase conveying	W>Ws, 3÷15	(0.5-0.8)W	20÷150	0.5÷6
4	Compact-phase conveying	Ws≤Ws, 0.5÷8	~ W	÷150	~6 and more
	TAKT-SCHUB ® conveying High-density pulse-phase conveying	Ws≤Ws, 2÷10	~0.6 W	÷150	0.5÷6

Figure 12-12. Typical methods of pneumatic conveying systems. (Courtesy of Buhler-Miag, Inc., Minneapolis, MN.)

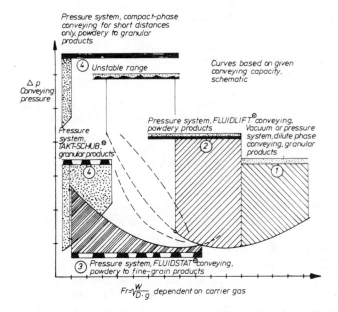

Figure 12-13. Operating ranges for various conveying systems. (Courtesy of Buhler-Miag, Inc., Minneapolis, MN.)

The advantages of low-velocity conveying include:

- Minimum particle breakage (decisive factor when conveying friable bulk materials)
- Low wear on the conveying system (an important consideration when handling abrasive products)
- Virtually no segregation of the material being conveyed, neither perpendicular to nor along the pipe axis
- Generally lower power requirements
- Smaller conveying-air volumes, therefore less filter area (if necessary at all), which is also an advantage when using conditioned air or, for example, nitrogen as a conveying medium

Whereas the rate of fall of the bulk material is the crucial property in dilute-phase conveying, its air permeability and air-retention capability are the decisive factors in low-velocity conveying.

With regard to these latter two criteria, two different methods of low-velocity conveying are distinguished:

1. Method of splitting up the plug of material
2. Method of conveying short slugs of material

Bulk materials tend to dam and pack in conveying pipes at velocities of 3–10 m/s, causing long plugs of material to form, with the material tightly wedged against the pipe wall.

These damming forces are all the stronger the less permeable the material is to air. For such products the conveying air must be supplied through a bypass pipe to the point where it is capable of conveying the product and splitting up the plug of material.

In the gas bypass-solid plug conveying, no additional air is required for breaking up the plug of material. When a plug occurs, air immediately bypasses it, going up into the bypass pipe and moving along to a point where the resistance of the plug is less than the force of the air. The long plug of material is thus divided up into slugs that are readily conveyed. These slugs are formed even over long conveying distances. A similar effect is achieved in other systems, where a pressurized air line equipped with booster valves is installed parallel to the conveying pipe, or where a porous fluidizing tube is integrated in the bottom of the conveying pipe over its entire length (Figure 12-14). In the case of these systems, additional air from a compressed-air system is boosted into the conveying line. It must be borne in mind, however, that the conveying velocity increases with the conveying distance, resulting in a transition to dilute-phase conveying.

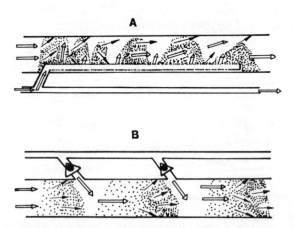

Figure 12-14. Illustration of the principle of splitting up a plug of material, for bulk materials impermeable to air: (A) splitting accomplished with the aid of additional air through a porous plate distributor; (B) splitting accomplished with additional air through a booster line. (Courtesy of Buhler-Miag, Inc., Minneapolis, MN.)

When bulk materials permeable to air are carried, the conveying air is able to penetrate into the plug of material, fluidizing it and limiting the damming forces. In addition, pressure compensation between the individual pockets of air and the slugs of material is possible without the aid of bypass or parallel booster lines.

Continuous air flow requires intermittent product feed, so that the slugs of some few meters in length are separated from each other by pockets of air. The pressure drops of all the individual slugs taken together are then substantially lower than the pressure required to move a single compact plug of material of the same length.

Few plants use all four conveying methods in the conveying systems of their production programs. Conveying systems handling highly adhesive and cohesive products such as paint pigments, foods containing fats, etc., belong to a special category. These materials can only be conveyed with flexible rubber or plastic tubes.

It is important to classify the various bulk materials according to their conveying properties, and to allocate them to the conveying method best suited for larger conveying distances (i.e., with the lowest possible conveying velocity). The lines between these categories of materials will necessarily be schematic, and it should be noted that there are transitions between the typical conveying methods that have been mentioned. Thus, it is frequently possible to use an alternative conveying method for a given bulk material, conveying distance, and material throughput rate.

With conventional conveying methods where velocity is the decisive factor, dense-phase conveying will work well for powdery products; granular materials, however, will tend to choke the conveying line. Similar situations will occur in a low-velocity system where the criteria of air permeability and air retention capability have not been given due consideration. Lines will choke in the low-velocity range if they are poorly designed. If the conveying-air volume is then increased, the conveying system will again become operational, but it will no longer be low-velocity conveying.

The important parameters to low-velocity conveying systems are particle size distribution, density, and product adhesion. Adequate materials are fines with wide particle size distributions. Bulk materials with steep characteristic curves in the granulation grid have poor air-retention capabilities and are therefore less well suited. The principle of short slugs of material (pulse-phase and compact-phase conveying) is best suited for granular products that have a narrow particle size distribution with good air permeability. A flatter characteristic curve in the granulation grid points causes unfavorable properties, due to the fact that the cavities between the individual particles are filled up, causing air permeability to deteriorate.

Table 12-2 summarizes conventional conveying methods. The table shows that low-velocity systems neither should nor can replace systems based on the conventional conveying methods.

The usually higher initial cost of a low-velocity conveying system is justified in cases where such a system has one or more outstanding advantages over other systems.

It is frequently necessary to test the practical performance of a low-velocity conveying system on a commercial scale to obtain the figures required for optimal operation. Data gained from tests and from operational systems in many cases, however, give sufficient information for the accurate assessment and sizing of conveying systems with grass roots designs.

Table 12-2
Conveying Selection Chart

			Principle: splitting up plug of material		Principle: short slugs of material
			Dilute phase conveying	Low-velocity conveying	
			Dense phase conveying		
			Vacuum/ pressure	FLUIDLIFT®	FLUIDSTAT®	TAKT-SCHUB®
Powders	normal	non-adhesive				
		adhesive	possibly R			
	slow-gentle	non-adhesive <100m<10 tlh				
		non-adhesive >100m>10 tlh				
		adhesive <100m<10 tlh				
		adhesive >100m>10 tlh	R			
Granulates	normal	non-adhesive				
		adhesive	possibly R			
	slow-gentle	non-adhesive				
		adhesive				P

R: Rubber Line; P: Plastic Line (Courtesy of Buhler-Miag, Inc., Minneapolis, MN.)

NOMENCLATURE

C   system frictional constant, vertical flow
C_D particle drag coefficient
C_H system frictional constant, horizontal flow
D   pipe inside diameter
D_c calculated equivalent line diameter with nonexpanded layer at velocities below the saltation velocity in horizontal flow

D_e actual equivalent line diameter at velocities below saltation in horizontal flow

d_p weight median particle diameter. The 50% point on a log probability plot of particle size versus cumulative wt%

f_g Darcy friction factor for gas = 4 × Fanning friction factor

f_s Darcy friction factor for solids

g gravitational acceleration

g_c gravitational constant needed in English system of units only = 32.2. In metric units use 1.0 with no dimensions

G_s solids mass flow rate per unit cross sectional area

H vertical height

k particle size distribution factor on saltation velocity

k_{el} elbow coefficient accounting for both reacceleration downstream and pressure drop by solids across an elbow

k_g coefficient accounting only for pressure drop across an elbow due to solids

L length of horizontal line

ΔP_e pressure drop due to presence of an elbow

$(\Delta P_f)_s$ frictional pressure drop due to solids in vertical flow

$(\Delta P_f)_{SH}$ frictional pressure drop due to solids in horizontal flow

ΔP_g pressure drop due to gas only

$(\Delta P_t)_s$ total pressure drop due to solids in vertical flow

$\Delta P_t)_H, \Delta P_H$ horizontal line pressure drop (excluding acceleration)

ΔP_v vertical flow pressure drop (excluding acceleration)

Re_p particle Reynolds number based on terminal velocity

U_b bubble rise velocity

U_{et} solids effective terminal settling velocity

U_o superficial solids velocity

U_s solids velocity in line

U_{so} single particle velocity

U_{to} single particle terminal settling velocity

V superficial gas velocity

V_c gas velocity at choking

V_{mf} minimum fluidization velocity

V_s saltation velocity

V_{so} effective single particle saltation velocity

W_s solids flow rate

Greek Symbols

ϵ voidage in line

ϵ_c voidage at choking

ϵ_{mf} voidage at minimum fluidization

η solids loading ratio in mass of solids per unit mass of gas

μ gas viscosity

ϱ_{dp} dispersed phase density
ϱ_g gas density
ϱ_p particle density
σ standard deviation of particle size distribution

REFERENCES

1. Zenz, F. A., *I&EC Fundamentals,* 3: 1 (Feb. 1964).
2. Halow, J. S., *Chem. Eng. Sci.,* 28: 1–12 (1973).
3. Rossetti, S., "Concepts and Criteria for Gas-Solids Flow," in *Handbook of Fluids in Motion,* N. P. Cheremisinoff and R. Gupta (Eds.), Ann Arbor Sci. Pub., Ann Arbor, MI (1983).
4. Yang, W. C., *Proc. of Pneumotransport 3,* BHRA Fluid Engineering, (April 1976).
5. Leung, L. S., R. J. Wiles, and D. J. Nicklin, *Ind. Eng. Chem. Process Design and Development* 2(10)183 (1971).
6. Yang, W. C., *AIChE J.,* 21 (5): 1,013 (1975).
7. Arundel, P. A., S. D. Bibb, and R. G. Boothroyd, "Dispersed Density Distribution and Extent of Agglomeration in a Polydisperse Fine Particle Suspension Flowing Turbulently Upwards in a Duct," *Powder Technology,* 4: 302–312 (1970/71).
8. Capes, C. E., and K. Nakamura, "Vertical Pneumatic Conveying: An Experimental Study with Particles in the Intermediate and Turbulent Flow Regimes," *Can. J. Chem. Eng.,* 51: 31, (Feb. 1973).
9. Nakamura, K. and C. E. Capes, "Vertical Pneumatic Conveying: A Theoretical Study of Uniform and Annular Flow Models," *Can. J. Chem. Eng.,* 51: 39, (1973).
10. Reddy, K. V. S., and D. C. T. Pei, "Particle Dynamics in Solids-Gas Flow in a Vertical Pipe," *I&EC Fundamentals,* 8: (3) 490 (1969).
11. Konno, H., and S. Saito, "Pneumatic Conveying of Solids Through Straight Pipes," *J. of Chem. Eng. of Japan,* 2: 2 (1969).
12. Leung, L. S., and R. J. Wiles, "A Quantitative Design Procedure for Vertical Pneumatic Conveying Systems," *I&EC Process Des. Dev.,* 15: 4 (1976).
13. Matsen, J. M., "Flow of Fluidized Solids and Bubbles in Standpipes and Risers," *Powder Technology,* 7: 93–96 (1973).

13

Gas Premixing Techniques

By Milind B. Ajinkya
Exxon Research and Engineering Company; Florham Park, New Jersey

CONTENTS

INTRODUCTION, 571

PIPELINE MIXING, 572

JET MIXING, 580
Coflowing Jets, 580
Cross-flowing Jets, 581

INDUSTRIAL MIXERS, 587

SUMMARY, 590

NOMENCLATURE, 590

REFERENCES, 591

INTRODUCTION

Mixing of two or more gases is encountered frequently in the process industry. In most cases mixing is a precursor to carrying out gas-phase reactions, the intention being the rapid mixing of gaseous reactants so that the desired reactions will take place in a more or less homogeneous gas phase. The purpose of this chapter is to outline some of the current practices in industry used to achieve mixing of gases as efficiently as possible. The emphasis is on pipeline and jet mixing, with different configurations thereof. The techniques described are of importance to fluidization engineering because they constitute a feed pretreatment operation.

Before moving onto the main subject matter, a few examples of gas mixing of industrial importance follow:

1. *Chlorination of gaseous hydrocarbons*—Allyl chloride is an intermediate formed in the process of making epichlorohydrin and synthetic gylcerine.[1,2] It is made by premixing propylene and chlorine and reacting the gases in the gas phase at elevated temperatures. Several parallel and series reactions are possible;[3] hence, the yields of the desired products depend highly on how well propylene and chlorine are mixed before reacting.
2. *Oxidation of ethylene*—Ethylene oxide is formed by reacting air or oxygen and ethylene over a catalyst. The two gases are premixed before entering the reactor. In addition to the product selectivity and yield of the process, safety is a major consideration since ethylene and oxygen form explosive mixtures in certain proportions. It is extremely important, therefore, that the mixture of ethylene and air/oxygen be as homogeneous as possible.
3. *Air oxidation of ammonia*—In the oxidation of ammonia to produce nitric acid, mixing of air with ammonia in the shortest possible time is desirable. This is essential to avoid product loss from side reactions.
4. *Air pollution*—Gas-gas mixing finds application in the abatement of air pollution, for example, where stack gases disperse into the crosswinds in the form of jets.

These are but a few of a number of gas-mixing problems encountered in the process industry. Although some research articles have appeared on modeling turbulent-fluid mixing in recent years, mixer design is still a highly empirical procedure, and much engineering judgment is called for. The state of the art has not progressed to the point where a practicing design engineer can use reliable correlations to design mixers. If the engineer has access to laboratory facilities and has the time, he can design scaled-down models of the commercial design and study the critical scale-up issues, e.g., the dynamic similarities or the geometric similarities. Even for troubleshooting a malfunctioning commercial mixer design, the latter is the approach followed by many industrial labs.

Although pipeline mixing is a special case of jet mixing, it is relatively easier to practice and hence is treated separately below.

PIPELINE MIXING

Pipeline mixing is usually the simplest means of mixing two or more gases. The process is slow but if enough pipe length is available, as in most interconnecting process piping, adequate mixing can take place. In many instances, though, "enough pipe length" can be as much as 250 pipe diameters from the injection of the secondary gas stream. In order to reduce the mixing length required to a few diameters, say 2–10, various devices have been proposed and used. Some depend on the methods of admitting the added gas to the primary flow, others on internals like baffles of different designs to enhance the mixing process. Use of internals such as baffles often causes considerable pressure drop and hence is not as popular as simple pipeline mixing without internals.[4]

Chilton and Genereaux[5] were two of the first to investigate pipeline mixing by different methods of admitting the second gas into the primary flow. Their experimental method consisted of observing the flow of two gaseous streams (generally air) in glass tubes, with smoke added to make one stream visible. The quality of mixing was judged by the distance downstream from the point of injection at which the smoke appeared to be completely diffused. Mixing was considered good when visual observation showed that the smoke was diffused completely in 2–3 pipe diameters, and poor when it took several pipe diameters for complete diffusion. Titanium tetrachloride was used as a smoke producing agent. Chilton and Genereaux varied the velocity ratio and also the ratio of diameters of the primary and the secondary flows. Using a 0.5-in. diameter tube perpendicularly connected to the 1.75-in. diameter main tube (T-junction) and air flowing in both of them, they were able to establish visually that the optimum linear velocity ratio for good mixing was 2.7. Below a velocity ratio of 2, the mixing was poor. Ratios between 3.5 to 6 also yielded poor mixing. Again above a velocity ratio of 6, mixing improved owing to the rebound of the side-entering air. The absolute values of the velocities did not have an effect on the mixing quality as long as the velocity ratio was maintained at a desired value. In order to study the effect of changing the diameter of the tube carrying the secondary air flow, Chilton and Genereaux varied the diameter ratio from 1.16 to 7 (main airflow tube diameter/secondary airflow tube diameter) and found that the optimum velocity ratio for good mixing decreased from 3.2 to 1.7 as the diameter ratio decreased from 7 to 1.16. Simultaneously the lower limit of the velocity ratio for good mixing decreased from 2.5 to 1.0. These results are shown in Table 13-1.

By experimenting with side-entering gases other than air, such as sulfur dioxide, carbon dioxide, and ammonia, whose density is different from air density, Chilton and Genereaux were able to establish that it is the momentum ratio and not the linear velocity ratio that influences the mixing process. Thus keeping the linear velocity ratio as low as 1.2 for SO_2/air system with a 0.5-in. diameter tube for the sec-

Table 13-1
Effect of Changing Side Tube Diameter[5]

Side Tube Diameter	Ratio of Diameters	Lower Limit of Velocity Ratio for Good Mixing	Best Ratio for Good Mixing
0.25″	7.0	2.5	3.2
0.50	3.5	2.0	2.7
0.875	2.0	1.5	2.2
1.50	1.16	1.0	1.7

Main tube: 1.75-in. diameter—mixing two air streams.

ondary gas (SO_2) flow, they demonstrated that good mixing was obtained because the ratio of mass velocities was 3.0–3.1 (see Table 13-2). If air is used in both the streams, the linear velocity ratio is the same as the mass velocity ratio, hence the criterion does not change.

In order to support their visual observation method by quantitative analysis, Chilton and Genereaux experimented with oxygen entering through the secondary tube into the main air flow in the form of a T-junction. Two different diameters were used for the former (0.5-in. and 0.25-in.) and samples were taken 8-in. downstream (i.e., 4.6 diameters from the entrance of the side stream) at $1/4$ diameter from the top, $1/4$ diameter from the bottom and also at the center line of the main pipe in the same plane. They were analyzed for oxygen content to determine the mixing efficiency. The results are summarized in Table 13-3. It is seen that the O_2 analysis corroborated the visual observations.

Besides using simple T-junctions, they also experimented with other geometries, which are summarized in Figure 13-1. None of the other geometries were found particularly more advantageous over a simple T-junction for the mixing efficiency, and hence their conclusion was that T-junctions are an efficient and yet a simple method of mixing gases. Especially inefficient was the configuration IX in Figure 13-1.

A more recent study on pipeline mixing was done by Reed and Narayan[8] (see also Reference 21) and is reported in detail in Reference 6. The objective of their study was to verify the common belief that when separate fluids are introduced into a pipe under turbulent flow, a homogeneous mixture quickly results. They concluded from their study that this is often not the case, particularly when fluids are introduced parallel to each other. Narayan[6,8] essentially tried three configurations which are shown in Figure 13-2. They are: head-on flow (I), perpendicular flow (II), and parallel flow (III). The tests were made by combining carbon dioxide and air (the secondary flow) with mainstream air flow. The Reynolds number for the mixed flow was 50,000. The CO_2/air stream flowed in a 0.5-in. pipe whereas the air stream flowed through a 2-in. pipe. Samples were drawn downstream at different radial positions in the main pipe.

Results of the parallel flow configuration are shown in Figure 13-3. Until 250 pipe diameters, the mixing was not complete. This essentially confirmed Chilton and Genereaux's[5] observations as noted earlier, that parallel flow is a very inefficient way of mixing gases. Results of the tests with head-on flow and T-mixing (perpendicular flow) are summarized in Table 13-4. Narayan[6] found that for the head-on configuration, complete mixing took place within about 5 pipe diameters whereas for T-mixing, complete mixing was observed in about 9 pipe diameters. Reed and Narayan concluded from their studies, that homogeneous mixture can be achieved by T-mixing and by maintaining a significant pressure (or velocity) differential between the two gases. They recommend a minimum pressure differential of 5 psi in most cases. A proprietary device[18] is patented using the principle of right-angle entry. The patent claims that pressure differentials up to 30 psi are used when the molecular weights of the two gases are very different. For example, Reed and Narayan[8] claim that ΔP's up to 10 psi are required to mix n-butane with 98%

Table 13-2
T-Mixing with Gases Other Than Air[5]

Gases	Main Velocity (ft/s)	Added Velocity (ft/s)	Ratio Linear Velocities	Main Mass Velocity (lb/ft²/s)	Added Mass Velocity (lb/ft²/s)	Ratio Mass Velocities	Quality of Mixing
SO_2	10.75	14.8	1.2	0.0056	0.0175	3.1	Good
and	11.6	15.6	1.2	0.0061	0.0184	3.0	Good
air	11.6	5.8	0.4	0.0061	0.0067	1.1	Poor
CO_2	10.4	16.7	1.6	0.0055	0.0136	2.5	Good
and	16.5	16.7	1.0	0.0086	0.0136	1.6	Fair
air	25.5	16.0	0.6	0.0133	0.0131	1.0	Poor
	64.5	16.7	0.3	0.0328	0.0136	0.4	Poor
NH_3	11.6	33.2	2.9	0.0062	0.0104	1.7	Fairly good
and	11.6	27.2	2.3	0.0062	0.0084	1.4	Fair
air	11.6	22.4	1.9	0.0062	0.0069	1.1	Poor
	20.2	35.0	1.7	0.0105	0.0109	1.0	Poor
	20.2	16.0	0.8	0.0105	0.0049	0.5	Poor

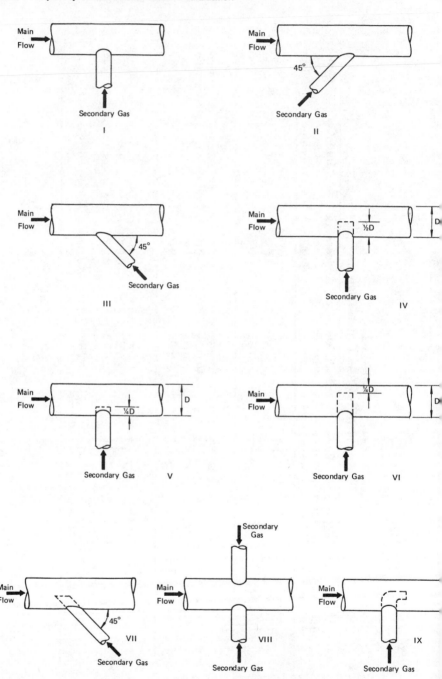

Figure 13–1. Different geometries for admitting secondary gas as tried by Chilton and Genereax.[5]

pure hydrogen, since their molecular weights are very different. The same is probably true for two streams whose molecular weights may or may not be very different but whose temperatures may be so different as to cause a significant density difference.

As noted earlier, pipeline mixing as described previously is a special category of jet mixing in general and was treated separately because of its prominence in indus-

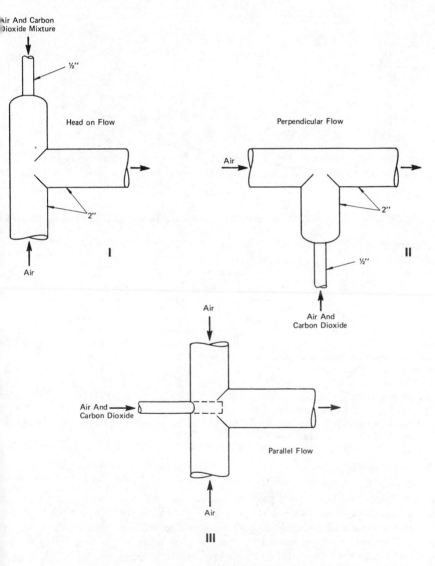

Figure 13-2. Mixer arrangements tried by Narayan. [6,8]

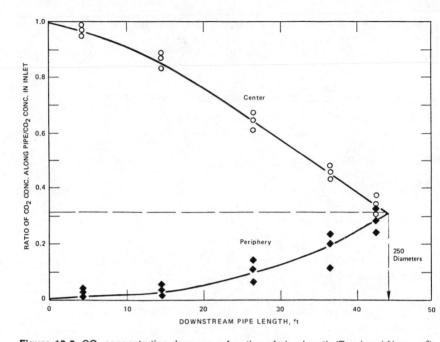

Figure 13-3. CO_2 concentration decay as a function of pipe length (Reed and Narayan[8]).

Table 13-3
Quantitative Measurements with T-Mixers Using O_2 Tracer[5]

Run	1	2	3
Added velocity, ft/s	41.25	16.5	73.5
Main velocity, ft/s	16.5	16.5	17.5
Ratio of linear velocities	2.5	1.0	4.2
Ratio of mass velocities	2.8	1.1	4.6
Ratio of diameters	3.5	3.5	7.0
Quality of mixing, by smoke	Good	Poor	Good
Oxygen %, 1/4 diameter from top	32.7	21.1	25.0
Oxygen %, center line	34.3	28.5	24.5
Oxygen %, 1/4 diameter from bottom	32.9	32.2	24.6

trial practice. In order to treat pipeline mixing quantitatively, some insight into the fundamentals of jet phenomena is necessary. The following will give the reader a flavor of the state of understanding jet mixing. The existing literature on "jets" is so vast that no attempt is made to discuss it all in a few pages here. Instead, the interested reader may refer to the various references listed at the end of the chapter for further details.

Table 13-4
Mixing Efficiency with Perpendicular and Head-On Configurations[8]

Type Flow	L=length, (ft)	Length/ diameter	Y=inlet CO_2 Concentration (mole%)	$X=CO_2$ Concentration at L (mole %)		X/Y	
				Center	Periphery	Center	Periphery
Head-on flow	0.75	4.35	19.44	4.792	4.938	0.246	0.254
				4.928	4.728	0.253	0.243
				4.841	4.850	0.249	0.251
	2.3	13.35	17.94	4.503	4.557	0.251	0.254
				4.584	4.512	0.255	0.252
				4.458	4.485	0.248	0.250
	4.25	24.67	18.60	4.548	4.641	0.245	0.249
				4.631	4.492	0.249	0.241
				4.565	4.604	0.246	0.247
Perpendicular flow	1.5	9.71	19.64	5.018	4.919	0.255	0.250
				4.939	4.890	0.251	0.249
				4.949	4.998	0.252	0.254
	8.3	13.35	16.72	4.213	4.238	0.252	0.253
				4.121	4.264	0.246	0.255
				4.163	4.180	0.249	0.250

JET MIXING

When a gas is added to the primary gas parallel to its direction of flow, as shown in Figure 13-4, it is done through a coflowing jet. When pipeline mixing is attempted using the concept of coflowing jets as in the ninth arrangement of Chilton and Genereaux[5] (see Figure 13-1), and the third configuration of Reed and Narayan[8] (see Figure 13-2), the efficiency of mixing is reported to be very poor. Hence, from a practical standpoint, coflowing jets are not interesting to a designer. Nevertheless, so the fundamentals of jet behavior may be understood, we will discuss some characteristics of coflowing jets.

Coflowing Jets

A coflowing jet is shown schematically in Figure 13-4. The fluid issuing through the nozzle has a uniform velocity U_o. The surrounding medium has a uniform velocity V. The respective densities are denoted by ϱ_o and ϱ_∞. The jet expands by drawing some of the surrounding fluid into itself and also by slowing down. There is a core region of the jet, called the potential or initial region corresponding to a core length X_c. The velocity in the core is constant at U_o. The jet has a main region after a distance X_n in which the jet has a velocity profile with U_m being the cen-

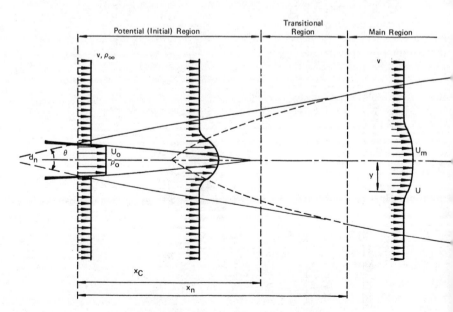

Figure 13-4. Schematic of a coflowing jet.

terline velocity and V being the velocity at the jet boundary, which is the same as the velocity of the surrounding medium. In between the jet core length X_c and the beginning of the main region after a distance X_n is a region called the transitional region. For most purposes, its separate existence is neglected and it is lumped into the main region. Typically the total included angle of the jet θ is 14°.

The jet Reynolds number remains constant throughout the jet and is equal to its value at the nozzle exit. When the jet Reynolds number is less than 300, the jet is considered to be laminar.[7] Between the jet Reynolds number of 300 and 1,000, there is unsustained turbulence in the jet boundary layer, and above 1,000, the jet is fully turbulent. Simpson[7] has briefly summarized several available results for coflowing jets, which allow one to determine the decay of the jet velocity, the amount entrained from the surrounding medium, the core length as a function of jet Reynolds number, etc. It is beyond the scope of the present chapter to discuss that here, but the interested reader is urged to refer to Simpson[7] and a number of pertinent original references cited therein.

From a designer's viewpoint, however, having the added gas jet perpendicular to the main flow (called a cross-flowing jet) is the most interesting configuration. In the preceding section on pipeline mixing, we have already seen the efficiency of cross-flow configuration as shown in Figures 13-1 and 13-2. We shall now summarize some recent quantitative results on jets in cross flow.

Cross-flowing Jets

A cross-flowing jet is schematically shown in Figure 13-5. Near the inlet, the jet entrains ambient pipe fluid and bends over in the cross-flow. Since this constitutes a three-dimensional turbulent shear flow embedded in a fully developed turbulent pipe flow, the analytical solution to the problem seems unlikely.

Various mixing criteria have been used by experimentalists to determine conditions of optimum mixing at a T-junction. With either gases like air, CO_2, etc. or liquids like water, several investigators have used tracer injection to study the effectiveness of mixing, by measuring the tracer distribution at a given downstream position and comparing it with a given mixing criterion. Table 13-5 summarizes most of the available experimental results, including the range of parameters and mixing criteria used.

Forney and Lee[9] have recently proposed some simple scaling laws which assure optimum pipeline mixing of constant density fluids at a T-junction. These correlations are summarized below:

$$\frac{d}{D} = \frac{0.27}{Rf^2} \qquad\qquad \text{for } R < 6 \qquad\qquad (13\text{-}1)$$

and

$$\frac{d}{D} = \frac{0.28}{Rg^{.667}} \qquad\qquad \text{for } R > 6 \qquad\qquad (13\text{-}2)$$

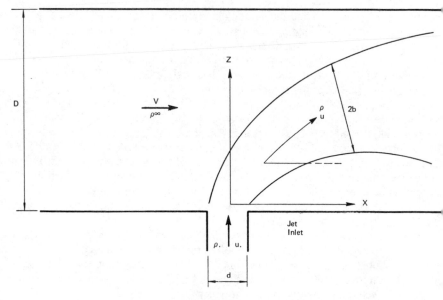

Figure 13-5. Schematic of a cross-flowing jet.

where d = diameter of the side-entering T-junction
         D = diameter of the main pipe
         R = velocity ratio U_o/V where U_o is the jet velocity and V is the main pipe
             flow velocity

f and g = empirical functions of $R^{15,9}$ as follows:

$$f = \frac{0.17}{0.1 + 0.35/R^{1.25}} \tag{13-3}$$

and

$$g = 0.83 + 0.2 \ln R \tag{13-4}$$

(see also Figure 13-6)

Since the flow ratio

$$\frac{q}{Q} = \left(\frac{d}{D}\right)^2 R \tag{13-5}$$

Table 13-5
Summary of Experimental Results on Cross-Flow Jets[9]

Jet Fluid	Pipe Fluid	Jet Diameter (cm)	Pipe Diameter (cm)	R (U_o/V)	Pipe Re	Jet Re_j	Measurement Point in Pipe Diameters	Measured Variable	Mixing Criterion	Reference
Air and $TiCl_4$	Air	0.68–2	4.45	1.5–3	4.3×10^3 -1.8×10^4	$>1.8 \times 10^4$	2–3	Visual smoke concentration	Visual smoke uniformity	Chilton and Genereaux[5]
Aq. 0.5N HNO_3	Aq. 0.5N NaOH	0.635	0.635	1	$1. \times 10^4$ -4×10^4	$1. \times 10^4$ -4×10^4	6–7	Temperature	97% of final temperature rise	Swanson[20]
Aq. NaCl	Water	0.08–0.32	15.24	6–24	$6. \times 10^4$	7.5×10^3	20–120	Electrical conductivity	Concentration stand. deviation	Ger and Holley[11]
Air and $TiCl_4$	Air	0.42–1.5	5.0	1.5–3.3	4×10^3 2×10^4	$>1. \times 10^4$	2–3	Visual smoke concentration	Visual smoke uniformity	Winter[14]
Air and 1% CH_4	Air	0.16	6.35	2–7	$2. \times 10^3$ $-9. \times 10^4$	5×10^2 -2.5×10^4	2–5	CH_4 concentration	Maximum concentration on pipe axis	Forney and Kwon[10]
Air 25°C	Air~35°C	0.5–1.3	5.1	3–4	1.6×10^4 -6.3×10^4	8.2×10^3 -2.3×10^4	2–10	Temperature	Temperature standard deviation	Maruyama, Suzuki and Mizushina[13]
Air 19% CO_2	Air	1.58	5.25	2.7	4.6×10^4	3.74×10^4	10	CO_2 concentration	Equal CO_2 concentration at pipe axis and periphery	Reed and Naravan[8]
Air and 0.3% CH_4	Air	0.1–1.27	11.43	2.9–28.3	$1/3 \times 10^4$ -3.2×10^4	1.1×10^3 -7.2×10^3	2–10	CH_4 concentration	Maximum concentration centered on pipe axis	Lee[12]

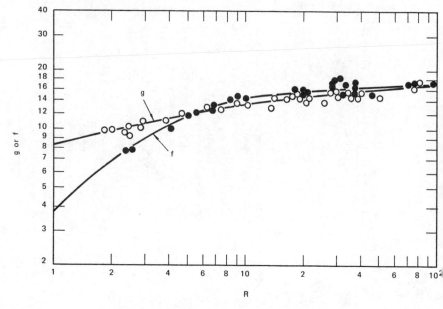

Figure 13-6. Plot of function "f" and "g" (Wright[15]).

where   q = jet inlet flow rate
        Q = main pipe flow rate

The expressions for optimum flow ratio are[9]

$$q/Q = \frac{0.073}{Rf^4} \qquad \text{for } R < 6 \tag{13-6}$$

and

$$q/Q = \frac{0.077}{Rg^3} \qquad \text{for } R > 6 \tag{13-7}$$

Forney and Lee[9] using Wright's[15] expressions for f and g (as previously given) and the available experimental data of several investigations, including their own, have shown how well the correlations in Equations 13-1, 13-2, 13-6, and 13-7 represent the data (see Figures 13-7, 13-8). Forney and Lee[9] also took measurements of the decay of the maximum methane concentration in the jet, C_m, as a function of the

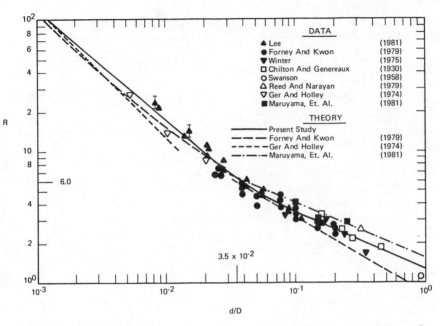

Figure 13-7. Optimum velocity ratio R = U_0/V vs. T-mixer dimension ratio d/D (Forney[9]).

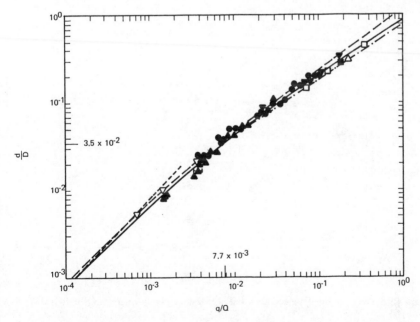

Figure 13-8. Optimum flow rate ratio q/Q vs. T-mixer dimension ratio d/D (Forney[9]).

distance down the pipe axis from the injection point. The data are shown in Figures 13-9 and 13-10 and are represented by the correlations

$$\frac{C_m}{C_o} = \frac{1}{R(X/D)^{0.5}} \qquad \text{for } R < 6 \qquad (13\text{-}8)$$

and

$$\frac{C_m}{C_o} = \frac{0.32}{R(X/D)^{0.666}} \qquad \text{for } R > 6 \qquad (13\text{-}9)$$

where C_o = inlet methane (tracer) concentration
X = downstream distance from the point of injection
D = main pipe diameter
R = jet to mainstream velocity ratio U_o/V

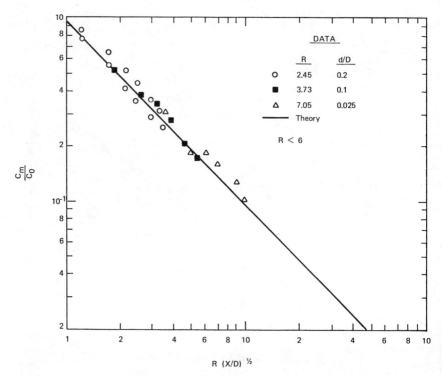

Figure 13-9. Decay of maximum jet tracer concentration with downstream distance for R < 6 (Forney[9]).

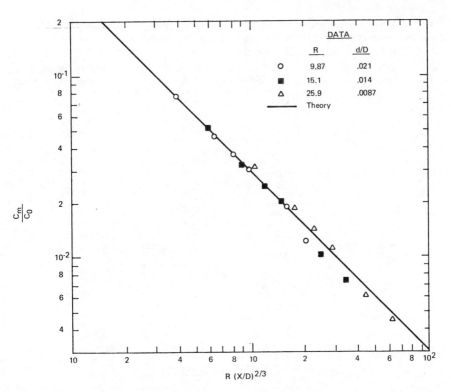

Figure 13-10. Decay of maximum jet tracer concentration with downstream distance for $R > 6$ (Forney[9]).

There are several additional references available on jets in cross flow. Their inclusion would be beyond the scope of this chapter. Some of them are listed at the end of the chapter and the interested reader is urged to refer to them.

We shall close the chapter by discussing some of the commonly used industrial mixer designs.

INDUSTRIAL MIXERS

Having gained some insight into the basics of pipeline mixing and jet mixing, it would seem appropriate to consider some of the commonly used mixer designs.

Simpson's[4] excellent comprehensive work on the topic is of practical interest for those involved in design and engineering. The reader is referred to Figure 13-11, in which four basic designs are depicted. In designs I and II, multiple jets are used to achieve good mixing in the shortest possible mixing length. Simpson gives a detailed algorithm to design types I and II mixers and suggests the following criteria as being important:

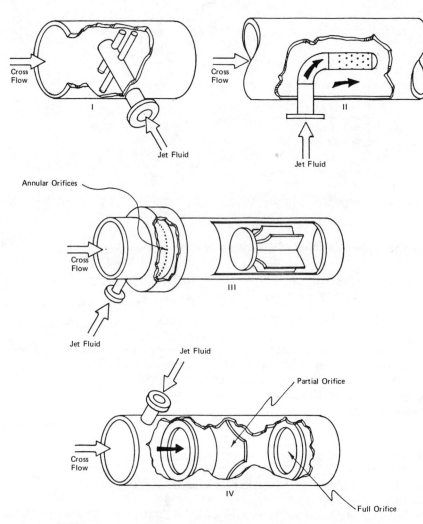

Figure 13-11. Illustrations of industrial mixers (Simpson, [4,7] Ajinkya[21]).

Figure 13-12. Schematic of a baffled mixer (Hartung,[16] Ajinkya[21]).

1. The design pressure drop ΔP, should be known.
2. The number of total orifices should be between 50 and 200.
3. The jet flow (orifice) velocity should be substantially greater than the main pipe flow velocity.
4. The orifice Reynolds number should be greater than 5,000.
5. In the first mixer, a good flow distribution along the length of each finger will be ensured if the finger cross-sectional area is a minimum 1.5 times the total orifice area in that finger.
6. There should be sufficient lengths of main piping upstream and downstream of the mixer to avoid pressure and velocity variations across the main pipe.

Type III mixer is used primarily for rapid mixing of reactants for fast gas-phase reactions. Type IV mixers involve installation of full or partial orifices. Details of these are found in Simpson.[7] These mixers are especially suitable for installation in existing process piping systems.

Hartung and Hiby[16] have experimented with the mixer design shown in Figure 13-11. Each baffle occupied half the pipe cross section and was placed one pipe diameter apart from the next baffle. Though Hartung and Hiby used this design to investigate liquid mixing, the design seems equally suitable for gas mixing.

There are at least two patented gas-gas mixer designs: one assigned to the John Zinc Company (Reed[18]) and the other to the Shell Oil Company (Son[19]). Both are based on a cross-flowing-jets configuration.

Like coflowing and cross-flowing jets, jets in swirling flow are also used for mixing gases rapidly. Many combustors use swirling flows.[17] It is an extensively developed, separate field and will not be treated here. Again, the interested reader can refer to the references noted at the end of this chapter.

In addition several motionless or stationary mixers are available commercially, e.g., Kenics or Koch mixers. The term motionless signifies that they have no moving parts. They are frequently used for mixing viscous fluids but are applicable in the turbulent mixing of gases also. There are several references available on the performance of static mixers. They are listed at the end of the chapter.

SUMMARY

This chapter has touched on a special topic of gas-gas mixing as practiced in the industry. As can be surmised from the sections above, a clear-cut design methodology has yet to emerge. A number of researchers have been active in the field of jets and their characterization, as is evidenced in the section on jet mixing. In spite of such a heavy emphasis on studying the jet behavior in different configurations, a designer is bewildered when he has to design a mixer. A unifying approach with the designer in mind is needed to bring all the relevant literature together and simplify his work.

NOMENCLATURE

b   jet radius
C_m maximum jet tracer concentration
C_o inlet tracer concentration
d, d_n jet inlet diameter
D   pipe diameter
f   empirical function $= 0.17/(0.1 + 0.35/R^{1.25})$
g   empirical function $= 0.83 + 0.2 \ell nR$
q   jet inlet flow rate $= \pi/4d^2U_o$
Q   pipe flow rate $= \pi/4D^2V$
R   velocity ratio $= U_o/V$
X   downstream distance from jet inlet
X_c core length of jet
U   jet velocity
U_o inlet jet velocity
V   mainstream velocity

Greek Symbols

ϱ_o jet fluid density
ϱ_∞ mainstream fluid density
θ included angle of jet in coflow
ϕ angle between jet direction and cross-flow direction

REFERENCES

1. Groll, H. P. A., and G. Hearne, *Ind. Eng. Chem.*, 31:1,530 (1939).
2. Fairburn, A. W., H. A. Cheney, and A. J. Cherniavsky, *Chem. Eng. Prog.*, 43:280 (1947).
3. Smith, J. M., *Chemical Engineering Kinetics*, 3rd Ed., McGraw-Hill Book Co., NY (1981).
4. Simpson, L. L., *Chem. Eng. Prog.*, 70:77 (1974).
5. Chilton, T. H., and R. P. Genereaux, *AIChE Trans.* 25(102) (1930).
6. Narayan, B. C., M.S. Thesis, University of Tulsa, Tulsa, OK (1971).
7. Simpson, L. L., *Turbulence in Mixing Operations*, R. S. Brodkey (Ed.) Academic Press, Inc., NY (1975).
8. Reed, R. D. and B. C. Narayan, *Chem. Eng.*, 86:131 (1979).
9. Forney, L. J., and H. C. Lee, *AIChE J.*, 28:980 (1982).
10. Forney, L. J., and T. C. Kwon, *AIChE J.*, 25:623 (1979).
11. Ger, A. M., and E. R. Holley, *Hydraulic Eng. Series #30*, Univ. of Illinois, Urbana, IL (1974).
12. Lee, H. C., M. S. Thesis, Dept. of Chem. Eng., Georgia Inst. of Tech., Atlanta, GA (1981).
13. Maruyama, T., S. Suzuki, and T. Mizushina, *Int. Chem. Eng.*, 21:205 (1981).
14. Winter, D. D., M. S. Thesis, Univ. of Illinois, Urbana, IL (1975).
15. Wright, S. J., Ph.D. Thesis, Calif. Inst. of Tech., Pasadena, CA (1977).
16. Hartung, K. H. and J. W. Hiby, *Chem. Eng. Tech.* 44:1,051 (1972).
17. Beer, J. M., and N. A. Chigier, *Combustion Aerodynamics*, Halstead Press NY (1972).
18. Reed, R. D., U.S. Patent #3,332,442 (1965).
19. Son, J. S., U.S. Patent #3,702,619 (1972).
20. Swanson, Unpublished data (1958).
21. Ajinkya, M. B. "Mixing of Gases"—*Handbook of Fluids in Motion,"* Ann Arbor Science, Ann Arbor, MI (1983), Ch. 9.

BIBLIOGRAPHY

Jets in Cross Flow

Abramovich, G. N., *The Theory of Turbulent Jets* The MIT Press, Cambridge, MA(1963).

Callaghan, E. E., and R. S. Ruggeri, NACA TN 61615 (1948).
Campbell, J. F., and J. A. Schetz. AIAA J. 11:242 (1973).
Crabb, D., D. F. G. Durao, and J. H. Whitelaw, *ASME J. Fluids Eng.* 103:142 (1981).
Daniel, T. L., S. Chan, and J. F. Kennedy, 11HR Report No. 140 (August 1972).
Harsha, P. T., Arnold Engineering Development Center, Tech. Report AEDC-TR-71-36 (1971).
Kamotani, Y., and I. Greber, NASA CR-2392 (March 1974).
Keffer, J. F., and W. D. Baines, *J. Fluid Mech.* 15:481 (1963).
Makihata, T., and Y. Miyai, *ASME J. Fluids Eng.* 101:217 (1979).
Norster, E. R., and C. S. Chapman. "Combustion and Fuels" paper presented at the A.R.C. meeting (May 11, 1962).
Patankar, S. V., D. K. Basu, and S. A. Alpay, *AMSE J. Fluids Eng.* 99:758 (1977).
Patrick M. A., *J. Inst. Fuel* (1967), p. 425
Stoy, R. L., and Y. Ben-Haim, *ASME J. Fluids Eng.* 95:551 (1973).
Sucec, J., and W. H. Bowley, *ASME J. Fluids Eng.* 98:656 (1976).

Motionless Mixers:

Azer, N. Z., S. T. Lin, and L. T. Fan, *I and EC Proc. Design Devel.*, 19:246 (1980).
Chen, S. J., *Chemical Eng. Prog.* 71:80 (August 1975).
Fan, L. T., S. T. Lin, and N. Z. Azer, *Int. J. Heat and Mass Trans.*, 21:849 (1978).
Morris, W. D., and R. Proctor, *I and EC Proc. Design Devel.*, 16:406 (1977).

14

Particulate
Capture—Dry Methods

CONTENTS

INTRODUCTION, 593

GRAVITATIONAL SEPARATION, 595

ELECTROSTATIC PRECIPITATION, 599

CYCLONE SEPARATORS, 602

FABRIC FILTER DUST COLLECTORS, 623

NOMENCLATURE, 638

REFERENCES, 640

INTRODUCTION

The motion of solid particles in gaseous mediums is all too frequently encountered in engineering applications. Unit operations directed at the separation of these heterogeneous systems include sedimentation in settling chambers, separation of particles in cyclone separators, particle capture in electrostatic fields, and filtration.

The widespread and successful applications of these particle-capturing techniques to a large number of industrial problems is based on the ability to take advantage of one or a combination of four primary forces, namely, gravity, centrifugal, pressure, and electric. Gravity is the controlling force for separations achieved in settlers; centrifugal force is applied to cyclone separators; and pressure forces are employed in air classification and in filters. Proper design of this equipment requires a fundamental understanding of fluid mechanics and particle aerodynamics.

During viscous flow over a stationary body or particle, certain resistances arise. To overcome these resistances or drag and to provide more uniform fluid motion, a certain amount of energy must be expended. The developed drag force and consequently the energy required to overcome it depend largely on the flow regime and the geometry of the solid body. Laminar flow conditions prevail when the fluid medium flows at low velocities over small bodies or when the fluid has a relatively high viscosity. Flow around a single body is illustrated in Figure 14-1.

As shown in Figure 14-1A, when the flow is laminar, a well-defined boundary layer forms around the body and the fluid conforms to a streamline motion. The loss of energy in this situation is primarily due to friction drag. If the fluid's average velocity is sufficiently increased, the influence of inertial forces becomes more pronounced and the flow becomes turbulent. Under the action of inertial forces the fluid adheres to the particle surface, forming only a very thin boundary layer and generating a turbulent wake as shown in Figure 14-1B. The pressure in the wake is significantly lower than that at the stagnation point on the leeward side of the particle. Hence, a net force, referred to as the *pressure drag*, acts in a direction opposite to that of the fluid's motion. Above a certain value of the Reynolds number, the role of pressure drag becomes significant, and the friction drag can be ignored.

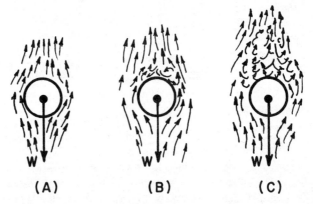

(A)   **(B)**   **(C)**

Figure 14-1. Illustration of flow around a solid particle: (A) laminar flow; (B) transition flow; (C) turbulent flow.

In Chapter 1 a dilute system, which is described as a low concentration of noninteracting solid particles carried along by a gas stream, was analyzed. In this system the solid particles are far enough removed from one another so that they may be treated as individual particles; that is, each particle individually contributes to the overall character of the flow. This discussion is most pertinent to understanding the rudimentary design principles outlined in this chapter.

GRAVITATIONAL SEPARATION

Settling equipment for removing solid particles from gas streams is designed for:

1. Cleaning of ventilation air or flyash removal from flue gases
2. Product-quality improvement
3. Recovery of valuable products
4. Powdered-product collection

The forces utilized for separating particles from gas streams may be classified as

1. Gravity settling
2. Inertial deposition
3. Flow-line interception
4. Diffusional deposition
5. Electrostatic deposition
6. Thermal precipitation
7. Sonic agglomeration

We shall discuss gravitational settling in this subsection.

Particle separation by this method is achieved in a chamber in which the velocity of a gaseous suspension is reduced to enable particles to settle out by the action of gravity. In order to decrease the trajectory path of a particle and consequently the time of settling, horizontal plates are sometimes positioned within the chamber. These plates significantly improve the collection efficiency of the discrete phase. Figure 14-2 illustrates a typical multiplate settling chamber.

To establish the length of the chamber required to remove particles of a certain minimum size (or to determine the size particles removed by an existing chamber with a specified loading), the particle settling velocity must be evaluated. If the particulates in question follow Stokes' law and are approximately spherical, the familiar settling velocity expression developed earlier may be applied:

$$u = \frac{d^2(\gamma_p - \gamma)}{18\mu} \qquad (14\text{-}1)$$

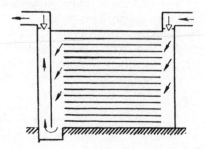

Figure 14-2. Multiplate settling chamber.

Since $\gamma_p >> \gamma$, Equation 14-1 simplifies to:

$$u = \frac{d^2\gamma_p}{18\mu} \tag{14-2}$$

For very large particles (typically above several hundred microns), the Allen equation may be used to estimate settling velocity.

$$u = \frac{0.153 \; d^{1.14}\gamma_p^{0.71}}{\left(\dfrac{\gamma}{g}\right)^{0.29} \mu^{0.43}} \tag{14-3}$$

If for a given heterogeneous system the settling velocity of the smallest particles that will separate out is u and the height of the chamber (or the distance between horizontal plates) is H, then the settling time will be H/u. The time required for a unit volume of gas to remain in the chamber (i.e., the gas residence time) must at least be equal to the settling time to allow the smallest particles to be removed. The linear gas velocity is equal to the volumetric flow rate, V, divided by the cross-sectional area of the chamber, F. For a chamber of length L, the residence time of the gas in the chamber is L(V/F). Since this time must be equal to that of the smallest particle we may equate the two times to give:

$$L = \frac{HV}{uF} \tag{14-4}$$

This expression shows that at a constant gas velocity, V/F, the length of the chamber, L, is proportional to its height H. Obviously, the smaller the height, the smaller the chamber length required for a desired separation, which thus explains the advantage of a plate design (Figure 14-2) over a simple chamber.

Because the smallest particles will settle according to Stokes' law, we may substitute Equation 14-2 for u into Equation 14-4:

$$L = \frac{18HV\mu}{Fd^2\gamma_p} \tag{14-5}$$

Thus, the length of a settling chamber is inversely proportional to the square of the particle diameter. If it is desirable to separate out particles that, for example, are two times smaller than the selected size, then the length of the chamber must be increased by a factor of four. Equation 14-5 may also be used to determine the smallest particle diameter that can be removed by a chamber of specified dimensions.

The following example problem illustrates some of these design principles.

Example Problem 1

Determine the dimensions of a simple settling chamber (illustrated in Figure 14-3) required to remove 50-μm-size particles under the following set of operating conditions:

Gas capacity Q $=$ 2,400 m^3/hr
Particle density ϱ_p $=$ 2,400 kg/m^3
Gas temperature t $=$ 20°C
Gas density ϱ $=$ 1.2 kg/m^3
Gas viscosity μ $=$ 1.8 $\times$ 10^{-5} N-s/m^2

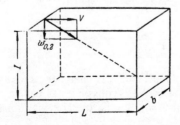

Figure 14-3. Simple settling chamber for Example Problem 1.

Solution

The settling regime for the particles must first be determined. Hence, the critical particle diameter is first computed:

$$d_{cr} = 2.62\left[\frac{\mu^2}{g(\varrho_p - \varrho)\varrho}\right]^{0.333}$$

$$d_{cr} = 2.62\left[\frac{(1.8 \times 10^{-5})^2}{9.81(2,400 - 1.2)1.2}\right]^{0.333} = 5.9 \times 10^{-5}\text{m} = 59\mu\text{m}$$

Since the size range of particles to be removed is less than the critical diameter, we are confident that particles will follow Stokes' law. Hence, the settling velocity for a 50 μm particle is:

$$W_o = \frac{d^2}{18} \times \frac{\varrho_p - \varrho}{\mu}g = \frac{(50 \times 10^{-6})^2}{18} \frac{2,400}{1.8 \times 10^{-5}}9.81 = 0.182 \text{ m/s}$$

The dimensions of the chamber shown in Figure 14-3 are determined based on the criterion that the time required for the particle to settle out is proportional to the chamber length:

$$t = \frac{H}{W_o} = \frac{L}{\nu}$$

If the chamber volume is V_c, then the residence time is:

$$t = \frac{3,600 \ V_c}{Q} = \frac{3,600 \ V_c}{2,400} = 1.5 \ V_c$$

Consequently, the maximum chamber height (m) is:

$$H = 1.5 \ W_o V_c = 1.5 \times 0.182 \times V_c = 0.273 \ V_c$$

The longitudinal cross-section of the chamber is:

$$B = \frac{V_c}{H} = \frac{V_c}{2.73V_c} = 3.7 \text{ m}^2$$

To determine the specific dimensions, the chamber's cross-section must be evaluated. This area is a function of the permissible gas velocity through the chamber. Assuming a gas velocity of $\nu = 0.2$ m/s, the cross-sectional area is:

$$S = \frac{Q}{3,600\nu} = \frac{2,400}{3,600 \times 0.2} = 3.33 \text{ m}^2$$

Since the two cross-sections of the chamber are now known, by selecting one dimension, based on acceptable space or headroom availability, the other dimensions can be established. For example, let H = 1 m, then:

$$b = \frac{S}{H} = \frac{3.33}{1} = 3.33 \text{ m}$$

$$L = \frac{B}{b} = \frac{3.7}{3.33} = 1.11 \text{ m}$$

Further examples and discussions are given by Green and Lane,[1] Drinker and Hatch,[2] Roberts,[3] and Cheremisinoff et al.[4,5]

ELECTROSTATIC PRECIPITATION

Particles typically less than 10 μm in size generally form a highly stable colloidal suspension in gas (called aerosols). These particles either will not settle out or will require an exceptionally long settling time. Recall that inertia forces are proportional to particle mass and hence, in the case of aerosols these small forces lead to very low settling velocities. Particle separation from the gas can be achieved on a practical basis by passing the heterogeneous system between a pair of high-voltage electrodes that ionize the gas. The discharge electrode, responsible for ionizing the gas, consists of a small cross-section which generates a high electrical field at its surface. The collecting electrode, serves to precipitate the charged particles. Particles migrate according to an EMF gradient and are attracted to the appropriately charged electrodes (i.e., the negatively charged particles are attracted to the positive electrode, and the positively charged particles to the negative electrode).

The direction of the velocity vector of the charged particles is determined by their sign and velocity and consequently their kinetic energy as determined by the field intensity. The electrical field forces responsible for particle precipitation may exceed inertia forces by orders of magnitude.

There are several types of electrostatic precipitators. Normally, the flow section of a precipitation chamber (simply called a precipitator) consists of a bundle of vertical tubes arranged in parallel fashion (usually a round or hexagonal cross-section), or as a packet of vertical parallel plates. Thin wires (approximately 2 mm in diameter) are suspended and stretched along the axes of the tubes, which are 150–300 mm in diameter. The same wires are stretched between the plate configurations. The wires and tubes are connected to a source of direct electrical current of high voltage (up to 90,000 V).

Cylindrical wires are connected to the negative terminal where a zone of ionized gas is generated. Gas molecules in this vicinity are composed of both positively and negatively charged ions. The negative ions are repelled to the walls of the tubes and plates and fill the total volume of the precipitator. The dispersed particulates are contacted by the ions and entrained to the surface of the tubes and plates. Here, the particles lose their charge and descend downward along the electrode surfaces.

The ionized gas layer in the vicinity of the wires dissipates an energy field in the form of a thin layer called the corona (hence, the name "wire corona-forming electrode"). The plates and tubes where the particles are precipitated are called collecting electrodes.

Depending on the shape of electrodes, the electrical field may be either homogeneous or heterogeneous. A homogeneous electrical field is observed in the gaseous space between flat parallel electrodes, as shown in Figure 14-4A. The lines of force uniformly fill the volume and are located in a parallel arrangement. A heterogeneous field is generated when the surface of one of the electrodes is greatly reduced by geometry changes; examples are the tubular precipitator, shown in Figure 14-4B, and the plate precipitator of Figure 14-4C. A thickening of the lines of force occurs around these electrodes, which corresponds to an increase in the field intensity. Hence, the field intensity E_x(V/s-m) in the tube will be at a maximum when x = r, which follows from the following theoretical formula:

$$E_x = \frac{\hat{\nu}}{x \ln \frac{\gamma_0}{x}}$$ (14-6)

where $\hat{\nu}$ = potential difference between the electrodes (volts)
  x = distance from the axis of the internal electrode (m)
  γ_0 = inside diameter of the tube, (m)
  r_{J} = radius of the internal electrode, (m) (see Figure 14-4)

The field intensity at any point between parallel plates is:

$$E = \frac{\hat{\nu}}{d}(V/m)$$ (14-7)

As E increases to its critical value E_{cr}, the gas gap, d, between parallel plates is "broken through" due to fast (cumulative) ionization. In the space between the plates a spark discharge is formed and the current greatly increases due to a shorting of electrodes. Such a process cannot be used for effective removal of particles.

The collision ionization in the heterogeneous field is initiated before achieving E_x at the surface of the wire and is not propagated on the total volume of the gap. A corona discharge occurs in this case with uniform ion formation (that is, the negative ions are repelled to the collecting electrode). The critical field intensity E_{cr} corresponds to the critical potential difference $\hat{\nu}_{cr}$. So far as $\hat{\nu}$ increases up to the spark potential, the current intensity is increased approximately by a square law (the electrical current in gases does not follow Ohm's law, and when $\hat{\nu} > \hat{\nu}_{spark}$ a spark discharge will also occur).

At the negative corona-forming electrode, ν_{cr} and ν_{spark} are higher. In addition, the mobility of the negative ions is greater, therefore, it is usually applied to the negative corona. It is evident that ions located in the force field are subjected to greater forces with an increase in $\hat{\nu}$ and E, which accelerates to the ion motion and

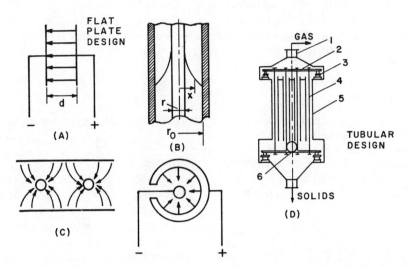

Figure 14-4. Different schemes for electrical precipitators: (1) duct outlet; (2) frame; (3) insulators; (4) corona-forming negative electrodes; (5) tubes; (6) duct for introducing suspension.

settling of charged particles. The applied potential difference must not be less than $\tilde{\mathcal{V}}_{spark}$, because at spark shorting, the intensity on the wires drops drastically resulting in the formation of a corona, and consequently, precipitation strongly degradates.

The primary design issue with a precipitator concerns the proper selection of the collecting electrode's geometry. The two primary configurations are tubular and plate. For the tubular design shown in Figure 14-4D the dust-laden gas enters into the lower chamber of the precipitator through the duct (6), passes by the tubes (5) upwards and exits through the duct (1). Corona-forming negative electrodes (4) are suspended on the frame (2), supported by insulators (3). The latter are removed from the gas flow to avoid fouling. By introducing the suspension from below, fouling of insulators is minimized. The electrodes are shaken with a percussion mechanism and the particles fall off the electrodes into the conical bottom of the precipitator. In the described precipitator, the ionization of the gas near the corona-forming electrode occurs simultaneously with the motion of the charged particles towards the collecting electrode.

The actual mechanical design of an electrostatic precipitator is simple; however, the phenomena occurring inside are extremely complicated. Because of this, a universal design procedure is unavailable. Hence, specific designs must be based upon experimental data and approximate formulas. For general guidelines, the current intensity for a tubular electrode may be taken as $I = 0.3–0.5$ ma/m, and for plate-type precipitators $I = 0.1–0.35$ ma/m. The field intensity is usually 4–450 kV/m (usually no more than 800 kV/m); with a working voltage of 35–70 kV.

For an electrical field length of 3–4 m, the allowable gas velocity is $W_g = 0.5$–1.0 m/s for plate-type precipitators. The gas residence time in a tubular precipitator depends on the particle settling velocity W_s:

$$t_o = \frac{\gamma_o}{W_o} \tag{14-8}$$

where W_o is determined from Stokes' law incorporating the expression for the force of the electrical field.

The collection efficiency of a precipitator is a function of the time that the gas remains in the active field and is in the range of 90%–99%.

For any given particle of uniform size and character the collection efficiency (eff) is related to the time (t, seconds) such that the gas remains in the active field.

$$\log(1 - \text{eff}) = t \log \dot{K} = tEC \tag{14-9}$$

where $\dot{K}$ = precipitation constant ($\dot{K} = 0.05 - 0.50$)
E = voltage
C = constant

Early works by Loeb,[6] Peek,[7] and more recent articles by Cheremisinoff et al.[8] provide good introductory reading to this subject.

CYCLONE SEPARATORS

A cyclone is a nonmechanical device which separates solid particulates from a relatively dry gas stream. Hydroclones are essentially the same device, which effect solids separations from liquids. Both devices are the simplest and most economical separators. Their operation is identical, whereby both inertial and gravitational forces are capitalized upon. Their primary advantages are high collection efficiency in certain applications, adaptability and economy in power. The main disadvantage lies in their limitation in achieving high collection efficiencies for small particles. In general, cyclones are not capable of high efficiencies when handling gas streams containing large concentrations of particulates less than 10 μm in size.

Cyclones generally are efficient handling devices for a wide range of particulate sizes. They are capable of collecting particles ranging in size from 10 to above 2,000 μm, with inlet loadings from less than one grain per scfm to greater than 100 grains per scfm. There are many design variations of the basic cyclone configuration. Because of its simplicity and lack of moving parts, a wide variety of construction materials can be used to cover relatively high operating temperatures of up to 2000°F.

Cyclones are employed in the following general applications:

1. Collection of coarse dust particles
2. Handling high solid concentration gas streams between reactors such as Flexi-cokers (concentrations typically above 3 grains/scf)
3. For classifying particulate sizes
4. In operations where extremely high collection efficiency is not critical
5. As precleaning devices in line with higher efficiency collectors for fine particles

Figure 14-5 shows the primary design features of a cyclone separator. The unit consists of a cylindrical barrel section (1) fitted with a conical base (2). The solids-laden gas stream enters through a tangential inlet (3) while collected solids fall through an outlet duct (5) and the cleaned fluid discharges through an exit duct (4).

The flow pattern in a cyclone is quite complex and has long been the subject of numerous investigations. There are three main flow patterns that prevail in all cyclones. These are:

1. *Descending spiral flow*—This pattern carries the separated dust down the walls of the cyclone to a dust hopper.
2. *Ascending spiral flow*—This rotates in the same direction as the descending spiral, but the cleaned gas is carried from the cyclone or the dust receptacle to the gas outlet.
3. *Radially inward flow*—This feeds the gas from the descending to the ascending spiral.

The final solids separation occurs in the dust-collecting hopper located below the exit duct (5). In the duct leading to the hopper (called the dipleg) the total gas flow reverses direction and transforms to an ascending spiral flow.

The flow patterns are generated by the creation of a double vortex, which centrifuges the dust particles to the walls. The two distinct vortices present in a cyclone are:

1. A large diameter descending helical current in the body and cone
2. An ascending helix of smaller diameter extending up from the dust outlet section, through the gas outlet.

Particles at the walls are transported into the collecting hopper, which is isolated from the influence of the spinning gases. The gas spirals downward and upward through the inside of the cyclone. Upon entering the cyclone, the gas undergoes a redistribution of its velocity, so that the tangential velocity component exceeds the inlet-gas velocity by several times. It is important to note that as the gas spins in a vortex in the cyclone body, the tangential velocities increase as the axis of the cyclone is approached at any horizontal plane. The tangential velocity at any radius appears to be relatively constant at all levels. However, tangential velocities at the extreme top of the cyclone are not included since the proximity of the cyclone cover slows the spin. When the downward gas flow is smooth and unbroken, the dust

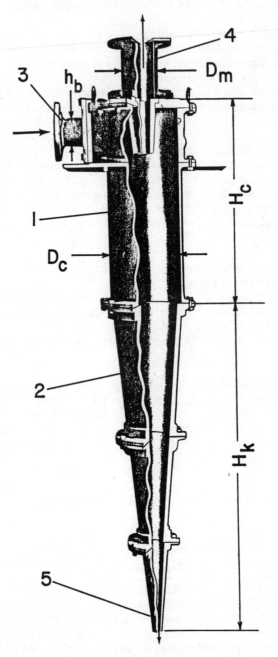

Figure 14-5. Illustration of a cross-section view of a cyclone separator suitable for gas or liquid services.

particles flow spirally downward and pass the bottom dust outlet without re-entrainment.

As illustrated in Figure 14-6, the dust-laden gas enters the tangential inlet and swirls through several revolutions in the body and cone while dropping its dust load. The clean gas is emitted through the axial cylindrical gas outlet. Dust particles, which were uniformly dispersed in the entering gas stream, tend to concentrate in the layer of gas next to the cyclone wall under the influence of centrifugal force. The helical motion of the downward-moving main gas stream and the small quantity of gas through the cyclone dust outlet help assist the separated solids into the receiving bin. Ideally, the gas should be distributed to a cyclone in a radially thin layer, so that the radial distance through which a particle must travel for separation is at a minimum. It is important that the inlet be exactly tangent to the body,

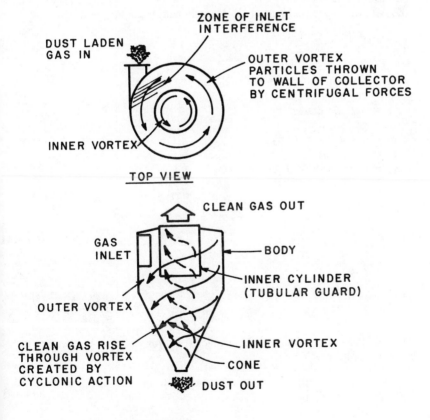

Figure 14-6. Details of internal flow patterns.

since separation is adversely affected by flow abnormalities. The gas discharge through the vertical exit duct maintains the upward helical pattern for some distance, until pipe bends and/or flow restrictions dampen out the spiral.

There are three forces that influence particle motion in a cyclone, namely: centrifugal, due to the particle rotation within the flow; gravity force; and Archimedes' force. The last two forces are small in comparison to centrifugal since the density of the medium is hundreds of times smaller than that of the solid particles.

In principle, the separation of finely dispersed solid particles from gases or liquids is governed by four factors, which are: the established centrifugal field; the radial velocity pattern; the residence time of the particles to be separated; and the turbulence that develops.

The criteria for particle separation is based on the concept of "equilibrium orbits." This term refers to the regions of the flow comprising circular tracks having such a radius that the outwardly directed centrifugal force, acting on a particle in this orbit, is in equilibrium with the inwardly directed drag according to Stokes' law, due to the radial flow.

In the case of a spherical particle this equilibrum leads to:

$$\frac{1}{6}\pi d^3 \varrho_1 \frac{\omega^2 r_1^2}{r_2} = 3\pi\mu d \frac{dr}{d\tau} \tag{14-10}$$

where τ = residence of gas in the cyclone
μ = viscosity of gas
d = particle diameter
ϱ_1 = gas density
ω = angular speed of gas
r_1 = outside radius of the exit pipe
r_2 = inside radius of the cyclone

Solving Equation 14-10 for τ, we obtain:

$$\int_0^\tau d\tau = \frac{18\mu}{d^2\omega^2\varrho_1} \int_{r_1}^{r_2} \frac{dr}{r} \tag{14-11}$$

or

$$\tau = \frac{18\mu}{d^2\omega^2\varrho_1} \ln \frac{r_2}{r_1} \tag{14-12}$$

For the separation of relatively large particles (i.e., for Re > 2) the general resistance law is applicable:

$$\frac{\pi d^3}{6}\varrho_1 \frac{\omega^2 r_1^2}{r_2} = \psi\varrho_2 d^2 \left|\frac{dr}{d\tau}\right|^2 \tag{14-13}$$

or

$$d\tau = \left(\frac{6\psi\varrho_2}{\pi d\varrho_1\omega^2}\right)^{0.5} \left(\frac{dr}{r^{0.5}}\right) \tag{14-14}$$

From which we obtain:

$$\tau = 2\left(\frac{6\psi\varrho_2}{\pi d\varrho_1\omega^2}\right)^{0.5}(r_2^{0.5} - r_1^{0.5})$$ (14-15)

From the residence time of the gas in the cyclone, the working volume can be obtained:

$$V_c = \nu_{sec} \times \tau \; (m^3)$$ (14-16)

where ν_{sec} is the gas flow rate (m³/s).
The height of the cylindrical part of the cyclone is:

$$H = \frac{V_c}{\pi(r_2^2 - r_1^2)} \; (m)$$ (14-17)

If the residence time of the gas is specified, then the minimum particle size that will be collected can be computed:

$$d_{min} = \left(\frac{18\mu}{\omega^2\varrho_1\tau} \ln \frac{r_2}{r_1}\right)^{0.5}$$ (14-18)

Typical tangential and axial velocity distributions in a cyclone are shown in Figure 14-7. The maximum values of the tangential velocities are observed close to the cyclone axis (but not on the axis—Figure 14-7A). Note that in following the tangential velocity component down the cyclone, the maximum shifts closer to the axis. This may be described by the following formula:

$$W = W_g\left(\frac{4}{3}\frac{d}{C_D}\frac{\varrho_{eff}}{\varrho}\frac{1}{R}\right)^{0.5}$$ (14-19)

Equation 14-19 was derived from the settling velocity expression,

$$W_s = \left(\frac{4}{3}\frac{d}{C_D}\frac{\varrho_{eff}}{\varrho}a\right)^{0.5}$$ (14-20)

Note that the acceleration term "a" is replaced by an expression for centrifugal acceleration:

$$a = \frac{W_g^2}{R}$$ (14-21)

where   d = particle diameter
C_D = drag coefficient
ϱ_{eff} = effective density ($\varrho_{eff} = \varrho_p - \varrho$; ϱ_p = particle density, ϱ = fluid density)
W_g = fluid rotational velocity
R = radius of particle rotation

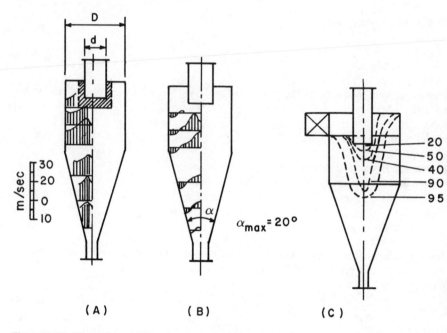

Figure 14-7. Illustration of the variations of velocities in a cyclone: (A) tangential; (B) axial; (C) collection efficiency at different zones of a cyclone.

In contrast, the maximum axial velocities fall exactly on the center-line axis at the lower elevations of the cyclone as shown in Figure 14-7B. The axial components of velocity decrease the collection efficiency since particles can be entrained into the discharge pipe. Due to the counterbalancing effects of the velocity components particle collection efficiency is not uniform in the different zones of a cyclone, as shown by Figure 14-7C.

Overall collection efficiency is defined as: $\eta = (c_1 - c_2)/c_1$ (where c_1 = particle concentration in the entering gas stream and c_2 = particle concentration in the exit gas). Efficiency depends on several factors, primary ones are the physical properties of the heterogeneous system (i.e., gas and particle densities, particle sizes, viscosity of the medium); the linear dimensions of a cyclone; solids loadings, and the gas inlet velocity.

Collection efficiency is a major parameter in the selection and design of a cyclone. Cyclones may be designed for any required efficiency; however, it is important to note that efficiency is both a function of the energy expended and the available space for the unit. Thus, proper optimization to an acceptable efficiency at moderate pressure drop within reasonable space requirements is necessary. Efficiency can be markedly improved at the expense of pressure drop without tampering with space requirements. The major parameter in the prediction of collection efficiency is particle size. For each particular cyclone design there is a critical-size particle at a given density upon which the centrifugal and inward viscous forces are balanced (that is, at the equilibrium state, the particle neither moves outward towards the walls nor inward towards the cyclone axis). Particles larger than this critical diameter (called the "theoretical cut;" measured in microns) are collected, while all smaller particulates escape.

Efficiency is enhanced as the axis of the cyclone is approached until the edge of the core is reached. The reason for this is that the centrifugal force increases more rapidly than the inward drift up to the edge of the gas core. As such, particles rotate in orbits whose radii depend on the balance between the viscous forces due to the inward drift and outward centrifugal force. Particles will then be transferred to the outer orbits, where they pick up finer particles by collision or are captured by turbulent eddy currents. A knowledge of the theoretical cut has very little direct significance in the prediction of collection efficiency. It does, however, give a rough indication of the cyclone performance.

The factors affecting particle settling depend on the relationship of forces which act on the particle in the flow.

$$\eta = \psi(C, G, R_D) \tag{14-22}$$

where

$$C = \frac{\pi d^3}{6} \varrho_1 \frac{\omega^2}{r} \tag{14-23}$$

$$G = \frac{\pi d^3}{6} \varrho_1 g \tag{14-24}$$

$$R_D = \psi \varrho_2 d^2 w_s^2 \tag{14-25}$$

and $\psi = \psi(Re)$ or $\psi = \psi\left(\dfrac{dw \varrho_2}{\mu}\right)$

Consequently, the drag force is also a function of viscosity.

Accounting for Equations 14-23 through 14-25, Equation 14-22 is restated as follows:

$$\eta = \psi(\varrho_1, d, \mu, \varrho_2, w_s, r, g) \tag{14-26}$$

where w_s is the settling velocity of a particle.

Because it is difficult to measure the actual velocity of a particle in a cyclone, the velocity of fluid is measured typically at the inlet, since it is most convenient. There is a definite relationship between the fluid velocity and the actual velocity of the particle. Hence, w_s may be approximated by the velocity of the fluid if particles are sufficiently small. Note that the radius of rotation of a particle (or the gas-solid mixture itself) is a variable. It, too, may be approximated by a specific dimension of the cyclone which is proportional to the other principal dimensions. The reference dimension, L, may be the cyclone radius, the diameter of the inlet duct, or some other convenient dimension.

Equation 14-26 may therefore be stated in the following form:

$$\eta = \psi(\varrho_1, d, \mu_1, \varrho_2, w_g, L, g) \tag{14-27}$$

By means of dimensional analysis, the functionality of cyclone collection efficiency is deduced.

$$\eta = \psi\left(Fr, \ Re, \ \frac{\varrho_2 L}{\varrho_1 d}\right) \tag{14-28}$$

For the laminar regime of flow (i.e., Re $\leq$ 2) the inertia of the medium may be ignored, and hence:

$$\eta = \psi(\varrho_1, d, \mu, w_g, L, g) \tag{14-29}$$

And on the basis of dimensional analysis we obtain:

$$\eta = \psi(St, Fr) \tag{14-30}$$

where $St = \dfrac{\varrho d^2 w_g}{\mu L}$

$$Fr = \frac{w_g^2}{gL}$$

The most common method of estimating total collection efficiency is by plotting a fractional efficiency curve or grade efficiency curve. A fractional efficiency curve is a plot of particle size versus percent collection. Figures 14-8 and 14-9 show the specific features of such a curve and a typical plot based on experimental data, respectively.

Figure 14-8 shows that the cyclone has 0% efficiency for all particles smaller than the cut size and 100% for all larger sizes.

Under actual operating conditions, however, a considerable amount of the particulates smaller than the cut size are separated along with the coarser particles. This can be explained by collision between particulates and particle agglomeration. Furthermore, a portion of the particles larger than the cut size escape collection (they are reentrained into the inner vortex either by eddies or by particle collisions). Little success has been achieved in accurately predicting efficiencies with particle sizes less than the cut size. The degree of collection efficiency in this range largely depends on the properties of the particles.

It is apparent that the curve in Figure 14-8 may be used accurately in predicting the total collection efficiency of a cyclone, only if the particle size distribution of the suspension is well known.

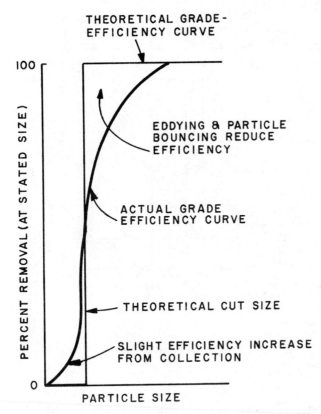

Figure 14-8. Illustration of a typical grade efficiency curve. Note that the cyclone has 0% collection efficiency for all particles that are smaller than the theoretical cut size, and 100% efficiency for all larger sizes. (These, of course, are theoretical limits.)

The specific operating parameters which efficiency depends on are:

1. Pressure drop
2. Particle size distribution
3. Inlet particle loading
4. Temperature of the inlet gas stream
5. Specific gravities of gas and solids

Table 14-1 summarizes the relationships of these factors to efficiency with the exception of pressure drop, which is considered separately.

There are several operating characteristics that contribute to lower collection efficiencies for particles exceeding the cut size. One important characteristic is that the distribution or drift is highly nonuniform. As noted by the contour plots shown

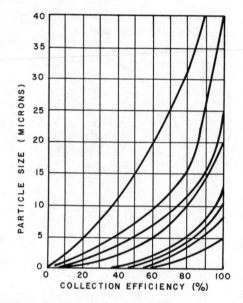

Figure 14-9. Typical collection efficiency curves. Data obtained on a 12-in. diameter cyclone using cracking catalyst.

Table 14-1
Factors Influencing Efficiency

Condition	Effect on Efficiency
Temperature	Decreases as temperature increases due to gas viscosity changes
Velocity	Increases with velocity and falls off sharply below 25 ft/s
Specific Gravity	Increases with higher specific gravity
Inlet Loading	Increases with inlet loading

earlier, at certain points in the cyclone local velocities may exceed the mean inlet velocity by a factor of 2 or 3. This is particularly pronounced at the ends of the cyclone where additional surfaces induce precession currents. A doubling or tripling of the drift velocity at any point results in particles 40% larger than the theoretical cut in reaching the exit.

Another effect responsible for poor separation of coarse particles from the gas is the presence of eddies in the vortex. The velocities of eddies normal to the main flow are generally one-fifth of the main flow. Thus, if the gases near the walls of the cyclone are spinning at about 50 ft/s, the eddies may add an additional 10 ft/s or more than the inward drift velocity. The inward drift velocity should only be on the order of 1 ft/s. The eddies will thus cause particles of the magnitude of three times or more than the cut size to appear in the exit stream.

The generation of double vortex eddies, superimposed in the vertical plane on the main flow, is also a problem. Figure 14-10 shows this phenomenon. Eddy currents tend to assist the particle descent into the collection hopper, but at the same time carry a portion of the collected particles back into the inner ascending vortex. Up-swept particles have an opportunity to be separated while being transported to the clean gas exit. The reason for this is that the gas spins very rapidly in the inner vortex. However, a large portion of particles does escape collection in this manner.

Base pickup is a major cause of excessive emissions. Some cyclone systems are designed with a predisengaging hopper (called a dustpot) before the final collecting hopper. Dustpots are designed to provide a disengagement space for recovering

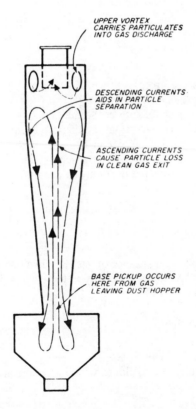

Figure 14-10. Illustration of eddying in a cyclone.

particles from the return gas; however, when the particles are undersized, an additional vertical flow is induced causing particulates to become reentrained.

One approach to minimizing particle reentrainment from the base and cyclone walls is to irrigate the vessel walls. A 5% to 15% purge from the bottom of the cyclone also reduces base pickup. However, the added expense usually outweighs any additional increase in efficiency.

Improved separation can be achieved by increasing the effective particle settling velocity. The velocity expression (Equation 14-20) implies that this can be achieved for a given heterogeneous system of known physical properties and cyclone capacity by increasing the peripheral gas velocity, W_g, or by decreasing the radius of the cyclone, or both. Note, however, that an increase in the gas flow leads to a dramatic rise in the hydraulic resistance of the cyclone.

Pressure drop is one of the most important factors affecting efficiency and design.

The total pressure in a cyclone consists of separate losses in the inlet pipe, the vortex, and the cyclone exit duct.

The pressure drop across a cyclone may be estimated from Bernoulli's equation:

$$\frac{\Delta P}{\gamma} = \frac{w_0^2}{2g} - \frac{w_1^2}{2g} + Z \tag{14-31}$$

where ΔP = total pressure drop
   γ = specific gravity of gas
   w_0 = superficial gas velocity at the inlet duct
   w_1 = superficial gas velocity at the discharge duct
   Z = total cyclone resistance consisting of the resistance inside the cyclone Z_0 and resistance at the discharge duct Z_1 where the gas resistance in the discharge duct may be computed from Darcy's equation:

$$Z_1 = \lambda \frac{L_1}{d_1} \frac{w_1^2}{2g} \tag{14-32}$$

As the first approximation the resistance of gas flow in a cyclone is proportional to kinetic energy of the gas. As the gas velocity in the cyclone is practically equal to the initial velocity w_0, we have:

$$Z_0 = K_0 \frac{w_0^2}{2g} \tag{14-33}$$

The resistance coefficient K_0 for cyclones with a rectangular inlet duct (h—height and b—width) is:

$$K_0 = 16 \frac{bh}{d_1^2} \tag{14-34}$$

Since the ratio w_0/w_1 is equal to the ratio of cross-sections F_1/F_0 (from continuity), Equation 14-31 may be rewritten as follows:

$$\frac{\Delta P}{\gamma} = \frac{w_0^2}{2g}\left[Z_0 + Z_1 - 1 + \left(\frac{F_0}{F_1}\right)^2\right] \tag{14-35}$$

The section F_0 is equal to bh, and the section of the discharge duct is $F_1 = \pi d_1^2/4$; and considering Equation 14-34, the pressure drop expression becomes:

$$\frac{\Delta P}{\gamma} = \frac{w_0^2}{2g}\left[\frac{16bh}{d_1^2} + \frac{4bh}{\pi d_1^2}\left(1 + \lambda\frac{L_1}{d_1}\right) - 1\right] \tag{14-36}$$

The resistance coefficient λ is determined from the well-known expressions for turbulent motion in pipes.

Shepherd et al.[9] have shown that the flow resistance in a cyclone decreases with increasing particle concentration. The pressure drop at a given gas velocity and particle concentration c may be described by the following relation:

$$\frac{\Delta P_0 - \Delta P}{\Delta P} = \dot{a}c^{0.5} \tag{14-37}$$

where ΔP_0 is the presure drop at the same cyclone capacity for a gas flow without solids and $\dot{a}$ is a characteristic constant for the specific cyclone.

The volumetric velocity of a clean gas V_0 and gas suspension V under the action of the same pressure gradient are related by the following expression:

$$\frac{V - V_0}{V_0} = bc^{0.5} \tag{14-38}$$

Excessive pressure losses can greatly reduce collection efficiency. Unfortunately, little can be done to correct for pressure drop. The spinning gases, at the exit from a cyclone, retain a great deal of the kinetic energy.

Attempts have been made to recover all or part of this lost kinetic energy. A few methods employed include the following arrangements:

1. A tangential exit pipe
2. A conical divergent pipe
3. Vanes in the exit pipe
4. Discs both inside and outside the pipe

Common cyclones, whose bodies are 3 to 5 times the diameter of the inlet duct, are useful where large gas handling capacity and moderate separating efficiencies are required. Particle sizes in excess of 50 μm generally experience good separation in these *large-diameter cyclones*.

To achieve high separating efficiencies for particulates above 30 μm in size, *small-diameter cyclones* are generally employed. Higher fluid-loadings handling capacities are generally achieved by clustering a multiple of cyclones as shown in Figure 14-11.

Figure 14-11. A cyclone cluster arrangement; all cyclones are fed from a common inlet manifold. (Courtesy of Krebs Engineers, Menlo Park, CA.)

A battery of cyclones composed of miniature units (barrel diameters typically 150–250 mm) is referred to as a multiclone arrangement. The individual cyclones are housed inside the retaining vessel. The cyclone units in Figure 14-12 are supported between two grids (2). The gas enters the battery through a duct (4) and is distributed among all the cyclone-elements. Upon passing through the cyclones, the gas enters into the general chamber and then the discharge duct. Particles are collected in the lower cone and part of the hopper and then evacuated from it.

In small-diameter, long-cone cyclones the heavy particles entering the cyclone reach the walls with comparatively small angular movement. The lighter particles entering at the same place must travel through a much greater angle to reach the cyclone wall. Hence, the smaller the particle size, the greater the angle of rotation. Also the greater the number of convolutions of the separating vortex, the smaller the particles that can be separated. High collection efficiencies are obtained from cyclones whose body diameters are less than one foot. For the highest separation, interiors must be well polished, with all eddy-forming projections eliminated. Efficiencies of more than 99% have been achieved in miniature cyclones handling average particle sizes of 5 μm. The capacities for larger units of similar design are proportional to the square of the diameter. Again, because of the limited capacity of a single unit, miniature cyclones can be installed in clusters and fed from the same duct. Greater pressure and more power is necessary to operate smaller combined units. The small-diameter cyclones tend to increase the gas stream's tangential velocity and centrifugal action, and because of their small size, the danger of choking is always imminent.

It is often more advantageous to employ several cyclones in parallel or series arrangements. Groups of cyclones, under some conditions and applications, can handle larger quantities of gas and more efficiently.

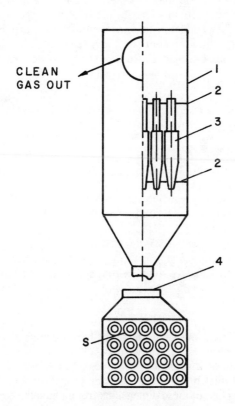

Figure 14-12. Schematic of a multiclone. Shown is a battery of cyclones: 1—hopper; 2—grid; 3—element of a battery-cyclone; 4—nozzle for entering gas suspension.

Parallel arrangements of cyclones can, however, present difficulties if proper design is not employed. Collection efficiency of a group in parallel could be less than one individual cyclone handling a comparable quantity of gas volume. This is brought about due to a difference in the pressures in various cyclone particle outlets, causing a circulation of gas within the receptacle from one cyclone to another.

The particular cyclone exhibiting a lower pressure at the outlet will discharge more gas from the hopper as it enters through other cyclones. The effect is that the ascending gas velocity increases without a corresponding increase in radial velocity, thus decreasing the overall efficiency. Fortunately, this can be overcome by minimizing the difference in pressure between the various particle discharges. This is accomplished by making all the cyclones feeding a common hopper dimensionally identical. Furthermore, operating and loading conditions in each unit should be identical.

Groups of cyclones in series are employed when it is desirable to operate at a higher efficiency than is possible with a single stage of collection alone or to handle higher gas volumes. This type of arrangement may prove more economical than a single high-efficiency cyclone that may have to handle a heavy concentration of abrasive particles. It generally involves the use of a two-stage arrangement; that is, a primary and secondary collector. In some applications a tertiary cyclone is used. Generally, the tertiary unit is smaller since it is required to handle a smaller solids loading. The following example illustrates some of the design principles discussed.[5]

Example Problem 2

Size a cyclone separator for removing particles above 100 μm in diameter entrained in a flue gas stream. The following information is supplied:

Gas volumetric flow V_{sec} = 1.8m^3/s
Particle density ϱ_p = 1,100 kg/m^3
Gas density ϱ = 1.2 kg/m^3
Gas kinematic viscosity ν = 2.25 $\times$ 10^{-5}m^2/s

The particles are approximately round with a shape factor of 0.77.

Solution

1. The relative dimensions (in terms of the barrel diameter) of one manufacturer's cyclone unit is given in Figure 14-13.
2. All dimensions of a cyclone of any design are selected depending on the width of inlet duct b or on the diameter of cyclone D_c. The problem is to properly select one of these dimensions from which the other dimensions are proportionally evaluated.
   The cyclone diameter, settling velocity, gas velocity, and parameters of the suspension to be separated are all interrelated parameters. Therefore, we se-

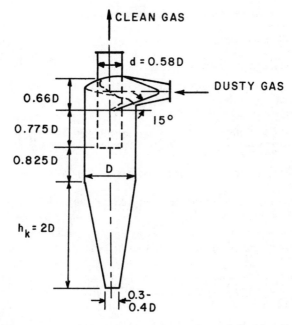

Figure 14-13. Schematic of cyclone for Example Problem 2.

lect a preliminary diameter for approximate calculations and then refine our
estimate to a more exact design.

The relative dimensions of the cyclone are specified as: $b = \alpha D_c$ and h_{in}
$= \beta D_c$.
For the chosen cyclone $\alpha = 0.21$ and $\beta = 0.66$.
The continuity equation for the inlet nozzle is:

$$bh_{in} = \frac{V_{sec}}{w_{in}} \tag{14-39}$$

where w_{in} is the inlet gas velocity; which for a primary cyclone operation is
typically 18 to 22 m/s.

Expressing b and h_{in} in terms of the barrel diameter D_c, Equation 14-39 is
rearranged to solve for the cyclone diameter:

$$D_c \left(\frac{V_{sec}}{\alpha \beta w_{in}} \right)^{0.5} = \left(\frac{1.8}{0.21 \times 0.66 \times 18} \right)^{0.5} = 0.85m$$

For design purposes, assume a value of 0.9 m for D_c.

3. The diameter of the discharge pipe (according to Figure 14-13) is:

$$D_d = 0.58D_c = 0.58 \times 0.9 = 0.52 \text{ m}$$

4. The gas velocity in discharge pipe is thus:

$$w_d = \frac{4V_{sec}}{\pi D_d^2} = \frac{4 \times 1.8}{3.14 \times 0.52^2} = 8.5 \text{ m/s}$$

5. Specifying a wall thickness $\delta = 5$ mm for the gas discharge pipe, its outside diameter will be:

$$D_{d.\,out} = D_d + 28 = 0.52 + 2 \times 0.005 = 0.53 \text{ m}$$

6. The width of the circular gap between the pipe and cyclone shell (refer again to Figure 14-13) is:

$$\ell = \frac{D_c}{2} - \frac{D_{d.\,out}}{2} = 0.45 - 0.265 = 0.185 \text{ m}$$

7. The height of the circular gap from a spiral surface to the lower edge of discharge pipe in Figure 14-13 is:

$$H = 0.775D_c = 0.775 \times 0.9 = 0.7 \text{ m}$$

8. The calculated dimensions of the cyclone can be checked by comparing the particle settling time:

$$\tau_0 = \frac{R_c - R_{d.\,out}}{w_0} = \frac{\ell}{w_0} \tag{14-40}$$

to the residence time of gas in the cyclone:

$$\tau = \frac{2\pi R_{av}n}{w_g} \tag{14-41}$$

where R_c and $R_{d.\,out}$ are the radii of the cyclone and discharge pipe, respectively; n = number of gas rotations around the discharge pipe (we may assume n = 1.5).

9. The peripheral velocity of gas is:

$$w_g = \frac{V_{sec}}{H\ell} = \frac{1.8}{0.7 \times 0.185} = 13.9 \text{ m/s}$$

For cyclones, this value must be in the range of 12 to 14 m/s.

10. The average radius of the gas rotation is:

$$R_{av} = \frac{D_{d.\,out}}{2} + \frac{\ell}{2} = \frac{0.53}{2} + \frac{0.185}{2} = 0.357 \text{ m}$$

11. The centrifugal acceleration (at the average radius) is:

$$a = \frac{w_g^2}{R_{av}} = \frac{13.9^2}{0.357} = 542 \text{ m/s}^2$$

12. The separation criterion is:

$$K_s = \frac{a}{g} = \frac{542}{9.81} = 55.2 \tag{14-42}$$

i.e., in this case, the centrifugal field in the cyclone is 55.2 times more intensive than the gravitational.

13. The Archimedes number is:

$$Ar = \frac{gd^3}{\nu^2} \times \frac{\varrho_f}{\varrho} = \frac{9.81 \times (10 \times 10^{-5})^3}{(2.25 \times 10^{-5})^2} \times \frac{1.1 \times 10^3}{1.2} = 17.8$$

where $\varrho_f = \varrho_p - \varrho \simeq \varrho_p$
The settling number is:

$$S_1 = Ar \times 1 \times K_s = 17.8 \times 55.2 = 980$$

14. Because $3.6 < S_1 < 82{,}500$ the flow regime through the cyclone is transitional. Therefore, the theoretical velocity of the particles is:

$$w = 0.22 \, d\left[\frac{(\alpha\varrho_f)^2}{\mu\varrho}\right]^{0.333} = 0.22 \, d\left[\frac{(\alpha\varrho_p^2)}{\nu\varrho^2}\right]^{0.333}$$

$$= 0.22 \times 10 \times 10^{-5}\left[\frac{(5.42 \times 10^2 \times 1.1 \times 10^3)^2}{2.25 \times 10^{-5} \times 1.2^2}\right]^{0.333} = 1.07 \text{ m/s}$$

15. The particles have a shape factor of $\psi = 0.77$ and the inlet gas stream contains a low volume of solid particles. Based on the operating conditions specified, the settling velocity is:

$$w_s = R\psi w = 0.77 \times 1.07 = 0.825 \text{ m/s}$$

Because the concentration of the suspension is low, we may assume $R = 1$.

16. The settling time is therefore:

$$\tau_0 = \frac{\ell}{w_s} = \frac{0.185}{0.825} = 0.224 \text{ s}$$

17. The residence time for the gas is:

$$\tau = \frac{2\pi R_{avg} n}{w_g} = \frac{2 \times 3.14 \times 0.357 \times 1.5}{13.9} = 0.24 \text{ s}$$

Since $\tau_0 < \tau$ the diameter of the cyclone selected is acceptable and we may now specify the other dimensions as based on the recommended proportions in Figure 14-13.

18. As a final calculation for the design, we evaluate the hydraulic resistance of the cyclone:

$$\Delta P = \tfrac{1}{2}C_D \varrho w_{in}^2 = 0.5 \times 7 \times 1.2 \times 18^2 = 1{,}360 \text{ N/m}^2$$

where C_D for a typical cyclone is equal to 7.

Now consider a multiclone arrangement. Normally, the allowable pressure drop is specified along with the conditional gas velocity for each cyclone element. For multiclones, typical pressure drop requirements and conditional inlet velocities are 350–600 N/m²(ΔP_{bc}) and 3–4 m/s (w_{cond}), respectively. A typical design problem often concerns determining the number of cyclone units required for a specified separation.

The continuity equation states:

$$V_{sec} = Z\frac{\pi d_{el}^2}{4} \, w_{cond} \; (\text{m}^3/\text{s}) \tag{14-43}$$

where Z is the number of cyclone elements having diameter d_{el}.

The hydraulic resistance of a battery-cyclone at the conditional velocity is:

$$\Delta P_{bc} = \tfrac{1}{2}\Sigma C_D \varrho w_{cond}^2 \tag{14-44}$$

From Equations 14-43 and 14-44 we obtain the number of elements with diameter d_{el}:

$$Z = 0.9 \frac{V_{sec}}{d_{el}^2 \left(\dfrac{\Delta P_{b.c.}}{\varrho \Sigma C_D}\right)^{0.5}} \tag{14-45}$$

From information on ΔP_{bc}, ΣC_D, and d_{el}, Z can be computed. Equation 14-43 may then be used to compute the conditional velocity w_{cond}, and resistance ΔP_{bc} can be estimated from Equation 14-44. If values computed from Equations 14-43 and 14-44 are within the recommended operating limits, the number of cyclone elements chosen represents an acceptable design.

Based on the specified number of cyclones, the principal dimensions of the retaining vessel can be sized through proper layout of the individual cyclone elements. The simplest vessel to design for is rectangular and a rough guideline for spacing between individual cyclones is 30 to 50 mm.

Assuming a gas velocity in the discharge pipe to be $w_{gd} = 14 - 18$ m/s, from the working expression:

$$V_{sec} = \frac{\pi d_d^2}{4} Z w_{gd} \tag{14-46}$$

we can determine the diameter of the discharge pipe; and from a specified pipe wall thickness, δ, compute the outside diameter of the discharge pipe $d_{d.\,out}$.

If Z_1 cyclone elements are positioned perpendicular to the gas flow in the retaining vessel, the width of the chamber is:

$$b = d_{e1}Z_1 + S(Z_1 + 1) \qquad (14\text{-}47)$$

The free passage in the entrance chamber is $b - Z_1d_{d. out}$.
The continuity equation then becomes:

$$V_{sec} = w_{in}h_{in}(b - Z_1d_{d. out}) \qquad (14\text{-}48)$$

From the specified gas entrance velocity, the chamber height can be computed.

References 10 through 74 have been compiled to provide further readings on general design, operational theory, applications, and problems associated with cyclone separators. See Appendix C for a partial list of U.S. cyclone manufacturers.

FABRIC FILTER DUST COLLECTORS

Filter fabrics have the ability to capture particles smaller than the smallest opening in the cloth. For example, even when the spaces between certain fibers of cloth measure 100 μm or more, particles as small as 1 μm can be captured. The principal mechanisms responsible for this collection phenomenon are interception, impingement, diffusion, gravity settling, and electrostatic attraction, in addition to, of course, simple particle sieving. These forces retain particles on the cloth fibers, forming a filter cake or mat which then leads to finer sieving.

Sieving refers simply to the fact that large particles will not pass through small holes. Particle velocity determines how far the solid will penetrate the cloth before it comes to rest. Since most dust particles are irregularly shaped, it is easy for many of the larger particles to build up and form a matrix of increasingly smaller holes. These smaller holes then enable the capture of smaller particles. In fine dusts and fumes, however, there may be only a small percentage having sizes greater than a few microns, and a precoat of coarse dust must then be applied onto the filter medium.

When an obstruction such as a cloth fiber is placed in the path of a fluid stream, the streamlines will curve around the obstruction. Particles suspended in and traveling with the gas stream will, depending on their inertia, either follow a single streamline or will leave it. Fabric filters are generally designed to operate in the laminar regime and hence, small inertialess particles will remain on single streamlines. As these streamlines pass close to the fibers of the cloth and within a distance equal to the radii of the particles, particles will contact and adhere to the fibers due to van der Waals forces (i.e., *particle inception*). Van der Waals forces exist between molecules of nonpolar compounds and are accounted for by quantum mechanics. As two nonbonded atoms are brought together, the attraction between them increases and reaches a maximum when the distance between the nuclei is equal to the sum of the van der Waals radii. If forced closer together, the attraction will be replaced by repulsion and the particle will want to back off to a comfortable distance. Particles smaller than 1 μm can be considered inertialess without serious error.

In laminar flow, streamlines are not affected by velocity, but rather the size of an obstruction, or in this case, the fiber strand.

The streamlines will pass closer to smaller-diameter fibers than to larger ones. Large particles are collected easily due to *impingement or inertial impact* because their streamlines need not pass as close to the fiber strand as smaller ones for the van der Waals forces to become important. As particle size increases, however, so does the mass, and the particles tend not to follow the streamline path but leave it when a distortion of the streamline occurs. At this point, the particle's high inertia carries it out of the gas stream in the original direction of motion. This condition is favored by high particle mass and high filtering velocity.

At low velocities, random particle movement (or Brownian motion) is a factor in bringing about the impact of fine particles in a gas stream in accordance with Stokes' law. The particle shape and mass along with the gas viscosity and velocity determine the particle's settling velocity on the filter medium. Hence, *diffusion* plays an important role in the capturing of small particulates.

Electrostatic attraction and repulsion are mechanisms which, while understood qualitatively, are as yet mysteries quantitatively where fabric filtration is concerned. These forces effect particle agglomeration and often determine the ease or difficulty of media cleaning. The degree to which electrostatic forces affect filtration efficiency is undefined. Polarity, charge intensity, and the dissipation rate of both the filter media and the dust particles are all important factors. Electrostatic charging of fabrics has been successfully demonstrated in laboratory experiments, but as yet has not found extensive use in industrial gas cleaning.

Fabric filters, more commonly called *baghouses,* have been in use since the turn of the century in the mining industry. Today's applications extend throughout the chemical process industries with primary emphasis in industrial air pollution control. Dry dust filters are available in sizes ranging from a few square feet up to several hundred thousand square feet of cloth. Gas flows that can be handled by individual units range from under 100 cfm to over 1,000,000 cfm. The fabric filter's design is similar to that of a large vacuum cleaner. It consists of bags of various shapes constructed from a porous fabric. Filter bags are available in two major configurations, namely, flat (envelope) bags and round (tubular) bags.

Figure 14-14 illustrates the operation of a baghouse. The dust-laden gas enters the module through an inlet diffuser that breaks up the stream and evenly disperses the dust. The heavier dust particles settle to the hopper and the fine particles rise through the tube sheet into the bags. Particles as small as 0.5 μm are collected on the inside of the bags, while the cleaned gas passes through the fabric.

Dust is removed from the bags by periodic shaking. The frequency of cleaning depends on the type of dust, the concentration, and the pressure drop which must be overcome. The dust shaken from the bags falls into the hopper below and is removed by a rotary airlock, screw conveyor, or other devices. Figure 14-15 shows specific design features.

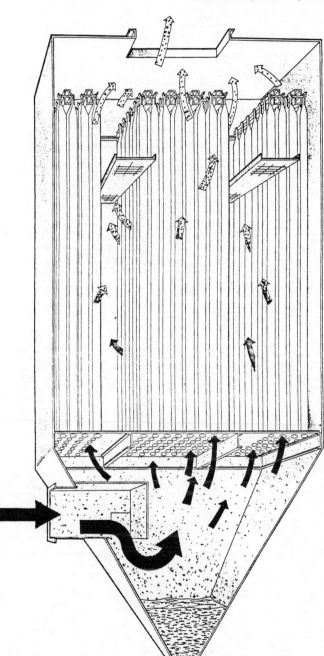

Figure 14-14. Illustration of the operation of a baghouse. (Courtesy of MikroPul Cor., Summit, NJ.)

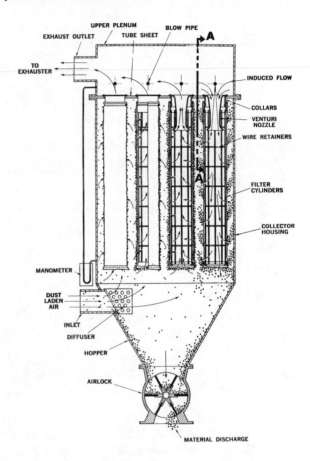

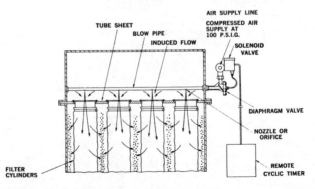

Figure 14-15. Principal design features of the baghouse. (Courtesy of MikroPul Corp., Summit, NJ.)

Series modules can be joined to provide any desired capacity. When two or more modules are joined together, a single module can be shut down for bag cleaning and then returned to service. The simple closing of an inlet or outlet damper diverts the dirty gas stream to other modules. Thus the gas is filtered continuously.

Multimodule installations typically employ a large single fan or small individual fans mounted on each module. Small fan arrangements are more flexible and eliminate the need for outlet ductwork and the foundation that are required for a large fan. Individual fans often simplify maintenance and permit fan, motor, drive, or other components to be changed readily without interrupting normal service. Any one module can be shut down and isolated from the rest of the system while still maintaining full operation and efficiency levels.

The particles to be removed play an important role in the selection of a fabric and filter efficiency. Specifically, the particulate density, concentration, velocity, and size are important. Each of these properties is interrelated with the pressure drop of the system, which is one of the most significant points affecting efficiency. Principal variables directly related to pressure drop are:

1. Gas velocity
2. Cake resistance coefficient
3. Weight of cake per unit area
4. Air-to-cloth ratio

The cake resistance coefficient is dependent on the particle size and shape, range of the particle sizes, and humidity. Weight of the cake per unit area is related to the concentration of particulates.

The design of fabric filters must satisfy two criteria, namely, high efficiency and low pressure drop. Attempts have been made to correlate the filtration efficiency to the operating conditions of the filter, but pressure drop has emerged as the primary factor determining efficiency. Prediction of the pressure drop and knowledge of its dependence on operating conditions of the filter are necessary for proper design.

There are several methods for predicting pressure drop across fibrous filters. The three chief methods of predicting pressure drop are based on the hydraulic radius theory, drag theory, and dimensional analysis. Experimental studies have shown dimensional analysis to be the most reliable. It is based on dimensional analysis of Darcy's law of flow through porous media, which relates the pressure drop to the filter porosity. Darcy's original equation is related as:

$$\frac{PF}{hQ} = ku \tag{14-49}$$

where F = cross-sectional area of filter
  P = pressure drop
  h = filter thickness
  Q = volumetric flow rate
  k = permeability of the medium
  u = gas velocity

Empirical forms of this equation assume the gas to behave ideally, however, a modfification of this is:

$$\frac{PF}{hQ} = \frac{k_3 u S_0^2 (1 - \epsilon)^2}{\epsilon^3} \tag{14-50}$$

where k_3 = constant
S_0 = surface area/unit volume of solid material
ϵ = bed porosity

From dimensional analysis,

$$k = \frac{PAd_e^2}{hQu} = 64(1 - \epsilon)^{1.5}[1 + 56(1 - \epsilon)^3] \tag{14-51}$$

where k = permeability coefficient
d_e = effective fiber diameter

This formula has shown accurate results for fiber diameters ranging from 1.6 to 80 μm and filter porosities ranging from 0.700 to 0.994.

Still another formula has been found through dimensional analysis:

$$\frac{PA\bar{d}^2}{hQu} = k''(1 - \epsilon)^{1.5} \tag{14-52}$$

where $\bar{d}^2$ = mean square fiber diameter
k'' = resistance coefficient

This expression predicts pressure drop for filters with porosities ranging from 0.88 to 0.96 and fiber diameters of about 0.1 to 3 μm.

A more useful formula is:

$$P = u_g \dot{V}_s (k_0 + k_1 W) \tag{14-53}$$

Again: P = pressure drop
u_g = gas velocity
$\dot{V}_s$ = air-cloth ratio (superficial velocity)
k_0 = weave resistance coefficient
k_1 = cake resistance coefficient (dependent on shape, concentration of particle, humidity)
W = weight of cake per square foot of surface

Typical values of k_1 and k_0 are given in Table 14-2 and 14-3, respectively.

Fabric filters composed of thicker felt materials have a complex orientation of fibers which can achieve a high collection efficiency with less dust buildup. Consequently, felt filters cannot be cleaned by mechanical shaking due to embedment of fine particles. Instead, a high pressure air stream (60 to 120 psi) is used to disengage the dust particles.

Table 14-2
Typical Values of k_0 for Different Types of Fiber[73]

Cloth	Thread Warp	Count Fill	Tensile Strength (lb/linear in.)	Coefficient of Resistance k_0 (in. H_2O/fpm)	Maximum Operating Temperature (°F)
Cotton	46	56	180	0.025	180
Wool	30	26	140	0.0091	215
Nylon	37	37	275	0.031	225
Asbestos			100	0.010	275
Orlon	72	72	170	0.012	275

Table 14-3
Typical Values for k_1 for Certain Industrial Dusts[73]

Dust	k_1 for Particle Size Less Than						
	20 Mesh	140 Mesh	375 Mesh	90μ	45μ	20μ	2μ
Granite	1.58	2.20				19.8	
Foundry	0.62	1.58	3.78				
Gypsum			6.30			18.9	
Feldspar			6.30			27.3	
Stone	0.96			6.30			
Lampblack							47.2
Zinc-oxide							15.7
Wood				6.30			
Resin (cold)		0.62				25.2	
Oats	1.58			9.60	11.0		
Corn	0.62		1.58	3.78	8.80		

The specific application dictates the type of fiber. For example, fiberglass filters can withstand higher temperatures than wool; nylon is a poor fiber to use for chemical resistance. The fabric is designed to withstand thermal, chemical, and mechanical action.

Fabric filters are categorized according to the particular cleaning method, the filter capacity, the type of filter media, the temperature capability, and the type of service (either intermittent or continuous). There are three major cleaning methods employed: shakers, reverse air, and pulse jet. The oldest and most widely used cleaning method is mechanical shaking. The casing is divided into an upper and lower portion by a tube sheet. The woven fabric tubular bags are located in the upper portion with a pyramid-shape hopper in the lower end. Each bag is supported between a flexible cap and a fixed thimble.

Gas velocity entering the hopper is reduced, causing the coarse particles to settle out. The gas enters the tube on the inside causing the fine particles to be collected, with the clean gas passing through the fabric into a common outlet manifold. After a certain dust buildup, the flexible support mechanically shakes the particle loose from the fabric into the hopper.

The reverse air cleaning baghouse operates in the same manner as the mechanical shaking arrangement, except a reverse air flow replaces the shaking process. An air vent located in the outlet manifold is opened allowing atmospheric air to enter the casing, thereby collapsing the bags and dislodging the dust particles (see Figure 14-16).

Baghouses incorporating the pulse jet cleaning method are constructed with an upper and lower compartment separated by a tube sheet. The upper portion serves as the discharge manifold. The felted filter bags are supported by a venturi-shaped thimble attached to the tube sheet. A compressed air jet is located above each filter bag to facilitate cleaning. Internal frames (mesh cages) with a closed bottom prevent collapse of the bags during the cleaning cycle.

Dirty gas enters the hopper and is then directed into the casing, passing through the filter bags. The dust is collected on the outside surface, allowing the clean air to pass through the fabric and out the discharge manifold. The filter bags are cleaned by the force of the pulse jet expanding the bags (see Figure 14-17).

Filters are grouped according to the capacity by volume as follows: small volumes (i.e., below 10,000 acfm), medium volumes (i.e., 10,000 to 100,000 acfm), and large volumes (i.e., > 100,000 acfm). The filter-media types include woven and felted media. Temperature capabilities of the media range from higher temperatures (> 400°F), to medium temperatures (200°F to 400°F) and low temperatures (< 200°F).

The ability of the fabric to collect fine particles and maintain a good cleaning process should serve as the basis in selection of a fabric. As the dust layer or so called filter cake layer builds up, flow resistance increases. Cleaning reduces the gas flow resistance and maintains the proper pressure drop across the filter.

Cloth filters are designed to remove three types of particles, and each type incorporates the basic principles of air filtration. Particles in the submicron size are collected as a result of the Brownian motion and bridging. As the particles build-up on the surface of the media, the collection surface areas increase causing particles to be captured. Collection efficiencies in excess of 99.95% are possible.[4]

Particles having diameters in the 1 to 10 μm range and coarse particles (above 10 μm) rely on inertial collection.[7] Efficiencies of 90%–95% are achieved with particles under 10 μm in size. Efficiencies of coarse particles fluctuate from 50%–99.9% efficiency. The reason for such variations in efficiency is a result of reentrainment caused by gas flows of high velocities. High velocities can force the particles through the pores of the fabric.

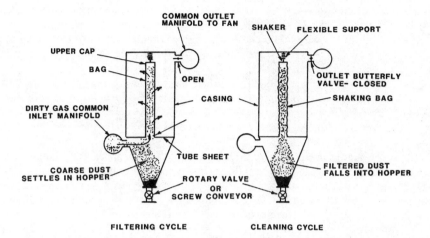

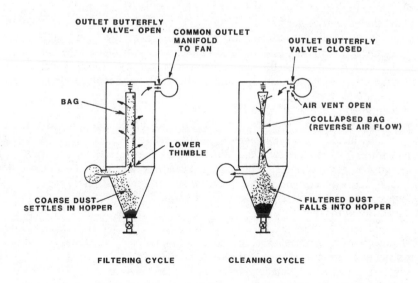

Figure 14-16. (A) Automatic conventional baghouse with mechanical shaker; (B) automatic baghouse with reverse airflow cleaning.

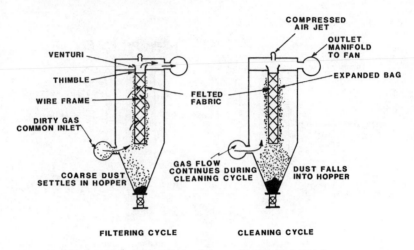

Figure 14-17. Automatic baghouse with pulse jet cleaning.

Fabric filters are made of natural fibers, such as cotton and wool or synthetic fibers, depending upon their application. Cotton and wool are available in spun form, which limits the individual fibers to a few inches in length. Spun fibers can produce characteristics not found in filament (continuous) fibers. Filters composed of spun fibers are thicker, bulkier, heavier and provide a higher permeability to air flow. Synthetic fibers can provide multifilament fabrics, which are the most widely used and produce characteristics not common on spun forms. Multifilament fabrics are light weight, of high tensile strength and high dimensional stability, abrasion resistant, and easy to clean.

Collection efficiency is affected by thread count, yarn size, and twist of the yarn. Permeability is increased by decreasing the thread count (either warp or fill), and subsequently increasing the pore area. Collection efficiency is reduced by increased permeability. A balanced weave is optimum for efficient operation. Permeability is also a function of the yarn size. The larger the yarn size, the lower the permeability. Yarn diameter, which can be altered by the twist of the yarn, also affects permeability; the smaller the diameter, the higher the permeability.

The ability of the gas stream to permeate the filter is also affected by the shrinking and elongation of the fabric. Elongation of the fibers results in increased pore space, and conversely shrinkage decreases the pore volume. Fabrics of good dimensional qualities are essential to fabric life and efficiency.

Fabric finishing steps enhance the collection efficiency of a system. The most commonly applied finishing steps include calendering, napping, singeing, glazing, and coating. Calendering is where surface fibers are pushed down onto the fabric medium by high pressure pressing on the fabric. Napping refers to scraping the filter medium, which raises the surface fibers. Singeing involves separate surface fibers that are removed by passing the filter medium over an open flame. Glazing involves surface fibers fused to the filter medium by high pressure pressing at elevated temperatures. Finally, coating involves a surface preparation over the fibers that reduces self-abrasion.

In order to specify a fabric filter, the emission problem must be well defined. The properties of the gas essential to the problem definition are volume, temperature, moisture content, and acid gas concentration. The dust properties of importance are the density, particle size, and dust loading.

The size of the fabric filter dust collector is directly related to the gas-to-cloth ratio, which can be calculated by dividing the total gas volume by the total area of cloth or filter medium as follows:

$$\text{Gas/cloth ratio} = \frac{\text{gas/volume}}{\text{cloth area}} = \frac{ft^3/\text{min}}{ft^2} = ft/\text{min}$$

Typical gas/cloth ratios are given in Table 14-4.

Corrections to the gas-to-cloth ratio are required for the volume of air introduced to the unit and to account for the area of cloth not exposed to the incoming gas:

$$\text{Gross gas/cloth ratio} = \frac{\text{total inlet gas volume}}{\text{total filter cloth in collector}}$$

$$\text{Net gas/cloth ratio} = \frac{\text{total inlet gas + cleaning volume}}{\text{on stream cloth}}$$

The type of fabric selected is a function of the cleaning process employed. For example, the pulse-jet cleaning method would be used in conjunction with the felt fabric to achieve proper cleaning and efficiency. The filter medium type is the next major consideration following the gas/cloth ratio and cleaning method. Table 14-5 gives typical temperature limitations and chemical resistance of fibers used in fabric filters.

Cotton bags are used in standard installations. A maximum operating temperature of 180°F is recommended for continuous use with 225°F allowed for surges. Wool bags are used for applications with dust particles of a combustible nature, or with operating temperatures of 200°F and an allowable surge of 250°F. Nylon has a greater tensile strength than cotton or wool and provides excellent abrasion resistance.

Fiberglass is most resistant to high temperatures, with a maximum operating temperature of 500°F. To increase the allowable temperature, fiberglass filters are silicone treated to permit their use in applications such as in carbon black production plants.

The carbon black is produced by burning oil or tar in furnaces. The exhaust gas leaves the furnace at a temperature of about 2000°F. A cooling process is required before filtration to lower the temperature below 600°F (the cooling process employed is usually high pressure water injected into the gas stream).

According to the American Society of Testing Materials (ASTM), the permeability of a fabric is defined as the quantity of clean atmospheric air expressed in cubic

Table 14-4
Typical Gas-to-Cloth Ratios[4]*

Dust	Shaker/Woven Reverse-Air/Woven	Pulse-Jet/Felt Reverse-Air/Felt
Alumina	2.5	8
Asbestos	3.0	10
Bauxite	2.5	8
Carbon black	1.5	5
Cement	2.0	8
Clay	2.5	9
Coal	2.5	8
Cocoa, chocolate	2.8	12
Cosmetics	1.5	10
Enamel frit	2.5	9
Feeds, grain	3.5	14
Feldspar	2.2	9
Fertilizer	3.0	8
Flour	3.0	12
Fly ash	2.5	5
Graphite	2.0	5
Gypsum	2.0	10
Iron ore	3.0	11
Iron oxide	2.5	7
Iron sulfate	2.0	6
Lead oxide	2.0	6
Leather dust	3.5	12
Lime	2.5	10
Limestone	2.7	8
Mica	2.7	9
Paint pigments	2.5	7
Paper	3.5	10
Plastics	2.5	7
Quartz	2.8	9
Rock dust	3.0	9
Sand	2.5	10
Sawdust (wood)	3.5	12
Silica	2.5	7
Slate	3.5	12
Soap, detergents	2.0	5
Spices	2.7	10
Starch	3.0	8
Sugar	2.0	7
Talc	2.5	10
Tobacco	3.5	13
Zinc oxide	2.0	5

* Generally safe design values; application requires consideration of particle size and grain loading.

feet per minute per square foot of media at a draft loss of 0.5 in water gauge. Typical ranges of permeability for the types of filter media commonly used are as follows:[7]

Fabric Type	Yarn Type	ASTM Permeability
Woven	Spun	20–100 cfm
Woven	Multifilament	10–50 cfm
Felt	Fiber	15–35 cfm

In start-up of new and clean filters the draft loss (difference of static pressure measured between the dirty and clean side of the bags) of a fabric filter will be under 0.5 in W.G. The efficiency gradually increases as the draft loss approaches 2.3 in. as the filter cake builds up. Increased operation results in a draft loss of about 6 in., at which time some form of cleaning method is required to reduce the filter cake thickness to achieve a draft loss of 2–3 in.

The major variables related to pressure drop are:

1. Gas velocity
2. Cake resistance coefficient
3. Weight of cake per unit area
4. Air-to-cloth ratio

The cake resistance coefficient is a function of the particle size and shape, range of the particles, and humidity. The concentration of particles determines the weight of cake per unit area.

Replacement of bag filters generates the highest maintenance and cost of the system. Typical causes of bag failure are:

- High gas/cloth ratio
- Metal-to-cloth abrasion
- Chemical attack
- Inlet velocity abrasion
- Too high temperature

The quality of the fabric and method of cleaning are additional factors to consider in evaluating maintenance costs.

If a filter bag tears, it is important to repair the bag as quickly as possible to prevent abrasion to adjacent bags by jet streams of dust discharging out of the damaged bag. This type of bag failure is limited to "inside bag collection" types of dust collectors. The speed of repair is determined by the opacity of the outlet bag. In a compartmentalized system, broken bags can be found by monitoring the emissions while isolating one compartment at a time. To prevent a higher filter velocity, damaged filter bags within a compartment should not be replaced with clean bags. The higher velocity could create greater pressure drop or failure due to dust abrasion. An alternative is to plug or tie off the flow.

In summary, the first step in selecting a fabric filter is to define the magnitude of the particulate loading. Knowledge of the particulates collected, properties of the

Table 14-5
Operating Ranges for Typical Fabrics[4]

Fiber	Generic Name	Fiber Properties					Recommended Operating Temperatures (°F)	
		Tensile Strength	Abrasion Resistance	Chemical Acids	Resistance Alkalies	Supports Combustion	Continuous	Upsets
Cotton	Natural fiber cellulose	Good	Average	Poor	Excellent	Yes	+180	+225
	Comment: Excellent selection in ventilation-type collector.							
Polypropylene	Polyolefin	Excellent	Good	Excellent	Excellent	Yes	+190	+190
	Comment: Strong fiber, low moisture absorption and possesses excellent chemical resistance.							
Glass	Glass	Excellent	Poor	Good	Poor	No	+500	+550
	Comment: All properties are highly dependent on fabric treatment. Can be used at high temperature and has high tensile strength							
Nylon	Polyamide	Excellent	Excellent	Poor	Excellent	Yes	+200	+250
	Comment: Rugged fiber with excellent resistance to abrasion and alkalies.							
Dacron[1]	Polyester	Excellent	Excellent	Good	Fair	Yes	+275[2]	+325[2]
	Comment: High tensile strength, good dimensional stability, excellent heat resistance. Susceptible to moist-heat hydrolysis.							
Orlon[1]	Acrylic	Average	Average	Very good	Fair	Yes	+240	+260

Table 14-5 (continued)
Operating Ranges for Typical Fabrics[4]

Fiber	Generic Name	Fiber Properties					Recommended Operating Temperatures (°F)	
		Tensile Strength	Abrasion Resistance	Chemical Acids	Resistance Alkalies	Supports Combustion	Continuous	Upsets
Microtain[3]	Acrylic	Average	Average	Very good	Fair	Yes	+260	+280
		Comment: Good at elevated temperatures and in acid conditions. Microtain fabrics possess excellent dimensional stability.						
Wool	Natural fiber protein	Poor	Average	Fair	Poor	No	+200	+250
		Comment: Good filterability.						
Nomex[1]	Aromatic polyamide	Very good	Very good	Fair	Very good	No	+400	+425
		Comment: Outstanding heat resistance and good resistance to abrasion.						
Teflon[1]	Fluorocarbon	Average	Below average	Excellent	Excellent	No	+450	+500
		Comment: Can be used at elevated temperatures and possesses excellent chemical resistance.						

[1] E.I. du Pont registered trademark.
[2] Dry heat.
[3] Registered trademark for Globe Albany 100% homopolymer acrylic fabrics.

gas stream, and the cleaning method are essential to proper design. Improper design leads to low efficiency and unscheduled maintenance.

Prior to selection, results from a related application should be investigated. An alternative is to operate a pilot unit to ensure the most optimum gas-to-cloth ratio for a specified pressure drop. With proper design, operation, and maintenance, better than 99.9% efficiency can be achieved, depending on the application.

A major advantage of fabric filters, is their ability to operate at a high efficiency at all loads from maximum down to zero gas flow. Some disadvantages of the system are the space requirements and high maintenance costs. Other problems associated with fabric filters are plugging of the fabric due to operation below the dew point or break down of the filter bags, resulting from high temperatures.

Fabric filters are more costly to operate and maintain than electrostatic precipitators, cyclones, and scrubbers; however, fabric filters are more practicable for filtration of specific dusts. For example: fabric systems are the typical control method for toxic dusts from insecticide manufacturing processes, salt fumes from heat treating, metallic fumes from metallurgical processes, and other applications. Any other control method may not be as efficient, nor economically feasible for such applications.

NOMENCLATURE

Ar	Archimedes number
a	acceleration
B	settling chamber longitudinal cross-sectional area
b	dimension
C	constant
C_D	drag coefficient
c	concentration
D	system diameter
d	particle diameter
d_e	effective fiber diameter
E	voltage potential
E_x	field intensity
F	cross-sectional area
Fr	Froude number
g	gravitational acceleration
H	height
h	filter thickness
$\dot{K}$	precipitation constant
K_0	cyclone resistance coefficient
K_s	dimensionless separation number (i.e., ratio of system acceleration to gravitational acceleration)
k	filter medium permeability

k''	resistance coefficient
k_0	weave resistance coefficient
k_1	cake resistance coefficient
k_3	filter cloth constant
L,ℓ	length
P	pressure
Q	volumetric flow rate
R_D	drag force
R	radius of particle rotation
Re	Reynolds number
r	radius
r_0	tube inside diameter
S	area
S_0	surface area per unit volume of filter material
St	Stokes number
t	settling or residence time
t_0	gas residence time
u	velocity
V	volume
V_{sec}	volumetric flow rate
$\dot{V}_s$	air to cloth ratio
W	weight of cake per unit filter surface area
w_g	fluid rotational velocity
w_0	settling velocity
w	velocity
x	distance
Z	total flow resistance

Greek Symbols

γ	specific gravity
ϵ	bed porosity
η	particle removal efficiency
λ	resistance coefficient (i.e., friction factor)
μ	viscosity
υ	kinematic viscosity
$\tilde{\nu}$	potential difference between electrodes
ϱ	density
τ	gas residence time in cyclone
ω	angular velocity
ψ	drag coefficient

REFERENCES

1. Green, H. L., and W. R. Lane, *Particulate Clouds: Dusts, Smokes and Mists*, Van Nostrand Reinhold Co., NY (1957).

2. Drinker, P., and T. Hatch, *Industrial Dust*, McGraw-Hill Book Co., NY (1954).

3. Roberts, R. T., *Power*, 83: 345, 392 (1939).

4. Cheremisinoff, P. N., and R. A. Young, *Air Pollution Control and Design Handbook, Part 1*, Marcel Dekker Inc., NY (1977).

5. Cheremisinoff, N. P., and D. Azbel, *Fluid Mechanics and Unit Operations*, Ann Arbor Science Pub., Ann Arbor, MI (1983).

6. Loeb, L. D., *Fundamental Processes of Electrical Discharge in Gases*, John Wiley and Sons, Inc., NY (1939).

7. Peek, F. W., *Dielectric Phenomena in High-Voltage Engineering*, McGraw-Hill Book Co., NY (1929).

8. Cheremisinoff, N. P., and P. N. Cheremisinoff, *Plant Engineering*, 27:25 (1973).

9. Shephard, C. B., and C. E. Lapple, *Ind. Eng. Chem.*, 31: 972 (1939).

9b. Shephard, C. B., and C. E. Lapple, *Ind. Eng. Chem.*, 32: 1,246 (1940).

10. Alphonso, N. A. D., and O. P. Goyal, "An Operational Appraisal of Fluid Catalytic Cracker with Regard to Solid-Gas Separation in Cyclone Systems," Hindustan Petroleum Corp., Ltd.; *Chem. Age India*, 27 (2): 224–30, (Feb. 1976).

11. "Concept of Effective Residence Time Applied to Cyclone Type Particle Collectors," Aslam, M. A., Univ. Cinc. Diss. (1974), see Abstr–Diss. Abst. Int. B. Vol. 35, No. 7, 3298 B (Jan. 1975).

12. Boulton, R. B., and D. G. Evans, "Predicting the Performance of Internal Separators," Australia Conf. On Hydraul. and Fluid Mech., *5th Proc.*, (Dec. 9–13, 1974).

13. Browne, J. M., and W. Strauss, "Pressure Drop Reduction in Cyclones," *Atmos. Environ.*, 12 (5) (1978).

14. Buonicore, A. J., and L. Theodore, "Monte Carlo Simulating to Predict Cyclone Performance, Energy & Environ.," *3rd Natl. Conc. Proc.*, (Sept. 29–Oct. 1, 1975), AIChE Pub.

15. Burrill, K. A., and D. R. Woods, "Separation of Two Immiscible Liquids in a Hydroclone," *Ind. Eng. Chem. Process Design and Development*, 9 (4) (Oct. 1970).

16. Calvert, S., I. L. Jashani, and S. Yung, "Entrainment Separators for Scrubbers," *J. Air Pollut. Control Assoc.*, 24 (10) (Oct. 1974).

17. Canton, A., "Clean Odour-Free Air from a Good West Scrub," *Process Eng.* (London), 84–85, 87 (Oct. 1978).

18. Chaston, I. R. M., "Heavy Media Cyclone Plant Design & Practice for Diamond Recovery in Africa," *Inst. of Min. and Metal.* (London) (1974).

19. Cheremisinoff, P. N., and N. P. Cheremisinoff, "Cyclone Dust Collectors," *Plant Eng.*, (July 25, July 11, 1974).

20. Ciliberti, D. R., and B. W. Lancaster, "Performance of Rotary Flow Cyclones," *AIChE J.*, 22 (2) (March 1976).

21. Collett, H., "Renkol Classifier May be Missing Link in Coal Preparation," *Coal Mining Process,* 10 (6) (June 1973).

22. Cooper, D. E. H., "Use of the Hydroclone in the Disposal of Particulate Solids Wastes," Inst. of Eng., Australia, Annv. Eng. Conf., Townsville, (May 10–14, 1976), Inst. of Eng., Aust., Sydney (1976), Pap. 468/2.

23. Cox, N. D., A. S. Richardson, and W. P. Jensen, "Energy Oriented Study of Industrial Cyclone Separators," Contract EY-76-C-07-1570, EG & Idaho Inc., Idaho Falls, U.S. Dept. Commerce Natl. Tech. Inf. Serv. Rep. N. Tree—1174 (Sept. 1977), see ERDA Energy Res. ABSTR. V-3-10654, (1978).

24. Crowe, C. T., and D. T. Pratt, "Analysis of the Flow Field in Cyclone Separators," *Computers & Fluids,* Vol. 2 (1974).

25. Crowley, M. S., "Inspection and Repair of Refractory Concrete Linings," *Chem. Engr. Progr.,* 66 (8) (Aug. 1970).

26. "Precipitator—Cyclone Combine Cuts CO-Boiler Emissions," *Crown Central Pet. Corp.,* Research-Cottrell Inc., *Oil & Gas J.,* 75 (16): 56 (April 18, 1977).

27. Davidenko, A. N., and A. N. Planovski, "Design of Cyclone and Jalousie Separators in Combined Operation," *Chem. Petrol. Eng.,* No. 1–2, (Jan/Feb. 1970).

28. Doerschlag, C., "Selecting Cyclone Dust Collectors," *Plant. Eng.,* 32 (21) (Oct. 12, 1978).

29. Doerschlag, C., and G. Miezek, "How to Choose a Cyclone Dust Collector," *Chem. Eng.,* 84 (4) 64–72 (Feb. 14, 1977).

30. Ebert, F., "Calculations of the Boundary Layer Flow in Cyclones," *Staub-Reinhalt Luft,* 29 (7) (1969).

31. Gelperin, N. T., et al., "Study of Hydraulics and Mass Transfer in Hydrocarbons for Liquid/Liquid Systems," *Russian Chem. Abstr.,* Vol. 86:- 108477, (1975).

32. Gerrard, A. M., and C. J. Liddle, "Optimal Choice of Multiple Cyclones," *Powder Technology* 13 (2) (March–April, 1976).

33. Grace, W. R., and J. A. Gray, "The Purpose, Application and Performance of the Baver Liquid Cyclone," *Combustion,* 44 (8): 30–35 (Feb. 1973).

34. Corishutin, K. S., and N. V. Makarov, "Study of Mazut Combustion in Industrial Cyclone Precombustion Chambers With Outlet Throats," *Russian Chem. Abstr. No. 124037,* 86 (18) (1975).

35. Gupta, J. P., and P. D. Grover, "Optimum Design of Hydroclones," *Chem. Process,* (London), 20 (6): 30–39, (June 1974).

36. Johnson, R. A., W. E. Gibson, and D. R. Libby, "Performance of Liquid-Liquid Cyclones," *Ind. Eng. Chem. Fund.*, 15 (2) (1976).

37. Johnston, I. R. W., and W. Strauss, "Dry Particulate Separation," *Inst. of Eng.*, Aust., Eng. Conf. Eng: Dev. A Better World Nat. Conf. Pub. (1978), p. 18/2.

38. Kelsall, D. R., "A Study of the Motion of Solid Particles in a Hydraulic Cyclone," *Trans. Instn. Chem. Engrs.*, Vol. 30 (1952).

39. Koch, W. A., and W. Licht, "New Design Approach Boosts Cyclone Efficiency," *Chem. Eng.*, 84 (24) (Nov. 7, 1977).

40. Lebedev, V. D., V. E. Maslov, and K. A. Lunegov, "Investigation of Efficiency of Centrifugal Scrubbers," *Thermal Eng.*, 19 (5) (May, 1972).

41. Lees, B., and R. W. Butcher, "Reducing Atmospheric Pollution from Oil-Fired Plant Development of Grit-Arresting Cyclones for Multiflue Chimneys," *J. Inst. Fuel,* 48 (397): 201–207 (Dec. 1975).

42. Lemmond, C., "Liquid Cyclone Separators Keep Products Ultra-Clean," (Industrial Service Co.), *Pipeline Gas J.,* 205 (10): 17–20, (Aug. 1978).

43. Littlejohn, R. F., and R. Smith, "Sampling Gasborne Solids: Some Factors Affecting the Characteristics of Miniature Cyclones," *Inst. Mech. Eng., (London) Proc.,* 192: 2–250 (Sept. 1978).

44. Loftler, F., and P. Meissner, "Pressure Drop Determination in Cyclone Separators, *Iran Congr. of Chem. Eng.,* 1st Proc., Shirat, Iran, (May 14–17, 1973, V.2). Publ. by Elsevier Sci. Publ. Co., No.4, (1974).

45. Lynch, A. J., T. C. Rao, and C.W. Bailey, "Influence of Design & Operating Variables on the Capabilities of Hydroclone Classifiers," *Int. J. Miner Process,* 2 (1): (Mar. 1975).

46. Morinianscky, E., and S. I. Cheng, "Modelling & Optimization of Gas Dust Separation by Hydraulic Cyclones," Summer Comput. Simulation Con., Inc., LaJolla, CA, Simulation Counc. Inc. (1973).

47. Martynenko, A. G., et al., "Use of Hydroclones During Urea Deparraffination," *Khim, Technol. Topl. Mastel,* (6): 18–20, (1977), Chem. Abstr. No. 138272, 87 (18).

48. McCabe, J. T., W. Garber, and P. Albrecht, "Development of a Particulate Control Cyclocentrifuge," Phase II Lab. Tests. Mo. Tech. Prog. Report No. 19, Jan. 1978–Feb. 1978. Attach. A—"Control of Alkali Metals in Low Btu Turbine Fuel Gas Using A Cyclocentrifuge," Mechanical Tech. Inc., Latham, NY, U.S. Dept. Commerce Natl. Tech. Inf. Serg., Rep. N. FE-2428-19 (Feb. 9, 1978)/Abstr.-ERDA Energy Res. Abstr. V-3-32568 (1978).

49. Muschelknautz, E., "Design of Cyclone Separators for Gases," *Chem. Ing. Tech.* 44 (1-2): 63–71 (Jan. 1972).

50. Muschelknautz, E., and W. Kranbrock, "Aerodynamic Parameters of a Cyclone Separator on the Basis of New and Improved Measurements," *Chem. Ing. Tech.,* 42 (5) (Mar. 1970).

51. O'Brien, E. J., and K. J. Sharpeta, "Water Only Cyclones: Their Functions and Performance," *Coal Age,* 81 (1) (Jan. 1976).

52. Pastala, A. L., "Contribution to the Design of Air Separation Equipment for Closed Circuit Grinding Systems," *Chem. Technol.,* 6 (4): (Jul.-Aug., 1975).

53. "Japanese Swirl Cyclone," Paul Weir Co., Chicago, IL, *Min. Eng.,* 30 (2) (Feb 1978).

54. Plitt, L. R., "Mathematical Model of the Hydrocyclone Classifier," *CIM. Bull.,* 69 (776) (Dec. 1976).

55. Rajagopolar, S., and S. K. Basu, "Theory and Design of Cyclones," *Chem. Age India,* 27 (1) (Jan. 1976).

56. Rao, K. N., and T. C. Rao, "Estimating Hydroclone Efficiency," *Chem. Eng.* (May 26, 1975).

57. Rozenhart, C. F. S., and J. Visman, "A Low-Pressure (Multiple Classifier) Cyclone for Desanding Industrial Waters," *Can. Petrol.,* 10 (10): 74–78 (Oct. 1969).

58. Rumpe, H., K. Borho, and H. Reichert, "Optimal Dimensioning of Cyclones by Means of Simplifying Model Calculations," *Chemie-Ingenieur-Technik,* 40 (21–22) (Nov. 18, 1968).

59. Schulz, F., "Contributions to the Theory of Cyclone Dust Collectors," *The Engineer's Digest,* 1 (5/6) (Nov./Dec. 1946).

60. Shah, Yatendra, M., and R. T. Price, "Calculator Program Solves Cyclone Efficiency Equations," *Chem. Eng.* 185 (19) (Aug. 28, 1978).

61. Skelly Oil Co., "Skelly Installs Cyclones at Refinery," *Oil & Gas J.,* 70 (23): 32 (6/5/72).

62. Shorg, H. P., "Separation of Liquids in a Conventional Hydroclone," *Sep. Purif. Methods,* 6 (1) (1977).

63. Sproull, W. T., "Effect of Dust Concentration Upon the Gas-Flow Capacity of a Cyclonic Collector," *J. Air Poll. Control Assoc.,* 16 (8) (Aug. 1966).

64. Svarovsky, L., "Gas Cyclone Selection Procedure," *Chem. Eng.* (London), No. 295, (Mar. 1975).

65. Tenney, E. D., "The Role of Cyclones in Refinery Air Pollution Control," Nat. Petrol. Refiners Assoc. Annu. Meet., (San Francisco 3/21–23/71), N.AM-71-12.

66. Thompson, B. W., and W. Strauss, "The Application of Vortex Theory to the Design of Cyclone Collectors," *Chem. Eng. Sci.,* Vol 26 (1971).

67. Tsarev, V. K., Troyankin, Y. U. R., "Influence of Design Parameters of an Annular Cyclone and of Non-Isothermal Conditions of the Flow on Velocity Distribution," *Thermal Eng.,* 18 (2) (Feb. 1971).

68. Usman, S., "Optimized Design of Cyclone Separators and Their Applications," *Chem. Age India,* 22 (1) (Jan. 1976).

69. Vevlorovskii, M. M., V. C. Sister, and M. V. Aizenbud, "Hydrodynamics of Centrifugal Separators," *Chem. Abst.* Vol 80-9: 7,783 (Russian) (1972).

70. Weismantel, S. E., R. A. Razyaitis, and O. Buxton, "Influence of Cone Design Upon Liquid Entrainment Separation for a Steam Cyclone Separator," *ASME* Paper No. 76-WA/Pwr-6, (Dec. 5, 1976).

71. Yuu, Shinich, et al., "Reduction of Pressure Drop Due to Dust Loading in a Conventional Cyclone," *Chem. Eng. Sci.*, 33 (12) (1978).

72. Zima, A. G., "New Weapon in the Fight Against Abrasion," *Rock Prod.*, 23 (6) (June 1970).

73. *Air Pollution Handbook*, McGraw-Hill Book Co., (1956), pp. 13–59.

74. Ross, R. D., *Air Pollution and Industry*, Van Nostrand Reinhold Co., NY, (1972), p. 362.

15

Particulate Capture In Venturi Scrubbers

CONTENTS

INTRODUCTION, 646

DESCRIPTION OF OPERATION, 646

DROPLET DYNAMICS, 647
Atomization, 648
Droplet Motion and Concentration, 658
The Mechanical Energy Balance, 659

COMPARISON OF SCRUBBER MODELS, 660

OPERATING VARIABLES AND PERFORMANCE, 663

HEAT AND MASS TRANSFER CONSIDERATIONS, 670

ADDITIONAL COMMENTS, 676

NOMENCLATURE, 680

REFERENCES, 682

INTRODUCTION

The venturi scrubber is a unique device because of the complexity of flow patterns and variables affecting capture efficiencies, and because it is employed in gas adsorption as well as particulate removal from gas streams. For this reason, a separate chapter is devoted to the device, with discussions revolving around the application of particle-gas separation. The principal advantages of the device are a high degree of removal efficiency for particles in the micron size range, the ability to handle large volumes of gas flows in comparatively small-size equipment, low initial capital investment, and simplicity in design.

The invention was first developed by the Pease-Anthony Equipment Co. of Newtonville, Massachusetts, and originally employed by the pulp and paper industry as a scrubbing device for salt cake fumes from black liquor furnaces.[1] The next major application was in the removal of iron oxide dust from open-hearth furnaces. Today, venturi scrubbers are integral components in a variety of process operations with heavy applications in air pollution control.

DESCRIPTION OF OPERATION

The principal design features of the venturi scrubber are illustrated in Figure 15-1. The process gas is passed through a venturi section where it is accelerated to a high velocity. The high velocity gas stream impinges onto a liquid stream causing the liquid to shatter into a fine distribution of liquid droplets. This atomization process generates a large surface area for particulates to impinge upon and soluble gases to dissolve in. As the two-phase flow exits the venturi's throat, further impaction takes place causing agglomeration of the droplets. These agglomerates are then removed in the separator portion of the scrubber.

There are two methods of operation commonly employed: one is the Pease-Anthony (P-A) method in which the liquid is injected into the throat of the venturi, and the other is the wet-approach (W-A) in which the liquid is introduced in such a manner that the entire convergent section is wetted by the liquid phase.

Scrubbing liquid can be introduced into the venturi throat in one of two ways. The first method involves the use of liquid jets, as shown in Figure 15-1A; and the second employs a weir (Figure 15-1B). The former has a higher particle capturing efficiency, but has operating difficulties when handling high dust loadings. Specifically, in such cases the scrubbing liquid is often recycled through the device, which has a tendency to plug the jet nozzles. With the weir-type design, this problem is eliminated; however, the atomization process is considerably less efficient and hence capture efficiencies are lower.

Venturi scrubbers can be classified according to their geometric configuration and type installation. Typical classifications are rectangular cross-section, cylindrical cross-section, fixed throat, variable throat, horizontal, and vertical.

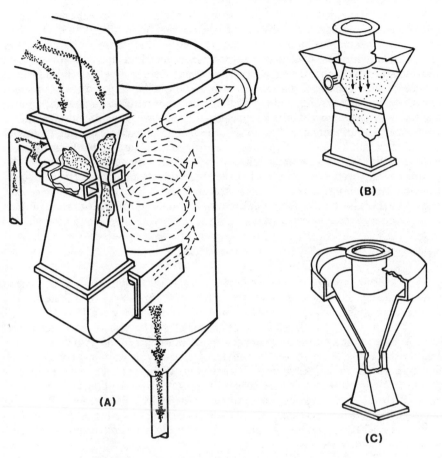

Figure 15-1. Principal configurations of venturi scrubbers.

DROPLET DYNAMICS

There are several physical mechanisms which combine to effect the removal of particulates in venturi scrubbers. These include inertial impaction and interception of particles and to lesser extents, diffusion, electrostatic, and mass and heat transfer phenomena. The contribution of any one mechanism depends on the particle and droplet sizes and their velocities relative to each other and the gas stream. The magnitude of each of these mechanisms depends on the scrubber's geometry and operating conditions. In typical installations, a range of particle sizes is introduced and the removal process becomes more complex due to the interactions between the separate classes of droplets and particles.

A number of theoretical analyses of scrubber performance appear in the literature, however, the majority of these have questionable or limiting assumptions that restrict their general usefulness as scale-up methods. Despite these shortcomings, such analyses are useful in that they provide insight into operating principles. Clearly though, complete design methodology must account for all variables, which includes system geometry, particle size distribution, inlet temperatures of gas and scrubbing liquid, humidity, and physical properties of particles, scrubbing liquor, and gas. Reasonable success has been achieved by the use of one-dimensional models. In the cases of mass and heat transfer, no large gradients exist in the direction normal to the flow due to turbulent eddy activity in the main stream. Tillman[2] provides a theoretical analysis on the effect of mainstream turbulence and reports little increase in the probability of collision between droplets and dust particles due to turbulent fluctuations. One of the more successful models is that of Placek and Peter,[3] to be discussed later. Some fundamental relations describing primary mechanisms need to be established first.

Atomization

As previously described, atomization takes place by the impingement of a high velocity stream onto a slower moving liquid. Figure 15-2 shows further details of the venturi and its converging section, which is responsible for accelerating the incoming gas stream. At the injection point, the high relative velocity between the gas and scrubbing liquid causes a violent disruption of the liquid into a distribution of spherical droplets. The particulate material suspended in the gas phase collides with the large, slower-moving droplets by means of the various collection mechanisms. Due to the drag forces, the droplets accelerate down the length of the venturi. Since the relative velocity decreases, the local collection efficiencies become smaller as the droplets move downstream. The gas decelerates in the diverging section, which provides for additional removal of the particulate material by collision with the now faster moving droplets.

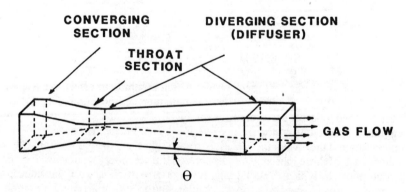

Figure 15-2. Schematic of venturi scrubber.

The atomization process is analogous to that of a conventional pneumatic nozzle, which typically produces a wide drop size distribution. The dispersion of a liquid into a gas requires a certain amount of work to overcome surface tension forces, in which the liquid must take on a form occupying the smallest possible surface area. Because of droplet formation, the overall surface of the original amount of liquid is increased. The required work for this purpose is:

$$dW' = \sigma dA \tag{15-1}$$

where W' = work
σ = surface tension
A = overall surface area of the liquid

Because the specific gravity of the droplets is greater than that of the gas, settling occurs. For small droplets in the Stokes region, the free-fall velocity is:

$$u_s = \frac{d_0^2(\varrho_1 - \varrho_2)}{18\mu} \tag{15-2}$$

where d_o = diameter of the droplet
ϱ_1 = density of the liquid
ϱ_2 = density of the gas
μ = viscosity of the gas

The settling of droplets can be counteracted by a gas flow in the opposite direction.

Atomization of a liquid jet being discharged from a given orifice into gas-filled space is the result of the interaction of the liquid stream and the gaseous environment. This interaction is extremely complex since not only does the jet itself break up but the independent primary droplets do so as well.

The initial conditions for the stream are the conditions for its discharge from the spray nozzle. These conditions are determined by the geometric configuration of the chamber, the spray-nozzle orifice, and the discharge velocity of the jet.

As for any flow in a gas-liquid system, the system is mathematically described by the equations of motion of the phases and by the conditions for their interaction at the boundaries. Here, because of considerable velocities of the liquid jet, gravitational forces can be comparable with inertia.

In the region where breakup takes place, the liquid-phase flow sets up strong turbulent perturbations in the surrounding gas. As such, the forces of molecular friction in the gas phase can also be disregarded.

The fundamental equations describing the break up of a simple jet are:

$$-\text{grad } P' + \mu' \nabla^2 \vec{w} = \varrho' \frac{D\vec{w}}{d\tau}$$

$$\text{div } \vec{w}' = 0$$

$$-\text{grad } P'' = \varrho'' \frac{D\vec{w}''}{d\tau}$$

$$\text{div } \vec{w}'' = 0$$

$$\mu'\left(\frac{\partial w'_\ell}{\partial x_k} + \frac{\partial w_k'}{\partial x_\ell}\right)_b = -\varrho''\overline{(v_\ell' v_k'')}_b$$

$$P' - 2\mu'\left(\frac{\partial w_k}{\partial x_k}\right)_b = P'' - \varrho''(v_k'^2)_b + \sigma\left(\frac{1}{R_1} + \frac{1}{R_2}\right)$$

$$\vec{w}'_b = \vec{w}''_b \tag{15-3}$$

where $P'P''$ = pressures
  μ = viscosity
  ϱ = density
  R_1R_2 = jet radii
  w = velocity
  τ = time
  D = diffusivity

and, v_{-i} and v_{-k} are the fluctuating velocity components.
These equations can be reduced to the following primary similarity criteria.

$$\left\{\frac{\Delta P}{\varrho' w'^2} \; ; \; \frac{w'\ell}{\nu'} \; ; \; \frac{\Delta P}{\varrho'' w''^2} \; ; \; \frac{\varrho'' w''^2 \ell}{\mu' w'} \; ; \; \frac{\Delta P\ell}{\sigma} \; ; \; \frac{w'}{w''}\right\} \tag{15-4}$$

And considering that

$$\frac{\Delta P}{\varrho' w'^2}\left(\frac{\varrho'' w''^2}{\Delta P}\right) = \frac{\varrho'' w''^2}{\varrho' w'^2} \tag{15-5}$$

and

$$\frac{\varrho'' w''^2 \ell}{\mu' w'} = \frac{\varrho' w'^2}{\varrho' w'^2}\left(\frac{w'\ell}{\nu'}\right) \tag{15-6}$$

we can write a system of criteria, strictly equivalent to Equation 15-4 but containing one less criterion:

$$\left\{\frac{\Delta P}{\varrho' w'^2} \; ; \; \frac{w'\ell}{\nu'} \; ; \; \frac{\varrho'' w''^2}{\varrho' w'^2} \; ; \; \frac{\Delta P\ell}{\sigma} \; ; \; \frac{w'}{w''}\right\} \tag{15-7}$$

The primary conditions which uniquely define the examined process are the geometric dimensions of the spray nozzle, flow velocities of the phases, and the physical constants in Equation 15-3. We now form combinations from the criteria in

Equation 15-7 so as to isolate the maximum number of groups composed only of quantities that are among the conditions uniquely defining the system.

$$\frac{\Delta P\ell}{\sigma}\frac{\varrho''w''^2}{\varrho'w'^2}\frac{\varrho'w'^2}{\Delta P} = \frac{\varrho''w''^2\ell}{\sigma}$$

$$\frac{\Delta P\ell}{\sigma}\frac{\varrho'w'^2}{\Delta P}\left(\frac{\nu'}{w'\ell}\right) = \frac{\mu'^2}{\sigma\varrho'\ell} \tag{15-8}$$

Consequently, the following is equivalent to the system described by Equation 15-7:

$$\left\{\frac{\Delta P}{\varrho'w'^2}\ ;\ \frac{\mu'^2}{\sigma\varrho'\ell^2}\ ;\ \frac{\varrho''w''^2\ell}{\sigma}\ ;\ \frac{\varrho''w''^2}{\varrho'w'^2}\ ;\ \frac{w'}{w''}\right\} \tag{15-9}$$

Four of these criteria are determining.

The higher the rate of the breakup process, the greater the dynamic interaction between the jet and the gas. This interaction depends on their relative velocity. Therefore, it is expedient to introduce the relative velocity of the gas into the criteria in Equation 15-9 rather than its absolute velocity:

$$w = w'' - w'$$

Taking this into account, any determinable criterion for the atomization process in geometrically similar spray nozzles is thus a certain function of the following determining dimensionless parameters:

$$\left\{\frac{\varrho''w^2\ell}{\sigma}\ ;\ \frac{\mu'^2}{\sigma\varrho'\ell}\ ;\ \frac{\varrho''w^2}{\varrho'w'^2}\ ;\ \frac{w'}{w}\right\} \tag{15-10}$$

As a liquid jet discharges, it begins to oscillate and to interact with the surrounding gas and finally breaks up into drops. The greater the gas density, the more complete is the disruption of the jet. The jet has an extremely pronounced wave character. The waves originate at the exit of the nozzle, and are gradually damped as they move away from the orifice. Once these waves have been completely damped, unstable waves develop whose amplitude continually increases along a jet and finally causes it to break up into drops.

The theory of jet break-up is based on the concept that the jet breaks up as a result of a disturbance of the equilibrium of the free surface of liquid under the effect of surface tension. The insignificant initial perturbations promote the formation of waves with spontaneously increasing amplitude. This process is accelerated by additional perturbations due to the relative motion of the liquid and the gas.

The equations of motion and continuity for the jet can be expressed in terms of the corresponding fluctuating components of velocity and pressure. In cylindrical coordinates; these equations are:

$$
\left.
\begin{aligned}
\varrho'\frac{Du}{d\tau} &= -\frac{\partial x'}{\partial z} + \mu'\left(\frac{\partial^2 u}{\partial z^2} + \frac{\partial^2 u}{\partial R^2} + \frac{1}{R}\cdot\frac{\partial u}{\partial R}\right) ; \\
\varrho'\frac{Dv}{d\tau} &= -\frac{\partial \pi'}{\partial R} + \mu'\left(\frac{\partial^2 v}{\partial z^2} + \frac{\partial^2 v}{\partial R^2} + \frac{1}{R}\frac{\partial v}{\partial R} - \frac{v}{R^2}\right) ; \\
\frac{\partial u}{\partial z} &+ \frac{\partial v}{\partial R} + \frac{v}{R} = 0 ;
\end{aligned}
\right\}
\qquad (15\text{-}11)
$$

where v, u = fluctuating velocities in the radial and axial directions, respectively
π' = fluctuating pressure in the jet.

The boundary conditions are given by Equation 15-3. These conditions can be expressed in a simpler form. Specifically, the tangential stresses on the jet surface are assumed to equal zero, from which we have:

$$
\left.
\begin{aligned}
\frac{dR}{d\tau} &= \nu_b \\
\mu'\left(\frac{\partial u}{\partial R} + \frac{\partial v}{\partial z}\right)_b &= 0 \\
\pi' + 2\mu'\left(\frac{\partial v}{\partial R}\right)_b &= \pi'' + \pi_0
\end{aligned}
\right\}
\qquad (15\text{-}12)
$$

where π'' = fluctuating pressure in the gas
π_σ = fluctuating pressure caused by the forces of surface tension

A solution of this system of equations for the time changes in the amplitude of oscillations has the form:

$$
\delta = F\left(\frac{R}{R_0} ; \xi\frac{Z}{R_0}\right)e^{q\tau}
\qquad (15\text{-}13)
$$

where q is the increment of oscillations in the jet, determined approximately by the following equation:

$$
q^2 + q\frac{3\mu}{\varrho'R_0^2}\xi^2 = \frac{\sigma}{2\varrho'R_0^3}(1 - \xi^2)\xi^2 + \frac{\varrho''w^2\xi^3}{2\varrho'R_0^2}f_0(\xi)
\qquad (15\text{-}14)
$$

where R_0 = mean radius of the jet
$\xi = 2\pi R/\lambda$ = wave number (λ is the wavelength of the oscillations)

Oscillations resulting in the breakup of the jet occur at q > 0. Upon examining Equation 15-15, it becomes apparent that two determining criteria corresponding to the first two criteria of the system Equation 15-10 materialize. Moreover, Equation 15-14 gives nondetermining criteria containing the increment and the wave number of the oscillation that leads to the breakup of the jet.

The behavior of a single drop entrained by a gas stream is a function of the interaction between the dynamic effect that the stream has on the drop and the "strength" of the drop, which depends on the surface tension and the viscosity of the liquid. The interaction of the liquid and gas is generally described by the system of Equation 15-3. Four determining criteria in Equation 15-10 result. For a single drop entrained by a stream, the velocity $\underline{w}'$ drops out of the conditions which uniquely define the process. Thus, the last two criteria of the system (Equation 15-10) cease to be determining.

For a drop of known size, breakup initiates at a specific velocity of the entraining stream. This velocity, denoted as $\underline{w}''_{cr}$, is a function of conditions that uniquely define the breakup process. It is assumed that:

$$We = \frac{\varrho'' w''_{cr} 2 r_0}{\sigma} = f\left(\frac{\mu'^2}{\varrho' \sigma r_0}\right) \tag{15-15}$$

where r_0 is the initial drop radius.

For low-viscosity liquids (when breakup does not depend on μ'), it follows from equation 15-15:

$$We = \frac{\varrho'' w''^2_{cr} r_0}{\sigma} = const \tag{15-16A}$$

$$w''_{cr} = const \left(\frac{\sigma}{\varrho'' r_0}\right)^{0.5} \tag{15-16B}$$

The Weber number (Equation 15-15) is one of the more significant parameters which is a measure of the ratio of the disruptive aerodynamic forces to the surface tension forces acting on a drop. When a certain value of We is exceeded, the aerodynamic forces are sufficient to overcome the surface tension forces and the drop deforms and breaks up into smaller drops. As the Weber number increases, the breakup time and the size of the droplets decrease. According to experiments[43] the interval where the drops become unstable is determined by the inequality:

$$7 > \frac{\varrho'' w''^2 r_0}{\sigma} > 5.3 \tag{15-17}$$

Lane[4] examined the breakup of water drops ranging from 0.5 to 5.0 mm in diameter both when falling down the axis of a small vertical wind tunnel and when exposed to a transient blast at the end of a shock tube. For the drops falling down the wind tunnel, he found the critical Weber number was 5.4.

From an examination of the data of Merrington and Richardson[5] for drops of various liquids allowed to fall down a tall tower, Hinze[6] decided that $We_{gc} \simeq 10$, with results ranging from 7 to 15. He deduced $We_{sc} \simeq 6$ for $\mu^2 d / \varrho d\sigma r \ll 1$, a condition for which the effect of viscosity was observed to be negligible. These results are about a factor of two greater than Lane's.

Hanson et al.[7] studied the breakup of drops of water, methyl alcohol, and three grades of silicone oil with diameters between 100 and 1,000 μm in a shock tube. They compared the critical velocities for water and methyl alcohol drops for a number of diameters, concluding that their ratio was closer to the cube root than the square root of the surface tension ratio. As the combination of liquid properties and drop sizes used produced values of $\mu^2 / \varrho \sigma r$ ranging from 2×10^{-4} to 10, they were able to demonstrate the effect of this nondimensional group on breakup. For those combinations where $\mu^2 / \varrho \sigma r < 0.1$ they found We_{sc} was in the range 3.6 to 8.4. They further observed that We_{sc} increased as the drop diameter decreased.

One must thus conclude that there are two limiting cases for the variation of relative velocity with time that have been studied. For the case of suddenly applied relative velocity, the critical Weber numbers found range from 2.25 to 8.4, while for gradually applied relative velocities they range from 5.4 to 15. In practical situations, sudden relative velocity changes are rare. However, if the rise time of the relative velocity is short compared with a drop's breakup time, it is reasonable to assume that the relative velocity has been suddenly applied.

A commercial oil burner is an example where the aerodynamic breakup of a drop is important. A 100 μm residual fuel oil (r.f.o.) drop exposed to a gas stream at a relative dynamic pressure of 1 kN m^{-2} has a Weber number of 4, both the drop diameter and the dynamic pressure being typical of those found in power station oil burners. Various studies[8-10] show that the critical Weber numbers vary from 2 to 18. If the lower value of 2 is applicable to r.f.o. drops, then a substantial proportion of the larger drops produced by atomizers in power station oil burners will be unstable in the combustion air stream and will experience secondary atomization. In contrast, a value in the region of 18 is applicable, then only the relatively large drops, of which there are few, if any, will be unstable. An examination of critical Weber numbers is therefore required to determine the degree of secondary atomization occurring.

In systems where the objective is to break up drops by relative fluid motion, as in the case of a venturi scrubber, a knowledge of the time to break up and the size of the residual droplets is needed before optimizing the system. As an example, consider a system in which drops are projected tranversely across an air jet, the aim being to produce droplets less than a specified size. Knowledge of breakup time would allow the minimum width of the air jet to be estimated, while a knowledge of droplet diameters would allow the minimum jet velocity to be calculated. These parameters together define the minimum power supply to the jet.

Quantitative conclusions on how breakup time and droplet size vary with ϵ' ($\epsilon' = \varrho_s / \varrho_d$ — density ratio, where subscripts s and d relate to surrounding gas and drop, respectively) are difficult. The important and dimensionless groups are the Reynolds number, the Mach number (Ma) (defined as U/C where U is the initial relative velocity between drop and stream and C is the speed of sound in the surrounding fluid) and the Hinze number (Hi) ($\mu_d / \varrho_d \sigma r_0 = Hi^2$).

From an incompressible analysis, the effect of drop accelerations appears to be small for $\epsilon' < .001$. For $\epsilon' > .001$, all that can be concluded is that breakup time might be expected to change and droplet size to increase. Baines and Buttery[12] provide some data for mercury drops in water ($\epsilon' = .073$). Their study indicates that changes in ϵ' appear to principally affect droplet size for $\epsilon' > .001$.

For the Reynolds number, the only available indicators of the regimes in which it is likely to have an effect are the sphere drag coefficient and We_{sc}; where We_{sc} is the critical Weber number for a suddenly applied relative velocity. As drag coefficient is constant over the range of Re from 10^3 to 10^5 for incompressible flow, it would be reasonable to expect the breakup of drops with We of the order of 10 to be little affected over this range as well. With an increasing We and with the finer liquid structures produced during breakup there is likely to be a corresponding increase in the value of Re below which breakup is affected.

At Ma < 0.6, the variations in drag coefficient suggest correspondingly little variation in breakup.[13]

For Hi, the effects on breakup are likely to occur above a limiting value which decreases with We. For low values of We, the limiting value of Hi is probably in the range 0.01 to 0.05. In general, increasing Hi will lead to increased maximum droplet size.[14] When Hi is increased to about 0.2, the photographs of Hanson, Domich, and Adams[7] show that the thickness of the bag's rim is reduced, resulting in a smaller maximum droplet size. Droplet size in this case has been found to correlate in terms of a nondimensional breakup time T, defined as $(\varrho_s/\varrho_d)^{0.5}(Ut/r)$.

The basic properties characterizing atomization are the fractional composition of the drops and the spray density distribution throughout the cross-section of the atomized jet. The mean drop diameter is determined from the property of weight as:

$$\overline{D} = \frac{\sum_n G_iD_i}{\sum_n G_i} \qquad (15\text{-}18)$$

where G_i is the total weight of drops of diameter D_i. This indicates to some extent the nature of liquid atomization by a given spray nozzle.

Figure 15-3 shows the relationship[15] between the relative mean drop diameter D/D_0 (where D_0 is the diameter of the spray-nozzle orifice) and the first group of Equation 15-10. In these experiments, the air velocity changed within the range from 43 to 121 m/s, and the liquid velocity within 0.55 to 2.3 m/s. No influence of the relative flow rate of the phases w'/w'' was observed. As shown in Figure 15-3, the experimental points fall properly on a logarithmic straight line with a slope n $= -0.45$. At the same time the distance of the drops from the spray nozzle orifice has no noticeably appreciable influence on the mean drop diameter. The proportionality factor in the relation is:

$$\frac{\overline{D}}{D_0} = A\left(\frac{\sigma}{\varrho''w^2D_0}\right)^{0.45} \qquad (15\text{-}19)$$

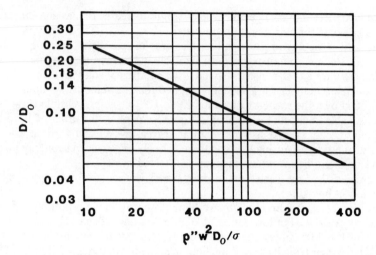

Figure 15-3. Plot of $\bar{D}/D_o$ vs. $\varrho''w^2D_o/\sigma$ from experiments with pneumatic spray nozzles[15].

This relationship varies for different liquids. This difference is determined only by the viscosity of the liquid and is characterized by the second criterion of Equation 5-10.

The data of Figure 15-4 show the following relationship:

$$\frac{\bar{D}}{D_0}\left(\frac{\varrho''w^2D_0}{\sigma}\right)^{0.45} = f\left(\frac{\mu'^2}{\varrho'\sigma D_0}\right) \tag{15-20}$$

The viscosity of the atomized liquids varied in these experiments from 0.067×10^{-3} to 54.5×10^{-3} kg $-$ 6/m². These data reveal that the effect of viscosity on drop size is only significant when

$$\frac{\mu'^2}{\varrho'\sigma D_0} > 0.1 \tag{15-21}$$

Experiments with a number of other spray nozzles have confirmed the indicated laws. The working formulas proposed by Vitman, et al.[15] have the form:

at $\dfrac{\mu'^2}{\varrho'\sigma D_0} > 0.5$:

$$\frac{\bar{D}}{D_0}\left(\frac{\varrho''w^2D_0}{\sigma}\right)^{0.45} = A_0 + 0.94\left(\frac{\mu'^2}{\varrho'\sigma D_0}\right)^{0.28} \tag{15-22}$$

at $\dfrac{\mu'^2}{\varrho'\sigma D_0} < 0.5$:

$$\dfrac{\overline{D}}{D}\left(\dfrac{\varrho''w^2D_0}{\sigma}\right)^{0.45} = A_0 + 1.24\left(\dfrac{\mu'^2}{\varrho'\sigma D_0}\right)^{0.63} \tag{15-23}$$

The quantity A_0 depends on the design of the spray nozzle. We may conclude that the fineness of liquid atomization by pneumatic type spraying is approximately inversely proportional to the square root of the kinetic energy of the gas.

The empirical expression most often applied for first approximation of drop size distributions generated by pneumatic type atomization is that of Nukiyama and Tanasawa:[16]

$$f(D) = \dfrac{\delta b^{3/\delta'}}{\Gamma(3/\delta')} D^2\exp(-bD^{\delta'}) \tag{15-24}$$

where the parameters b and δ' affect the dispersion and central value of the distribution and D is the droplet diameter in meters. The correlation was originally proposed as a relationship between mean droplet size and the physical properties and atomization conditions. For the air-water system, the correlation is expressed as follows:

$$\overline{D_{32}} = \dfrac{4.892 \times 10^{-3}}{V_{rel}} + 0.01206\ L^{1.5} \tag{15-25}$$

where the Sauter mean diameter, $\overline{D_{32}}$, is used, and is defined as that size of droplets that possess the same volume-to-surface-area ratio as the sum of all drops in the distribution. L is the liquid-to-gas loading ratio (m³ liquid/m³ gas), and V_{rel} is the

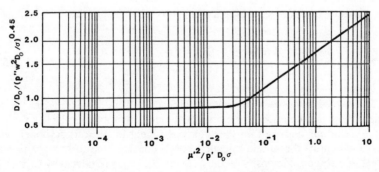

Figure 15-4. Generalized relationship between $\overline{D}D_0/(\varrho''w^2D_0/\sigma)^{0.45}$ and $\mu'^2/(\varrho'D_0\sigma)$ (Vitman et al.[15]).

relative velocity between liquid and gas phases at the point of injection (m/s). The Sauter mean diameter has been found to be useful in describing the efficiency of spray breakup processes and in describing mass transfer and particle collection processes.[17]

For a discrete droplet distribution, the Sauter mean diameter can be calculated from the expression:

$$\bar{D}_{32} = \frac{\sum_{j=i}^{j} D_j^3 f'(D_j)}{\sum_{j=i}^{j} D_j^2 f'(D_j)} \tag{15-26}$$

where $f'(D)$ is the fraction of drops in the interval having a characteristic diameter D_j.

For the Nukiyama-Tanasawa distribution function, the Sauter mean diameter is:

$$\bar{D}_{32} = b^{-(1/\delta')} \frac{\Gamma(6/\delta')}{\Gamma(5/\delta')} \tag{15-27}$$

Lewis et al.[18] observed for venturi atomizers that a δ' value of $1/4$ to $1/3$ provides a good representation of the distribution.

Equations 15-25 and 15-27 provide a discrete distribution in terms of the number of droplet classes, each having a known fraction of the total injected spray. Although the validity of the Nukiyama-Tanasawa distribution in describing the conditions in an operating venturi has been questioned by several investigators,[18,19] a universally accepted distribution function has not been advanced.

Droplet Motion and Concentration

The equation of motion describing a single spherical droplet can be stated as follows:

$$\frac{du_j}{dx} = \frac{3}{4} C_{Dj} \frac{\varrho(v - u_j) \mid v - u_j \mid}{u_j \varrho_s D_j} - \frac{3u_j dD_j}{D_j dx} \; ; j = 1, ..., j^* \tag{15-28}$$

The last term represents the momentum contribution from mass transfer. The drag coefficient, C_{Dj}, is a function of the droplet Reynolds number. Boll[20] has reviewed various correlations and data on the drag coefficient on venturi scrubber operations. At the venturi throat and injection point, considerable turbulence prevails. The effect of turbulence intensity on the drag coefficient is reviewed by Clift et al.[21]

The deposition rate or removal of particulates depends on the relative velocity between particles and droplets, the local target efficiency, and the number concentrations of particles and droplets. For a steady-state phenomenon, the equation describing this process is:

$$\frac{\partial(vn_jA)}{\partial x} = -\sum_{j=i}^{j} (v - u_j)n_jA \frac{\pi D_j^2}{4} E_{ij}N_j \qquad (15\text{-}29)$$

where v = gas velocity (m/s)
u = droplet velocity (m/s)
n = particle concentration (particles/m^3)
A = local cross-sectional area of the venturi (m^2)
x = distance measured along the axis (m^2)
D = droplet diameter (m)
E_{ij} = local target efficiency for the particles of the ith class being collected by droplets of the jth class, N is the droplet concentration (droplets/m^3). The summation sign denotes the collection of the particles by each droplet size class.

The local target efficiency, E_{ij}, indicates the relative ease by which particles belonging to the ith class are removed by droplets belonging to the jth class. E_{ij} is a function of the physical properties of the gas and liquid phases, the droplet and particle size distributions, as well as various dynamic, spacial characteristics. Placek and Peters[22] have developed expressions describing the various flow regimes which include the effects of mass and heat transfer. In Equation 15-29, the term "vn_j A" can be replaced by $\dot{n}_i$ which is the particle loading (i.e., number of particles per unit time).

The Mechanical Energy Balance

The pressure balance across a venturi scrubber can be derived from consideration of the momentum exchange between the gas phase and the wall of the device. Placek et al.[3] neglected the presence of the dust phase in deriving the mechanical energy balance on the basis of a dilute system flow. From a momentum balance about a control volume with differential length, dx, the energy balance is stated as:

$$A\frac{dP_T}{dx} + \dot{m}_g\frac{dv}{dx} + \sum_{j=1}^{j^*} \dot{m}_j\frac{du_j}{dx} + \frac{\dot{m}_s + \dot{m}_g}{\dot{m}_g} \frac{fv^2A}{2D_h} = 0 \qquad (15\text{-}30)$$

The first term in this equation denotes the pressure forces acting over the cross-sectional area, A; the second term represents the change in gas momentum; the third term refers to the change in droplet momentum for all droplet classes; and the last term accounts for momentum loss of the fluid to the wall as shear.

Boll[20] notes that an additional momentum loss term should be included due to the formation of the liquid film on the venturi wall. He notes that this is partly offset by the fact that the mixture density correction usually underestimates the wall friction term. Although Yoshida et al.[23] suggest the use of different friction factor correlations for various sections of a venturi, Boll[20] found that an average value of 0.027 was sufficient.

Combining Equation 15-30 with the droplet equation of motion, (Equation 15-28), the pressure gradient can be expressed as follows:

$$\frac{dP_T}{dx} = -\varrho v \frac{dv}{dx} - \sum_{j=1}^{j^*} \frac{3}{4} \frac{\varrho}{\varrho_s} \frac{\dot{m}_j}{D_j A} C_{Dj} \frac{(v - u_j) \mid v - u_j \mid}{u_j}$$

$$+ 3 \frac{\dot{m}_j u_j dD_j}{D_j A dx} - \frac{\dot{m}_s + \dot{m}_g}{\dot{m}_g} \frac{f \varrho v^2}{2 D_h}$$

(15-31)

The first and second terms on the right hand side allow for either pressure loss or recovery. The third term is zero for operations without mass and heat transfer. Hollands and Goel[24] present a nondimensionalized form of the mechanical energy balance and provide nomographs to estimate the pressure drop. However, numerical integration of Equation 15-31 is necessary to obtain the axial pressure distribution.

COMPARISON OF SCRUBBER MODELS

The performance of a scrubber in collecting particles belonging to the ith size class may be represented by the overall particle collection efficiency, E_{iov}, which may be expressed in terms of the inlet and exit dust loading rates.

$$E_{iov} = 1 - (\dot{n}_i)_{exit}/(\dot{n}_i)_{inlet}$$

(15-32)

Alternately, the venturi's performance can be expressed in terms of the penetration, P_{iov}:

$$P_{iov} = 1 - E_{iov}$$

(15-33)

or more conveniently, in terms of the number of transfer units, N_{Ti}, defined as:

$$N_{Ti} = \ln \left(\frac{1}{P_{Ti}} \right)$$

(15-34)

Performance data on a commercial venturi scrubber are reported by Brink et al.[25] Experiments in this study were aimed at evaluating the throat gas velocity, the spray liquid rate, the spray liquid velocity, and the number of injection jets. A cascade impactor was used to measure the particle size distribution at the venturi entrance and exit to establish the collection efficiency. Some of these results are compared

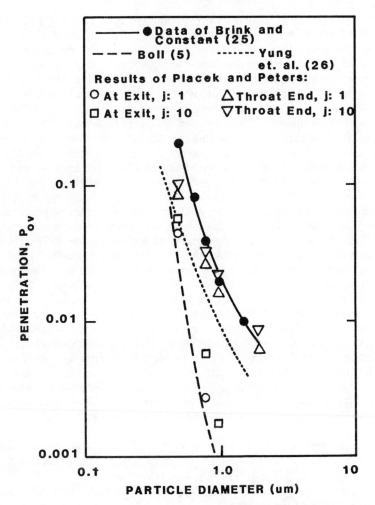

Figure 15-5. Comparison of different model predictions to the data of Brink and Contant.[25]

with model predictions of Boll[5] and Yung et al.[26] in Figure 15-5. As shown, the measured overall collection are overpredicted by these two models (recall Equation 15-33; $E_{iov} = 1 - P_{iov}$). The results reported by Boll[20] are essentially the same as those obtained assuming a drop size equal to the Sauter mean diameter. This overestimation of predicted collection efficiency is likely related to the nonuniform distribution of drops across the throat region.[20] The penetrations predicted by assuming a single drop class and 10 drop classes differing by 10%–50%, indicate the need to account for the variance of the droplet size distribution. Note from Figure 15-5 that Yung et al.'s[26] model did provide a better estimate of the penetration, which is somewhat surprising, since their model only considers particle collection to take place in the throat. This assumption would imply a lower efficiency than for the case of accurately represented geometry. The agreement between Yung et al.'s prediction and the data of Brink et al.[25] does not support the contention that scrubbers do not collect particles after the throat section. However, without specifically modeling the poor distribution of spray liquid and other effects, a better estimate might be obtained in some cases by only considering collection to occur in the throat.

Ekman and Johnstone[27] report measurements of the collection efficiency of 1-μm diameter dibutyl-phthalate particles using a laboratory-scale scrubber having a total length of approximately 0.5 m. Their results for the inward radial configuration are shown in Figure 15-6, plotted as a function of the performance parameter $L(St)^{0.5}$. This parameter by convention, gives a suitable variable for correlating performance data. The Stokes number is defined in terms of the Sauter mean diameter and the gas velocity in the throat. Data are compared again with the model of Placek et al.,[3] and as shown, their model overestimates the collection efficiency by 50%–100% in most cases. There are several reasons for this discrepancy. First the scrubber used by Ekman and Johnstone[27] was a laboratory scrubber, and units of this size are known to be susceptible to poor liquid distribution. Secondly, the spray was introduced by means of a single jet rather than multiple jets, in which case droplet interaction is ignored in the model. Thirdly, the scrubber was operated in a mode which produced values for $L(St)^{0.5}$ that are less than 0.002, corresponding to very low liquid loading ratios. This corresponds to operating the venturi at collection efficiencies less than 60%. Finally, oil aerosols are in general, more difficult to collect with a water spray scrubber, than solid particle aerosols. Whereas a soluble and hydrophilic particle may attach itself to a water drop as a result of a glancing collision, a more direct contact may be required for the capture of a hydrophobic particle.

Yung et al.'s[26] model accounts for a finite throat length rather than an infinite length as is assumed in other models. The principal assumptions of this model are:

1. The venturi scrubber consists of a straight throat section with water injection at the entrance of the throat.
2. A single droplet size is used.
3. The initial velocity for the drop phase is zero.
4. No mass or heat transfer effects are considered.
5. Collection occurs by inertial impaction only
6. A simplified empirical relationship is used to express the target efficiency in the potential flow regime ($E_{imp} = (1/K_p + 0.7)^2$, where the impaction parameter $K_p = 2St$).
7. The drag coefficient is represented by a simplified empirical expression, $C_D = 18.5/Re^{0.6}$.

In applying the model to actual scrubber geometries, their model tends to underpredict the overall efficiency since it does not account for collection mechanisms in other parts of the venturi.

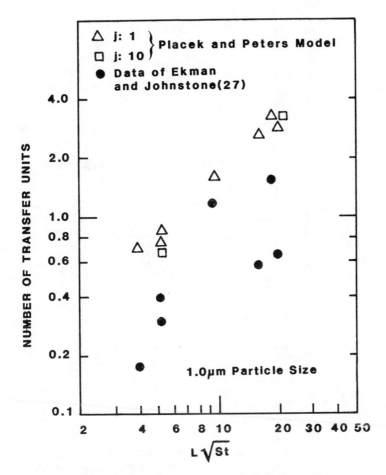

Figure 15-6. Comparison of data of Ekman et al.[27] to the model of Placek and Peters.[3]

OPERATING VARIABLES AND PERFORMANCE

The two parameters most often used in correlating venturi scrubber performance are the liquid loading ratio and the gas velocity. An increase in the liquid loading ratio results in an increase in the droplet Sauter mean diameter. This in turn causes a reduction in the Stokes number and hence a lower target efficiency. In addition, it directly increases the concentration of droplets.

The effect of gas velocity on performance is illustrated in Figure 15-7, which shows a plot of the number of transfer units versus $L(St)^{0.5}$. For a loading ratio

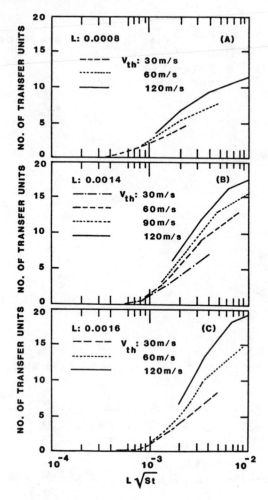

Figure 15-7. The effect of gas velocity on particle collection efficiency for different liquid-to-gas loadings (Placek and Peters[3]).

0.008 and constant injection point characteristics, an increase in the throat velocity results in greater collection efficiency. There are several explanations for this observation. To begin, the Nukiyama-Tanasawa drop size equation predicts that the spray continues to disintegrate into small droplets at higher throat velocity. Since both the higher velocity difference and the smaller drop size tend to increase the Stokes number, a higher collection efficiency would be expected. Also, since more drops can be formed from a given volume of liquid, their concentration is higher, which directly increases the collection rate. Figure 15-7 further shows that this effect is most important for values of $L(St)^{0.5}$ in excess of 0.001. At lower values of $L(St)^{0.5}$, collection efficiency appears less sensitive.

A plot of the number of transfer units versus $L(St)^{0.5}$ is shown in Figure 15-8. Note that a gas velocity of 30 m/s, increasing the liquid loading ratio can either increase or decrease the performance. At higher values of $L(St)^{0.5}$, the larger values

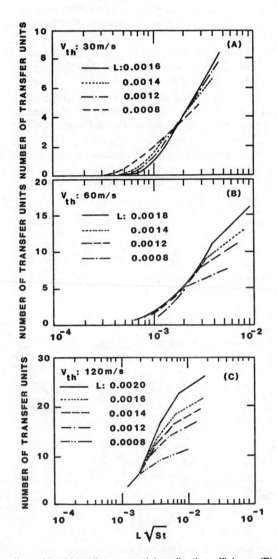

Figure 15-8. The effect of liquid loading on particle collection efficiency (Placek and Peters[3]).

of L resulted in improved performance since the larger volume of liquid results in greater droplet concentrations. However, since $\overline{D}_{32}$ varies with $L^{1.5}$ in the Nukiyama-Tanasawa equation, a trade-off exists since the larger drop size has a smaller Stokes number corresponding to a lower efficiency.

Placek and Peters[3] compared a distribution consisting of ten drop classes to that of a single droplet class, shown in Figure 15-9. As shown, the use of a single class results slightly in only an underestimate of the collection efficiency at low values of the Stokes numbers. This was attributed to changes in the target efficiency due both to impaction and interception mechanisms. Conceivably, a single drop size could duplicate the multiple drop class results; however, it is difficult to determine what that drop size should be.

Both the injection site and the initial liquid jet velocity have pronounced effects on performance. Figure 15-10 shows the effect of injection site reported by Placek et al.[3] For the particular geometry modeled, moving the location of the injection site varied the effective contact time of droplets in the venturi, and also altered the drop size distribution since the gas velocity used in the Nukiyama-Tanasawa equation is a function of position in the scrubber. The axial position of the injection site was moved from 0.2 m to 0.8 m from the beginning of the converging section in these experiments. This enabled a range of Sauter mean diameters of 231 μm to 148 μm. The effect of the injection location on performance is complex. For particle diameters less than 1.0 μm, performance was observed to increase as the injection site was moved closer to the throat, since the higher velocity at these positions

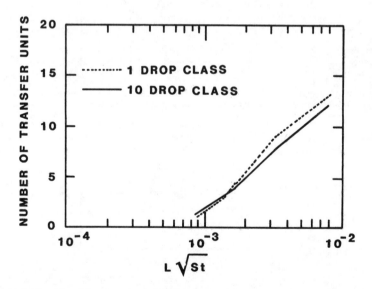

Figure 15-9. The effect of the number of droplet class intervals on collection efficiency (Placek and Peters[3]).

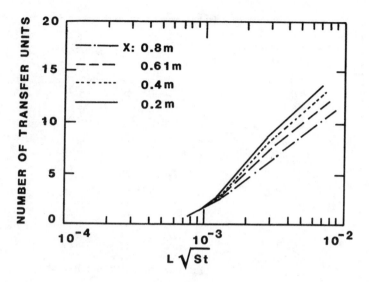

Figure 15-10. The effect of injection site location on particle collection efficiency (Placek and Peters[3]).

allowed for better capture of these small particles. For particles larger than 2.0 μm (those which are collected relatively easily), collection decreased as the injection site was moved toward the throat since the contact time was shorter.[3]

The throat length also plays an important role in scrubber performance. A longer throat favorably affects performance since it allows for a greater contact time between the liquid and dust. From an operating cost standpoint, however, too long a throat is undesirable since it consumes more mechanical energy in frictional losses to the walls.

Muir et al.[28] investigated the effects of venturi geometry, nozzle arrangement, method of water injection, etc., on performance at high liquid-to-gas ratios, attempting to show their effects as being secondary. Their study was based upon the Contacting Power Concept,[29-32] which implies that for a given gas and liquid and particle size distributions, a single correlation of collection efficiency as a function of power consumption exists, which is largely independent of scrubber design, type, or size. The relationship is of the form:

$$N_T = a' \Delta P^{b'} \tag{15-35}$$

where coefficients a' and b' are functions of the particular aerosol.

Two types of variable-throat configurations were examined along with several different methods of water injection; namely, even distribution of water around the

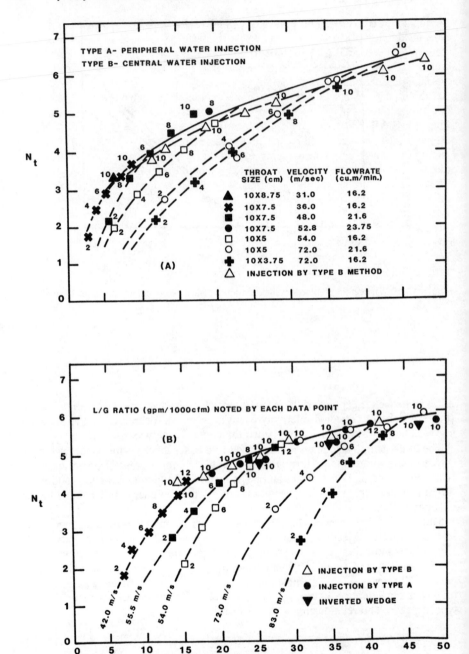

Figure 15-11. N_t versus ΔP correlations developed by Muir et al.[28] for two different venturi scrubber types.

periphery of the entry duct, distribution of water by a central spreader in the converging section of the venturi, and direct injection of water at the venturi throat—four jets on either side. The results of this study are summarized by the plots of N_T versus ΔP given in Figure 15-11. The highest collection efficiencies are almost invariably associated with high liquid-to-gas ratios (> 1.28 ℓ/m^3). The differences in scrubber performance due to throat position and velocity are significant at low liquid-to-gas ratios and at low pressure drops. They become progressively less sensitive at higher liquid-to-gas ratios. The low efficiencies characteristic of low liquid-to-gas ratios are attributed to the maldistribution of scrubbing liquid. Also, the method of water injection does not appear to be significant at high liquid-to-gas ratios. A comparison of the performance of both venturis on the same test dust showed large differences in the efficiencies of the two units at low liquid-to-gas ratios.[30] The open throat venturi (Type A) was shown to perform markedly better, but again, these differences tend to diminish as the liquid-to-gas ratio and pressure drop increase. A comparison of the performance of both venturis at L/G > 1.6 ℓ/m^3 is shown in Figure 15-12. A single correlation is shown for two different types of venturis, for a wide range of velocities and scrubber geometries, and for the three different methods of water injection. The test results of Muir et al.[29] thus support the Contacting Power Concept.

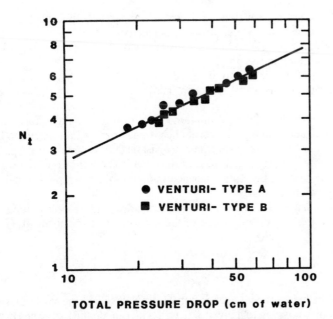

Figure 15-12. Comparison of performances of two venturi types studied by Muir et al.[28]

HEAT AND MASS TRANSFER CONSIDERATIONS

In addition to the complex hydrodynamic mechanisms and particle interactions causing droplet breakup and heat, mass exchanges play important roles in establishing dynamic drop size distributions that ultimately affect collection. The evaporation and/or condensation processes are complicated by the wide range of droplet sizes normally present in a scrubber, with each size class having changing velocities, temperature, and evaporation rates. Numerous investigations have been made on evaporation rates from single drops of pure liquids. Dickenson and Marshall[33] (see also Reference 34) studied the evaporation from sprays using different drop size distribution functions. Their investigation was limited to drops whose temperature remained constant with respect to time (i.e., adiabatic conditions). They found that the mean diameter (e.g., the Sauter mean), cannot adequately characterize a nonuniform spray with respect to its evaporation behavior; instead, the drop size distribution must be accounted for in any analysis.

Bailey and Liang[2] estimated the heat and mass transfer between multicomponent gas and liquid streams consisting of a number of different droplet size classes. They showed for the case of flue-gas scrubbing by spray quenching that scrubbing efficiency is critically dependent on the droplet size distribution. Placek and Peters[35] adapted and applied this analysis to the venturi scrubber case, considering only one component to be subject to mass transfer (an appropriate assumption for the air water system). For a single droplet experiencing evaporation/condensation, the following assumptions are made:[35]

1. The drops are spherical and uniform in temperature throughout.
2. Direct interaction between drops is neglected.
3. All resistance to heat and mass transfer is assumed to exist in a gas boundary layer surrounding the droplet.
4. The flow of gas and spray is one-dimensional.
5. Equilibrium exists at the gas/drop interface.

Kulic et al.[36] have shown the assumption of uniform drop temperature differences between a model describing the internal heat transfer resistance and a model developed to simulate no internal heat transfer resistance to be small for drops less than 1,000 μm in size.[36] Since the surface of the drop is at equilibrium, the vapor pressure of water vapor at the drop's surface is therefore known as a function of the droplet's temperature.

The rate of change of a single drop having mass M_j with respect to time is related to the partial pressure driving force of the evaporating component $(p_b - p_{dj})$ by:

$$\frac{dM_j}{dt} = \frac{d}{dt}\left(\frac{\pi}{6}D_j^3\varrho_s\right) = \dot{k}_{gj}MW_b\pi D_j^2(p_b - p_{dj}) \, ; \, j = 1, \ldots j* \qquad (15\text{-}36)$$

where $\dot{k}_{gj}$ is the mass transfer coefficient for droplets belonging to the jth size class. Since all drops belonging to a given size will undergo identical changes in temperature, velocity, and size, no drops move from one size class to another even though the typical size characterizing the class will decrease or increase. The balance can be restated as follows:[35]

$$\frac{dD_j}{dt} = 2\dot{k}_{gj}MW_b(p_b - p_{dj})/\varrho_s; \quad j = 1, \dots j* \qquad (15\text{-}37)$$

If the partial pressure of water vapor in the bulk gas exceeds the partial pressure at the drop surface, the diameter increases, which is the situation occurring during condensation conditions. When p_b is less than p_{dj}, evaporation occurs.

Rowe et al.[37] have reviewed the literature describing gas-liquid mass transfer coefficients and recommend the following expression for the Sherwood number:

$$Sh = 2.0 + BSc^{0.333}Re^{0.5} \qquad (15\text{-}38)$$

Literature values for B are reported to range from 0.362 to 0.60 depending on the gas-liquid system. Placek et al.[35] applied the correlation tested by Manning et al.[38] who studied heat and mass transfer to decelerating finely divided sprays in air. Manning et al. used the Ranz and Marshall[39] equation, which is stated as:

$$Sh_j = 2.0 + 0.6Sc_j^{0.333}Re_j^{0.5}; \quad j = 1, \dots j* \qquad (15\text{-}39)$$

where the dimensionless Sherwood, Schmidt, and Reynolds numbers are defined respectively, as follows:

$$Sh_j = \frac{k_{gj}MW_bD_jP_{afj}}{D_{abfj}\varrho_{fj}} \qquad (15\text{-}40)$$

$$Sc_j = \frac{\mu_{fi}}{D_{abfj}\varrho_{fj}} \qquad (15\text{-}41)$$

$$Re_j = \frac{D_j \mid v - u_j \mid \varrho_{fj}}{\mu_{fj}} \qquad (15\text{-}42)$$

Subscripts a, b, and f refer to air, water, and the conditions in the film, respectively.

For heat exchange to a single droplet, internal circulation and conduction are assumed to dampen out any temperature gradients within the drop volume.[35] An energy balance for the droplet includes energy transfer due to the temperature gradient across the film plus the energy transfer due to mass transfer.

$$\frac{dT_{dj}}{dx} = \frac{6h_{gj}(T_a - T_{dj})}{\varrho_sC_{ps}D_ju_j} + \frac{3}{C_{ps}D_j}\left[\lambda_j + C_{pb}(T_a - T_{dj})\right]\frac{dD_j}{dx} \qquad (15\text{-}43)$$

The heat transfer coefficient applied by Placek et al.[35] is analogous to Ranz and Marshall's[34] mass transfer correlation:

$$Nu_j = \frac{h_{gj}D_j}{k_{fj}} = 2.0 + 0.6 \, Pr_j^{0.333}Re_j^{0.5} \qquad (15\text{-}44)$$

where the Prandtl number is defined as:

$$Pr_j = \frac{C_{Hfj}\mu_{fj}}{(1 + H_{fj})k_{fj}}$$

(15-45)

where the terms refer to the mean film humid heat capacity, C_{Hfj}, the mean film humidity, H_{fj}, and the thermal conductivity of the film, k_{fj}.

For an adiabatic system, an overall energy balance for the gas and two phases is:

$$\dot{m}_{ai} \int_{T_{ai}}^{T_a} C_{pa}dT + \dot{m}_{bi} \int_{T_{ai}}^{T_a} C_{pb}dT$$

$$+ \sum_{j=1}^{j^*} \left(\dot{m}_{dj} \int_{T_{di}}^{T_{dj}} C_{pd}dT \right)$$

$$= (\dot{m}_{bi} - \dot{m}_b)\left(\lambda_b + \int_{T_{di}}^{T_{ai}} C_{pb}dT \right)$$

(15-46)

where the expression is integrated over the limits from T_{ai} to the local bulk gas temperature, T_a. The expression can be solved for T_a by numerical integration. An approximate procedure involves the use of a linear function to represent the heat capacities of air and water vapor from which a quadratic expression for T_a can be written as follows:

$$q_1 T_a^2 + q_2 T_a + q_3 = 0$$

(15-47)

The variables q_1, q_2, and q_3 are of the following forms:

$$q_1 = \frac{m_a}{2}(a_2 - b_2 H)$$

(15-48A)

$$q_2 = m_a(a_1 - b_1 H)$$

(15-48B)

$$q_3 = \sum_{j=1}^{j^*} m_{dj}C_{pd}(T_{dj} - T_{di})$$

$$- \frac{m_a}{2}(a_2 + b_2 H)T_{ai}^2 - m_a(a_1 + b_1 H)T_{ai}$$

$$-(H_i - H)m_a\left[\lambda_b + b_1(T_{ai} - T_{di})\right] + \frac{b_2}{2}(T_{ai}^2 - T_{di}^2)$$

(15-48C)

a_1, a_2, b_1, and b_2 are the coefficients of the linear heat capacity relationships.

$$C_{pa} = a_1 + a_2 T_a$$

(15-49A)

$$C_{pb} = b_1 + b_2T_a \qquad (15\text{-}49\text{B})$$

and

$$m_b = m_aH \qquad (15\text{-}49\text{C})$$

where H = local humidity
       H_i = humidity at the inlet

The local temperature T_a can now be evaluated by solving Equation 15-49A where q_1 and q_2 are both positive.

The local humidity, H, can be obtained from a mass balance for the water phase. Denoting F as the fraction of the original spray remaining,

$$F = \sum_{j=1}^{j^*} f(D_j)D_j^3 / \sum_{j=1}^{j^*} f(D_j)_i(D_j^3)_i \qquad (15\text{-}50)$$

where $f(D_j)$ is the fraction of droplets belonging to the jth drop size class. Following Placek et al.,[35] we denote w as the mass ratio of dry air to liquid spray introduced, from which humidity can be expressed as follows:

$$H = (1 - F - w'H_i)/w' \qquad (15\text{-}51)$$

Local collection efficiency is sensitive to the inlet gas temperature, humidity, and spray temperature. Hence, these parameters must be included in the analysis. By defining local dimensionless source strengths for each droplet class and noting that particle collection can occur in either a viscous or potential flow regime, two parameters materialize:

$$S_{pj} = \frac{\varrho_s u_j}{2\varrho_{bf} \mid v - u_j \mid} \frac{dD_j}{dx} \qquad (15\text{-}52)$$

$$S_{vj} = - \frac{\varrho_s D_j u_j}{4\varrho_{bf}v} \frac{dD_j}{dx} \qquad (15\text{-}53)$$

Expressions described earlier for the local target efficiency depend on S_{pj} or S_{vj}. These are known as the interception parameters, where the Stokes number is defined as follows in the target efficiency equation :

$$St = \frac{C_f(\varrho_p - \varrho)d^2 \mid v - u_j \mid}{18\mu D_j} \qquad (15\text{-}54)$$

The results of experiments to determine the dynamic behavior of primary variables and the effect of process variables are reported by Placek and Peters.[35] Figures 15-13 and 15-14 summarize some of their observations. Figure 15-13A shows measured axial velocity profiles. The gas velocity and the response of different droplet diameters are shown. The locations of the converging and throat sections are readily recognized in these velocity flow patterns. The break in the curve in the converging section (1-2) represents the point of liquid injection and shows the effect of the 350°K gas contacting the cooler liquid. It can also be observed that the gas velocity in the throat section increases only slightly due to the mass and heat transfer effects. An obvious observation is that the inlet and exit gas velocities are different even though the flow areas are the same; this is due to the change in gas density, which cannot be accounted for in the simpler models proposed by other investigators.

Figure 15-13B shows the temperature profiles for the simulation of a 350°K process gas being contacted with a 300°K spray liquid. The gas temperature decreases very rapidly within the first few centimeters, and then gradually approaches a steady value of slightly under 319°K over most of the remaining venturi. The dashed curve represents the adiabatic saturation temperature. The difference in behavior of the 210 μm drops and the 50 μm shows that the low thermal mass of the smaller drops tends to keep them more nearly in equilibrium with the surrounding gas than the larger drops. In all cases, the drops attempt to follow the adiabatic saturation temperature of the system rather than the actual gas temperature, although the two are not greatly different.

The pressure distribution in a typical scrubber is shown in Figure 15-14A. At the inlet of the converging section, the pressure begins to decline gradually due to the acceleration of the gas. At the injection location, a sharp decrease in the total pressure occurs due to the momentum exchange between the gas and the droplet phases. The pressure gradient is steepest at the injection site and then diminishes as the drops acquire higher velocities. Pressure recovery in the diverging section is due to the decrease in gas kinetic energy and to the droplets supplying kinetic energy.

The variation in local collection efficiency is shown by the plot in Figure 15-14B. Note that particles of 0.5 μm diameter are poorly collected, while 5.0 μm dust is collected with nearly 100% efficiency. This observation tantalizes further interest in developing design enhancements to increase collection efficiencies for small particles perhaps through the use of condensation techniques such as steam conditioning.

One approach to enhancing scrubber performance is by varying the humidity of the inlet gas stream. Placek et al.[35] reports measurements showing encouraging increases in collection efficiency with increasing relative humidity. This enhancement is a heat and mass transfer effect resulting from the motion of water vapor in the gas toward the cooler droplet surface during condensation. Since in many industrial applications process gas streams are already at relatively high humidity levels, a model which does not account for diffusiophoresis is of limited value since it will tend to predict lower collection efficiencies. In a complete description of the effect of humidity, one should also consider the hygroscopic nature of the particles since this could possibly affect both the particle size and the local humidity in the venturi.

To model the effect of inlet gas temperature on performance, Placek and Peters[35] conducted experiments at temperatures of 350°K, 500°K, and 700°K for dry air and a spray temperature of 300°K. The results of these simulations showed performance to decrease moderately as the gas temperature increased for particles in the range of 0.8 μm to 2.0 μm. The collection of 0.5 μm particles was observed to be only slightly affected by the increase in gas temperatures. One reason for this de-

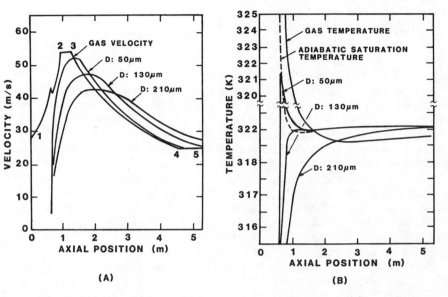

Figure 15-13. Axial distributions for different size particles: (A) velocity profiles; (B) temperature profiles (Placek and Peters[35]).

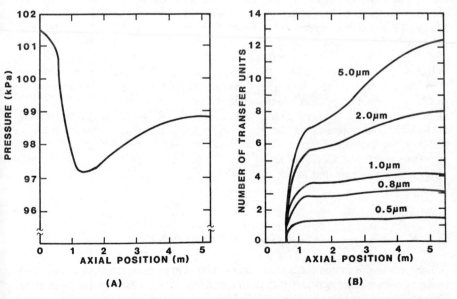

Figure 15-14. Axial profiles for (A) pressure; (B) collection efficiency; reported by Placek and Peters.[35]

crease is that the rapid evaporation of water from the drop surface, as the spray encounters the hot, dry gas, slightly retards the collection process. Another reason for the lower performance at high temperature is the change in gas density (and hence, velocity) as the gas cools. This reduces the relative velocity between the gas and droplets, thus lowering the Stokes number and collection efficiency.

An examination of their data at spray temperatures in the range of 275°K to 350°K with an inlet gas temperature of 350°K reveals that for submicron particles, increasing the inlet water temperature has little effect on collection. However, for particles larger than 2.0 μm, increasing the water temperature resulted in a lowering of performance. Thus, as the water temperature is increased, the relative importance of enhanced collection due to condensation decreases.

Increasing the initial water spray temperature tends to increase the exiting gas temperature, thereby raising the gas velocity over the length of the venturi. This causes large velocity differences between the gas and drops and also increases the collection efficiencies due to the larger Stokes numbers. It appears that the smaller particle sizes are most sensitive to the difference in the Stokes number while the condensation effect predominates for the larger particle sizes.

To evaluate the importance of mass transfer on overall collection efficiency, the effects due to evaporation and condensation must be separated. In the case of evaporation, the total time when mass transfer occurs is rather limited since the gas cools quickly to the adiabatic saturation temperature due to contact with the cool liquid. In these cases, the total amount of water transferred to the gas phase is quite small (only enough to saturate the gas at the ultimate adiabatic saturation temperature). On the other hand, if a gas at 350°K is initially saturated with water vapor and contacts the cool liquid stream, the system must transfer most of the water vapor to the droplet (all except that portion which is required to saturate the gas at the adiabatic saturation temperature). The greater magnitude of this effect relative to the evaporation process is reported by Placek et al.[35] In changing the relative humidity from 0% to 100%, the penetration of 0.5 μm particles changed from 0.270 to 0.204. This represents a 21% change in the number of transfer units. Although these effects are not very large, they are many times greater than the retarding effect which would be present under conditions where the spray was evaporating. A large fraction of the drop size distribution is less than the Sauter mean diameter, and the interception parameter may be significantly larger for some drop size classes. In addition, the analysis of target efficiency has shown that interception may be more important when considered as acting together with the impaction mechanism than when both are considered to act independently.

ADDITIONAL COMMENTS

The discussions in this chapter have been limited to particle removal, which obviously is not representative of this device's full potential—that of gas absorption. Discussions of the principles of gas absorption with specific relation to the operation of venturi scrubbers are given in References 36 through 54. A few remarks on this subject are worthy in this chapter.

Johnstone et al.[41,42] and Field[43] investigated the absorption of sulfur dioxide in water and alkaline solutions and measured the amount of sulfur dioxide absorbed in the liquid at various distances from the point of liquid injection. Kuznetsov et al.[44] report a correlation for the rate of gas absorption with chemical reaction in the throat and the divergent sections, relating the number of transfer units and the degree of absorption to the principal operating and design parameters. Their correlation was used by Boyadzhiev[45] to evaluate the optimal conditions for gas absorption with chemical reaction. Markant et al.[46] and others[47,48] also studied the absorption of SO_2 from dilute gas streams.

Gleason[49] reports an extensive data bank on SO_2 absorption by sodium carbonate solutions and calcium hydroxide solutions using a flooded disk scrubber, which is considered a type of atomizing scrubber. Atlay[50] studied the absorption of hydrocarbon vapors using surfactant solutions in an ejector venturi scrubber.

Uchida and Wen[51] report simulations of SO_2 absorption in various venturi scrubbers using a mathematical model that describes mass transfer and fluid flows in scrubbers for SO_2-H_2O and SO_2-alkaline solutions. A set of first order, nonlinear, ordinary differential equations was derived relating the liquid velocity, the SO_2 concentration in the liquid, and the SO_2 partial pressure along the axial direction of the scrubber. In their mechanical energy balance and equation of motion, the size distribution of droplets was not accounted for, but rather a mean droplet diameter was defined.

Virkar et al.[52] applied the theory of gas absorption with chemical reaction to estimate the effective interfacial area, a, and the liquid-side and gas-side mass transfer coefficients in a venturi scrubber operating in the wet-approach mode. Data were also reported for the Pease-Anthony mode of operation which provided comparison between the two modes of operation. They studied the hydrodynamic characteristics for the operating modes over a range of gas and liquid flow rates. In addition, they examined the effects of liquid viscosity and surface tension on the effective interfacial contact area. They reported that the former operating mode gives reasonably high values of interfacial area, liquid-side mass-transfer coefficient, and gas-side mass-transfer coefficient at relatively low values of pressure drop. The effective interfacial area for this mode was found to be independent of liquid viscosity over the range of variables studied. A decrease in the surface tension of the liquid phase resulted in an increase in the values of effective interfacial area for the Pease-Anthony operating mode. In this case, values of the gas-side mass-transfer coefficient were substantially higher, however, the pressure drop was found to be significantly higher than with the wet-approach.

Consider a stationary liquid droplet where physical absorption onto the surface is occurring. The following differential equation is obtained from a material balance:

$$\frac{\partial C_A}{\partial t} = \frac{D_A}{r^2} \frac{\partial}{\partial r}\left(r^2 \frac{\partial C_A}{\partial r}\right) \tag{15-55}$$

The initial and boundary conditions for this problem are

at $r = r_o$, $t > 0$; $C_A = C_{Ai}$

at $r = 0$, $t > 0$; $\partial C_A/\partial r = 0$ $\qquad\qquad$ (15-56)

Equation 15-55 can be solved analytically for the rate of absorption at time t:[51]

$$N_A = \frac{2D_AC_{Ai}}{r_o} \sum_{m-1}^{\infty} \exp\left(\frac{-D_Am^2\pi^2t}{r_o^2}\right)$$
(15-57)

The mass transfer coefficient for physical absorption into the drop k_{LP} is defined as follows:

$$k_{Lp} = \frac{2D_A}{r_o} \sum_{m-1}^{\infty} \exp\left(\frac{-D_Am^2\pi^2t}{r_o^2}\right)$$
(15-58)

Assuming the reaction to be instantaneous and both the diffusivities of the gas and the reactant species in the liquid are the same,[53] then the liquid phase mass-transfer coefficient can be expressed as:

$$k_L = \left[1 + \left(\frac{C_{Bo}}{C_{Ai}}\right)\right]k_{LP}$$
(15-59)

where C_{Ai} is the interfacial concentration

$$C_{Ai} = \frac{(C_A{}^* - C_{Bo}R')}{(1 + R)}$$
(15-60)

and $R' = k_{Lp}H_h/k_g$.

The rate of absorption is:

$$N_a = k_L C_{Ai}$$
(15-61)

For the SO_2-water system, the equilibrium concentration is:

$$C_A^* = H_h p_A + C_{Ao}$$
(15-62)

where the critical values are $H_h = 1.688 \times 10^{-6}t_L^2 - 1.90 \times 10^{-4}t_L + 6.38 \times 10^{-3}$ and $C_{Ao} = 1.125 \times 10^{-9}t_L^2 - 1.375 \times 10^{-7}t_L + 6.263 \times 10^{-6}$. The applicable ranges of this correlation are $p_A = 0.005 \sim 0.002$ atm and $t_L = 10 \sim 50°C$.[51]

Uchida et al.[51] give the following general system of differential equations for the absorption of gas A into the liquid phase.

$$\frac{dC_A}{dx} = \left[a\varrho_Mk_L/(L_m/S)\right]\Delta C_A$$
(15-63A)

$$\frac{dP_A}{dx} = -\left[aPk_L/(G_m/S)\right]\Delta C_A$$
(15-63B)

The liquid side-mass transfer coefficient is strictly applicable to droplets. A correction must be made to account for the relative velocity of the droplets to the gas in the case of the venturi scrubber. The analysis of Uchida and Wen[5] is shown to give good predictions of absorption removal for the SO_2-water system. Figure 15-15 shows a comparison of predicted SO_2 removal for this model versus experimental values reported by various investigators.

In general, the venturi scrubber is a highly efficient device but for particulate capture and gas absorption applications. However, like its predecessor, the cyclone separator, venturi scrubbers are difficult to design for large capacity systems; largely due to the complex flow mechanisms and interactions of heat and mass transfer mechanisms. The most advanced model to date, attempting to describe these complex interactions, is that of Placek and Peters.[3,22,35] It accounts for the principal system parameters such as geometry, gas throat velocity, liquid-to-gas loading ratio, and collector droplet and particle-size distributions. Liquid loading ratio and gas velocity are found to be the two most important variables, while the dispersity of the droplet size distribution only slightly affects collection efficiency over the operating range normally encountered. Location of the liquid injection site and throat length are also important design considerations. While particle collection in venturi scrubbers has typically been assumed to occur in the potential flow regime, Placek and Peter's results show that collection can also occur under the

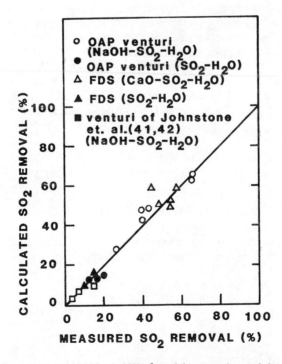

Figure 15-15. Comparison of Uchida and Wen[5] model to experimental data on SO_2 removal.

collecting droplets. The transition Reynolds number used to change from the potential to viscous flow equation affects performance predictions.

Normal operation is usually at nonisothermal conditions, since the gas to be cleaned frequently enters at a higher temperature than the scrubbing liquid. The temperature of the inlet gas stream can significantly alter the collection efficiency. The major effect is to increase the gas density causing a corresponding decrease in the gas velocity in the throat. Evaporation from the droplet surface is not important since the gas rapidly cools due to contact with the fine liquid spray.

Most models have ignored interception as an important collection mechanism for particulate removal by arguing that the dust particles are small compared to the Sauter mean diameter of the liquid drop. However, a significant fraction of the distribution is smaller than the Sauter mean diameter, hence, interception likely accounts for a measurable amount of removal. This distribution also plays an important role in gas absorption, since it is directly proportional to the effective interfacial contact area. Further theoretical and experimental investigations on drop spray patterns in operating venturis are warranted to assess the impacts on overall collection efficiency. Spray distribution at the point of injection is probably one of the least understood areas of wet scrubber operations and may be one of the most important in terms of performance. Experimental work would provide additional data to evaluate the limitations of those models that assume a uniform liquid spray pattern, and also elucidate conditions under which poor distribution might be expected. Such studies might futher reveal more desirable techniques for achieving uniform droplet injection, thereby improving scrubber performance significantly. Perhaps the most poorly understood area is that of droplet-droplet and drop-particle interactions. Droplets themselves undergo collisions, which dynamically alters the size distribution. By incorporating the dynamic nature of the drop size distribution into models, an important feature of scrubber operation may be analyzed. In future models, a description of the hydroscopic nature of particles is desirable since particle growth from condensation on the surfaces can occur. This process could also affect the degree of saturation of the bulk gas. Additional discussions on the applications of venturi scrubbers are given by Cheremisinoff et al.[40]

NOMENCLATURE

A_o nozzle coefficient in Equation 15-23
A local venturi cross-sectional area or surface area
a' parameter
a contact area per unit volume
B parameter in Equation 15-38
b, b' parameter
C speed of sound
C_A mole concentration of component A
C_{Ai} mole concentration of A at interface

C_A mole concentration of A in equilibrium with partial pressure of A in gas phase

C_D drag coefficient

C_H humid heat capacity

C_p heat capacity at constant pressure

D_{ab}, D_A diffusivity

D   droplet diameter

$\underline{D_h}$ hydraulic diameter of venturi

$\overline{D_{32}}$ Sauter mean diameter

d_o droplet diameter

E_{ij}-   local target efficiency for particles of the ith class being collected by droplets of the jth class

E_{iov}-   overall collection efficiency for particles of the ith class

f   friction factor

f(d)   fraction of droplets with characteristic diameter D

$F'(D_j)$ fraction of droplets in size interval having characteristic diameter D_j

F   fraction of injected spray remaining as liquid

G_i weight of sample class

G_m molar gas flow rate

h'_g heat transfer coefficient corrected for high flux rate

H   local humidity

H_h Henry's law constant

Hi   Hinze number

k_f thermal conductivity

k_g mass transfer coefficient

k_{LP}, K_L mass transfer coefficient for gas absorption without reaction

L   liquid-to-gas loading ratio

L_m molar liquid flow rate

ℓ characteristic size

$\dot{m}$ rate of mass moving through the control volume

M   droplet mass

Ma   Mach number

MW   molecular weight

n   particle concentration, i.e., number particles per unit volume

$\dot{n}$ particle loading, i.e., number particles per unit time

N   droplet concentration, i.e., number droplets per unit volume

N_A absorption rate of A

N_T number of transfer units

Nu   Nusselt number

P   pressure drop

P_{iov} particle penetration for ith class

P_T total pressure

P   partial pressure or vapor pressure

Pr   Prandtl number

p' local pressure

q_1, q_2, q_3 parameters

R   radius of jet

R′   group defined in Equation 15-60
Re   Reynolds number
r_0 drop radius
Sc   Schmidt number
Sh   Sherwood number
S_p source strength (potential regime)
St   Stokes number
S_v source strength
t   time
T   absolute temperature
u   droplet velocity
u_s droplet settling velocity
v   gas velocity
V_{rel} relative velocity between liquid and gas phases at injection
W′   work
We   Weber number
W_{cr} critical jet velocity
w′   ratio of dry air to liquid injected
w   jet velocity
x   distance measured along the x-axis

Greek Symbols

δ amplitude of jet oscillations
δ' parameter in Equation 15-24
ϵ' density ratio
λ wavelength of jet oscillations
λ_{jip} latent heat of vaporization
μ viscosity
ξ wave number
π'' pressure fluctuation
ϱ density
σ surface tension
τ characteristic time or frequency

REFERENCES

1. Collins T. T., Jr., C. R. Seaborne, A. W. Anthony, Jr., Paper Trade Journal, (Jan. 1948).

2. Tillman, E. S., Jr., paper presented at the 64th Annual Meeting of Air Pollution Control Association, Atlantic City, NJ (1971).

3. Placek, T. D., and L. K. Peters, *AIChE J.*, 27 (6) (1981).

4. Volynskiy, M. S., *Dan SSR*, 68 (2): (1949).

5. Merrington, A. C., and E. G. Richardson, *Proc. Phys. Soc.*, 59 (1): 1 (1947).

6. Hinze, J. D., *Appl. Sci. Res.*, A1: 263 (1948).

7. Hanson, A. R., E. G. Domich, and H. S. Adams, *Phys. Fluids*, 6 (8): 1,070 (1963).

8. Putnam, A. A., et al., USAF WADC Technical Reports 56-344 (Mar. 1957), p. 5–41.

9. Habler, G., *Proc. 3rd Int. Conf. Rain Erosion and Associated Phenomena*, A. A. Fyall & R. B. King (Eds.), organized by RAE Farnborough (1970), pp. 707–725.

10. Dyner, H. B., and J. A. F. Hill, Proc. 3rd Int. Conf. Rain Erosion and Associated Phenomena, A. A. Fyall and R. B. King (Eds.), organized by RAE Farnborough (1970), pp. 669–690.

11. Sarjeant, M., *Proc. 3rd European Conf. on Mixing*, Vol. 1, Univ. of York, England, B.H.R.A. Fluid Eng. (April 4–6, 1979), p. E2.

12. Baines, M., and N. E. Buttery, paper presented at the International Meeting on Nuclear Power Reactor Safety, Am. Nuc. Soc. and Euro. Nuc. Soc. Joint Conf. (October 16–19, 1978).

13. Bailey, A. B., *J. Fluid Mech.*, 65 (2): 401–410 (1974).

14. Dodd, K. N., *J. Fluid Mech.*, 9: 175–182 (1960).

15. Vitman, S. B., et al., *Nauchnykh Rabot Inzh. f-ta*, Leningrad, Inst. Melchnizatsii Selskogo khozyaystva, Vol. X (1953).

16. Nukiyama, S., and J. Tanasawa, *Trans. Soc. of Mech. Eng.*, (Japan) 4: 128 (1938).

17. Mugele, R. A., and H. D. Evans, *Ind. Eng. Chem.*, 43: 1,317 (1951).

18. Lewis, H. C., D. G. Edwards, and M. J. Goglia, *Ind. Eng. Chem.*, 40: 67 (1948).

19. Boll, R. H., et al., *J.A.P.C.A.*, 24: 943 (1974).

20. Boll, R. H., *Ind. Eng. Chem. Fund.*, 12: 40 (1973).

21. Clift, R., and W. H. Gauvin, *Can. J. Chem. Eng.*, 49: 439, (1971).

22. Placek, T. D., and L. K. Peters, *J. of Aerosol Science*, 11: 521 (1980).

23. Yoshida, T., N. Morishima, and M. Hayashi, *Kagaku Kogaku*, 24: 20 (1976).

24. Hollands, K. G. T., and K. C. Goel, *Ind. Eng. Chem. Fund.*, 14: 16 (1975).

25. Brink, J. A., and C. E. Contant, *Ind. Eng. Chem.*, 50: 1,157 (1958).

26. Yung, S. C., et al., *Environ. Sci. Tech.*, 12: 456 (1978).

27. Ekman, F. O., and H. F. Johnstone, *Ind. Eng. Chem.*, 43: 1,958 (1951).

28. Muir, D. M., C. D. Grant, and Y. Miheisi, Dust Control and Air Cleaning Conf., Olympia, London (1977) (see also *Filtration and Separation* (May 1978)).

29. Lapple, C. E., and H. J. Kamack, *Chem. Eng. Prog.*, 51: 110 (1955).

30. Semrau, K. T., *J.A.P.C.A.*, 10 (3): 200 (1960).

31. Semrau, K. T., et al., *Ind. Eng. Chem.*, 50: 1,615 (1958).
32. Semrau, K. T., *J.A.P.C.A.*, 13 (12): 587 (1963).
33. Dickenson, D. R., and W. R. Marshall, Jr., *AIChE J.*, 14: 541 (1968).
34. Baile, J. E., and S. F. Liang, *Ind. Eng. Chem. Process Design and Devel.*, 12: 334 (1973).
35. Placek, T. D., and L. K. Peters, *AIChE J.*, 28: 1 (1982).
36. Kulic, E., and E. Rhodes, *Can. J. Chem. Eng.*, 53: 252 (1975).
37. Rowe, P. N., K. T. Claxton, and J. B. Lewis, *Trans. Inst. of Chem. Eng.*, 43: T14 (1965).
38. Manning, W. P., and W. H. Gauvin, *AIChE J.*, 6: 184 (1960).
39. Ranz, W. E., and W. R. Marshall, Jr., *Chem. Eng., Progr.*, 48: 141 (1952).
40. Cheremisinoff, P. N., and R. A. Young, *Pollution Engineering Practice Handbook*, Ann Arbor Science Pub., Ann Arbor, MI (1975).
41. Johnstone, H. F., and M. H. Robert, *Ind. Eng. Chem.*, 41: 2,417 (1949).
42. Johnstone, H. F., T. B. Fields, and M. C. Tassler, *Ind. Eng. Chem.*, 46: 1,601 (1954).
43. Field, R. B., M.S. Thesis, Univ. of Illinois (1950).
44. Kuznetsov, M. D., and V. I. Oratovskii, *Ind. Chem. Eng.*, 2: 185 (1962).
45. Boyadzhiev, Kh., *Int. Chem. Eng.*, 4: 22 (1964).
46. Markant, H. P., R. A. McIroy, and R. E. Matty, *Tappi Journ.*, 45: 849 (1962).
47. Elenkov, D., and K. Boyadzhiev, *Ind. Chem. Eng.*, 7: 191 (1967).
48. Volgin, B. P., T. F. Efimova, and M. S. Gofman, *Ind. Chem. Eng.*, 8: 113 (1968).
49. Gleason, R. J., "Pilot Scale Investigation of a Venturi-type Contactor for Removal of SO_2 by the Limestone Wet Scrubbing Process,"—EPA Final Report Draft (1971).
50. Atay, I., M.S. Thesis, New Jersey Inst. of Technology (1980).
51. Uchida, S., and C. Y. Wen, *Ind. Eng. Chem. Process Design and Development*, 12 (4): 437 (1973).
52. Virkar, P. D., and M. M. Sharma, *Can. J. Chem. Eng.*, 53: 512–516 (1975).
53. Brunson, R. J., and R. M. Wellek, *Chem. Eng. Sci.*, 25: 904 (1970).
54. Brady, J. D., and L. K. Legatski, "Venturi Scrubbers," in *Air Pollution Control and Design Handbook,"* Part 2, P. N. Cheremisinoff, and R. A. Young (Eds.), Marcel Dekker, Inc., NY (1977), pp. 747–777.

Appendix A

Source Listing and Abstracts of the Fluidized Bed Literature

The following international citations and abstracts cover various aspects of fluidization and fluid-bed reactor systems. The listings are divided into three general areas:

Section I - Hydrodynamics of Fluidized Beds and Reactor Systems: References 1-266 pertain to various studies on bubble dynamics, fluid bed modeling and studies on mass transfer in fluidized beds. Key papers pertaining to three-phase fluidization are also listed in this section.

Section II - Mixing and Segregation in Fluidized Beds: References 267-351 pertain to various experimental investigations aimed at understanding particle-particle interaction and causes of segregation when fluidizing heterogeneous solids mixtures.

Section III - Heat Transfer in Fluidized Systems: References 352-545 pertain to both experimental and design-related literature for estimating heat transfer coefficients in fluid beds with and without internals. Various fluid bed processes are covered including coal gasi-

fication, fluid-bed combustion, and liquefaction systems. Most
of the literature reviewed pertains to experimental studies, however,
some citations on theoretical models are given.

I. HYDRODYNAMICS OF FLUIDIZED BEDS AND REACTOR SYSTEMS

1. The Dynamic (Behavior) of Bubbles and Entrained Particles in
the Rotating Fluidized Bed.

Chevray, R; Chan, Y.N.I.; Hill, F.B.

AIChE J., V.26, N.3, 390-98 (May 1980).

Abstract: The Dynamics of Bubbles and Entrained Particles in Rotating
Fluidized Beds used, e.g., in the combustion of gas and oil, are determined from equations expressing a balance among inertial, centrifugal,
Coriolis, gravity, and drag forces. Using the modified Davies and Taylor
equation for the rise of a spherical cap bubble in an inviscid liquid, an
isolated bubble arising through the bed was accurately discussed for the
case of the gas-solid fluid bed. Significant deflections from a radial
path existed for large bubbles due to Coriolis forces. It was observed
that the fate of single particles injected into the freeboard region
depended on their size. Large particles were returned to the bed, small
particles were elutriated, and particles of intermediate size were retained
in circular orbits in the freeboard region. Comparisons between the elutriation properties of rotating and gravitational beds were made indicating
that particles of the same size were elutriated from both beds, but at a
flow rate which was greater in the rotating bed than in the gravitational
bed by the ratio of the radial to gravitational accelerations.

2. Fluidized Bed Bubbles Observed Simultaneously by (A Light)
Probe and by X-Ray.

Rowe, P. N.; Masson, H.

Chem. Eng. Sci., V.35, N.6, 1443-47 (1980).

Abstract: Fluidized Bed Bubbles were simultaneously measured by a light probe by X-ray cine equipment, pulsed to give a framing rate of 40/sec. The fluidized bed consisted of alumina particles that were 500μm in size and had a minimum fluidization velocity of 18.8 cm/sec.   The column was a 15 cm ID cylindrical vessel fitted with a uniform high-pressure drop porous plate distributor.   The bed height at minimum fluidization was 40 cm, and the fluidizing gas was air at room temperature with a superficial velocity of 25.5 cm/sec.   Results indicate that X-ray cine pictures are likely to give more reliable measurements of bubble size and velocity than probes.

3.   Effect of Bubble Interaction on Interphase Mass Transfer In Gas-Fluidized Beds.

Sit, S.P.; Grace, J.R.

72nd AIChE Annu. Meet. (San Francisco 11/25-29/79) Prepr. N. 26A 33P.

Abstract: The paper discusses the effects of Bubble Interaction on Interphase Mass Transfer in Gas-Fluidized Beds.   A non-interfering technique was used to measure the concentration of ozone in pairs of bubbles injected into a bed of inactive 390 μm glass beads fluidized by ozone-free air.   The transfer of the ozone tracer from the bubble phase to the dense phase was enhanced when compared with the transfer from isolated bubbles with the same particles in the same column.   Bubble growth was also greater when pairs of bubbles were introduced than when isolated bubbles were present.   A comparison with previous studies showed that enhancement of interphase mass transfer for interacting bubbles increases with particle size.   Thus, bubble interaction apparently leads to enhancement of the convective component of transfer, whereas the diffusive component is not affected.   New equations were derived for estimating interphase mass transfer in freely bubbling two- and three-dimensional fluidized beds.

4. The Significance of Particles Entrained in Bubbles on the Products of Fluidized Bed (Coal) Gasification.

Wood, R. M.; U.K. National Coal Board

Trans. Inst. Chem. Eng., V. 57, N. 3 213-14 (July 1979).

Abstract: The Significance of Particles Entrained in Bubbles on the Products of Fluidized-Bed Coal Gasification is discussed. Char gasification experiments in fluidized beds showed that the yield of carbon monoxide is much higher with air as the fluidizing gas than with a 21:79 carbon dioxide-nitrogen mixture. Using air, the CO yield increased rapidly over the 650° - 750°C range and then was fairly constant until about 900°C. Theoretical results obtained for gasification with air, with the particle temperatures of solids dispersed in bubbles were 50°, 100°, and 150°K higher than the particulate phase temperature. This indicated that if particle ignition in the bubbles is gradually occurring at 600° - 700°C, the CO yield will increase rapidly and follow the experimental trend.

5. Heat and Mass Transfer Between Bubbles and Dense Phase In a Fluidized Bed.

Borodulya, V.A.; Dikalenko, V.I.; Kovenskii, V.I.

Teplo- Massoobmen Mnogofaznykh Mnogokomponentyn YKG Sist. 3-17 (1978). See Russian Chem. Abstr.   Abstract No. 23032, V. 91, N. 3-4.

6. Particle and Bubble Behavior and Velocities in a Large-Particle Fluidized Bed with Immersed Obstacles.

Loew, O., Shmutter, B.; Resnick, W.

Powder Technol. 22(1) 45-57 (1979). See English Chem. Abstr. Abstract No. 206541, V. 90, N. 25-26.

7. Change in the Characteristics of Gas Bubbles with Respect to
Fluidized Bed Height in Apparatus with a Porous Gas Distribution Grid.

Vakhrushev, I.A.; Vladimirov, A.I.; Basov, V.A.

Mosk. Inst. Neftekhim Gazov Prom. Moscow, USSR.

Teor. Osn. Khim. Tekhnol. 13(1) 77-85 (1979). See Russian

Chem. Abstr. Abstract No. 206483, V. 90, N. 25-26.

8. A Bubble Growth Theory of Fluidized Bed Reactors.

Darton, R.C.

Trans. Inst. Chem. Eng., V.57, N. 2, 134-38 (April 1979).

Abstract: A Bubble Growth Theory of Fluidized Bed Reactors based on
stagewise coalescence of the bubbles was used to predict, with minimum
experimental information, the bed expansion and interchange of gas between
bubbles and dense phases in a fluidized chemical reactor. In this model
the dense phase was assumed to be perfectly mixed and the bubble phase was
in plug flow. A comparison of model predictions with literature reported
data on the catalytic decomposition of ozone in a fluidized bed of 177 μm
diameter impregnated sand particles was made, showing satisfacory agreement
with the theory in view of the approximations made in the model's development.

9. An Analysis of the Distribution of Flow Between (The Bubble and
Particulate) Phases in a Gas-Fluidized Bed.

Yacono, C.; Rowe, P.N.; Angelino, H.

Chem. Eng. Sci., V. 34, N. 6, 789-800 (1979).

Abstract: An Analysis of the Distribution of Flow between Gas and Particulate Phases in a Gas-Fluidized Bed was made, based on the hydrodynamic
models of Davidson, Harrison, and Murray. The theory distinguishes
between bubbles with and without clouds and makes no assumptions about

the value to be attributed to the average dense-phase porosity. The
model requires an expression relating it to permeability. The theory was
applied to data obtained in a rectangular bed using 262 μm mean diameter
silicon carbide particles supported by a "steel ball distributor" and
fluidized at 6, 18, and 32 cm heights above the top of the balls with
air at 1.57, 2.75, or 3.93 cm/sec velocities. The dense-phase porosity
and the interstitial gas velocity were found to decrease with height. In
the region of the distributor, a high concentration of small bubbles,
which were slow moving and therefore without clouds, was observed. This
proportion decreased sharply with an increase in height. These results
explain the good conversion usually observed in the regions close to the
gas distributing systems of fluidized-bed reactors.

10. A Critical Review of the Theory of Potential Flow of Solids
Around Rising Bubbles in Gas-Solid Fluidization in Relation to the Structure and Rheology of the Dense Phase.

Rieteman, K.

Chem. Eng. Sci., V. 34, N. 4, 571-78 (1979).

Abstract: The paper presents a Critical Review of the Theory of Potential
Flow of Solids around Rising Bubbles in Relation to the Structure and
Rheology of the Dense Phase. Evidence is presented which indicates that
the potential flow theory is not an acceptable model for the flow of
solids around a rising bubble, as in a gas-fluidized bed, including evidence based on measurements with cracking catalyst that all the particles
in the dense phase of a gas-fluidized bed are in continuous contact. It
is postulated that the dense phase has a mechanical structure and an
elasticity, and that a shear stress is generated by the rising bubble.
The requirements from which the existence of a cloud phase of circulating
particles near each bubble can be proven, and which can explain the much
faster bubble rise than predicted by potential flow theory (that can be

satisfied by an adequate rheology model of solids flowing around rising
bubbles) are discussed.

11. Rise Velocity Equation for Isolated Bubbles and for Isolated
Slugs in Fluidized Beds.

Allahwala, S.A.; Potter, O.E.

Ind. Eng. Che., Fundam., V.18, N. 2, 112-16 (May 1979).

Abstract: The paper presents a Rise Velocity Equation for Isolated
Bubbles and for Isolated Slugs in Fluidized Beds. Rise velocities of
465 bubbles of various sizes injected into two 22.4 and 61 cm ID fluidized
beds, each containing 59, 68, or 198 μm diameter glass beads, were measured
using capacitance probes. Measurements were obtained in the transition
region between the bubbling and slugging regimes, i.e., equivalent bubble
diameter to vessel diameter ratios of 0.3:1 to 0.9:1. The measured values
together with published data for the bubbling and slugging regimes, were
used to derive a simple generalized bubble rise velocity equation which
can be used in developing computer models simulating the behavior of
fluidized beds in all three (bubbling, transition, and slugging) regimes.
The empirical correlation was also compared with those reported in the
literature for gas-liquid systems.

12. Some Aspects of Bubble Formation in Fluidized Systems.

Doichev, K.

God. Vissh. Khim.-Tekhnol. Inst., Sofia 23(3) 133-40 (1978) In
Bulgarian, See Chem. Abstr. Abstract No. 106378, V. 90, N. 13-14.

13. A Possibility for Determination of Initial Bubble Size in
Heterogeneous Fluidized Systems.

Doichev, K.; Dimitrov, V.

God. Vissh. Khim.-Tekhnol. Inst., Sofia 23(3) 125-32 (1978)
In Bulgarian, see Chem. Abstr. Abstract No. 106377, V. 90, N. 13-14.

14. <u>Measurement of Solid Exchange Between the Bubble Wake and the</u> <u>Emulsion Phase in a Three-Dimensional Gas-Fluidized Bed.</u>

Chiba, A.; Chiba, T.; Tanimoto, H.; Kobayashi, H.

43rd Soc. Chem. Eng. Jap. Annu. Meet. (Nagoya 4/4/78) J. Chem. Eng. Jap., V. 12, N. 1, 43-45 (Feb. 1979).

Abstract: Measurements of Solid Exchange Between the Bubble Wake and the Emulsion Phase in a Three-Dimensional Gas-Fluidized Bed are reported. Tracer experiments were conducted in a 19 cm diameter column. Bed expansion due to the injection of a single bubble and bubble height were measured in addition to the tracer distribution. The solids exchange coefficient for the bubble wake/surrounding emulsion phase decreased with increasing bubble size, and were found to agree with predictions calculated from a previously developed simple model.

15. <u>Bubble-Size Distribution in a Fluidized Bed by the Hot-Wire</u> <u>Scope Technique.</u>

Yamazaki, M.; Ito, N.; Jimbo, G.

Kagaku Kogaku Rombunshu 3(3) 272-6 (1977). See Japanese Chem. Abstr. Abstract No. 57096, V. 90, No. 7-8.

16. <u>Measurement of Temperature in Bubble and Emulsion Phases in</u> <u>Fluid-Beds.</u>

Yamazaki, M.; Miyauchi, T.

Kagaku Kogaku Rombunshu 3(3) 261-5 (1977). See Japanese Chem. Abstr. Abstract No. 56822, V. 90, No. 7-8.

17. <u>Letters to the Editors/Comments on 'The Division of Gas</u> <u>Between Bubble and Interstitial Phases in Fluidized Beds of Fine Powders'</u> <u>by Row, Santoro, and Yates.</u>

Geldart, D.; Row, P.N.; Santoro, L.; Yates, J.G.

Chem. Eng. Sci. V. 34, No. 1, 155-56 (1979).

Abstract: A short note is presented on measurements of the dense-phase

voidage in bubbling and nonbubbling beds of fine particles by the bed

collapse method.   It is shown that the values of the dense-phase voidage

(0.31-0.38) quoted in a paper are much too low; in fluidizing fine powders

similar to that used by the authors, voidages were found to range from

0.45 to 0.65 depending on the mean size, shape, and size distribution of

the powder.   A reply by the authors, P. N. Rowe, J. G. Yates, and L.

Santoro is given.

18.   Formation of Bubbles at an Orifice in Fluidized Beds.

Hsiung, T.P.; Grace, J.R.

Fluid., Proc. Eng. Found. Conf., 2nd 19-24 (1978) In English,

See Chem. Abstr.   Abstract No. 25422, V. 90, No. 3-4.

19.   Unsteady Mass Exchange Between a Bubble and the Dense Phase in

a Fluidized Bed.

Gupalo, Yu, P.; Ryazantsev, Yu, S.; Yu A Sergeev.

Inst. Probl. Mech. Moscow USSR.

Fluid., Proc. Eng. Found. Conf., 2nd 162-6 (1978) in English.

See Chem. Abstr.   Abstract No. 25369, V. 90, No. 3-4.

20.   Modeling of Homogeneous and Heterogeneous Flow in Fluidized

Beds and Bubble Columns.

Riquarts, H.P.

VDI - GVC 'Multiphase Flow', Comm. Meet. (Duesseldorf 5/11-12/78)

Chem. - Ing. - Tech., V. 51, No. 1, 52-60 (Jan. 1979) In German.

21.   Certain Regularities Governing the Motion of Gas Bubbles in a

Fluidized Bed.

Teplitskii, Yu S.; Tamarin, A.I.

Inzh. -Fiz. Zh. 34(3) 409-16 (1978) In Russian, See Chem.
Abstr. Abstract No. 91642, Vol. 89, No. 12.

22. Study of the Parameters of the Bubble Phase in a Developed
Fluidized Bed.

Oigenblik, A.A.; Zheleznov, A.S.; Slinko, M.G.; Barannikov, V.I.

Dokl. Akad. Nauk SSSR 238(3) (Chem. Tech.) 653-6 (1978) in
Russian. See Chem. Abstr. Abstract No. 61747, Vol. 89, No. 8.

23. Gas Bubble-Condensed Phase Overall Mass Transfer Coefficient in
a Fluid Bed.

Morooka, S.

Kagaku Kogaku 41(6) 300-3 (1977) in Japanese. See Chem.
Abstr. Abstract No. 123132, Vol. 88, No. 18.

24. Frequency of the Passage of Bubbles in a Fluidized Bed.

Tamarin, A.I.; Teplitskii, Yu S.; Livshits, Yu E.

Teplo- Massoobmen Dvukhfaznykh Sist. Fazovykh Khim. Prevrashch.
46-53 (1976) in Russian. See Chem. Abstr. Abstract No. 39413, V. 88, No. 6.

25. Experimental Study of the Mixing of Solid Particles in a
Fluidized Bed by Gas Bubbles During Their Chain Motion.

Vakhrushev, I.A.; Tolkachev, V.M.

Teor. Osn. Khim. Tekhnol. 11(3) 405-10 (1977) in Russian.
See Chem. Abstr. Abstract No. 39400, V. 88, N. 6.

26. Bubble Wake Solids Content in Three-Phase Fluidized Beds.

El-Temtamy, S.A.; Epstein, N.

2nd Pac. Chem. Eng. Congr. (Denver 8/31/77) Int. J. Multiph.
Flow, V. 4, N. 1, 19-31 (March 1978) .

Abstract: The paper presents a new model for calculating the relative holdup in the wake of gas bubbles in liquid-fluidized beds. The model assumes that the wake corresponds to the sphere-completing volume of a spherical bubble cap but does not require assumptions for the solids content of the wake. The model was derived from the generalized wake equation of Bhatia and Epstein and resulted in an equation for the solids holdup in the wake relative to that in the liquid-fluidized portion of the bed as a function of experimentally measurable quantities, (i.e., the gas, liquid, and solid phase velocities). The study indicates that a gas bubble initially collects a wake containing a solids concentration equal to that of the liquid-fluidized bed, and that the solids tend to settle out as a function of their terminal velocity and the liquid circulation in the wake.

27.   The Physical and Mass-Transfer Properties of Bubbles in Gas-Fluidized Beds of Carbon.

Pereira, J.R.; Calderbank, P.H.

Inst. Fuel Symp. Ser. (London) 1 (Fluid. Combust.), B2/1-B2/11 (1975). See English Chem. Abstr. Abstract No. 9456, V. 88, N. 2.

28.   Some Aspects of the Behavior of Gas Bubbles in Heterogeneous Fluidized Beds.

Tamarin, A. I.; Teplitskii, Yu S.

Protsessy Perenos V Apparatakh S. Dispers. Sistemami, 3-26 (1976) in Russian, See Chem. Abstr. Abstract No. 8990, V. 88, N. 2.

29.   Bubble Control in Gas-Fluidized Beds with Applied Electric Fields.

Colver, G.M.

Powder Technol., 17(1) 9-18 (1977), in English, see Chem. Abstr. Abstract No. 169897, V. 87, N. 22.

30. Experimental Verification of the Bubble-Bed Model of Lateral
Solid Mixing in Shallow Fluidized Beds.

      Chmielewski, A.G.; Selecki, A.

      Pr. Inst. Inz. Chem. Politech. Warsaw, 5(3), 35-47 (1977), in
Polish. See Chem. Abstr. Abstract No. 169826, V. 87, N. 22.

31. Simulation of Bubble Populations in a Gas-Fluidized Bed.

      Shah, B.H.; Ramkrishna, D.; Borwanker, J.D.

      Chem. Eng. Sci., V. 32, N. 12, 1419-25 (1977).

Abstract: The paper reviews the dynamics of bubble populations in
gas-fluidized beds, based on a model derived from the work of Argyriou et al
A simulation technique was used to show that coalescence may reduce bubble
populations sufficiently to produce considerable fluctuation around an
average value. Such fluctuations could affect conversions in fluidized bed
reactors.

32. The Physical and Mass Transfer Properties of Bubbles in
Fluidized Beds of Electrically Conducting Particles.

      Calderbank, P.H.; Pereira, J.M.; Burgess, J.

      Fluid. Technol., Proc. Int. Fluid. Conf., 1975, 1, 115-67
(1976). See English Chem. Abstr. Abstract No. 86750, V. 87, N. 12.

33. Correction for Wall Effect in Point Probe Measurements of
Bubble Size (In a Fluidized Bed).

      Nakamura, K.; Capes, C.E.

      Chem. Eng. Sci., V.32, N. 11, 1339-43 (1977).

Abstract: The paper presents a theoretical analysis on the basis of
geometry and probability of bubble size as measured by a probe technique.
The analysis indicates that measurements are influenced by the existence of

a bed boundary when the measurable bubble length exceeds half the distance between the wall and the probe. The effect increases with the normalized deviation of bubble size and decreases with the wake angle for the range 200° - 240°F. Graphical results of the analysis are given which can be used to correct experimental probe measurements for the boundary effect. The application is demonstrated to electroresistivity probe measurements made on a 2-ft diameter bed of fluidized coke particles.

34. Gas Backmixing, Solids Movement, and Bubble Activities in Large-Scale Fluidized Beds.

Nguyen, H.V.; Whitehead, A.B.; Potter, O.E.

AIChE J., V.23, N. 6, 913-22 (Nov. 1977).

Abstract: Experiments results from a 1.22 m square bed of silica sand fluidized with air at 15.2 and 24.4 cm/sec and injected with carbon dioxide as tracer gas are presented. The study confirmed the strong backmixing predicted by the countercurrent backmixing model. The downward movement of solids occurred at about the expected order of magnitude. The solids movement was related to the bubble pattern, and gas movement in the particular phase was related to the solids movement. At 15.2 cm/sec, the stable bubble pattern in the upper region of the bed left a persistent central area relatively bubble-free, and a pronounced solids downflow occurred in this area which was attributed to strong gas backmixing. At 24.4 cm/sec, however, an unstable bubble pattern with concomitant variations in solids flow regimes was evident. This was reflected by short-term variations in the pressure profile recorded at the bed base. An important conclusion is that since the overall pattern of gas and solids mixing in large fluidized beds depends on the fluidizing velocity; sampling in large beds (e.g., coal combustion) will not be reliable if it is not done systematically and extensively throughout the bed.

35.   Mass Transfer from a Bubble to the Dense Phase in a Fludized-
Bed Reactor.

Gupalo, Yu P.; Ryazantsev Yu S.; Sergeev, Yu A.

Chem. React. Eng., Proc. Int. Symp., 4th, 162-8 (1976), see
English Chem. Abstr. Abstract No. 55079, V87, N.8.

36.   Simulation of Complex Reactions in Fluidized Beds.   Effect of
Thermal Instabilities of Dispersed Solids in Bubbles on Product Selectivity.

Yoshida, K.; Mii, T.; Kunii, D.

Fluid. Ses Appl., C. - R. Congr. Int. 1973, 512-23 (Pub. 1974),
see Chem. Abstr. Abstract No. 157628, V.86, N. 22.

37.   On Void Fractions Around a Bubble in a Two-Dimensional
Fluidized Bed.

Nguyen, X.T.; Leung, L.S.; Weiland, R.H.

Fluid. Ses Appl., C.-R. Congr. Int., 1973, 230-9 (Pub. 1974),
see Chem. Abstr. Abstract No. 142203, V.86, N. 20.

38.   Solid Exchange Between the Bubble Wake and the Emulsion Phase
in a Gas-Fluidized Bed.

Chiba, T.; Kobayashi, H.

36th Soc. Chem. Eng. Jap. Annu. Meet. (Tokyo 4/471), J. Chem.
Eng. Jap., V.10, N.3, 206-10 (June 1977).

39.   Mean Velocity of Bubbles in a Fluidized Bed with Packing.

Tamarin, A.I.; Borisenko, V.P.; Galershtein, D.M.; Zabroskii, S

Inzh-Fiz Zh 1976, V.31, N.4 601-6 in Russian, see Chemical
Abstract V86-92452.

40. Application of the Bubble Assemblage Model to the Hydrane

Process Fluid Bed Hydrogasifier.

Wen, C.Y.; Gray, J.A.; Mori, S.; Yavorsky, P.M.; U.S. Bureau

of Mines.

AIChE Symp. Ser., V. 73, N. 161, 86-99, (1977).

41. The Over-All Mass Transfer Coefficient Between the Bubble Phase

and the Emulsion Phase ((K)) In a Free and (An) Eight-Stage (Air-) Fluidized

Bed.

Nishinaka, M.; Morooka, S.; Kato, Y.

Kagaku Kogaku Ronbunshu, V.2, N.1, 71-76 (1976) (Transl.) Int.

Chem. Eng. V.17, N.2, 254-60 (April 1977).

42. Regularities of Gas Bubble Motion in a Fluidized Bed.

Tamarin, A.I.; Teplitskii, Yu S.; Livshits, Yu E.

Inzh-Fiz Zh 1976, V.31, N.2, 323-7 in Russian, see Chem. Abstract

V86-45201.

43. Dependence of Local Heat Transfer Coefficient on Bubble

Properties in a Fluidized Bed.

Masson, H.; Jottrand, R.

Int. Congr. Chem. Eng. Chem. Equip. Des Autom. (Proc.), 5th

1975 D. D3.3 6pp. in English, see Chemical Abstract V85-126508.

44. Bubble Control in Gas Fluidized Beds with Applied Electric

Fields.

Colver, G.M.

ASME Natl. Heat Transfer Con. (St. Louis 8/8-11/76) Paper

No. 76-HT-69, Mech. Eng. V. 98, N. 11, 88-90 (Nov. 1976).

45. Bubble-Induced Heat Transfer in Gas-Fluidized Beds.

    Kubie, J.

    Int. J. Heat Mass Transfer, V.19, N.12, 1441-53 (Dec. 1976).

46. A Low-Reynolds-Number Analysis of Gas Bubbles in Fluidized Beds.

    Weiland, R.H.

    Ind. Eng. Chem. Fundam., V.15, N.3, 189-96 (August 1976).

47. Synopses/Significance of Bubble Coalescence for the Design of
Gas/Solid Fluidized Beds.

    Werther, J.

    VDI - GVC Annu. Meet. (Karlsruhe 9/30-10/2/75), Chem-Ing.-Tech.

V.48, N. 4, 339 (April 1976), in German.

48. Instability Waves and the Origin of Bubbles in Fluidized
Beds--1. Experiments.

    El-Kaissy, M.M.; Homsy, G.M.

    Int. J. Multiph. Flow, V.2, N.4, 379-95 (Feb. 1976).

49. Stability of Bubbles in Fluidized Beds.

    Weber, M.E.; Clift, R.; Bhatia, V.K.; Grace, J.R.

    Ind. Eng. Chem. Fundam., V.15, N.1, 86-87 (Feb. 1976).

50. Behavior of Rising Bubbles in a Gas-Fluidized Bed at Elevated
Temperature.

    Kawashima, M.; Tone, S., Shibata, T.; Otake, Td.

    8th Soc. Chem. Eng. Jap. Autumn Meet. (Tokyo, Oct. 1974), J.

Chem. Eng. Jap., V.8, N.5, 388-92 (Oct. 1975).

51. Bubble Activity and the Packet Theory of Fluidized Bed Heat
Transfer.

Scheldorf, J.J.; Selzer, V.W.; Thomson, W.J.

68th AIChE Annu. Meet. (Los Angeles 11/16-20/75), Paper N. 44C

41P.

52. Heat Transfer During Bubble Formation in Gaseous Fluidized Beds.

Mori, S.

Heat Transfer, Jap. Res. 1973, V.2, N.4, 37-40, see Chemical

Abstract V81-27667.

53. Mass Transfer Between Bubbles and the Continuous Phase in a
Fluidized Bed.

Gupala, Yu P.; Sergeev, Yu A.; Ryazantsev, Yu S.

Izv Akad Nauk SSSR Mekh Zhidk Gaza 1973, N.4, 42-9, see Chem.

Abstract V81-4999, in Russian.

54. A Low Reynolds-Number Analysis of Gas Bubbles in Fluidized Beds.

Weiland, R.H.

Res. Results Serv. Manuscr. (Manuscript), ACS Single Artic

Announce., V5, N.16 1 (8/28/75), N. 75-140, 31p.

55. Ascent Velocity of Single Gas Bubbles In (Liquids and Extension
To) Liquid-Fluidized Beds (Of Solids).

Vakhrushev, I.A.; Verbitskii, B.G.

Khim Tekhnol. Topl. Masel, N.4, 36-39 (1974) (Transl.) Int.

Chem. Eng., V.15, N.2, 277-79 (April 1975), in Russian.

56. Behavior of Bubbles in Fluidized Beds of a Gas-Solid System.

Nakatani, Y.; Ito, S.; Kajiuchi, T.; Matsui, S.

Kagaku Kogaku 1974, V.38, N.11, 824-8, see Chemical Abstract V82-74972, in Japanese.

57. The Distribution of Bubble Size in Gas-Fluidized Beds.

Yacono, C.; Rowe, P.N.

Trans. Inst. Chem. Eng., V.53, N.1, 59-60 (Jan. 1975).

58. Importance of Dispersed Solids in Bubbles for Exothermic Reactions in Fluidized Beds.

Kunii, D.; Aoyagi, M.

Chem. Eng. Commun. 1974, V.1, N.4, 191-7, see Chemical Abstract V82-45839.

59. The Shapes of the Bubbles in a Two-Dimensional Gas Fluidized Bed

Goldsmith, J.A.; Rowe, P.N.

Chem. Eng. Sci., V.30, N.4, 439-40 (April 1975).

60. The Estimation of Bubble Diameter in Gaseous Fluidized Beds.

Wen, C.Y.; Mori, S.

AIChE J., V.21, N.1, 109-15 (Jan. 1975).

61. Behavior of Gas Bubbles in a Fluidized Bed in an Electromagnetic Field.

Shumkov, S. Kh.; Ivanov, D.G.

Khim Ind. (Sofia), 1974, V.46, N.3, 108-10, see Chemical Abstract V81-172101, in Bulgarian.

62.   Characteristics of Large Two-Dimensional Air Bubbles in Liquids
and in Three-Phase Fluidized Beds.

Ostergaard, K.; Henriksen, H.K.

Chem. Eng. J. (Lausanne), 1974, V.7, N.2, 141-6.

63.   (A Semi-Empirical Correlation for The) Estimation of Bubble
Diameter in Gaseous-Fluidized Beds.

Wen, C.Y.; Mori, S.

67th AIChE Annu. Meet. (Washington, DC 12/1-5/74), Paper
N. 25D, 24p.

64.   Reaction Mechanisms in a Fluidized Bed Reactor. Transfer
Mechanism of the Gas in a Bubble.

Okada, T.; Matsuno, Y.

Asahi Garasu Kogyo Gijutsu Shoreikai Kenkyu Hokoku 1973,
V.22, 303-16, see Chemical Abstract V81-155136, in Japanese.

65.   Simulation of Fluidized-Bed Reactor Performance by a Modified
Bubble Assemblage Model (And Confirmation with Data from Catalytic Fluidized-
Bed Experiments).

Mori, S.; Wen, C.Y.

Res. results Serv. Manuscr. (Manuscript) ACS Single Artic
Announce. V.4, N.18, 1-2 (9/27/74), N. 74-192, 37p.

66.   Coalescence of Bubble Pairs in a Three-Dimensional Fluidized
Bed.

Clift, R.; Grace, J.R.

Can. J. Chem. Eng., V.52, N.3, 417-19 (June 1974).

67.   (Fluidized-Bed Reactor Design Calculations Based Only on Bubble Size).

> Kobayashi, H.; Chiba, F.

> Eur. Fed. Chem. Eng. "Fluidized Bed Technol." Symp. (Toulouse 10/1-5/73) (German Abstract). Chem-Ing.-Tech., V.46, N.12, 525-28 (June 1974)

68.   (A Theoretical Determination of the Optimum Solid Particle Size for Minimum Bubble Size in a Three-Phase Fluidized Bed for Alpha-Methylstyren Hydration).

> Sherrard, A.J.; Lee, J.C.; Buckley, P.S.

> Eur. Fed. Chem. Eng. "Fluidized Bed Technol." Symp. (Toulouse 10/1-5/73) (German Abstract). Che.-Ing.-Tech., V.46, N.12, 525-28 (June 1974)

69.   (Entrainment of Solid Particles by Bubbles in Three-Phase Fluidized Beds).

> Harrison, D.; Page, R.E.

> Eur. Fed. Chem. Eng. "Fluidized Bed Technol." Symp. (Toulouse 10/1-5/73) (German Abstract) Chem-Ing.-Tech., V.46, N.12, 525-28 (June 1974).

70.   (A Model for Three-Phase Fluidized Beds that Accounts for the Effect of Bubble Wakes on the Fluidized Bed).

> Bhatia, K.K.; Epstein, N.

> Eur. Fed. Chem. Eng. "Fluidized Bed Technol." Simp. (Toulouse 10/1-5/73) (German Abstract). Chem.-Ing.-Tech. V46, N.12, 525-28 (June 1974).

71.   (An Experimental Study of Gas Motion in the Vicinity of Bubbles in Fluidized Beds.

> Anwer, J.; Pyle, D.

> Eur. Fed. Chem. Eng. "Fluidized Bed Technol." Simp. (Toulouse 10/1-5/73) (German Abstract). Chem.-Ing.-Tech., V.46, N.12, 525-28 (June 1974)

72.   (Measurement of Particle Density and "Emulsion" Phase Viscosity in the Vicinity of Bubbles in Fluidized Beds.

Weiland, R.H.; Leung, L.S.; Nguyen, X.T.

Eur. Fed. Chem. Eng. "Fluidized Bed Technol." Sump. (Toulouse 10/1-5/73) (German Abstract). Chem-Ing-Tech, V.46, N.12, 525-28 (June 1974).

73.   (Disintegration of Bubbles in Fluidized Beds by a Mechanism of "Finger Formation" and Splitting).

Pyle, D.L.; Upson, P.D.

Eur. Fed. Chem. Eng., "Fluidized Bed Technol." Symp. (Toulouse 10/1-5/73) (German Abstract) Chem-Ing-Tech. V.46, N.12, 525-28 (June 1974).

74.   (The Velocity of Particles in the Wake of Bubbles in Fluidized Beds).

Geldart, D.; Bayerns, J.

Eur. Fed. Chem. Eng. "Fluidized Bed Technol." Symp. (Toulouse 10/1-5/73) (German Abstract) Chem-Ing-Tech. V.46, N.12, 525-28 (June 1974).

75.   (Piezoelectric Detection of Particle Motion in the Region Between Minimum Fluidizing and Bubble-Forming Velocities).

Patureaux, T.; Vergnes, F.; Legoff, P.

Eur. Fed. Chem. Eng. "Fluidized Bed Technol." Symp. (Toulouse 10/1-5/73) (German Abstract) Chem-Ing-Tech., V.46, N.12, 525-28 (June 1974).

76.   (A Relationship Between the Size of Vertical Empty Spaces and Channels Observed at Less than Minimum Bubble-Formation Velocity in Fluidized Beds and Interparticle Forces).

Massimilla, L.; Donsi, G.

Eur. Fed. Chem. Eng. "Fluidized Bed Technol." Symp. (Toulouse 10/1-5/73) (German Abstract) Chem-Ing-Tech. V.46, N.12, 525-28 (June 1974).

77. (Mass Transfer in the Absorption of Carbon Dioxide, Ethylene Chloride, or Benzene from Large Bubbles into Water in a Three-Phase Fluidized Bed).

Roland, S.; Vanderschuren, J.; Schrayen, J.P.

Eur. Fed. Chem. Eng. "Fluidized Bed Technol." Symp. (Toulouse 10/1-5/73) (German Abstract). Chem-Ing-Tech. V.46, N.12, 525-28 (June 1974).

78. The Ascent Rate of Individual Gas Bubbles in a Pseudo-Fluidized Liquid Layer.

Vakhrushev, I.A.; Verbitskii, B.G.

Khim Tekhnol Topl Masel, N.4, 36-39 (1974) in Russian - All Union Sci. Res. Inst. Pet. Ind. -- Mosc. Inst. Petrochem. & Gas Ind.

79. On the Mechanism of Breakup of Large Bubbles in Liquids and Three-Phase Fluidized Beds.

Oestergaard, K.E.; Oestergaard, K.E.; Henriksen, H.K.

Chem. Eng. Sci., V.29, N.2, 626-29 (Feb. 1974), Tech. Univ. Den.

80. Dispersion of Gas in the Track of Tracer Bubbles Injected intc a Two-Dimensional Fluidized Bed.

Evans, T.J.; Rowe, P.N.

Chem. Eng. Sci., V.29, N.1, 293-94 (Jan. 1974).

81. The Interaction Between Solid Particles and Gas Bubbles in Three-Phase Fluidized Beds.

Oestergaard, K.

VDI Verfahrenstech Ges "Multiphase Flow" Comm. Symp. (Duesseldorf 4/9-10/73) (German Abstract) Chem-Ing-Tech, V.46, N.1, 38-44 (Jan. 1974) Dan Tek Hoejsk Lyngby.

82. Stability of Bubbles in Fluidized Beds.

Grace, J.R.; Weber, M.E.; Clift, R.

Ind. Eng. Chem. Fundam., V.13, N.1, 45-51 (Feb. 1974).

83. The Pressure Field Around a Two-Dimensional Gas Bubble in a

Fluidized Bed.

Littman, H.; Homolka, G.A.J.

Chem. Eng. Sci., V.28, N.12, 2231-43 (Dec. 1973).

84. The Mechanisms of Heat Transfer and Bubble Formation in Gas-

Solid Fluidized Beds.

Lisa, R.E.

Purdue Univ. Diss. (1973), 331p. (Abstract) Diss. Abstr. Int.

B, V.34, N.6, 2592B (Dec. 1973).

85. Effect of the Adsorption Capacity or Heat Capacity of Particles

on Gas Transfer or Heat Transfer Between a Bubble and an Emulsion Phase in a

Fluidized Bed.

Oita, M.; Hotta, H.; Toei, R.; Matsuno, R.

Teplo-Massoperenos, 1972, V.5, N.1, 206-29, Chem. Abstract

V79-80818, in Russian.

86. Bubble Motion in Liquids and Fluidized Beds.

Davidson, J.F.

Proc. Roy. Inst. Gt. Britain, 1972, V.45, 161-77.

92.   An Experimental Investigation of the Distribution of Gas Between the Bubble and Suspension Phases, and the Spatial Distribution of Bubbles in Freely Bubbling Fluidized Beds.

Molerus, O.; Werther, J.

4th Int. Chem. Eng. Chem. Equip. & Autom. Congr. (Prague 9/11-15/72), see German Abstract CHEM-ING-TECH, V.45, N.8, 567-68 (April (1973).

93.   Solid-Particle Flow at the Wall of a Fluidization Column Induced by Isolated Bubbles.

Crescitelli, S.; Donsi, G.; Massimilla, L.; Volpicelli, G.

Chim. Ind. Genie Chim., V.106, N.9, 637-38, (April 1973), in French.

94.   Evidence of Maximum Stable Bubble Size in a Fluidized Bed.

Matsen, J.M.

65th AIChE Annu. Meet. (NY 11/26-30/72), AIChE Symp. Ser. V.69, N.128, 30-33 (1973).

95.   Bubble Behavior Around Immersed Tubes in a Fluidized Bed.

Thomson, W.J.; Hager, W.R.

65th AIChE Annu. Meet. (NY 11/26-30/72) AIChE Symp. Ser. V.69, N.128, 68-77 (1973).

96.   (Instantaneous Local Wall-to-Bed) Heat Transfer (Coefficients) Around Single Bubbles in a Two-Dimensional (Air-) Fluidized Bed.

Tuot, J.; Clift, R.

65th AIChE Annu. Meet. (NY 11/26-30/72) AIChE Symp. Ser. V.69, N.128, 78-84 (1973).

97. Behavior of Gas During a Bubble Formation in a Gaseous Fluidized Bed.

Muchi, I.; Miwa, K.; Mori, S.

Kagaku Kogaku 1973, V.37, N.3, 295-302, in Japanese.

98. Heat Transfer During a Bubble Formation in a Gaseous Fluidized Bed.

Mori, S.

Kagaku Kogaku, 1973, V.37, N.3, 317-19, in Japanese.

99. Bubble Size Variation in Two-Phase Models of Fluidized Bed Reactors.

Potter, O.E.; Fryer, C.

Powder Technol. 1972, V.6, N.6, 317-22, see Chemical Abstract V78-18276.

100. Measurement of Local Bubble Size Distribution in Gas-Solid Fluidized Beds.

Werther, J.

VDI-Verfahrenstech Ges Annu. Meet. (Cologne 10/3-5/72) (Condens) Chem-Ing-Tech, V.45, N.6, 375-77 (March 1973), in German.

101. The Effect of Bubbles on Heat Transfer from Immersed Tubes in a Freely Bubbling Fluidized Bed.

Hager, W.R.

Univ. Idaho Diss. (1973) 210p. (Abstract) Diss. Abstract Int. B, V.33, N.9, 4257B (March 1973).

102. (Behavor of Gas Bubbles in Fluidized Beds).

Pigford, R.L.; Rieke, R.D.

AIChE J., V.19, N.2, 415-16 (March 1973).

103.   Behavior of Gas Bubbles in Fluidized Beds.

Clift, R.; Grace, J.R.; Garcia, A.

AIChE J., V.19, N.2, 369-70 (March 1973).

104.   Gas Transfer from Bubbles in a Fluidized Bed to the Dense
Phase--2. Experiments.

Drinkenburg, A.A.H.; Rietema, K.

Chem. Eng. Sci., V.28, N.1, 259-73 (Jan. 1973).

105.   Stability of Bubbles in Fluidized Beds.

Grace, J.R.; Clift, R.; Weber, M.E.

Res. Results serv. Manuscr. (Manuscript) ACS Single Artic
Announce. V.3, N.5, (3/15/73), N.73-18 43p.

106.   The Mechanism of Bubble Break-Up in Fluidized Beds.

Clift, R.; Grace, J.R.

Chem. Eng. Sci., V.27, N.12, 2309-10 (Dec. 1972).

107.   The Structure of Bubble-Free Gas-Fluidized Beds of Fine Fluid
Cracking Catalyst Particles.

Zucchini, C.; Massimilla, L.; Donsi, G.

Chem. Eng. Sci., V.27, N.11, 20005-15 (Nov. 1972).

108.   The Capacitance Effect on the Transfer of Gas or Heat Betwee
a Bubble and the Continuous Phase in a Gas-Solid Fluidized Bed.

Oichi, M.; Toei, R.; Fujine, Y.; Hotta, H.; Matsuno, R.

5th Soc. Chem. Eng. Jap. Autumn Meet. (Osaka, Oct. 1971),
J. Chem. Eng. Jap., V.5, N.3, 273-79 (Sept. 1972).

109. Transfer of Heat from Bubbles in a Fluidized Bed.

Seth, H.K.; Williams, K.A.; Barile, R.G.

Chem. Eng. J. (London), 1970, V.1, N.4, 263-72 Chemical

Abstract V76-101688.

110. Motion of Single Gas Bubbles in a Fluidized Bed.

Kulbachnyi, V.G.

Khim. Prom. (Moscow), 1971, V.47, N.12, 920-2, Chemical

Abstract V76-87826, in Russian.

111. The Coalescence of Bubble Chains in Fluidized Beds.

Clift, R.; Grace, J.R.

Trans. Inst. Chem. Eng., V.50, N.4, 364-71 (Oct. 1972).

112. Gas Transfer from Bubbles in a Fluidized Bed to the Dense

Phase -- 1. A Theory.

Drinkenburg, A.A.H.; Rietema, K.

Chem. Eng. Sci., V.27, N.10, 1765-74 (Oct. 1972).

113. Gas Exchange Between the Bubble and Emulsion Phases in Gas-

Solid Fluidized Beds.

Chiba, T.; Kobayashi, H.
1st Int. AIChE - Eur. Fed. Chem. Eng.-ACS "CChem. Reaction

Eng" Symp (Wash. DC 6/8-10/70) (Condens) Adv. Chem. Ser. N. 109, 132-33 (1972).

114. Expansion of Beds of Fine (Cracking-Catalyst) Particles

Fluidized with Gas in the Absence of Bubbles.

Donsi, G.; Massimilla, L.; Zucchini, C.

Soc. Chim. Ital. Campana Sect. Meet. (Naples 3/15/72)

(Italian Abstract) Chim. Ind. (Milan)., V.54, N.7, 657 (July 1972).

115. Effect of Dispersing Air Bubbles into Liquid-Fluidized Beds
(Of Wettable and Partially Wettable Solids) on Solid-Liquid Mass-Transfer Rate

Rao, K.V.; Veerabhadra, Rao K.; Rao, K.V.; Nirmalkumar, H.;
Dakshinamurty, P.

Research Results Serv. Manusc. (Manuscript) ACS Single Artic
Announce., V.2., N.17, (9/15/72), N.72-207, 17p.

116. Holdup of Gas Bubbles and Longitudinal Dispersion Coefficien
of Solid Particles in Fluid-Bed Contactors for Gas-Solid Systems.

Morooka, S.; Kato, Y.; Miyauchi, T.

J. Chem. Eng. Japan, V.5, N.2, 161-67 (June 1972).

117. Behaviour of Bubbles in Gas-Solid Fluidized Beds, The Initia
Formation of Bubbles.

Terashima, K.; Chiba, T.; Kobayashi, H.

Chem. Eng. Sci., V.27, N.5, 965-72 (May 1972).

118. The Interrelationship Between Bubble Motion and Solids Mixin
in a Gas-Fluidized Bed.

Haines, A.K.; King, R.P.; Woodburn, E.T.

AIChE J., V.18, N.3, 591-99 (May 1972).

119. The Formation of Primary Bubbles in a Fluidized Bed.

Basov, V.A.; Vakhrushev, I.A.

Khim. Prom. N. 6, 467-71 (1971) (Transl.) Int. Chem. Eng.,
V.12, N.2, 319-24 (April 1972), in Russian.

120. Gas Flow Through a Bubble in a Fluidized Bed.

Pyle, D.L.; Hargreaves, J.H.

Chem. Eng. Sci., V.27, N.2, 433-37 (Feb. 1972).

121. (An Inductance) Probe for Bubble Detection and Measurement in

Large Particle Fluidized Beds.

Cranfield, R.R.

Chem. Eng. Sci., V.27, N.2, 239-45 (Feb. 1972).

122. Heat Transfer Between the Emulsion Phase and Gas Bubbles in

Fluid-Bed Catalytic Contactors.

Yamazaki, M.; Miyauchi, T.

34th Soc. Chem. Eng. Jap. Annu. Meet. (Tokyo April 1969), J.

Chem. Eng. Jap., V.4, N.4, 324-30 (Nov. 1971).

123. Transfer of Heat from Bubbles in a Fluidized Bed.

Seth, H.K.; Barile, R.G.; Williams, K.A.

Chem. Eng. J. (London), 1970, V.1, N.4, 263-72.

124. Behavior of Fluidized Beds Based on the Bubble Assemblage Model.

Yoshida, K.; Wen, C.Y.

63rd AIChE Annu. Meet. (Chicago 11/29-12/3/70), AIChE Symp.

Ser., V. 67, N.116, 151-58 (1971).

125. Coalescence of Bubbles in Fluidized Beds.

Clift, R.; Grace, J.R.

3rd Inst. Ing. Quim. P.R. - AIChE Joint Meet. (San Juan,

P.R. May 1970), AIChE Symp. Ser., V.67, N.116, 23-33 (1971).

126. Fluidized Bed Bubbles Viewed by X-Rays -- 1. Experimental

Details and the Interaction of Bubbles with Solid Surfaces. 2. The Transition

from Two to Three Dimensions of Undisturbed Bubbles. 3. Bubble Size and
Number when Unrestrained Three-Dimensional Growth Occurs.

Rowe, P.N.; Everett, D.J.

Trans. Inst. Chem. Eng., V.50, N.1, 42-48, 49-54, 55-60,
(Jan. 1972), in English.

127. Behavior of Bubbles in a Gaseous Fluidized Bed.

Muchi, I.; Kato, T.; Miwa, K.; Mori, S.

Kagaku Kogaku, V.35, N.7, 770-76 (July 1971) (Transl.)
Int. Chem. Eng., V.12, N.1, 187-94 (Jan. 1972), in Japanese.

128. Behavior of Gas Bubble(s) in Fluid Beds.

Miyauchi, T.; Morooka, S.; Tajima, K.

Kagaku Kogaku, V.35, N.6, 680-86 (June 1971), Translated
Int. Chem. Eng., V.12, N.1, 168-74 (Jan. 1972), in Japanese.

129. A Note on Bubble Clouds in Fluidized Beds.

Grace, J.R.

Chem. Eng. Sci., V.26, N.11, 1955-57 (Nov. 1971).

130. Transfer of Gas Between Bubbles and Dense Phase in a Two-
Dimensional Fluidized Bed.

Evans, T.J.; Middleton, J.C.; Rowe, P.N.

Chem. Eng. Sci., V.26, N.11, 1943-48 (Nov. 1971).

131. The Contribution of Solids Dispersed in Bubbles to Mass
Transfer in Fluidized Beds.

Wakabayashi, T.; Kunii, D.

J. Chem. Eng. Jap., V.4, N.3, 226-30 (Aug. 1971).

132.   Formation of Primary Bubbles in a Fluidized Bed.

Vakhrushev, I.A.; Basov, V.A.

Khim. Prom. (Moscow, 1971, V.47, N.6, 467-71, in Russian.

133.   Behavior of Gas Bubbles in Fluidized Beds.

Morooka, S.; Tajima, K.; Miyauchi, T.

Kagaku Kogaku, 1971, V.35, N.6, 680-6, in Japanese, see

Chemical Abstract V75-78568.

134.   Gas Interchange Between Bubble Phase and Continuous Phase
in Gas-Solid Fluidized Bed at Coalescence.

Nishitani, K.; Matsuno, R.; Ryozo, T.

Mem. Fac. Eng. Kyoto Univ., 1970, V.32 (Pt. 2) 194-209.

135.   Boundary Effects on a Bubble Rising in a Finite Two-Dimensional
Fluidized Bed.

Gabor, J.D.

Chem. Eng. Sci., V.26, N.8, 1247-57 (Aug. 1971).

136.   Pressure Field Around Two Dimensional Bubbles in Gas Fluidized
Beds.

Homolka, G.A.J.

Rensselaer Polytech. Inst. Diss. (1971), 223p. (Abstract),
Diss. Abstract INT. B, V.32, N.2, 906B-907B (Aug. 1971).

137.   Bubble Coalescence and the Simulation of Mass Transport and
Chemical Reaction in Gas-Fluidized Beds.

Orcutt, J.C.; Carpenter, B.H.

Chem. Eng. Sci., V.26, N.7, 1049-64 (July 1971).

138. A Note on the Initial Motion of a Fluidization Bubble.

Murray, J.D.; Collins, R.

Chem. Eng. Sci., V.26, N.6, 995-96 (June 1971).

139. Single Bubbles Injected into a Gas-Fluidized Bed and Observed by X-Rays.

Rowe, P.N.; Matsuno, R.

Chem. Eng. Sci., V.26, N.6, 923-35 (June 1971).

140. Bubble Interaction in Fluidized Beds.

Clift, R.

McGill Univ. Diss., (1970), (Abstract) Diss. Abstract INT B V.32, N.1, 261B (July 1971).

141. Experimental Age Distribution of Bubbles and Emulsion in Fluidized Beds.

Navarette, A.E.

Ill. Inst. Technol. Diss. (1970), 240p (Abstract) Diss. Abstract INT B V.31, N.5, 2655B (Nov. 1970).

142. Initial (Shape and) Motion of a Bubble in a Fluidized Bed.

Leung, L.S.; Sandford, I.C.

Inst. Chem. Eng. Aust. Nat. Comm. Chemica 70 Conf. (Univ. Melbourne & Univ. N.S. Wales, Aug. 1970).

143. Self- and Cross-Correlations in Measurements of Local Bubble Size and Rise Velocity in Gas-Solid Fluidized Beds.

Molerus, O.; Werther, J.

Verfahrenstech Ges Annu. Meet. (Munich 10/13-15/70), see CHEM-ING-TECH, V.43, N.5, 271-73 (March 1971).

144. Bubble Growth by Coalescence in Gas Fluidized Beds (Including Fluidized Cracking Catalyst).

> Argyriou, D.T.; List, H.L.; Shinnar, R.
>
> 60th AIChE Annu. Meet. (New York 11/26-30/67), AIChE J.,

V.17, N.1, 122-30 (Jan. 1971).

145. Bubble Coalescence in Fluidized Beds: Comparison of Two Theories.

> Clift, R.; Grace, J.R.
>
> AIChE J., V.17, N.1, 252-54 (Jan. 1971).

146. Properties of Bubbles in Three Phase Fluidized Beds as Measured by an Electroresistivity Probe.

> Rigby, G.R.; Van Blockland, G.P.; Capes, C.E.; Park, W.H.
>
> Chem. Eng. Sci., V.25, N.11, 1729-41 (Nov. 1970).

147. Bubble Interaction in Fluidized Beds.

> Clift, R.; Grace, J.R.
>
> 62nd AIChE Annu. Meet. (Washington, DC 11/16-20/69), Chem.

Eng. Progr. Symp. Ser., V.66, N.105, 14-27 (1970).

148. Bubble Rise Velocities in Two-Dimensional Gas-Fluidized Beds from Pressure Measurements.

> Homolka, G.A.J.; Littman, H.
>
> 64th AIChE Nat. Meet. (New Orleans 3/17-20/69), Chem. Eng.

Progr. Symp. Ser., V.66, N.105, 37-46 (1970).

149. The Distribution of Bubbles in a Gas-Fluidized Bed.

> Matsuno, R.; Rowe, P.N.
>
> Chem. Eng. Sci., V.25, N.10, 1587-93 (Oct. 1970).

150. Bed Expansion and Bubble Wakes in Three-Phase Fluidization.

Capes, C.E.; Rigby, G.R.

Can. J. Chem. Eng., V.48, N.4, 343-48 (Aug. 1970).

151. Bubble Interaction in Fluidized Beds.

Clift, R.; Grace, J.R.

62nd AIChE Ann. Mtg. (Washington, DC 11/o6-20/69) Preprint

N. 39A, 46p.

152. On the Percolation of Fluid Through Bubbles in Fluidized Bed

Leung, L.S.; Sandford, I.C.

Chem. Eng. Sci., V.24, N.8, 1391-94 (Aug. 1969).

153. The Effect of a Bubble on Gas Flow in a Plane Fluidized Bed
of Finite Width - Two Theories Compared.

Collins, R.

Chem. Eng. Sci., V.24, N.8, 1291-1307 (Aug. 1969).

154. Bubble Assemblage Model for Fluidized Bed Catalytic Reactor

Kato, K.; Wen, C.Y.

Chem. Eng. Sci., V.24, N.8, 1351-69 (Aug. 1969).

155. Minimum Stable Bubble Volumes and Bubble Collapse Rates in
Gas Fluidized Beds.

Richardson, J.F.; Godard, K.

Can. J. Chem. Eng., V.47, N.4, 350-52 (Aug. 1969).

156. Gas Transfer Between a Bubble and the Continuous Phase in a

Gas-Solid Fluidized Bed.

Komagawa, Y.; Matsuno, R.; Miyagawa, H.; Nishitani, K.;

Toei, R.

Kagaku Kogaku, V.32, N.6, 565-70 (1968) (Transl.) Int. Chem.

Eng., V.9, N.2, 358-64 (April 1969).

157. The Properties of Bubbles in Fluidized Beds of Conducting

Particles as Measured by an Electroresistivity Probe.

Capes, C.E.; Kang, W.K.; Osberg, G.L.; Park, W.H.

Chem. Eng. Sci., V.24, N.5, 851-65 (May 1969).

159. Bubble Growth by Coalescence in Gas Fluidized Beds.

Argyriou, D.T.

City Univ. New York Diss. (1968), 299p, (Abstract) Diss.

Abstract B V29, N.7, 2407B (Jan. 1969).

160. Bubble Assemblage Model for Fluidized Bed Catalytic Reactors.

Kato, K.; Wen, C.Y.

64th AIChE Nat. Mtg. (New Orleans 3/16-20/69), Preprint

N.48B 38p.

161. Bubble Assemblage Model for Fluidized Bed Catalytic Reactors.

Kato, K.; Wen, C.Y.

Res. results serv. MS (Manuscript), N.68-449, 30p, Ind. Eng.

Chem., V.60, N.12, 66-68 (Dec. 1968).

162. Gas Exchange Between the Bubble and Emulsion Phases in Gas-Solid Fluidized Beds.

Chiba, T.; Kobayashi, H.

1st Int. "Chem. Reaction Eng." Symp. (Washington 6/8-10/70), Chem. Eng. Sci., V.25, N.9, 1375-85 (Sept. 1970).

163. Behavior of Fluidized Beds Based on Bubble Assemblage Model.

Wen, C.Y.; Yoshida, K.

63rd AIChE Ann. Mtg. (Chicago 11/29-12/3/70), Preprint N.16C, 36p.

164. Experimental Age Distributions of Bubbles and Emulsion in a Fluidized Bed (Studied with Petroleum Coke).

Fitzgerald, T.J.; Navarrette, A.E.

63rd AIChE Ann. Mtg. (Chicago 11/29-12/3/70), Program Paper No.15E.

165. Design of Gas Distributors and Prediction of Bubble Size in Large Gas-Solids Fluidized Beds.

Leung, L.S.

Res. results serv. MS (Mauscript) Ind. Eng. Chem., V.62, N.10, 79-80 (Oct. 1970), N.70-257, 24p.

166. Residence Behavior of Gas and Mass Transfer at a Bubble in a (Two-Dimensional) Fluidized Bed.

Wessely, R.; Dolling, E.; Reuter, H.

Chem-Ing-Tech., V.42, N.17, 1109-15 (Sept. 1970).

167.   Measurement of Local Bubble Size and Rising Velocity in an Actual Gas-Solid Fluidized Bed by a Correlation Method.

Werther, J.

Ver Deut. Ing. Dust. Technol. Comm. - Verfahrenstech Ges. "Multiphase Flow", Comm. Joint Conf. (Duesselforf 3/9-10/70).

168.   Flow Mechanics in Bubble-Forming Fluidized Beds.

Molerus, O.

Ver Deut. Ing. Process Eng. Ann. Mtg. (Bayreuth 9/30-10/2/69) Chem-Ing.-Tech., V.42. N.7, 488-93 (April 1970).

169.   Effects of Voidage Variation on Throughflow in Bubbles in a Fluidized Bed.

Leung, L.S.; Mak, F.K., Sandford, I.C.

Chem. Ehg. Sci., V.25, N.1, 220-21 (Jan. 1970).

170.   (Effects of Bubble Formation On) Axial Mixing in Gas/Liquid Fluidized Beds.

Michelsen, M.L.; Oestergaard, K.

3rd Int. Chem. Eng. Chem. Equip. & Automat. Congr.(Marienbad 9/15-20/69).

171.   The Behavior of Gas Bubbles in a Fluidized Bed.

Mikhalev, M.F.; Murzin, A.R.; Pravdin, G.V.

Zh. Prikl. Khim. V.42, N.12, 2356-59 (Oct. 1969).

172.   Gas Exchange Between (Stationary) Bubbles and a Fluidized Bed (Of Cracking Catalyst).

Drinkenburg, A.A.H.; Koolen, J.L.A.; Rietema, K.

3rd Int. Chem. Eng. Chem. Equip. & Automat. Congr. (Marienbad 9/15-20/69).

173. Bubble Coalescence in Fluidized Beds.

Lin, S.P.

AIChE (Amer. Inst. Che. Eng.) J., V.16, N.1, 130-33 (Jan.1970).

174. Prediction of Voidage Fraction Near Bubbles in Fluidized Beds.

Stewart, P.S.B.

Chem. Eng. Sci., V.23, N.4, 396-97 (June 1968)

175. Bubble-Driven Fluid Circulations.

De Nevers, N.

AIChE (Am. Inst. Chem. Engrs.) J., V.14, N.2, 222-26 (Mar. 1968)

176. Bubble Growth by Coalescence in Gas-Fluidized Beds.

List, H.L.; Argyriou, D.T.

60th AIChE Ann. Mtg. (New York 11/26-30/67) Program Abstract No. 33D.

177. Experimental Comparison of the Mixing Processes in Different Two-Phase Flow Systems (i.e., Fluidized Beds and Bubble Columns).

Diboun, M.; Schuegerl, K.

2nd Chisa Intern. Congr. (Marianske Lazne 1965) Chem. Tech. (Berlin), V.19, N.7, 403-7 (July 1967).

178. Gas Interchange Between Bubbles and Continuous Phase in a Fluidized Bed.

Richardson, J.F.; Davies, L.

Brit. Chem. Eng., V.12, N.8, 1223-26 (Aug. 1967).

179. On Bubble Flow in Liquids and Fluidized Beds.

Turner, J.C.R.

Chem. Eng. Sci., V.21, N.11, 971-74 (Nov. 1966).

180. Gas Interchange Between Bubbles and the Continuous Phase in
a Fluidized Bed.

Davies, L.; Richardson, J.F.

Trans. Inst. Chem. Engrs. (London), V.44, N.8, T293-T305 (1966).

181. On the Growth of Air Bubbles Formed at a Single Orifice in
a Water Fluidized Bed (Of Sand).

Oestergaard, K.

Chem. Eng. Sci., V.21, N.5, 470-72 (May 1966).

182. The Effect of Dispersing Air Bubbles into Liquid Fluidized
Beds on Heat Transfer and Hold-Up at Constant Bed Expansion.

Viswanathan, S.; Kakar, A.S.; Murti, P.S.

Chem. Eng. Sci., V.20, N.10, 903-10 (Oct. 1965).

183. An Extension of Davidson's Theory of Bubbles in Fluidized Beds.

Collins, R.

Chm. Eng. Sci., V.20, N.8, 747-55 (Aug. 1965).

184. Cloud Formation Around Bubbles in Gas Fluidized Beds.

Rowe, P.N.; Partridge, B.A.; Lyall, E.

Chem. Eng. Sci., V.19, N.12, 973-85 (Dec. 1964).

185. Bubble Rise in Liquid and Fluidized Systems...A Reinterpretation.

Pyle, D.L.; Stewart, P.S.B.

Chem. Eng. Sci., V.19, N.10, 842-43 (Oct. 1964).

186.   The Evolution of Gas Bubbles in Liquids and Fluidized Systems.

Angelino, H.; Charzat, C.; Williams, R.

Chem. Eng. Sci., V.19, N.4, 289-304 (April 1964).

187.   Oxygen Mass Transfer in Bubble Columns and Three-Phase Fluidized Beds.

Alvarez-Cuenca, M.

Univ. West. Ont., Diss. (1979), Diss. Abstract INT. B, V.40, N.10, 4916B (April 1980).

Abstract: The paper discusses bubble columns in the limiting case of three-phase fluidization. Reactor systems for fermentation and wastewater treatment are hindered by the technical difficulties of conjugating large liquid and gas flow rates, such as oxygen mass transfer, economically. The experimental systems used air, deaerated water, and glass beads, in which two well defined regions could be observed in the mass transfer columns: the grid zone covering 20% of the column height but producing 95% of the oxygenation, measured at the exit; and the second or bulk zone of much lower oxygenation. Computer-derived concentration contour diagrams were reported which permitted detailed observation of hydrodynamic characteristics of these systems. They showed that bubble columns transfer oxygen more efficiently than three-phase fluidized beds using 1 or 3 but not 5 mm diameter particles. Comparison of the results with calculations by the plug flow, axial dispersion, and complete mixing models showed that none of the models adequately described the observed concentrations. For the models examined, liquid-side volumetric mass transfer coefficients increased, with increasing gas and liquid superficial velocities.

188.   Bubble Frequency in Fluidized Beds of Binary Mixtures.

Sankarshana, T.; Rao, P.S.; Rao, S.N.

Pet. Chem. Ind. Dev. 13(8) 9-13 (1979).

189. On the Formation of Bubbles in Gas-Particulate Fluidized Beds.

Fanucci, J.B.; Ness, N.; Yen, R.H.

J. Fluid Mech. 94(2), 353-67 (1979).

190. Formation of Bubbles in Gas-Particulate Fluidized Beds.

Fanucci, J.B.; Ness, N.; Yen, R.H.

U.S. Dept. Commerce Natl. Tech. Inf. Serv. Rep. N. METC/CR-78/9

(July 1978), 91p., in English, see ERDA Energy Res. Abstract V-4-6879 (1979).

191. Bubble Distribution and Eruption Diameter in a Fluidized Bed with a Horizontal Tube Bundle.

Nguyen, H.V.; Potter, O.E.; Whitehead, A.B.

Chem. Eng. Sci., V.34, N.9, 1163-64 (1979), in English.

Abstract: Bubble flow patterns at the surface of a 1.2 sq. m. fluidized bed of sand, with and without a tube bundle, were determined. For open beds, the bubbling points at 15.2 cm/sec velocity were observed concentrated in the four corners of the square bed. Bubbles appeared at lower concentrations elsewhere. The study indicated that the downflow of solids can be expected to occur strongly in the center and to a lesser extent, at the corners and walls. With a tube bundle in the bed, the bubbles are uniformly distributed and bubble eruption diameters are one-third to one-half of that for the open bed. The tubes appear to induce splitting of bubles since bubble diameters in the presence of tubes are always less than the bubble diameters in the open bed at the same level.

192. Emergence Rate of Gas Bubbles in a Heterogeneous Fluidized Bed.

Mirzakhanyan, R.M.; Mirzakhanyan, A.G.

Mezhvuz. Sb. Nauchn. Tr. - Frevan. Politekh. Inst. Im. K. Marksa, Ser. 19, 3 117-19 (1977), in Russian, see Chem. Abstr. Abstract No. 59452, V.91, N.7-8.

193. Bubble Chains in Large Diameter Gas Fluidized Beds.

Werther, J.

J. Powder Bulk Solids Technol. 1(1), 14-21 (1977), refer to English Chem. Abstr. Abstract No. 23139, V.91, N.3-4.

194. Synopses/Modeling of the Homogeneous and Heterogeneous Flow in Fluidized Beds and Bubble Columns.

Riquarts, H.P.

Verfahrens-Ing. Annu. Meet. (AACHEN 9/27-29/78), Chem.-Ing.-Tech. V.51, N.5, 520-21 (May 1979), in German.

Abstract: The author presents an analysis of bubble columns and fluidized beds, showing that in the homogeneous flow regime, gas holdup and porosity can be calculated by utilizing the balance of volume, pressure, and flow forces that act on the particle cloud. To evaluate the particle cloud flow resistance for these calculations, a correlation was developed for the flow resistance coefficient in terms of single particle flow resistance, dispersed phase volume fraction, the Reynolds number based on the relative rates of the phases, the particle diameter, and the kinematic viscosity of the dispersed phase, the Reynolds number based on final particle velocity, and a correction factor. For the heterogeneous flow regime, the bubble growth mechanisms were found to differ in the two systems. The fluidized bed mechanism was modeled on the assumption of gas entrainment (rather than the generally accepted coalescence) and treated as a deterministic (rather than stochastic) growth process. Model predictions showed that bubble-forming fluidized beds always have a lower porosity than homogeneous beds under identical conditions.

195. Letters to the Editor/Prediction of Bubble Size in a Gas-Fluidized Bed.

Whitehead, A.B.

Chem. Eng. Sci., V.34, N.5, 751 (1979).

Abstract: In relation to Rowe's and Potter's comments on the deficiency
of mathematic models of bubble coalescence phenomena in gas-solid fluidized
beds (based on assuming some type of ordered progression in the coalescence
mechanism), an analysis of published experimental data showed that an increase
in bed depth or gas flow rate enhances the speed of bubble coalescence in the
immediate vicinity of the distributor. This is attributed to the development
of large-scale circulation patterns called "Gulf Streaming." Thus bubble
coalescence models which take this effect into account are needed to produce
expressions that are sufficiently accurate to allow for extrapolation into the
industrial operating ranges.

196.   A Method for Measurement of Spatial Distribution of Bubbles
in a Fluidized Bed.

Yamazaki, M.; Jimbo, G.; Matsumoto, T.; Mizutani, A.; Yogo, S.;
Shiraya, H.; Ito, N.

Kagaku Kogaku Rombunshu, 3(3) 266-71 (1977).

197.   Bubbling Behavior of Fluidized Beds at Elevated Pressures.

Subzwari, M.P.; Clift, R.; Pyle, D.L.

Fluid., Proc. Eng. Found. Conf., 2nd 50-4 (1978).

198.   Size Distribution of Bubbles in Gas Fluidized Beds.

Yoshida, K.; Nakajima, K.; Hamatani, N.; Shimizu, F.

Fluid., Proc. Eng. Found. Conf., 2nd 13-18 (1978).

199.   Influence of the Distributor Design on Bubble Characteristics
in Large Diameter Gas Fluidized Beds.

Werther, J.

Fluid., Proc. Eng. Found. Conf., 2nd 7-12 (1978).

200.   Measurement of Local Bubbles Properties in a Fluidized Bed.

Masson, H.; Jottrand, R.

Fluid., Proc. Eng. Found. Conf., 2nd 1-6 (1978).

201.   Experimental Study of Gas Exchange Between Bubbles and the
Emulsion Phase in a Two-Dimensional Fluidized Bed.

Dikalenko, V.I.

Teplo- Massoobmen Dvukhfaznykh Sist. Fazovykh Khim. Prevrashcl
31-7 (1976), in Russian, see Chemical Abstract. Abstract No. 138409, V.88, N.2

202.   Model of a Bubble Forming Fluidized Bed.

Riquarts, H.P.

Verfahrenstechnik (Mainz), 11(3), 164-8 (1977), in German,
see Chem. Abstr. Abstract No. 9038, V.88, N.2.

203.   The Division of Gas Between Bubble and Interstitial Phases
in Fluidized Beds cf Fine Powders.

Rowe, P.N.; Santoro, L.; Yates, J.G.

Chem. Eng. Sci., V.33, N.1, 133-40 (1978), in English.

Abstract: Data is reported on the division of gas between bubble and
interstitial phases in fluidized fine powders of a commercial silica base
catalyst. Measurements of interstitial phase voidage and bed height over a
wide range of gas velocities are reported. Voidage measurements were made
by comparing the X-ray absorption of the interstitial phase of the freely
bubbling catalyst with that of a calibration wedge containing the same materia
X-ray photography was also used in the measurement of bed height. Increasing
the fines content of a fluidized powder led to an increase in the relative
proportion of gas flowing interstitially at all fluid velocities. The
interstitial gas flow was up to 25 times greater than the minimum fluidization

value for the powder containing the highest proportion of fines. This means

that catalytic and similar fluidized bed chemical reactors using fine powders

will be more efficient than the two-phase theory predicts.

204. Bubble Growth Due to Coalescence in Fluidized Beds.

Darton, R.C.; Lanauze, R.D.; Davidson, J.F.; Harrison, D.

Trans. Inst. Chem. Eng., V.55, N.4, 274-80 (Oct. 1977).

Abstract: The authors presented a model of bubble coalescence in fluid-

ized beds. The model is based on the assumption that the distance traveled

by the bubble before coalescence with another is proportional to their hori-

zontal separation. Rising bubbles tend to rise in preferred paths and move

slowly and laterally. For the case of extreme height and small diameter, the

model leads to a single path and a slug at the top of the bed. An equation

derived for bubble diameter depends on the fluidization velocity, height in the

bed, and catchment area at the distributor plate. Model predictions agree well

with published data on bubble size when bubble growth is not limited by the

presence of an appreciable amount of fine particles.

205. Bubble Characteristics in Three-Phase Fluidized Beds.

Kim, S.D.; Baker, C.G.J.; Bergougnou, M.A.

Chem. Eng. Sci., V.32, N.11, 1299-1306 (1977).

Abstract: Data on bubble size and rising velocity were reported for

freely bubbling liquid-gas and liquid-gas-solid fluidized beds using a movie

photography technique. The gas in all cases was air and the solids consisted

of 1 mm diameter and 6 mm diameter glass beads and 2.6 mm gravel. The fluid

phases were: water and aqueous acetone, sugar, and carboxymethyl-cellulose

solutions. Bubble size and rising velocity both increased with increasing

gas velocity but were relatively insensitive to liquid velocity, viscosity, and

surface tension. At the high gas rates used, the bubble characteristics were independent of particle size. The authors give correlations for calculating

bubble size and rising velocity. The work may be of practical interest in the

hydrogenation of residual oils.

206. Letters to the Editor/Prediction of Bubble Size in a Gas-
Fluidized Bed.

Potter, O.E.; Rowe, P.N.

Chem. Eng. Sci., V.32, N.8, 979 (1977).

207. Gas Motion Around Bubbles in Fluidized Beds.

Anwer, J.; Pyle, D.L.

Fluid. Ses. Appl., C.-R. Congr. Int. 1973, 240-53 (Pub. 1974)

in English.

208. Bubble Chains in Large-Diameter Gas Fluidized Beds.

Werther, J.

Int J. Multiph. Flow, V.3, N.4, 367-81 (June 1977).

209. Estimation of the Properties of Bubbles in Screen-Packed
Fluidized Beds.

Ramamoorthy, S.; Subramanian, N.

Indian J. Technol., 1976, V.14, N.8, 379-80, see Chemical

Abstract V86-108620.

210. Bubble Growth in Large Diameter Fluidized Beds.

Werther, J.

Fluid Technol. Proc. Int. Fluid Conf., 1975 (Pub. 1976),

V.1, 215-35.

211. Formation of Gas Bubbles in a Fluidized Bed.

Melik-Akhnazarov, T. Kh.; Basov, V.A.; Markhevka, V.I.;

Orochko, D.I.

Teor. Osn. Khim. Tekhnol, 1976, V.10, N.3, 471-3, in Russian,

see Chemical Abstract V86-75171.

212. Material Transfer During the Rise of a Large Gaseous Bubble

in a Liquid Fluidized Bed.

Roland, S.; Schrayen, J.P.; Vanderschuren, J.

Fluid Ses. Appl. C-R Congr. Int. 1973 (Pub. 1974), 351-64,

in French.

213. Formation of Bubbles in Gas-Fluidized Beds.

Haribabu, P.; Sarkar, M.K.; Subba, Rao, D.

Can. J. Chem. Eng., V.54, N.5, 451-52 (Oct. 1976).

214. Letters to the Editors/Fluidized Bed Bubbles and Froude Number.

Epstein, N.

Chem. Eng. Sci., V.31, N.9, 852 (1976).

215. Bubble Sizes in a Fluidized Bed at Elevated Temperatures.

Geldart, D.; Kapoor, D.S.

Chem. Eng. Sci., V.31, N.9, 842-43 (1976).

216. Prediction of Bubble Size in a Gas-Fluidized Bed.

Rowe, P.N.

Chem. Eng. Sci., V.31, N.4, 285-88 (1976).

217. Diffusion of Bubble Gas in Two-Dimensional Fluidized Bed.
I. Diffusion of Gas When Alpha More Than 1.

Fuchigami, K.; Matsuno, Y.; Okuda, T.

Kyushu Kogyo Daigaku Kenkyu Hokoku Kogaku, 1975, V.30,

57-64.

218. The Effective Rate of Gas Exchange in a Bubbling Fluidized Bed

Walker, B.V.

Trans. Inst. Chem. Eng., V.53, N.4, 255-66 (Oct. 1975).

219. A Model of (Single) Bubbles Rising in a Fluidized Bed.

Buyevich, Yu A.

Int. J. Multiph. Flow, V.2, N.3, 337-51 (Dec. 1975).

220. The Measurement of Bubble Properties in Two-Phase Dispersions
3. Bubble Properties in a Freely Bubbling Fluidized Bed.

Burgess, J.M.; Calderbank, P.H.

Chem. Eng. Sci., V.30, N.12, 1511-18 (1975).

221. Lateral Distribution of Bubble Sizes in Two-Dimensional
Gas-Fluidized Beds.

Chiba, T.; Kobayashi, H.; Terashima, K.

J. Chem. Eng. Jap., V.8, N.2, 167-69 (April 1975).

222. The Measurement of Bubble Parameters in Two-Phase Dispersions
1. The Development of an Improved Probe Technique.

Burgess, J.M.; Calderbank, P.H.

Chem. Eng. Sci., V.30, N.7, 743-50 (July 1975).

223. Deformation and Splitting of a Bubble in a Two-Dimensional
Fluidized Bed....Experimental Results. Theoretical Calculations.

Yamamoto, K.; Oichi, M.; Matsuno, R.; Toei, R.

7th Jap. Soc. Chem. Eng. Autumn Meet. (Oct. 1973), J. Chem.
Eng. Jap., V.7, N.6, 447-50, 451-55 (Dec. 1974).

224. Formation of Bubbles in a Fluidized Bed.

Soo, S.L.

Powder Technol., 1974, V.10, N.4, 211-16.

225. Glow Discharge Probes for Fluid Bed Applications.

Crescitelli, S.; Macchiaroli, B.' Egiziano, L.

Quad. Ing. Chim. Italy, 1974, V.10, N.2, 23-6.

226. On the Origin of Bubbles in Gas-Fluidized Beds.

Verloop, J.; Heertjes, P.M.

Chem. Eng. Sci., V.29, N.5, 1101-7 (May 1974).

227. Variation in Shape with Size of Bubbles in Fluidized Beds.

Widmer, A.J.; Rowe, P.N.

Chem. Eng. Sci., V.28, N.3, 980-81 (Mar. 1973).

228. A Note on Bubble Formation at an Orifice in a Fluidized Bed.

Nguyen, X.T.; Leung, L.S.

Chem. Eng. Sci., V.27, N.9, 1748-50 (Sept. 1972).

229. Throughflow in Bubbles in a Fluidized Bed.

Leung, L.S.; Mak F.K.; Nguyen, X.T.

63rd AIChE Annu. Meet. (Chicago 11/29-12/3/70) AIChE Symp.
Ser., V.67, N.116, 34-37 (1971).

230. Initial Motion of Liquid Bubbles in Liquid-Solid Fluidized Bed

Leung, L.S.; Mak, F.K.

Powder Technol. 1971, V.4, N.3, 167-70.

231. Behavior of Gas Bubbles in Fluidized Beds.

Pigford, R.L.; Rieke, R.D.

64th AIChE Nat. Meet. (New Orleans 3/16-20/69), AIChE J.,

V.17, N.5, 1096-1101 (Sept. 1971).

232. Interaction Effects on the Fluid Dynamics of Bubbles in a

Fluidized Bed Chain of Rising Bubbles in an Infinite Three-Dimensional Medium

Gabor, J.D.; Koppel, L.B.

64th AIChE Nat. Meet. (New Orleans 3/17-20/69), Chem. Eng.

Progr. Symp. Ser., V.66, N.105, 28-36 (1970).

233. Fluidized Beds Take on New Life.

Rowe, P.N.; Yates, J.G.; Harrison, D.; Busyman, P.J.;

Gunn, D.J.; Whitehead, A.B.; Elliott, D.E.; FMC Corp.; Iowa State University.

Chem. Eng. News, V.48, N.52, 46-48 (12/14/70).

234. Interaction Effects on the Fluid Dynamics of Bubbles in a

Fluidized Bed...A Chain of Rising Bubbles in an Infinite Two-Dimensional Mediu

Gabor, J.D.

Ind. Eng. Chem. Fundam., V.8, N.1, 84-91 (Feb. 1969).

235. Bubble Rise Velocities in Two-Dimensional Gas Fluidized Beds

(Calculated) From Pressure Measurements.

Homolka, G.; Littman, H.

64th AIChE Nat. Mtg. (New Orleans 3/16-20/69), Program Paper

No. 48A.

236.   (Mechanism Of) Leakage into Single Bubbles in a Fluidized Bed.

Pigford, R.L.; Rieke, R.D.

64th AIChE Nat. Mtg. (New Orleans 3/16-20/69), Program Paper

N. 47C.

237.   (Theoretical Study Of) Interaction Effects on the Fluid

Dynamics of Bubbles in a Fluidized Bed...Chain of Rising Bubbles in an Infinite

Three-Dimensional Medium.

Gabor, J.D.; Koppel, L.B.

64th AIChE Nat. Mtd. (New Orleans 3/16-20/69), Program Paper

N. 47B.

238.   Gas Solid Catalyzed Reactions in a Fluidized Bed.

Zabransky, R.F.

Ill. Inst. Technol. Diss (1969), (Abstract). Diss. Abstract

INT B V30, N.1, 187B (July 1969).

239.   Studies in Bubble Formation -- 4. Bubble Formation at Porous

Discs.

Kumar, R.; Bowonder, B.

Chem. Eng. Sci., V.25, N.1, 25-32 (Jan. 1970).

240.   Distribution of Gas Flow in a Fluidized Bed.

Harrison, D.; Lockett, M.J.; Richardson, J.F.; Davidson, J.F.;

Godard, K.

Chem. Eng. Sci., V.23, N.6, 660-61 (Aug. 1968).

241.   Isolated Bubbles in Fluidized Beds...Theory and Experiment.

Stewart, P.S.B.

Trans. Inst. Chem. Engrs. (London), V.46, N.2, T60-T66 (Mar.1968).

242. The Coalescence of Bubbles in a Gas-Solid Fluidized Bed.

Matsuno, R.; Mori, M.; Sumitani, T.; Toei, R.

Kagaku, Kogaku, N.9, 861-67 (1967) (Transl.) Intern. Chem.
Eng., V.8, N.2, 351-57 (Apr. 1968).

243. Bubble Formation in Fluidized Beds.

Kuloor, N.R.; Kumar, R.

Chem. Tech. (Berlin), V.19, N.12, 733-37 (Dec. 1967).

244. Theory and Applications of Fluidized Solids.

Reuter, H.

Deut. Ges. Fettwiss Mtg. (Hannover 10/25/66) Fette Seifen
Anstrichmittel, V.69, N.12, 899-905 (Dec. 1967).

245. The Influence of Bubble Shape on the Rising Velocities of
Large Bubbles.

Grace, J.R.; Harrison, D.

Chem. Eng. Sci., V.22, N.10, 1337-47 (Oct. 1967).

246. Some Properties of Bubbles in Fluidized Beds.

Pyle, D.L.

Cambridge Univ. Diss. (Sept. 1965) (Abstract), Brit. Chem.
Eng., V.12, N.8, 1258 (Aug. 1967).

247. On the Two-Phase Theory of Fluidization.

Harrison, D.; Lockett, M.J.; Davidson, J.F.

Chem. Eng. Sci., V.22, N.8, 1059-65 (Aug. 1967).

248. Pressure Behind a Bubble Accelerating from Rest...Simple
Theory and Applications.

Jameson, G.J.; Kupferberg, A.

Chem. Eng. Sci., V.22, N.7, 1053-55 (July 1967).

249. A Note on (J.D.) Murray's Paper on Bubbles in Fluidized Beds.

Murray, J.D.; Partridge, B.A.; Rowe, P.N.

J. Fluid Mech., V.23, N.3, 583-84 (1965) (Abstract) Chim.

Ind. (Paris) - Genie Chim., V. 97, N.12, 1963 (June 1967).

250. On the Mechanism of Bubble Formation in a Fluidized Bed.

Muntean, O.; Ruckenstein, E.

Can. J. Chem. Eng., V.45, N.2, 95-97 (Apr. 1967).

251. The Rising Velocity of Bubbles in Two-Dimensional Fluidized

Beds.

Harrison, D.; Pyle, D.L.

Chem. Eng. Sci., V.22, N.4, 531-35 (Apr. 1967).

252. In Fluid Beds - Flowing Solids Displace Bubble Voids.

Zenz, F.A.

Hydrocarbon Process., V.46, N.4, 171-75 (Apr. 1967).

253. (A Mechanism Of) Coalescence of Bubbles in a Gas-Fluidized

Granular Bed.

Reuter, H.

Deut. Ges.Chem. Apparatewesen Ann. Mtg. (Frankfurt 6/30-7/1/66),

Abstract, Chem-Ingr.-Tech., V.38, N.11, 1208 (Nov. 1966).

254. Fluidization Research

U.K. Science Research Council; Rowe, P.N.

Fuel, V.45, N.5, 418 (Sept. 1966).

255.   Bubble Formation in Fluidized Bed.

Kuloor, N.R.; Kumar, R.

Res. Results Serv. MS N. 66-338, 17p., Abstract in Ind. Eng.
Chem., V.58, N.10, 92 (Oct. 1966).

256.   The Behavior of Bubbles in a Gas-Fluidized Bed.

Toei, R.

Mem. Fac. Eng. Kyoto Univ., V.27, 475 (1965), Abstract in
Chem. Ingr. Tech., V.38, N.8, 901 (Aug. 1966).

257.   (Experiments) on the Nature of the Bubbles in Gas- and Liqui
Fluidized Beds.

Reuter, H.

Chem. Eng. Progr. Symp. Ser., V.62, N.62, 92-99 (1966).

258.   Mathematical Aspects of Bubble Motion in Fluidized Beds.

Murray, J.D.

Chem. Eng. Progr. Symp. Ser., V.62, N.62, 71-82 (1966).

259.   Bubble Chains in Gas-Fluidized Beds.

Botterill, J.S.M.; George, J.S.; Besford, H.

Chem. Eng. Progr. Symp. Ser., V.62, N.62, 7-14 (1966).

260.   The Motion of Gas Bubbles in Fluidized Particle Beds in
Rectangular Columns.

Volpicelli, G.; Raso, G.; Maitz, C.

Ing. Chim. Ital., V.1, 157-67 (1965), Abstract in J. Appl.
Chem. (London), V.16, N.4, I-291 (Apr. 1966).

261. Bubble Rise Velocity in Gas-Solid Fluidized Beds.

Reuter, H.

Ges. Verfahrens Tech. Ann. Mtg. (Karlsruhe 4/ 28-29 /64),

Chem.Ingr.Tech., V.37, N.10, 1062-66 (Oct. 1965).

262. An X-Ray Cine Study of Bubbles in Fluidized Beds.

Rowe, P.N.; Partridge, A.

Trans. Inst. Chem. Engrs. (London), V.43, N.5, T157-T175

(June 1965).

263. A Mechanism of Incipient Bubble Destruction and Particulate

Fluidization.

Zenz, F.A.

AIChE (Am. Inst. Chem. Engrs.) J., V.11, N.3, 560-62, 573-76

(May 1965).

264. Chemical Reaction in Bubbling Fluidized Beds.

Pyle, D.L.; Rose, P.L.

Chem. Eng. Sci., V.20, N.1, 25-31 (Jan. 1965).

265. The Mechanism of Bubble Formation in a Gas-Solid Fluidized

Bed.

Reuter, H.

Tech. Hochschule AACHEN Diss. (1963), Abstract in VDI (Ver

Deut. Ingr.) Z, V.106, N.11, 452 (4/11/64).

266. A Note on the Motion of a Bubble Rising Through a Fluidized Bed.

Rowe, P.N.

Chem. Eng. Sci., V.19, N.1, 75-77 (Jan. 1964).

II . MIXING AND SEGREGATION IN FLUIDIZED BEDS

267.   Temperature Effect on Solid Mixing in a Gas-Fluidized Bed.

Kim, H.S.; Lee W.K.

Hwahak Konghak 17(2) 109-16 (1979), refer to Chemical

Abstract No. 76131, V.91, N.9-10.

268.   Mixing of the Solid Phase (Heat Transfer) in a Fluidized

System.

Teplitskii, Yu S.

Teplo - Massoobmen Mnogofaznykh Mnogokomponentnykh Sist.,

29-35 (1978), in Russian.

269.   Study of Solid Phase Mixing in a Pulsating Layer of Finely

Divided Material.

Zabrodskii S.S.; Efremtsev, V.S.; Kalinnikov, S.V.;

Dolidovich, A.F.

Teplo - Massoobmen Mnogofaznykh Mnogokomponentnykh Sist.,

62-9 (1978), in Russian.

270.   Solid Mixing in a Fluidized Bed.

Jottrand, R.; Dang Tran K.; Masson, H.

C.R. - Int. Symp. Mixing Paper D5 (1978), 12p., in French.

271.   Mixing of Large Particles in Two-Dimensional Gas-Fluidized

Beds.

Fan, L.T.; Chang, Y.

Kans. State University

Can. J. Chem. Eng., V.57, N.1, 88-97 (Feb. 1979).

Abstract: Tests were conducted in a 330.2 x 38.1 x 4.45 cm bed with

dyed 3.65 cm diameter table tennis balls as a nonsegregating system and similar

balls where some had been weighted with sand as a segregating system. The

systems were described by a nonstationary random walk model. Each particle

was found to oscillate around a fixed position in the bed prior to the onset

of bubbling. The transition from bubbling to slugging-bed conditions was

found to be rapid. Bubble- or slug-induced drift was the predominant mixing

mechanism; wake mixing was negligible, and radial mixing was more rapid than

axial mixing. In the segregating system, axial mixing was more rapid when

the lighter particles were initially at the bottom rather than at the top.

Both systems yielded a unique equilibrium concentration distribution with the

lighter particles at the top. At low or moderate air rates, a concentration

gradient existed only near the bottom of the bed.

272.   Discrete Model of Segregation of Solid Particles in a

Fluidized Bed.

Zakharenko, V.V.; Ainshtein, V.G.

Deposited Doc. (Viniti) 3307-77 (1977), 20p., in Russian.

Refer to Chemical Abstract No. 153921, V.90, N.19-20.

273.   Particles Segregation in Liquid-Solid Fluidized Beds.

Juma, A.K.A.; Richardson, J.F.

Chem. Eng. Sci., V.34, N.1, 137-43 (1979).

Abstract: A pressure transducer incorporating a variable-position

stainless steel probe was used to measure the pressure gradient throughout the

depth of a bed of particles of different sizes of glass ballotini (2, 3, and 4 mm

diamter) fluidized by water (243, 174, and 53.2 mm/sec velocities) in a 104 mm

diameter column. Experimental results showed that a pressure transducer can be

used satisfactorily to explore particle segregation in a liquid-solid fluidized bed by measuring local pressure gradients, from which local bed voidages may be calculated, and that the magnitude and frequency of pressure fluctuations can be found. As would be expected for particulate fluidization, by analogy with sedimentation, segregation is more marked when the difference in particle size is large and when the voidage (or fluid velocity) is high. Note that this is in contrast to the behavior of a bubbling gas-solid bed where the mixing is improved as the flow rate is increased.

274. A New Method for Solid Mixing Studies in a Gas Fluidized Layer.

Masson, H.A.

Textes Conf. Cadre Congr. Int. 'Contrib. Calc. Electron. Dev. Genie Chim. Chim. Ind.' D85-9 (1978).

275. Axial Mixing of the Solid Phase in a Fluidized Bed. Retarded Bed.

Teplitskii, Yu S.; Tamarin, A.I.

Inzh.-Fiz. Zh. 33(4) 603-10 (1977), in Russian. Refer to Chemical Abstract, Abstract No. 217276, V.89, N.26.

276. Mixing in a Fluidized-Bed Dryer.

Menshikov, V.V.; Zlotnikov, E.S.; Khomichev, S.A.

Deposited Doc. (Viniti) 2947-76 (1976), 5p., in Russian. Refer to Chemical Abstract, Abstract No. 181648, V.89, N.22.

277. Solids Mixing in Fluidized Beds of Large Particles.

Cranfield, R.R.

69th AIChE Annu. Meet. (Chicago Nov.-Dec. 1976), AIChE Symp. Ser., V.74, N.176, 54-59 (1978), in English.

278. Multicomponent Solid-Solid Mixing in a Fluidized Bed.

Jain, R.C.; Sengupta, P.

Chem. Petro-Chem. J., V. 9, N. 2, 9-13 (1978).

279. Axial Mixing of Liquid in Liquid-Solid Fluidized Bed.

Ogiwara, K.; Ohashi, H.

Akita Kogyo Koto Semmon Gakko Kenkyu Kiyo 12 61-5 (1977),
refer to Japanese Chemical Abstract, Abstract No. 148622, V. 89, N.18.

280. Lateral Mixing of Solid Particles in Gas Fluidized Beds.

Chmielewski, A.G.; Selecki, A.

Inz. Chem. 7(3), 549-60 (1977), in Polish, refer to Chemical
Abstract, Abstract No. 113274, V.89, N.14.

281. Solids Mixing in Fluidized Beds.

Jottrand, R.; Dang Tran K.; Masson, H.

Faculte Polytech. Mons Int. 'Mixing' Symp. (Mons 2/21-24/78),
Abstract appears in Chem. Ing. Tech., V.50, N.9, 736-41 (Sept. 1978), in German.

282. Hydrodynamical Studies on Fluidized Beds. Part 4 Studies on
the Particle Mixing Phenomena in Dual-Cell Fluidized Beds Using Isotope Tracer
Techniques.

Szentmarjay, T.; Csukas, B.; Ormos, Z.

Hung. J. Ind. Chem., V. 5, N. 3, 213-24 (1977).

283. Axial Mixing of the Solid Phase in a Fluidized Bed. Loose
Bed.

Teplitskii, Yu S.; Tamarin, A.I.

Vestsi Akad., Navuk BSSR, Ser. Fiz.-Energ. Navuk, (4), 88-94
(1977), in Russian. refer to Chemical Abstract, Abstract No. 193429, V.88, N.26.

284. <u>Experimental Study of the Mixing of Solid Particles in a</u> <u>Fluidized Bed by Gas Bubbles During Their Chain Motion.</u>

Vakhrushev, I.A.; Tolkachev, V.M.

Teor. Osn. Khim. Tekhnol., V. 11, N. 3, 405-10 (1977).

285. <u>Effect of the Size of Solid-Phase Particles on the Intensity</u> <u>of Their Mixing During Fluidization of a Polydispersed Material.</u>

Chechetkin, A.V.; Pavlov, V.A.; Apostolova, G.V.; Dementev, A.I.; Romanova, T.T.

Deposited Doc. (Viniti) 1696-74 (1974), 9p., in Russian.

286. <u>Evaluation of the Solid-Phase Longitudinal Mixing Coefficient</u> <u>in a Fluidized Bed.</u>

Emelyanov, I.D.; Meshcheryakov, V.D.

Teor. Osn. Khim. Tekhnol., V. 11, N. 2, 300-2 (1977), in Russian.

287. <u>Gas Backmixing, Solids Movement, and Bubble Activities in</u> <u>Large-Scale Fluidized Beds.</u>

Nguyen, H.V.; Whitehead, A.B.; Potter, O.E.

Abstract: Experiments were conducted in a 1.22 m square bed, using silica sand fluidized with air at 15.2 and 24.4 cm/sec. Carbon dioxide injected as tracer gas confirmed the strong backmixing predicted by the counter-current backmixing model. The downward movement of solids occurred at about the expected order of magnitude. The solids movement was related to the bubble pattern, and gas movement in the particular phase was related to the solids movement. At 15.2 cm/sec, the stable bubble pattern in the upper region of the bed left a persistent central area relatively bubble-free, and a pronounced solids downflow occurred in this area, associated with strong gas backmixing. At 24.4 cm/sec, however, an unstable bubble pattern with concomitant variation in solids flow regimes was evident. This was reflected by short-term variations

in the pressure profile recorded at the bed base. Since the overall pattern
of gas and solids mixing in large fluidized beds depends on the fluidizing
velocity, sampling in large beds (e.g., in coal combustion), will not be reliable
if it is not done systematically and extensively throughout the bed.

288. Particle Mixing in a Gas Fluidized Bed.

Baeyens, J.; Geldart, D.

Fluid. Ses. Appl., C.-R. Congr. Int. 1973, 182-95 (Pub. 1974).

289. Solids Mixing in Slugging Fluidized Beds.

Potter, O.E.; Thiel, W.

Fluid Technol. Proc. Int. Fluid Conf. 1975 (Pub. 1976), V.2,
185-92.

290. Solids Mixing in Fluidized Beds of Large Particles.

Cranfield, R.R.

69th AIChE Annu. Meet. (Chicago 11/28-12/2/76) Prepr. N. 103B,
20p.

291. Holdup, Mass Transfer, and Mixing in Three-Phase Fluidization.

Oestergaard, K.

69th AIChE Annu. Meet. (Chicago 11/28-12/2/76) Prepr. N. 119B,
10p.

292. Solids Mixing in Fluidized Bed of Large Particles.

Cranfield, R.R.

69th AIChE Annu. Meet. (Chicago 11/28-12/2/76).

293. Mixing of Phases in a Spouting Layer in the Liquid-Solid
System.

Zobrin, V.V.; Mukhlenov, I.P.; Gorshtein, A.E.

Izv Vyssh Uchebn Zaved Khim Khim Tekhnol, 1975, V.18, N.5, 825-7, in Russian.

294. Fluidization (And Mixing) Characteristics of Binary Solids Mixtures.

Chu, C.H.

Univ. West. Ont. (Canada), Diss. (1974) (Abstract) Diss. Abstract INT B V.35, N.3, 1242B (Sept. 1974).

295. A Technique for Studying the Mixing of Solid Particles in a Fluidized Bed.

Putilov, A.V.; Zhorov, Yu M.; Panchenkov, G.M.

Khim Tekhnol. Topl. Masel, V.18, N.7, 32-35 (1973), in Russian.

296. A Technique for Studying the Mixing of Solid Particles in a Fluidized Bed.

Putilov, A.V.; Panchenkov, G.M.; Zhorov, Yu M.

Khim. Tekhnol. Topl. Masel, N.7, 32-35 (1973) (Transl.) Int. Chem. Eng., V.14, N.1, 105-7 (Jan. 1974), in Russian.

297. Circulation and Mixing of a Solid Phase in a Fluidized Bed.

Shakhova, N.A.; Klassen, P.V.

Teor. Osn. Khim. Tekhnol., 1973, V.7, N.3, 457-60, in Russian.

298. Solids Mixing in Batch Operated, Tapered and Non-Tapered Gas Fluidized Beds.

Leipziger, S.; Lee, B.S.; Babu, S.P.; Weil, S.A.

65th AIChE Annu. Meet. (NY 11/26-30/72), AIChE Symp. Ser. V. 69, N.128, 49-57 (1973).

299. Role of Solid Mixing in Fluidized-Bed Reaction Kinetics.

Squires, A.M.

64th AIChE Annu. Meet. (San Francisco 1971), AIChE Symp. Ser.
V.69, N.128, 8-10 (1973).

300. The Effect of Solid Mixing on Noncatalytic Solid-Gas Reactions
in a Fluidized Bed.

Ishida, M.; Wen, C.Y.

64th AIChE Annu. Meet. (San Francisco 1971), AIChE Symp. Ser.
V.69, N.128, 1-7 (1973).

301. Fluid Mixing in Particulate Fluidized Beds.

Elgin, J.C.; Letan, R.

Chem. Eng. J. (London), 1972, V.3, N.2, 136-44.

302. Holdup and Axial Mixing Characteristics of Two- and Three-
Phase Fluidized Beds.

Baker, C.G.J.; Bergougnou, M.A.; Kim, S.D.

Can. J. Chem. Eng., V.50, N.6, 695-701 (Dec. 1972).

303. Fluctuational Methods for Determining the Coefficient of
Solid-Phase Mixing in a Two-Dimensional Fluidized-Bed Model.

Todes, O.M.; Sheinina, L.S.

Inzh-Fiz. Zh. 1972, V.22, N.4, 589-96, refer to Chemical
Abstract V77-22160, in Russian.

304. Holdup and Fluid Mixing in Gas-Liquid Fluidized Beds.

Michelsen, M.L.; Oestergaard, K.

Chem. Eng. J. (London), 1970, V. 1, N.1, 37-46.

305. The Mechanisms by Which Particles Segregate in Gas-Fluidized Beds....Binary Systems of Near-Spherical Particles.

Agbim, A.J.; Nienow, A.W.; Rowe, P.N.

Inst. Chem. Eng. "Mixing Powders Pastes + Non-Newtonian Fluids" Symp. (1/6/72) Trans. Inst. Chem. Eng., V.50, N.4, 310-23 (Oct. 1972).

306. Fluidizing Characteristics and Solids Mixing in Batch Operated Tapered and Non-Tapered Gas Fluidized Beds.

Babu, S.P.

Ill. Inst. Technol. Diss. (1971), 202p. (Abstract) Diss. Abstract INT B V. 33, N.3, 1151B (Sept. 1972).

307. The Interrelationship Between Bubble Motion and Solids Mixing in a Gas-Fluidized Bed.

Haines, A.K.; King, R.P.; Woodburn, E.T.

AIChE J., V.18, N.3, 591-99 (May 1972).

308. A Fluctuation Method for Determining the Effective Mixing (Diffusion) Coefficient of the Solid Phase in a Fluidized Bed and Analogous Systems.

Bogomaz, E.L.; Skvortsov, V.P.; Todes, O.M.; Bondareva, A.K.; Petrenko, I.I.; Sheinina, L.S.

Khim. Prom., N.7, 535-41 (1971) (Transl.) Int. Chem. Eng., V.12, N.2, 263-70 (Apr. 1972), in Russian.

309. Mixing in Fluidized Beds.

Bergougnou, M.A.

Br. Chem. Eng. Process Technol., V.17, N. 1, 5 (Jan. 1972).

310.   Procedure of Mixing and Combustion in a Gas-Solid Fluidized
Bed.

  Boehm, E.

  Verfahrenstechnik (Mainz), 1971, V.5, N.3, 102-8, in German.

311.   Fluctuation Method for Determining the Effective Mixing
(Diffusion) Coefficient of the Solid Phase in a Fluidized Bed and Analogous
Systems.

  Todes, O.M.; Petrenko, I.I.; Skvortsov, V.P.; Bogomaz, E.L.;
Sheinina, L.S.; Bondareva, A.K.

  Khim. Prom. (Moscow), 1971, V.47, N.7, 535-41, in Russian,
refer to Chemical Abstrict V75-89533.

312.   Algorithm for Calculation of Processes in a Fluidized Bed
Allowing for Mixing of the Solid Phase.

  Korsunskii, V.I.; Svetozarova, G.I.; Lyubimov, Yu K.

  Teor. Osn. Khim. Tekhnol, 1971, V.5, N.3, 408-16, in Russian,
Chemical Abstract V75-38453.

313.   Equation for the Mixing Coefficients of Solid Particles in
a Vibration Fluidized Bed.

  Jinescu, G.I.

  Rev. Chim. (Bucharest), 1971, V.22, N.3, 159-64, in Rumanian,
refer to Chemical Abstract V74-143720.

314.   Effect of Geometric Parameters of Gas-Distributing Networks
on the Fluidized-Bed Mixing of Material.

  Volkov, V.F.; Ukhlov, V.V.

  Izv. Vyssh. Ucheb. Zaved. Khim. Khim. Tekhnol, 1970, V.13,
N.7, 1042-5, in Russian.

315. Qualitative Study of Solid-Phase Mixing in a Fluidized Bed by a "Freezing" Method.

Budkov, V.A.; Maslovskii, M.F.; Prozorov, E.N.

Khim. Prom. (Moscow), V. 6, N. 3, 216-17 (1970), in Russian.

316. Gas-Solids Mixing and Heat Transfer Studies in Incipiently Fluidized Beds of Nonuniform Cross-Sectional Area.

Zenz, F.A.; Edwards, R.M.

Ind. Eng. Chem. Process Des. Develop, V.8, N.4, 598 (Oct. 1969)

317. Gas-Solids Mixing and Heat Transfer Studies in Incipiently Fluidized Beds of Nonuniform Cross-Sectional Area.

Edwards, R.M.; Miller, K.J.

Ind. Eng. Chem. Process Des. Develop, V.8, N.2, 232-40, (Apr. 1969).

318. Mixing of Solids in Gas-Solid Fluidized Beds.

Geyer, H.; Lehmann, W.; Mueller, F.; Pippel, W.; Runge, K.

Kammer Tech. Hochsch Magdeburg Joint "Fluidized Bed Technol" Mtg. (Magdeburg 9/11/68), Chem. Tech. (Berlin), V. 20, N.12, 750-55 (Dec.1968).

319. Investigation of a Multizone Apparatus Having (Two) Fluidize Beds with Limited Mixing.

Fraiman, R.S.; Luzanova, T.I.

Khim. Prom., V.44, N.9, 701-3 (1968).

320. Effect of a Gas-Distributor Grid on the Mixing of the Solid Phase and Heat Transfer in a Fluidized Bed.

Babenko, V.E.; Genin, L.S.; Goikhman, I.D.; Kaganovich Yu Ya Oigenblik, A.A.; Teminkov, V.I.

Khim. Prom., V.44, N.8, 615-18 (Aug. 1968).

321.   Solids Movement in Liquid Fluidized Beds -- 2.   Measurements of Axial Mixing Coefficients.

Carlos, C.R.; Richardson, J.F.

Chem. Eng. Sci., V.23, N.8, 825-31 (Aug. 1968).

322.   Mixing of Solids in Gas-Solid Fluidized Beds.(Equipment Design from Small-Scale Experiments).

Geyer, H.; Lehmann, W.; Mueller, F.; Pippel, W.; Runge, K.

Kammer Tech-Tech Hochschule Otto Von Guericke Joint Mtg. (Magdeburg 9/11-13/68).

323.   A Determination of the Solids Mixing Coefficient in a Gas Fluidized Bed.

Weislehner, G.

Chem. Ing. Tech., V.42, N.8, 524-30 (Apr. 1970).

324.   Experimental Investigation of Longitudinal Mixing of Solids in Gas-Solid Fluidized Bed Equipment.   Special Channels.

Lehmann, W.

3rd Int. Chem. Eng. Chem. Equip. & Automat. Congr. (Marienbad 9/15-20/69).

325.   The Mechanism of Mixing of Gas in a Fluidized Bed of Granular Material.

Kozlova, I.D.; Mukhlenov, I.P.

Zh. Prikl. Khim. V.42, N.10, 2251-53 (Oct. 1969).

326.   A Study of Solid-Phase Mixing in a Sectioned Fluidized Bed Apparatus.

Chernysheva, R.K.; Gazanchiyants, M.G.; Martyushin, I.G.; Morina, I.M.

Izv. Vyssh. Ucheb. Zaved Khim. I Khim. Tekhnol., V12, N.5, 664-67 (1969) (Translated in Int. Chem. Eng., V.10, N.1, 27-30 (Jan. 1970)).

327. (Axial) Mixing of Solids in Gas/Solid Fluidized Beds -- 2.

Mueller, F.; Schramm, W.; Zemitzsch, H.; Lehmann, W.

Chem. Tech. (Berlin), V.21, N.11, 682-86 (Nov. 1969).

328. Mixing in Packed and Fluidized Beds.

Gunn, D.J.

Chem. Eng. (London), N.219, CE153-CE172 (June 1968).

329. Study of the Intensity of Mixing of Solid Particles in Adjacent Fluidized Layers by a Nonstationary Method.

Baskakov, A.P.; Gimpelman, E.Ya.

Khim. Prom., V.44, N.6, 412-14 (June 1968).

330. Local Mixing of Solid Particles in (Multistage) Packed Fluidized Beds.

Schuegerl, K.

Eur. Federation Chem. Eng. Inter. "Fluidization" Symp. (Eindhoven Neth June 1967), Paper N. 9 5.

331. Experimental Comparison of the Mixing Processes in Different Two-Phase Flow Systems (i.e., Fluidized Beds and Bubble Columns).

Dibourn, M.; Schuegerl, K.

2nd Chisa Intern. Congr. (Marianske Lazne 1965), Chem. Tech. (Berlin), V.19, N.7, 403-7 (July 1967).

332.   An Investigation of Solids Distribution, Mixing, and
Contacting Characteristics of Gas-Solid Fluidized Beds -- 1. Study of Solid
Concentration Profiles in a Gas-Solid Fluidized Bed.

El Halwagi, M.M.; Gomezplata, A.

AIChE (Am. Inst. Chem. Engrs.) J., V.13, N.3, 503-12
(May 1967).

333.   Mixing Processes in Multiphase Flow Systems.

Schuegerl, K.

Ver Deut. Ingr. Verfahrenstech Ges. Tech. Reaktion Mtg.
(Bad Duerkheim 4/5-6/66), Abstract in Che. Ing. Tech., V.38, N.11, 1214
(Nov. 1966).

334.   Movement and Mixing of the Solid Particles in a Fluidized Bed.

Todes, O.M.; Bondareva, A.K.; Grinbaum, M.B.

Khim. Prom., V.42, N.6, 408-13 (June 1966).

335.   Axial Solids Mixing in Fluidized-Packed Beds.

Gabor, J.D.

58th Am. Inst. Chem. Engrs. Natl. Mtg. (Dallas 2/6-9/66),
Chem. Eng. Progr. Symp. Ser., V.62, N.67, 35-41 (1966).

336.   The Effects of Solids Mixing in Fluidized Beds and Solid-
Phase Conduction in Packed Beds on the Interpretation of Gas-Particle Heat
Transfer Measurements -- 1.   Models and Preliminary Data.

Littman, H.; Barile, R.G.

58th Am. Inst. Chem. Engrs. Natl. Mtg. (Dallas 2/6-9/66),
Chem. Eng. Progr. Symp. Ser., V.62, N.67, 10-27 (1966).

337. Annual Review/Mixing.

Oldshue, J.Y.

Ind. Eng. Chem., V.58, N.11, 50-57 (Nov. 1966).

338. Gas-Fluidized Beds -- 9. Solids Mixing in Gas-Fluidized Beds

Alfke, G.; Baerns, M.; Schiemann, G.; Schuegerl, K.

Dechema. Ann. Mtg. (Frankfurt 6/24/65), Chem.Ingr.Tech, V.38

N. 5, 553-60 (May 1966).

339. The Mixing of Solid Particles in a Fluidized Bed.

Jinescu, G.; Teoreanu, I.; Ruckenstein, E.

Can. J. Chem. Eng., V.44, N.2, 73-76 (Apr. 1966).

340. Mixing of the Gas Phase in a Fluidized Bed.

Planovskii, A.N.; Levin, B.D.; Lyandres, S.E.; Inozemtseva,

E.E.; Akopyan, L.A.

Khim I Tekhnol Topliv I Masel, V.11, N.3, 21-25 (Mar. 1966).

341. Kinetics of Sorption and Chemical Reaction Over a Catalyst

Having a Uniform Surface, In a Fluidized Bed Under Conditions of Complete

Mixing of Solids and Gas.

Rozental, A.L.; Lavrovskii, K.P.

Kinetika I Kataliz, V.7, N.1, 151-56 (Jan.-Feb. 1966).

342. The Mechanisms of Solids Mixing in Fluidized Beds.

Cheney, A.G.; Henwood, G.A.; Lyall, E.; Partridge, B.A.;

Rowe, P.N.

Trans. Inst. Chem. Engrs. (London), V.43, N.9, T271-86 (1965

343.   The Lateral Mixing Rate of Fluidized Solids Through Meshed
and Unmeshed Apertures.

Lochiel, A.C.; Sutherland, J.P.

Chem. Eng. Sci., V.20, N.12, 1041-53 (Dec. 1965).

344.   Solids Mixing Effects on Fluid-Particle Heat Transfer in
Fluidized Beds by Frequency Response Techniques.
Littman, H.; Barile, R.G.
58th Am. Inst. Chem. Engrs. Natl. Mtg., (Dallas 2/6-9/66).

345.   Lateral Transport in a Fluidized-Packed Bed -- 1. Solids
Mixing.

Gabor, J.D.

AIChE (Am. Inst. Chem. Engrs.) J., V.11, N.1, 127-29
(Jan. 1965).

346.   Solids Mixing in Straight and Tapered Fluidized Beds.
Littman, H.
47th Am. Inst. Chem. Engrs. Natl. Mtg. (Baltimore 5/20-23/62),
AIChE (Am. Inst. Chem. Engrs.) J., V.10, N.6, 924-29 (Nov. 1964).

347.   Some Segregation Effects in Packed-Fluidized Beds.
Sutherland, J.P.; Wong, K.Y.
Can. J. Chem. Eng., V.42, N.4, 163-67 (Aug. 1964).

348.   Homogeneous Fluidization: A Kinetic Theory of the
Homogeneous Fluidized Bed, and Its Application to Axial Mixing.
Ruckenstein, E.
Ind. Eng. Chem. Fundamentals, V.3, N.3, 260-68 (Aug. 1964).

349. A Resistance Probe Method for Determining Local Solid Particle Mixing Rates in a Batch Fluidized Bed.

>   Hayakawa, T.; Graham, W.; Osberg, G.L.

>   Can. J. Chem. Eng., V.42, N.3, 99-103 (June 1964).

350. Solids Mixing Studies in Gas Fluidized Beds -- 2. The Behavior of Deep Beds of Dense Materials.

>   Rowe, P.N.; Sutherland, K.S.

>   Trans. Inst. Chem. Engrs. (London), V.42, N.2, T55-T63

(Mar. 1964).

351. Mixing Processes in Fixed or Fluidized Beds.

>   Ruckenstein, E.; Teoreanu, I.

>   Zh. Prikl. Khim., V.36, N.11, 2426-32 (Nov. 1963).

III. HEAT TRANSFER IN FLUIDIZED BED SYSTEMS

352. Effect of Oxygen Transfer into Solid Catalyst on its State in a Fluidized Bed.

>   Makhotkin, O.A.; Ostrovskii, N.M.; Kuznetsov, Yu I.; Slinko, M.G

>   Dokl. Akad. Nauk SSSR, 249(2) (Phys. Chem.), 403-6 (1979),

in Russian.

353. Current Temperature of Particles of a High-Temperature Fluidized Bed of Corundum on the Heat Exchange Surface.

>   Pikashov, V.S.; Kuchin, G.P.; Makhorin, K.E.

>   Khim.Tekhnol. (Kiev), V. 6, 26-7 (1979), in Russian.

354. Experimental and Theoretical Investigations of Heat Transfer
Between a Gas-Solid Fluidized Bed and Immersed Tubes.

Grewal, N.S.

Univ. Ill. Chic. Circle, Diss. (1979), 350p, in English
Abstract INT. B, V. 40, N. 9, 4427B (Mar. 1980).

Abstract: Experimental heat transfer coefficients (hw) between an
electrically heated single horizontal tube and square air-solid fluidized
beds of glass beads, dolomite, sand, silicon carbide, and alumina particles
and the maximum value of hw were inadequately reproduced by existing tube-to-
bed heat transfer correlations.   New correlations are presented in the thesis.
Experimental results for the total heat transfer coefficient between 12.7 mm
copper tubes with four different rough surfaces and different-sized glass
beads suggested that the coefficient depended strongly on the ratio of roughness
pitch to the average particle diameter. Experimental data were obtained for the
heat transfer coefficient between horizontal smooth tube bundles (12.7 and 28.6
mm diameter. and V-thread finned tube bundles (28.6 mm diameter) and square beds
of silica sand and alumina (167-504 µm avg. diameter) as a function of air
fluidizing velocity.   An extension of a modified form of the alternate-slab
model of Gabor was used to evaluate the radiative contribution to the total
heat transfer from a high temperature fluidized bed system of air and sand to
an immersed surface.   The results were compared with other predictions and
experimental data.

355. Local Heat-Transfer Coefficients Around Horizontal Tubes in
(Air-) Fluidized Beds.

Chandran, R.; Chen, J.C.; Staub, F.W.

J. Heat Transfer, V.102, N.1, 152-57 (Feb. 1980).

Abstract: Local heat-transfer coefficients around horizontal tubes in
(air-) fluidized beds of glass beads (125-1580 µm diameter) were measured under

steady-state conditions at 100-400 kPa, both for a single tube and a ten-row

bare tube bundle. The local heat-transfer coefficients were strongly influenced

by angular position and gas flow rate, as well as by particle size and system

pressure. The heat transfer coefficients, averaged around the circumference

of the tube, showed a general tendency to increase with decreasing particle

size and increasing system pressure. The heat transfer coefficients for a tube

in an inner-row position within the bundle were slightly higher than those for

a tube in the bottom row. Comparisons of measured average coefficients with

published correlations showed poor agreement, with deviations up to several

hundred percent.

356.   Synopse/Einfluss der Stromungsmechanik Auf Den Warmeubergang

in Gas/Feststoff-Wirbelschichten.   Synopses/The Effect of the Flow Mechanics

on Heat Transfer in Gas/Solids Fluidized Beds.

Bock, H.J.; Molerus, O.

Verfahrens-Ing. Annu. Meet. (Nuernberg 9/26-28/79), Chem.

Ing. Tech., V.52, N.3, 260-61 (Mar. 1980), in German.

Abstract: Heat transfer was measured at single pipes or tube bundles

immersed vertically into fluidized beds in 19, 40, or 100 cm ID vessels with

porous and valve-plate air distributors. Measurements were made at various

radial and axial positions. Measured heat transfer coefficients reflected the

nonuniform distribution of the rising gas bubbles which provided intensive

mixing of solids relative to the heated surfaces, that is, zones of high

bubble concentrations moved towards the vessel axis with increasing height from

the distributor plate, and became less distinct with increasing gas loading.

A model describing nonsteady-state heat conductance, which related the heat

transfer coefficient to the degree of fluidization, material parameters of the

solids, the contact time, and the relative bubble content of the bed was

presented. The calculated heat-transfer coefficients were in good agreement

with measured values, including values measured in moving beds, where longer
contact times could be realized.

357. Heat and Mass Transfer in Fluidized Beds.

Martin, H.

Verfahrens-Ing. Annu. Meet. (Nuernberg 9/26-28/79), see·
Chem. Ing. Tech., V.52, N.3, 199-209 (Mar. 1980), in German.

Abstract: A model describing the particle-convective contribution to
the heat transfer at column inserts in fluidized beds is presented. It
expresses the particle-convective heat transfer coefficient as a function of
particle diameter, type of gas, temperature, pressure, volumetric heat capacity
of the particles, and bed porosity. Predicted temperature and pressure
dependences of the heat transfer coefficients were in good agreement with
available data for cylindrical surfaces in argon-fluidized coke, and anthracite
beds, and at copper spheres in fluidized sand and clay beds. Available methods
for calculating maximum fluidization velocity, bed expansion, and particle-to-
fluid heat and mass transfer were reviewed.

358. Plate Heat Exchanger with a Fluidized Bed.

Granier, M.; Couderc, J.P.

Univ. Compiegne 'Technol. Lits. Fluidises. Appl. Ind.',
Colloq. (10/22-23/79), Inf. Chim, N.198, 95-99 (Jan.-Feb. 1980), in French.

Abstract: Heat transfer between hot gas and a cooled vertical, plane
reactor wall through a two-dimensional fluidized bed of solid particles was
studied. The experimental column consisted of an air-preheating furnace and a
38 cm high and 8, 81, or 31 mm thick bed of 225, 450, or 715 μm diameter glass
beads fluidized by an upward flow of hot air from the furnace. The heat-exchange
coefficients, calculated from a thermal balance equation, increased to plateau
values with increasing air flow. As the bed thickness and particle diameter
decreased, heat transfer became very efficient. In addition, direct cine-

photographic observations were made. The study showed that a strong relation
between the heat exchange and the bubbling phenomenon in the fluidized bed
exists. Several theoretical heat transfer models were evaluated, and that of
Couderc et al. (Chem. Eng. Sci. 22:99 (1967)) yielded the best predictions of
heat transfer coefficients from hydrodynamic parameters of the beds.

359. The Influence of Jetting-Emulsion Mass and Heat Interchange
in a Fluidized-Bed Coal Gasifier.

Weimer, A.W.; Clough, D.E.

72nd AIChE Annu. Meet. (San Francisco 11/25-29/79), Prepr.
N. 26B, 45p.

Abstract: A model was developed for a low-pressure, steam-oxygen,
fluidized bed, coal-gasifying reactor. The model includes the effect of the
grid region and describes the adiabatic and continuous gasification of coal
particles by pyrolytic devolatilization and both heterogeneous and homogeneous
reactions. The bulk bubbling region of the bed is modeled according to a
modified two-phase theory which considers bubbles to be free of particles.
The bubbles are assumed to develop at the top of the jets and coalesce and grow
in size as they rise, and the emulsion phase consists of particles and the
surrounding interstitial gas. The dilute-phase jet and bubbles are assumed in
plug flow and the emulsion-phase gas and particles are assumed perfectly mixed
Simulations indicate that the jetting-emulsion mass and heat interchange has
a significant effect on overall carbon conversion, product gas composition, and
bed temperature close to the inlet gas distributor, i.e., an increase of inter
change increases carbon conversion. Changes in grid geometry which affect
interchange characteristics can eliminate the presence of hot spots caused by
rapid homogeneous combustion reactions within the jetting region.

360. Heat Transfer to an Endothermic Gas-Solid Reaction Using a
Particulate Heat Transfer Medium.

Hussein, F.D.; Maitra, P.P.; Jackson, R.

72nd AIChE Annu. Meet. (San Francisco 11/25-29/79), Prepr.
N. 26G,41p.

Abstract: Tests were conducted on preheated limestone chips and 2.3,
3.35, and 4.6 mm glass beads descending through an air-fluidized bed of 530 μm
diameter polystyrene beads. The experiments demonstrated the main features of
the mechanical behavior of these systems, which are being considered for supplying heat to endothermic gas-solid reactions, such as in the Battelle/Union
Carbide Ash Agglomerating and the Conoco CO_2 Acceptor Steam gasification of
coal. Experiments on a two-dimensional fluidized bed, with opaque balls
dropped singly or in groups on the surface of the bed, showed that the principal
ball descent mechanism involves the interaction of balls with the rising
bubbles. Descending balls tend to form clusters which then move down more
rapidly. Cluster formation may account for the decrease in residence time with
increasing ball feed rate. At high rates, the residence time passes through
a minimum and increases again as flooding is approached. As the ball holdup
increases, larger clusters form, and flooding occurs when one of these reaches
a critical size determined by the ability of the cluster to compact the bed
below it.

361. The Calculation of the Governing Equation for a Seriated
Unequal Velocity, Equal Temperature Two-Phase Continuum.

Lyczkowski, R.W.; Solbrig, C.W.

AIChE J., V.26, N.1, 89-98 (Jan. 1980).

Abstract: The authors show that the calculation of the governing
equation for a seriated unequal velocity, equal temperature two-phase continuum
such as encountered in fluidized beds can be accomplished by a simple implicit

iterative procedure. The equations can predict phase flow reversal, counter-current flow and flooding-like behavior. The procedure is illustated for problems involving the acceleration of an initially motionless stratified mixture of steam and water in a horizontal pipe at uniform pressure and energy the prediction of countercurrent flow and flow reversal in a vertical tube during a transient, and the analysis of the effect of wall heat flux on the phase flow transients in a vertical pipe. The performance of the present meth is compared with the equivalent equal phase velocity, equal phase temperature theory.

362.   Gas-Particle Heat Transfer in a Packed Fluidized Bed.

Kato, K.; Ito, H.; Omura, S.

J. Chem. Eng. Jap., V.12, N.5, 403-5 (Oct. 1979).

Abstract: Gas-particle heat transfer in a packed fluidized bed was measured by drying fluidized wet alumina particles in a bed of open-ended cylindrical wire nets of various sizes. Nusselt numbers for the gas-to-particle heat transfer were found to increase with increasing particle size, increasing particle Reynolds number, and decreasing bed height. An empirical relationship is reported.

363. Effect of Distributor Design on Heat Transfer from an Immersed Horizontal Tube in a Fluidized Bed.

Grewal, N.L.; Saxena, S.C.; Dolidovich, A.F.; Zabrodskii, S.

Chem. Eng. J. (Lausanne), V. 18, N. 3, 197-201 (1979).

364. Heat Transfer Mechanisms near Horizontal Heat Exchange Tubes in an Air Fluidized Bed of Uniformly Sized Glass Particles.

Krause, W.B.; Peters, A.R.

ASME, AIChE Jt. Heat Transfer Conf. (San Diego 8/6-8/79), Abstracted in Mech. Eng., N.79-HT-88, V.101, N.11, 102-8 (Nov. 1979).

365. An Analytical Study of Heat Transfer to a Horizontal Cylinder in a Large Particle Fluidized Bed.

George, A.H.; Welty, J.R.; Catipovic, N.M.

ASME - AIChE Jt. Heat Transfer Conf. (San Diego 8/6-8/79), Abstracted in Mech. Eng., N. 79-HT-78, V.101, N.11, 102-8 (Nov. 1979).

366. Heat Transfer to Horizontal Tubes in the Freeboard Region of a Gas-Fluidized Bed.

George, S.E.; Grace, J.R.

72nd AIChE Annu. Meet. (San Francisco 11/25-29/79), Prepr. N. 7E, 22p.

Abstract: Heat transfer to horizontal tubes in the freeboard region of a gas-fluidized bed was found to be nearly as favorable as in the bed proper when the tubes were in the splash zone immediately above the expanded bed surface. Fluidization was performed at 120-145°C using silica sand having average particle diameters of 102-890 μm and a density of 2630 kg/cu m with air flowing at up to 1.7 m/sec to give a static bed height of 0.22-0.75 m. The beds probably never reached the turbulent regime. For the larger particle sizes, the heat transfer coefficient decreased quickly with increasing height above the bed surface, approaching the values for particle-free air; and for the smallest particle size, the heat transfer coefficient did not approach the value for particle-free air with increasing height. The heat transfer coefficient decreased with increase in particle diameter from 100 to 900 μm, and the decrease with distance above the bed was less rapid at higher air velocities. For the shallower bed, heat transfer coefficients for a single tube were up to 20% lower than the wide pitch bundle. For the deeper bed, single tube transfer coefficients were lower than coefficients for the wide pitch bundle up to air velocities of 0.55 m/sec, above which the single tube transfer coefficients were between those of the wide and narrow pitch bundles.

367. <u>Heat Transfer Between a Fluidized Bed and an Immersed Vertic</u>
<u>U-Tube</u>.

Saxena, S.C.; Chatterjee, A.

Energy (Oxford), V. 4, N. 2, 349-56 (1979).

368. <u>Heat Transfer to Horizontal Tubes in Fluidized Beds Experim</u>
<u>and Theory</u>.

Catipovic, N.M.

Oregon State Univ., Diss. (1979), 242p, Diss. Abstract INT.
B V.40, N.2, 845B (Aug. 1979), in English.

<u>Abstract</u>:   The thesis reports the results of experiments conducted in a
fluidized bed of 0.48 m x 0.13 m cross-section with air as the fluidizing gas
at room temperature and 1 atm with a single immersed tube and with a closely
spaced tube array for particle sizes of 0.37-6.6 mm and superficial gas velocities of 0.1-5.6 m/sec. Voidage at the tube surface varied much less with
gas velocity than did the overall bed voidage. The gas convective component
of heat transfer was found to be unaffected by the superficial velocity. The
Adams analytical model of heat transfer for large particles gave accurate
predictions of local instantaneous and time-averaged coefficients, with and
without the presence of bubbles. A theoretical model was developed in which
heat exchange occurs by three parallel paths, namely, by packets of particles,
by gas percolating between the particles and the tube surface, and by gas
bubbles or slugs. Correlations were derived for the corresponding particle
convective, gas convective, and bubble heat transfer coefficients, as well as
for the voidage around the tube. The theoretical predictions agreed with the
reported experimental results and with published data for intermediate and
large particles.

369. Heat Transfer Between a Gas-Solid Fluidized Bed and a Small
Immersed Surface.

Richardson, J.F.; Shakiri, K.J.

Chem. Eng. Sci., V.34, N.8, 1019-29 (1979).

Abstract: Mean heat transfer coefficients from a small electrically
heated element to beds of powders (i.e., 25-520 μm glass ballotini, Diakon,
a cracking catalyst, and aluminum dust) fluidized by gas (i.e., hydrogen,
air, carbon dioxide, and Freon 12) were measured as a function of gas velocity
at bed static pressures of 0.03-1.48 MPa. For all conditions, the heat transfer
coefficients showed the same general dependence on gas flow rate, generally
passing through a maximum and a minimum. A general relationship between the
maximum Nusselt number (0.10-0.80), Galileo number (1-220) and the Prandtl
number of the gas was derived. From a plot of the element temperature versus
time, the corresponding instantaneous values of the heat transfer coefficient
were calculated. At any gas flow rate, the mean heat transfer coefficient
could be expressed in terms of the coefficient at the incipient fluidization
point and a term characterizing the fluctuations. The effects of particle and
gas properties, gas pressure, and of particle shape on heat transfer are discussed.

370. Heat Transfer Between Gas Fluidized Bed and Vertical Tubes.

Kim, S.D.

Hwahak Konghak, V. 17, N. 2, 85-98 (1979).

371. Heat Transfer Between A Gas Fluidized Bed and Immersed Tubes.

Saxena, S.C.; Grewal, N.S.; Gabor, J.D.; Zabrodskii, S.S.;
Galershtein, D.M.

Adv. Heat Transfer, V. 14, 149-247 (1978).

372.   Mechanism of Coal Combustion and Sulfur Removal in a
Fluidized Bed with a Submerged Heat Exchanger.

Lorkiewicz, Z.; Tomeczek, J.

Zesz. Nauk. Politech. Slask., Energ., V. 68, 143-50 (1978), in
Polish.

373.   Energy Storage in Fluidized Beds.

Harker, J.H.; Hindmarch, C.E.

J. Inst. Energy, V.52, N.410, 45-48 (Mar. 1979).

Abstract: Preliminary experiments were carried out to determine the
amount of heat which can be stored and recovered by fluidizing a 75 mm diameter
bed of 80-530 μm ballotini particles with hot and cold air. Even with the
modest lagging used (25 mm thick sheet of woven fiber glass) losses were
negligible for about 40 min. when the bed was at 330°K and for 10 min. when
the bed was at 490°K. Losses increased with a decrease in bed height. The
recovery efficiency tended to decrease at higher bed temperatures, presumably
owing to greater heat losses, though an optimum value would seem likely since
a decrease in bed temperature reduces the capacity of the system. The geometry
of the bed appeared to be an important factor; in particular, the bed height-
to-width ratio (where the maximum volume of bed with the minimum surface area
occurs) proved to be a beneficial means of reducing heat losses during storage

374.   Heat Transfer/Particle Size Effects in Fluidized-Bed
Combustion.

Golan, L.P.; Cherrington, D.C.; Diener, R.; Scarborough, C.
Weiner, S.C.; Exxon Research & Engineering Co.; U.S. Department of Energy.

Chem. Eng. Prog., V.75, N.7, 63-72 (July 1979).

Abstract: As part of a joint U.S. Department of Energy and Exxon

Research & Engineering Co. study of fluidized-bed combustion for indirect-fired

process heaters, experiments involving variations in limestone particle sizes

(top sizes, 1410-5600 μm with wide and narrow distributions), 25 and 45 cm

tube-to-grid spacings, and bed inventories (25-52 cm above the grid) were

performed to determine the effect of these factors on heat transfer to an

optimum tube bundle configuration. The presence of finer material in the

particle blends was the major factor in reducing heat transfer. It was found

that the larger particles had minor effects; and the overall size distribution

had little effect. Measured head transfer coefficients correlated well with

the bundle space velocity/minimum fluidization velocity ratio. The tube-to-

grid spacing, or the bed inventory, did not affect significantly the bed-to-

tube heat transfer coefficients. The study involved four limestone blends,

variable fluidization air rates of up to 290 cu m/min, and several arrangements

of the 10 cm tubes.

375.   Synopses/Heat Transfer Between a Fluidized Bed and Internals..
A Problem of Heat Transfer During Short Contact Times.

Heyde, M.; Klocke, H.J.

Verfahrens-Ing. Annu. Meet. (Aachen 9/27-29/78), see Chem.
Ing. Tech., V.51, N.4, 318-19 (Apr. 1979), in German.

Abstract: Relationships were developed for calculating the optimum gas

rate and the corresponding heat transfer coefficient for heating or cooling

coils in fluidized beds for any technically applicable bed height. Predictions

were within $\pm$ 20% of measured values at 30° - $1000^{\circ}C$ and 1-7 bar for beds of

7-600 cm diameter, 100-4400 sq. mm heat exchange surfaces, and 1000-11,000 kg/cu

m solids concentrations, and with air, nitrogen, carbon dioxide, ammonia,

hydrogen, and their mixtures as the fluidizing media.

376. <u>Industrial Application Fluidized Bed Combustion. Category</u>
<u>III. Indirect Fired Heaters. Monthly Technical Report No. 10, August 1-31,</u>
<u>1977.</u>

Cherrington, D.C.

U.S. Dept. Commerce Natl. Tech. Inf. Serv. Report No. FE-2471-14 (15 Sept. 1977), 11p, in English, refer to ERDA Energy Res. Abstract V-3-43483 (1978).

377. <u>Investigations of Heat Transfer from Immersed Tubes in a</u>
<u>Fluidized Bed.</u>

Grewal, N.S.; Saxena, S.C.

Proc. Natl. Heat Mass Transfer Conf., 4th, 53-8 (1977).

378. <u>Aerodynamics of the Fluidizing Agent in Heterogeneous</u>
<u>Fluidized Systems.</u>

Doitchev, K.; Boitchev, G.

God. Vissh. Khim.-Tekhnol. Inst., Sofia 23(3) 91-8 (1978), in Bulgarian, refer to Chemical Abstract No. 106328, V.90, N.13-14.

379. <u>Synopses/Heat Transfer Between Gas-Fluidized Beds and</u>
<u>Vertical Heat Exchanger Surfaces.</u>

Wunder, R.; Mersmann, A.

Verfahrensing. Annu. Meet. (AACHEN 9/27-29/78), see Chem. Ing. Tech., V.51, N.3, 241 (Mar. 1979), in German.

<u>Abstract</u>:   The results of experiments performed with glass, aluminum, porous polymer, lead, and other spheres and irregular particles fluidized in 80, 200, and 690 mm diameter beds heated with a central copper rod, are reported. The heat transfer at the solid particle was modeled under the assumption that the gas layer is constantly renewed. The heat transfer was relatively insensitive

to the design parameters compared with its responses to operating parameters,

e.g., a gas velocity change from twice the minimum fluidization velocity to the

solids discharge velocity for a bed of 0.05 mm particles varied the heat

transfer coefficient by a factor larger than that obtainable by any change

(40-fold or more) in particle size. The change in the heat transfer coefficient

obtained by varying the flow mechanics was comparable with the influence of

material parameters in an air-fluidized bed when the temperature was increased

from 200° to 800°C.

380. Heat Transfer from a Flat Surface to a Two-Phase Fluidized Bed.

Mrowiec, M.; Pabis, A.

Tub-Dok. Aktuell (2, Verfahrenstech. Chem. Apparatebau),

249-75 (1978), in Polish.

381. Heat Transfer in Three-Phase Fluidized Beds.

Baker, C.G.J.; Armstrong, E.R.; Bergougnou, M.A.

Powder Technol., V. 21, N. 2, 195-204 (1978).

382. Mechanisms of Momentum and Heat Transfer Between Gas Jets

and Fluidized Beds.

Donadono, S.; Massimilla, L.

Fluid., Proc. Eng. Found. Conf., 2nd, 375-80 (1978), in

English.

383. Mechanical Stirring of Fluidized Beds Potential Improvements

in the Control of Heat Transfer.

Rios, G.; Gibert, H.

Fluid., Proc. Eng. Found. Conf., 2nd, 357-61 (1978).

384.   Heat Transfer Between a Fluidized Bed and a Small Immersed
Surface.

Khan, A.R.; Richardson, J.F.; Shakiri, K.J.

Fluid., Proc. Eng. Found. Conf., 2nd, 351-6 (1978).

385.   Measuring Particle Temperature and Emissivity in a High
Temperature Fluidized Bed.

Makhorin, K.E.; Pikashov, V.S.; Kuchin, G.P.

Fluid., Proc. Eng. Found. Conf., 2nd, 93-7 (1978).

386.   Lateral Thermal Diffusivities in Packed Fluidized Beds of
Horizontal Flow Type.

Hirama, T.; Yumiyama, M.; Tomita, M.; Yamaguchi, H.

Kagaku Kogaku Rombunshu, 3(4), 344-8 (1977), refer to
Japanese Chemical Abstract No. 40738, V.90, N.5-6.

387.   An Investigation of the Heat Transfer Mechanisms Around
Horizontal Bare and Finned Heat Exchange Tubes Submerged in an Air-Fluidized
Bed of Uniformly Sized Particles.

Krause, W.B.

Univ. Nebraska- Lincoln, Diss. (1978), 160p, in English,
(Abstract) Diss. Abstract INT. B V.39, N.8, 3982B-3983B (Feb. 1979).

Abstract: The heat transfer coefficient between the heated bare tube and
the fluidized bed and the convective heat transfer coefficient on the sides
of the tube were determined in this study. The results correlated well with
the Mickley-Fairbanks packet theory and Ziegler particle theory. Selected
serrated finned tubes showed better heat transfer capacity than did bare tubes
for similar fluidization conditions. Fin efficiency and fin effectiveness
factors were determined as a function of mass velocity and a fin length parameter

Surface heat transfer coefficients were found to be a function of the bed
particle size, density, and thermophysical properties, and on the fluid velocity
and thermophysical properties, the temperature difference between the tube
surface and the bulk medium, and the tube geometry. The data for bare heat
exchange tubes were correlated in a manner similar to fluid flow past a cylinder.
Heat transfer coefficients for the finned tubes were found by accounting for
radial fin temperature distribution. No general phenomenological model could
be developed due to the large numer of variables involved.

388. Effect of Tube Bank and Gas Density on Flow Behavior and
Heat Transfer in Fluidized Beds.

Staub, F.W.; Canada, G.S.

Fluid., Proc. Eng. Found. Conf., 2nd, 339-44 (1978), Schenect-
ady, NY, refer to Chem. Abstract, Abstract No. 8257, V.90, N.1-2.

389. Heat Transfer to Surfaces Immersed in Fluidized Beds,
Particularly Tube Arrays.

Xavier, A.M.; Davidson, J.F.

Fluid., Proc. Eng. Found. Conf., 2nd, 333-8 (1978), Cambridge,
England.

390. Wall-to-Bed Heat Transfer in a Fluidized Bed.

Hoebink, J.H.B.;   Rietema, K.

Fluid., Proc. Eng. Found. Conf., 2nd, 327-32 (1978), refer to
English Chem. Abstract, Abstract No. 8255, V.90, N.1-2.

391. Lateral Thermal Diffusivities in Packed Fluidized Beds of
Horizontal Flow Type.

Hirama, T.; Yumiyama, M.; Tomita, M.; Yamaguchi, H.

Heat Transfer - Japanese Res., V. 7, N. 1, 74-81 (1978).

392. Heat Transfer from the Surface of a Body Fixed in a Fluidized Bed.

Yasutomi, T.; Yokota, S.

Kagaku Kogaku Rombunshu V. 2, N. 2, 205-11 (1976), refer to Japan Chemical Abstract, Abstract No. 8249, V.90, N.1-2.

393. Heat Transfer from Wall to Packed and Fluidized Bed for Gas-Liquid Cocurrent Up-Flow.

Kato, Y.; Ohshima, S.; Kago, T.; Morooka, S.

Kagaku Kogaku Rombunshu V. 4, N. 3, 328-30 (1978).

394. Heat Transfer Between a Dispersed System and a Vertical Heating or Cooling Surface.

Mersmann, A.B.; Wunder, R.

Heat Transfer, Int. Heat Transfer Conf., 5th, V. 4, 31-6 (1978). Munich, Germany.

395. Particle-Fluid Heat Transfer in Fixed and Fluidized Beds.

Pandey, D.K.; Upadhyay, S.N.; Gupta, S.N.; Mishra, P.

J. Sci. Ind. Res., V. 37, N. 5, 224-49 (1978).

396. Heat Transfer in the Fluidized Bed.

Druga, L.; Wanyorek, C.

Constr.Mas. V. 30, N. 2, 80-1 (1978), see Rumanian Chemical Abstrac Abstract No. 181594, V.89, N.22.

397. Gas Convective Heat Transfer to Packed and Fluidized Beds.

Botterill, J.S.M.; Denloye, A.O.O.

69th AIChE Annu. Meet. (Chicago Nov.-Dec. 1976), AIChE Symp. Ser., V.74, N.176, 194-202 (1978), in English.

398. Large-Particle Fluidization and Heat Transfer at High Pressures.

Canada, G.S.; McLaughlin, M.H.

69th AIChE Annu. Meet. (Chicago Nov.-Dec. 1976), AIChE Symp.
Ser., V.74, N.176, 27-37 (1978), in English.

Abstract: Two-phase flow and heat transfer data were reported for
closed-loop air and R-12 fluidized beds of 650 or 2600 μm glass beads, extending
previous 1 atm test results. Heat transfer data were obtained with 3.2 cm OD
bare tubes in 5 and 10 row banks; the tubes were located in a staggered pitch
array. Results showed that the average heat transfer coefficient tends to
decrease by 20% when the particle diameter is increased from 650 to 2600 μm.
The heat transfer coefficient is not a strong function of bed depth and is
relatively insensitive to the height of the bed for both particle sizes. There
is less indication of apparent slug flow in open bed runs at 5 and at 10 atm
than at 1 atm. There is a more gradual transition from bubbly flow through a
mixed flow regime to turbulent flow. The heat transfer coefficients increase
with increasing pressure but the general variation of the average heat transfer
coefficient as a function of the ratio of superficial gas-to-thermal velocities
is about the same at all pressures and gas flows.

399. Average Residence Times of Emulsion and Void Phases at the
Surface of Heat Transfer Tubes in Fluidized Beds.

Ozkaynak, T.F.; Chen, J.C.

15th AIChE Natl. Heat Transfer Con., (San Francisco Aug. 1975),
AIChE Symp. Ser., V.74, N.174, 334-43 (1978).

400. An Experimental Study of Heat Transfer from Plain and
(Helical) Finned Tubes in (Air-) Fluidized Beds.

Chen, J.C.; Withers, J.G.

15th AIChE Natl. Heat Transfer Conf. (San Francisco, Aug.
1975), AIChE Symp. Ser., V.74, N.174, 327-33 (1978).

Abstract: Fluidized solids consisting of glass beads 60.005-0.024 in. average diameter, were used in this study. The bedside heat transfer coefficients were obtained for eight different test sections, including two different plain tubes and four different finned copper tubes. General behavior was similar for finned tubes and the plain tubes with the highest heat transfer occurring in the bed of smallest diameter particles. The heat transfer coefficients for finned tubes were generally 0.5 to 1.2 times those for plain tubes operating under similar fluidized conditions. The optimum geometry depended on the particle size, fin height, fin gap, and also on the excess air mass velocity

401. Heat Transfer from Spiral Tubing in an Air-Fluidized Bed.

Genetti, W.E.; Everly, D.

71st AIChE Annu. Meet. (Miami Heach 11/12-16/78), Paper No. 46F, 20p, in English.

Abstract: Heat transfer data was obtained from coiled spiral and plain copper tubes (7 in. ID coil) in an air-fluidized bed of glass beads (0.0076, 0.0109, and 0.0164 in. average diameter). Measurements were made to determine the effect of groove depth, number of flutes, flute pitch, and air mass velocity on heat transfer. The heat transfer coefficients generally increased with increasing fluidizing velocity, reaching a maximum at high air mass velocities and then decreasing. The coefficients increased with decreasing particle size for all geometries. The spiral tube with four flutes gave the best heat transfer duty, with gains as large as 40% over plain tubes. A correlation based on a particle mode mechanism fit the data within the range of experimental error

402. Particle Temperature Measurement in a Gas-Solid Fluidized Bed

Singh, A.N.; Ferron, J.R.

Chem. Eng. J. (Lausanne), V. 15, N. 3, 169-78 (1978), in English.

403. Study on the Heat Transfer of Gas-Solid Suspensions. Part 1.

Effects of Free Turbulence on Heat Transfer.

Maeda, M.; Saigusa, T.; Ikai, S.

Nippon Kikai Gakkai Rombunshu, 42(355), 866-76 (1976), refer

to Japanese Chemical Abstract, Abstract No. 76804, V.89, N.10.

404. Moving Bed Heat Transfer for Advanced Energy Applications.

Thornton, T.A.; Schluderberg, D.C.

Proc. Condens. Pap. - Miami Int. Conf. Alternative Energy

Sources, 837-7 (1977).

405. Temperature Distribution of Particles in Continuous Fluidized

Beds.

Lu, W.M.; Huang, C.G.

J. Chin. Inst. Chem. Eng. V. 8, N. 2, 155-64 (1977), in English.

406. Prediction of Temperature Profiles in Fluid Bed Boilers.

Hodges, J.L.; Hoke, R.C.; Bertrand, R.; Exxon Research

& Engineering Co.

AIChE, ASME Heat Transfer Conf. (St. Louis 8/9-11/76),

Paper N. 76-HT-66, in J. Heat Transfer, V.100, N.3, 508-13 (Aug. 1978), in

English.

Abstract: Data from Exxon Research & Engineering Co.'s pilot-scale

pressurized fluid bed boiler indicate that the arrangement and orientation

of internal boiler tubes has a strong influence on the measured bed temperature

profile. Horizontally oriented tubes yield much steeper temperature gradients

than vertical tubes. Excessive vertical temperature gradients in coal-fired

fluid bed boilers can either limit coal feed rates or result in the formation

of agglomerates of solid materials, which are destructive of bed internals.

A backmixing model for solids recirculation was developed, which may be useful in the design of large-scale commercial fluid bed boilers. The concept of a solids mixing height was extended to estimate solid movements in fluids with immersed tubes. The solids mixing height and vertical boiler tube dimensions were correlated and showed good agreement between theoretical and experimental bed temperature profiles.

407. Bed to Surface Heat Transfer in a Fluidized Bed of Large Particles.

Denloye, A.O.O.; Botterill, J.S.M.

Powder Technol., V. 19, N. 2, 197-203 (1978).

408. Transfer of Heat or Mass to Particles in Fixed and Fluidized Beds.

Gunn, D.J.

Int. J. Heat Mass Transfer, V.21, N.4, 467-76 (Apr. 1978).

Abstract: The author gives a correlation of the Nusselt number with Reynolds number, Prandtl number, and bed porosity (valid in the 0.35-1.0 porosity range). The correlation was derived on the basis of a stochastic model of the fixed bed. The analysis considered the interaction of convection, conduction, and interphase transfer based on statistical properties of the flow field and the diffusion field. The analysis shows that the Nusselt number approaches a constant value with decreasing Reynolds number. Available heat and mass transfer data for air and water in fixed beds were predicted accurately above Re = 500; at lower Reynolds numbers, experimental points were scattered owing to a low sensitivity of the experimental response to the Nusselt number. Heat and mass transfer at single spheres were correctly predicted for Re > 20. For fluidized beds, the increased bed porosity was approximately balanced by the particle Reynolds number.

409. Heat Transfer from the Surface of a Body Fixed in a Fluidized Bed.

    Yasutomi, T.; Yokota, T.

    Heat Transfer - Japanese Res. V. 6, N. 3, 26-35 (1977).

410. Heat Transfer in a Fluidized Bed.

    Bukur, D.B.

    Kem. Ind. V. 26, N. 4, 161-7 (1977), refer to Serbo-Croat. Chem. Abstract No. 107293, V.88, N.16.

411. Advances in Liquid Fluidized-Bed Heat Exchanger Development.

    Grimmett, E.S.; Fanous, A.F.; Allen, C.A.

    Am. Soc. Mech. Eng., (Paper) 77-HT-66 (1977), 11p.

412. Research Needs in Heat Transfer for a Rational Design of Fluidized-Bed Gasifier and Combustors.

    Wen, C.Y.

    Dep. Fluid., Therm. Aerosp. Sci. Rep. FTAS/TR (Case Western Reserve Univ.), FTAS/TR-75-117, Workshop Heat Mass Transfer Porous Media, PB-252, 387, 153-61 (1974).

413. Mechanical Stirring of Gas Fluidized Beds. II. Thermal Study in Steady Operation.

    Rios, G.; Gibert, H.; Couderc, J.P.

    Chem. J. (Lausanne), V. 13, N. 2, 111-18 (1977), in French.

414. Heat Transfer to Vertical Gas-Solid Suspension Flows.

    Matsumoto, S.; Ohnishi, S.; Maeda, S.

    38th Soc. Chem. Eng. Japanese Annu. Meet. (Tokyo Apr. 1973), J. Chem. Eng. Japan, V.11, N.2, 89-95 (Apr. 1978).

Abstract: Air velocity profiles, radial particle concentration distributions, frequency of particle collisions with the wall, and inlet and outlet
temperatures in a heated section of vertical copper tube were measured for
12,000-24,000 Reynolds air flows, with and without 72-1130 μm glass and copper
beads at solids loading ratios up to 10:1. The velocity profiles were not
affected by solids up to a 5:1 loading ratio. The 181 μm and 72 μm glass beads
concentrated near the tube center. Particle collisions with the tube wall were
found not to affect the heat transfer rate at the wall. The total heat transfer
rate increased when solids were added to the gas flow, but the heat transfer to
the gas phase decreased. Heat transfer coefficients for the glass beads
decreased with increasing loading ratio to about 3:1, and then increased. For
copper beads they decreased monotonically. A generalized correlation for the
heat transfer coefficient at the wall of a reactor such as a fluid catalytic
cracking or reforming unit, was derived and verified using literature data.

415.   A Theoretical Model of Heat Transfer to a Packed or Quiescent
Fluidized Bed.

Botterill, J.S.M.; Denloye, A.O.O.

Chem. Eng. Sci., V.33, N.4, 509-15 (1978).

Abstract: The authors present a theoretical model describing the heat
transfer between an immersed heater and unrestrained packed or quiescent
fluidized bed. The bed was divided into two regions of constant bed voidage
and gas velocity: a region of increased voidage close to the heat transfer
surface; and the area outside this. Heat transfer was assumed to take place
by steady-state conduction, and effective conductivities were used to characterize the heat transfer in both regions. Experimental measurements were made with
air and copper (620 μm diameter) and sand (1020 and 2370 μm diameter) particles.
The measured packed bed to surface heat transfer coefficient was observed to
increase linearly with the particle Reynolds number over the range of experimenta

variables studied. The predictions of the proposed model agreed with the packed

bed results and were also in agreement with the experimental quiescent bed

coefficients within 25%.

416.   Liquid Fluidized Bed Heat Exchanger - Horizontal Configuration
Experiments and Data Correlations.

    Allen, C.A.; Fukuda, O.; Grimmett, E.S.; McAtee, R.E.

    Proc. - Inteosoc. Energy Convers. Eng. Conf., 12 Vol. 1, 824-31
(1977).

417.   Fluidized Bed Combustion for Industrial Applications Process
Heaters.

    Cherrington, D.C.; Golan, L.P.; Halow, J.S.; Hammitt, F.G.

    Prepr. AIChE Paper, Natl. Heat Transfer Conf., 17th, 9-14
(1977).

418.   Heat Transfer in a Fluidized Countercurrent Bed.   Interim
Report, November 1976 - January 1977.   Contract EX-76-C-01-2231.

    Jackson, R.

    U.S. Dept. Commerce Natl. Tech. Inf. Serv. Rep. N. FE-2231-3
(Feb. 1977), 15p, see ERDA Energy Res. Abstract V-2-47131 (1977).

419.   Model Studies of Tube to Bed Heat Transfer in a Vibro-
Fluidized Bed.

    Kosenko, G.D.; Reshetnikov, E.G.; Syromyatnikov, N.I.;
Sapozhnikov, B.G.

    Inst. Fuel Symp. Ser. (London) 1(Fluid. Combust.), B4/1-B4/5
(1977).

420. <u>Towards More Versatile Fluidized-Bed Heat Exchangers.</u>

Sanderson, P.R.; Howard, J.R.

Appl. Energy, V. 3, N. 2, 115-25 (1977).

421. <u>Heat Transfer in Liquid-Fluidized Beds.</u>

Ipfelkofer, R.; Blenke, H.

Verfahrens. Ing. Annu. Meet. (Stuttgart, Germany 9/28-30/77),
see also Chem. Ing. Tech., V.50, N.3, 212 (Marc. 1978), in German.

<u>Abstract</u>: The authors made heat transfer measurements in a 15 mm diameter stainless steel tube that was heated electrically (1.5-130 w/sq cm) and was placed horizontally in a water-fluidized glass bead bed initially at 15°, 50°, and 66°C. In the nonboiling region, local mass transfer was much greater at the underside than at the upper side of the tube. In the subcooled boiling region, upward and downward heat transfer became more uniform, but was less in the fluidized bed than in a flow of pure water. In full bubble boiling, transfer differences between the fluidized bed and pure water flow disappeared. The results were correlated by a dimensionless relationship.

422. <u>Heat Transfer from a Simulated Plate Element to Liquid-Fluidized Beds.</u>

Romani, M.N.

Proc. Pak. Acad. Sci., V. 12, N. 2, 77-84 (1975).

423. <u>Heat Transfer. 3. Heat Transfer in Stationary and Fluidized Packed Beds.</u>

Bauer, R.; Muchowski, E.; Schluender, E.U.

Fortschr. Verfahrenstech., Abt. A 14, 54-9 (1976), in German.

424.   An Analytical Model of Heat Transfer to a Horizontal

Cylinder Immersed in a Gas Fluidized Bed.

Adams, R.L.

Oregon State Univ., Dissertation (1977).   See Abstract INT.

B V.38, N.6, 2799B (Dec. 1977).

Abstract: The model was developed taking into account flow within

attached bubbles and within the interstitial voids but neglecting gas property

variations.   The interstitial flow is approximated as flow within a series of

double-cusped channels and analyzed by a Stokes approximation for the corner

boundary layer flow matched to a two-dimensional integral analysis for the flow

in the central region.   Radiative heat transfer from hot particles was included

to extend the model to combustion conditions.   Computer calculations by the

model of heat convection for a horizontal cylinder immersed in a bubbling two-

dimensional bed gave results that were in agreement with published data.   The

presence of a single bubble having a diameter equal to the cylinder diameter

had little effect on the total heat transfer but did affect the local Nusselt

number distribution.

425.   Heat Transfer and Combustion in Centrifugal Fluidized Beds.

Broughton, J.; Elliott, D.E.

Inst. Chem. Eng. Symp. Ser. (High Temp. Chem. React. Eng.),

V. 43, N. 11 (1975), 6p.

426.   Heat Transfer in a Gas-Fluidized Bed Assisted by an

Alternating Electric Field.

Elsdon, R.; Shearer, C.J.

Chem. Eng. Sci., V.32, N.10, 1147-53 (1977).

427. Fluidized Bed Combustion as an Example of the Performance
of Exothermic Gas-Solid Reactions in a Fluidized Bed Reactor.

Janssen, K.; Schilling, H.D.

Inst. Chem. Eng. Symp. Ser. (High Temp. Chem. React. Eng.),
V.43, 7 (1975), 9p, in German.

428. Fluidized Bed Combustion for the Stirling Engine.

Thring, R.H.

Int. J. Heat Mass Transfer, V.20, N.9, 911-18 (Sept. 1977),
in English.

429. Steam Gasification of Coal in an Indirectly Heated Fluidized
Bed.

Feistel, P.P.; Van K.H.; Juenthen, H.

Inst. Chem. Eng. Symp. Ser. (High Temp. Chem. React. Eng.),
V.43, N.9, (1975), 9p, in English.

430. Heat Transfer Between a Single Sphere and a Vibrated
Fluidized Bed.

Lu, W.M.; Chen, C.C.; Chiu, C.S.

J. Chin. Inst. Chem. Eng., V.7, N.2, 83-94 (1976), in English

431. Investigation of Heat Transfer Coefficient Pulsations and of
the Mechanism of Heat Transfer from a Surface Immersed into a Fluidized Bed.

Baskkakov, A.P.; Vitt, O.K.; Kirakosyan, V.A.; Maskaev, V.K.
Filippovskii, N.F.

Fluid. Ses. Appl., C-R Congr. Int. 1973, 293-302 (Pub. 1974)

432. Fluidized Bed Heat Transfer...The Packet Theory Revisited.

Thomson, W.J.; Selzer, V.W.

68th AIChE Annu. Meet. (Los Angeles 1975), AIChE Symp. Ser.

V.73, N.161, 29-37 (1977).

433. Heat Transfer from Helical Finned Tubes in a Fluidized Bed.

Genetti, W.E.; Kratovil, M.T.

83rd AIChE Natl. Meet. (Houston 3/20-24/77), Paper No. 4B,

32p.

434. Heat Exchange in a Three-Phase System with Fluidized Bed.

Durych, A.; Wiechowski, A.

Inz. Chem. 1976, V.6, N.1, 71-9, in Polish.

435. Heat Transfer Between a Heated Surface and a Fluidized Bed

in Sublimation.

Vitovec, J.

Chem. Eng. J. (Lausanne), 1975, V.10, N.3, 235-9, in English.

436. Gas Convective Heat Transfer in Fluidized Beds.

Botterill, J.S.M.; Denloye, A.O.O.

Int. Congr. Chem. Eng. Chem. Equip. Des. Autom. (Proc.),

5th, 1975 D D3.5, 11pp.

437. New Fields of Fluidization Employment for Intensification

of Heat-Mass Transfer Processes.

Karpensko, A.I.; Sydromyatnikov, N.I.; Vasanova, L.K.;

Kulikov, V.M.; Korolev, V.N.; Evplanov, A.I.; Bader, V.I.; Denisova, S.A.

Int. Congr. Chem. Eng. Chem. Equip. Des. Autom. (Proc.) 5th, 1975 D   D3.4, 6pp.

438.   Dependence of Local Heat Transfer Coefficient on Bubble Properties in a Fluidized Bed.

Masson, H.; Jottrand, R.

Int. Congr. Chem. Eng. Chem. Equip. Des. Autom. (Pric.), 5th, 1975 D D3.3, 6pp.

439.   (Wall-to-Bed) Heat Transfer in Aggregative and Particulate Liquid-Fluidized Beds.

Patel, R.D.; Simpson, J.M.

Chem. Eng. Sci., V.32, N.1, 67-74 (1977).

440.   The Development of a Mechanism for Gas-Particle Heat Transfer in Shallow Fluidized Beds of Large Particles.

McGaw, M.R.

Chem. Eng. Sci., V.32, N.1, 11-18 (1977).

441.   (In Studies On) Heat Transfer in a Pulsed Fluidized Bed.

Bhattacharya, S.C.; Harrison, D.

Trans. Inst. Chem. Eng., V.54, N.4, 281-86 (Oct. 1976).

442.   Gas-Convective Heat Transfer to Packed and Fluidized Beds.-- 2.   Experimental Results.

Botterill, J.S.M.; Denloye, A.O.O.

69th AIChE Annu. Meet. (Chicago 11/28-12/2/76), Preprint No. 103E-2, 25p.

443. Gas-Convective Heat Transfer to Packed and Fluidized Beds --
1. A Theoretical Model.

Denloye, A.O.O.; Botterill, J.S.M.

69th AIChE Annu. Meet. (Chicago 11/28-12/2/76), Prepr. N.
103E-1, 26p.

444. Bubble-Induced Heat Transfer in Gas-Fluidized Beds.

Kubie, J.

Int. J. Heat Mass Transfer, V.19, N.12, 1441-53 (Dec. 1976).

445. Heat Transfer in Fluidized Beds of Low Density, Large-Sized
Particles.

Arora, V.K.

Univ. Mass. Diss. (1976), 186p, Diss. Abstract INT B V37,
N.1, 349B (July 1976).

446. Particle Circulation Downstream from a Tube Immersed in a
Fluidized Bed.

Hager, W.R.; Schrag, S.D.

Chem. Eng. Sci., V.31, N.8, 657-59 (1976).

447. Heat Transfer from Immersed Surfaces in Liquid Fluidized Beds.

Shakiri, K.J.; Romani, M.N.; Richardson, J.F.

Chem. Eng. Sci., V.31, N.8, 619-24 (1976).

448. Heat Transfer in Shallow Crossflow Fluidized Bed Heat
Exchangers -- 1. A Generalized Theory. 2. Experimental.

McGaw, D.R.

Int. J. Heat Mass Transfer, V.19, N.6, 657-63, 665-71 (June 1976).

449. On Fluidized-Bed-To-Surface Heat Transfer.

Zabrodsky, S.S.; Parnas, A.L.; Antonishin, N.V.

Can. J. Chem. Eng., V.54, N.1-2, 52-58 (Feb.-Apr. 1976).

450. Heat- and Mass-Transfer Studies in Semifluidized Beds... A
Review.

Murthy, J.S.N.; Sarma, K.J.R.; Roy, G.K.

Chem. Eng. World, V.11, N.2, 55-58 (Feb. 1976).

451. A Note on Heat Transfer Mechanism as Applied to Flowing
Granular Media.

Kubie, J.; Broughton, J.

Unilever Res. Ltd.

Int. J. Heat Mass Transfer, V.19, N.2, 232-33 (Feb. 1976).

452. Effect of Particle Residence Time Distribution on Heat
Transfer in Fluidized Bed Heat Exchangers.

McGaw, D.R.

Powder Technol., 1975, V.11, N.1, 33-6.

453. Bubble Activity and the Packet Theory of Fluidized Bed Heat
Transfer.

Scheldorf, J.J.; Selzer, V.W.; Thomson, W.J.

68th AIChE Annu. Meet. (Los Angeles 11/16-20/75), Paper N.
44C, 41p.

454. Evaluation of Emulsion Phase Residence Time and Its Use in
Heat Transfer Models.

Ozkaynak, T.F.; Chen, J.C.

68th AIChE Annu. Meet. (Los Angeles 11/16-20/75), Paper

N.44D, 44p.

455. Heat Transfer During Bubble Formation in Gaseous Fluidized

Beds.

Mori, S.

Heat Transfer. Japanese Res. 1973, V.2, N.4, 37-40.

456. Heat Transfer in Multistage Inclined Fluidized Beds.

Arai, N.; Hasatani, M.; Sugiyama, S.

Heat Transfer, Japanese Res. 1973, V.2, N.4, 18-25.

457. Heat Transfer Between a Vertical Wall and a Gas Fluidized Bed.

Baeyens, J.; Goossens, W.R.A.

Powder Technol., 1973, V.8, N.1-2, 91-6.

458. Heat Transfer Through a Wall to a Batch Fluid Bed.

Gopichand, T.; Rao, D.P.

Indian Chem. Eng., 1972, N.1, 15-21.

459. Flow Characteristics of Circulation Systems with Two-Fluidized

Beds.

Kunii, N.; Yuzawa, O.; Kunii, D.; Kunugi, T.

Kagaku Kogaku, 1973, V.37, N.9, 949-53, refer to Chemical

Abstract V79-147739, in Japanese.

460. Fluid-to-Particle Heat Transfer in Fluidized Beds.

Bhattacharyya, D.; Pei, D.C.T.; Rowe, P.N.

Ind. Eng. Chem. Fundam., V.14, N.3, 281-82 (Aug. 1975).

461. Fluid-Particle Heat Transfer in Gas Fluidized Beds.

Balakrishnan, A.R.; Pei, D.C.T.

Can. J. Chem. Eng., V.53, N.2, 231-33 (Apr. 1975).

462. Two-Diemensional Recirculating Bed Data with Simulated Heat

Transfer Surface in the Downcomers.

U.S. Environmental Protection Agency; Yang, W.D; Keairns, D.L.

Ind. Eng. Chem. Process Des. Dev., V.14, N.3, 259-63

(July 1975).

463. Heat Transfer from a Grid Jet in a Large Fluidized Bed.

Bergougnou, M.A.; Behie, L.A.; Baker, C.G.J.

Can. J. Chem. Eng., V.53, N.1, 25-30 (Feb. 1975).

464. Configuration of Horizontal Tube Bundles in Gas-Fluidized

Bed Reactors from the Thermotechnical Viewpoint.

Neukirchen, B.

Univ. Stuttgart Diss. (1973) (Abstr.) VDI (Ver Dtsch. Ing)

Z V.117, N.4, 203 (Feb. 1975).

465. A Model of (Surface-to-Bed) Heat Transfer in Gas-Fluidized Beds

Kubie, J.; Broughton, J.

Int. J. Heat Mass Transfer, V.18, N.2, 289-99 (Feb. 1975).

466. Investigation of Packet Residence Time and Its Relation with

the Heat Transfer Coefficient in Fluidized Beds.

Ozkaynak, F.T.

Lehigh Univ. Diss. (1974), 181p, see Diss. Abstract INT B

V.35, N.8, 3930B (Feb. 1975).

467. Heat Transfer in Vibro-Fluidized Bed. The Effect of Pulsated
Gas Flow.

Jimbo, G.; Kanagawa, Y.; Yamazaki, R.

38th Soc. Chem. Eng. Japanese Annu. Meet. (Tokyo 4/3/73),
J. Chem. Eng. Japan, V.7, N.5, 373-78 (Oct. 1974).

468. Heat and Mass Transfer in Fluidized Beds.

Jullien, G.A.; Shridhar, M.; Pfafflin, J.R.

65th AIChE Annu. Meet. (NY 11/26-30/72), AIChE Symp. Serv.
V.70, N.141, 69-72 (1974).

469. Heat Transfer at Horizontal, Longitudinally-Finned Tubes in
Gas-Fluidized Beds.

Blenke, H.; Natusch, H.J.

Verfahrenstechnik (Mainz), V.8, N.10, 287-93 (Oct. 1974),
in German.

470. Population Balance Model for Heat Transfer in Fluidized Beds.

Chin, L.Y.; Lu, W.M.; Wang, T.L.

J. Chinese Inst. Chem. Eng., 1974, V.5, N.1, 15-25.

471. Flow Characteristics of Circulation Systems with Two
Fluidized Beds.

Yuzawa, O.; Kunugi, T.; Kunii, N.; Kunii, D.

Kagaku Kogaku, V.37, N.9, 949-53 (1974). (Transl.) Int.
Chem. Eng., V.14, N.3, 588-93 (July 1974), in Japanese.

472. Fluid-to-Particle Heat Transfer in Fluidized Beds.

Bhattacharyya, D.; Pei, D.C.T.

Ind. Eng. Chem. Fundam., V.13, N.3, 199-203 (Aug. 1974).

473. A New Method for Measuring Heat Transfer in Fluidized Beds.

Elmas, M.

Eur. Fed. Chem. Eng. "Fluidized Bed Technol." Symp.
(Toulouse 10/1-5/73), refer to Chem. Ing. Tech., V.46, N.12, 525-28 (June 1974).

474. Heat Transfer at a Vertical Wall in a Fluidized Bed Described
by the Film Penetration Model.

Goossens, W.R.A.; Hellinck, X.L.

Eur. Fed. Chem. Eng. "Fluidized Bed Technol." Symp.
(Toulouse 10/1-5/73), see Chem. Ing. Tech. V.46, N.12, 525-28 (June 1974).

475. Heat Transfer at Horizontal and Vertical Cylinders and at a
Sphere Immersed in Fluidized Beds.

Samson, T.

Eur. Fed. Chem. Eng. "Fluidized Bed Technol." Symp.
(Toulouse 10/1-5/73), refer to Chem.Ing.Tech., V.46, N.12, 525-28 (June 1974).

476. (In Studies Of) Momentum & Heat Transfer in Fixed and
Fluidized Beds.

Bhattacharyya, D.

Univ. Waterloo (Canada) Diss. (1973), Diss. Abstract INT B V.34,
N.10, 4933B-4934B (Apr. 1974).

477. Fluid-Particle Heat Transfer in Fixed and Fluidized Beds.

Gupta, S.N.; Chaube, R.B.; Upadhyay, S.N.

Chem. Eng. Sci., V.29, N.3, 839-43 (Mar. 1974).

478. Flow and Transfer Behavior of Fluidized Beds.

Reh, L.

Verfahrens-Ing. Annu. Meet. (Berlin 10/2-4/73), Chem. Ing.

Tech., V.46, N.5, 180-89, (Mar. 1974), in German.

479. A Mechanism of Bed- (To) -Wall Heat Transfer in a Fluidized

Bed at High Temperatures.

Kunii, D.; Yoshida, K.; Ueno, T.

Chem. Eng. Sci., V.29, N.1, 77-82 (Jan. 1974).

480. The Mechanisms of Heat Transfer and Bubble Formation in Gas-

Solid Fluidized Beds.

Lisa, R.E.

Purdue Univ. Diss. (1973), 331p, Diss. Abstract INT B

V.34, N.6, 2592B (Dec. 1973).

481. Unsteady State Thermal Responses of Fluidized Beds.

Pfafflin, J.R.; Shridhar, M.; Ziegler, E.N.; Lees, L.H.

J. Inst. Fuel, V.46, N. 388, 335-39 (Sept. 1973).

482. Heat Transfer to Liquid Fluidized Beds.

Simpson, J.M.

Polytech. Inst. Brooklyn Diss. (1973), 181p. Diss. Abstract

INT B V.34, N.5, 2005B (Nov. 1973).

483. Heat Transfer at Finned Tubes in Gas-Fluidized Beds.

Natusch, H.J.; Blenke, H.

4th Int. Chem. Eng. Chem. Equip. & Autom. Congr. (Prague

9/11-15/72), Verfahrenstechnik (Mainz), V.7, N.10, 293-96 (Oct. 1973), in German.

484. An (Experimental) Study of the Kinetics of Mass and Heat Transfer in a Fluidized Bed of Packing Irrigated in Counterflow.

Mrowiec, M.; Durych, A.

Chim. Ind. Genie Chim., V.106, N.11, 848-50 (May-June 1973), in French.

485. Heat Transfer in a Fluidized Bed of Small Particles.

Hughmark, G.A.

AIChE J., V.19, N.3, 658-59 (May 1973).

486. Solid-Particle Flow at the Wall of a Fluidization Column Induced by Isolated Bubbles.

Crescitelli, S.; Donsi, G.; Massimilla, L; Volpicelli, G.

Chim. Ind. Genie. Chim., V.106, N.9, 637-38 (Apr. 1973), in French.

487. Bubble Behavior Around Immersed Tubes in a Fluidized Bed.

Thomson, W.J.; Hager, W.R.

65th AIChE Annu. Meet. (NY 11/26-30/72), AIChE Symp. Ser. V.69, N.128, 68-77 (1973).

488. Bed-to-Surface Heat Transfer.

Botterill, J.S.M.

64th AIChE Annu. Meet. (San Francisco 1971), see AIChE Symp. Ser. V.69, N.128, 26-27 (1973).

489.   Heat Transfer from a Horizontal Bundle of (Seven) Bare and

(Serrated) Finned Tubes in an Air-Fluidized Bed.

Genetti, W.E.; Bartel, W.J.

72nd AIChE Natl. Meet. (St. Louis 5/21-24/72), AIChE Symp.

Ser. V. 69, N. 128, 85-93 (1973).

490.   Heat Transfer During a Bubble Formation in a Gaseous

Fluidized Bed.

Mori, S.

Kagaku Kogaku 1973, V.37, N.3, 317-19, Chem. Abstr. V78-

138336, in Japanese.

491.   Analogies and Differences in the Variation of the Heat-

Transfer Coefficient in Fluidized Beds.

Bibolaru, V.

Bul. Stiint. Teh. Inst. Politeh. Timisoara. Ser. Chim. 1970,

V.15, N.2, 205-12, see Chem. Abstract V78-99661, in Rumanian.

492.   Wall-to-Bed Heat Transfer in Fluidized Beds.

Simpson, J.M.; Patel, R.D.

Chem. Eng. Sci., V.28, N.2, 669-70 (Feb. 1973).

493.   The Effect of Bubbles on Heat Transfer from Immersed Tubes

in a Freely Bubbling Fluidized Bed.

Hager, W.R.

Univ. Idaho Diss. (1973), 210p., Diss Abstract INT. B, V. 33,

N.9, 4257B (Mar. 1973).

494. Bed to Surface Heat Transfer.

Botterill, J.S.M.

Chim. Ind. Genie Chim. V.105, N.25, 1829-30 (Dec. 1972).

495. Effect of Mechanical Stirring on Heat Transfer in
Homogeneous Fluidization.

Angelino, H.; Varela, B.; Couderc, J.P.

Can. J. Chem. Eng., V.50, N.6, 719-23 (Dec. 1972), in French

496. The Capacitance Effect on the Transfer of Gas or Heat
Between a Bubble and the Continuous Phase in a Gas-Solid Fluidized Bed.

Oichi, M.; Toei, R.; Fujine, Y.; Hotta, H.; Matsuno, R.

5th Soc. Chem. Eng. Japanese Autumn Meet. (Osaka Oct. 1971),
J. Chem. Eng., Japan, V.5, N.3, 273-79 (Sept. 1972).

497. Limiting Factors in Gas-Fluidized-Bed Heat Transfer.

Desai, M.; Botterill, J.S.M.

Powder Technol., 1972, V.6, N.4, 231-8.

498. Rate of Heat Transfer Between a Fluidized Bed and The Tube
Wall at High Temperatures.

Asaki, Z.; Awakura, Y.; Nagase, T.; Kondo, Y.; Fukunaka, Y.;
Nakano, I.

Mem. Fac. Eng. Kyoto Univ., 1972, V.34 (Pt. 1), 1-10, refer
to Chemical Abstract V77-63962.

499. Mechanism of Heat Transfer in Liquid Fluidized Beds.

Tripathi, G.; Pandey, G.N.; Varma, R.L.

Indian J. Technol., 1971, V.9, N.8, 277-80.

500. Influence of Vertical Vibrations on the Efficiency of
Fluidized Beds.

Jinescu, G.I.

Rev. Chim. (Bucharest), 1972, V.23, N.1, 41-8, in Romanian.

501. Heat Transfer in Vibrated Fluidized Layers.

Bratu, Em A.; Jinescu, G.I.

Rev. Roumanian Chim. 1972, V.17, N.1-2, 49-56, in Rumanian.

502. Transfer of Heat from Bubbles in a Fluidized Bed.

Seth, H.K.; Williams, K.A.; Barile, R.G.

Chem. Eng. J. (London), 1970, V.1, N.4, 263-72, refer to
Chemical Abstract V76-101688.

503. Examinations of Heat Transfer in Particle Aggregation.
Pallai-Varsany, E.
Proc. Conf. Appl. Phys. Chem. 2nd, 1971, V.2, 115-20,
Research Inst. Tech. Chem. Hung. Acad. Sci., Veszprem, Hungary.

504. Momentum, Heat, and Mass Transfer for Fixed and Homogeneous
Fluidized Beds.

Hughmark, G.A.

AIChE. J., V.18, N.5, 1020-24 (Sept. 1972).

505. Heat Transfer in Semifluidized Beds.

Tripathi, G.; Pandey, G.N.; Varma, R.L.

Indian J. Technol., V.10, N.1, 11-15 (Jan. 1972).

506. Heat and Mass Transfer and Flow in Multistage Trickle-Tray Fluidized Beds.

Brauer, H.; Mewes, D.

Chem. Ing. Tech., V.44, N.5, 357-60 (Mar. 1972), in German.

507. Laws Governing Flow and Mass and Heat Transfer in Single-Stage Fluidized Beds.

Mewes, D.; Brauer, H.

Chem. Ing. Tech., V.44, N.3, 141-44 (Feb. 1972), in German.

508. Heat Transfer from a Horizontal Tube to a Fluidized Bed in the Presence of Unheated Tubes.

Kermode, R.I.; Lese, H.K.

Canadian J. Chem. Eng., V.50, N.1, 44-48 (Feb. 1972).

509. Heat Transfer at a Pipe by Cross Flow in a Liquid-Fluidized

Blenke, H.; Neukirchen, B.; Noack, R.

Verfahrenstechnik (Mainz), V.6, N.3, 80-83 (Mar. 1972), in German.

510. Heat Transfer from a Horizontal Bundle of Tubes in an Air Fluidized Bed.

Bartel, W.J.

Montana State Univ. Diss. (1971), 177p; Diss. Abstract INT B V. 32, N 9, 5193B-5194B (Mar. 1972).

511. Heat Transfer Between the Emulsion Phase and Gas Bubbles in Fluid-Bed Catalytic Contactors.

Yamazaki, M.; Miyauchi, T.

34th Soc. Chem. Eng. Japanese Annu. Meet. (Tokyo Apr. 1969), J. Chem. Eng. Japanese, V.4, N.4, 324-30 (Nov. 1971).

512. Transfer of Heat from Bubbles in a Fluidized Bed.

Seth, H.K.; Barile, R.G.; Williams, K.A.

Chem. Eng. J. (London), 1970), V.1, N.4, 263-72.

513. Fluid-Bed Heat Transfer Between Solid and Fluid.

Sen Gupta, P.

Chem. Age. India 1971, V.22, N.9, 631-5.

514. A Model of Heat Transfer in Fluidized Beds.

Hwang, C.L.; Fan, L.T.; Chung, B.T.F.

ASME Paper N. 71-HT-Z, J. Heat Transfer, V.94, N.1, 105-10,

(Feb. 1972).

515. Heat Transfer in a Screen-Packed Bed.

Jain, S.C.; Chen, B.H.

69th AIChE Natl. Meet. (Cincinatti 5/16-19/71), AIChE.

Symp. Ser. V.67, N.116, 97-105 (1971).

516. Heat Transfer in Liquid-Fluidized Beds with A Concentric Heater.

Brea, F.M.; Hamilton, W.

Trans. Inst. Chem. Eng., V.49, N.4, 196-203 (Oct. 1971).

517. Heat Transfer in Vibrofluidized Beds of Alumina and Basic

Aluminum Ammonium Sulfate.

Dabrowski, A.; Marcinkowski, R.

Bull. Acad. Pol. Sci. Ser. Sci Chim., 1971, V.19, N.1,

71-5, refer to Chemical Abstract V75-50837.

518. Pulsed-Bed Approach to Fluidization.

Kobayashi, M.

U.S. at Energy Comm. 1969, ANL-7592, 157pp; refer to Chemica
Abstract V74-33005.

519.   Heat Transfer in Liquid Fluidized Beds.

Tripathi, G.; Pandey, G.N.

Indian J. Technol., 1970, V.8, N.8, 285-9.

520.   Heat Transfer in Liquid-Fluidized Beds.

Zahavie, E.

Int. J. Heat Mass Transfer, V.14, N.6, 835-57 (June 1971).

521.   Mathematical Determination of Heat Transfer Between a Wall
and A Fluidized Bed.

Klose, E.; Heschel, W.

Chem. Tech. (Leipzig), V.23, N.4-5, 219-24 (Apr.-May 1971).

522.   Heat Transfer at Horizontal Tubes in Fluidized Beds.

Noack, R.

Univ. Stuttgart Diss. (1970); Abstract VDI (Ver Deut. Ing.),
Z V.113, N.2, 184 (Feb. 1971).

523.   Heat Transfer from a Horizontal Tube to a Fluidized Bed in
the Presence of Unheated Tubes.

Lese, H.K.

Univ. KY Diss. (1970), 339p; Diss. Abstract INT B V.31, N.9,
5343B-5344B (Mar. 1971).

524.   Continuous High-Temperature Heat Exchange (Between Two Gases)
Via Moving (Heat)Storage Particles.

Sonnenschein, H.

Verfahrenstech Ges. Annu. Meet. (Munich 10/13-15/70),

Chem.Ing.Tech., V.43, N.5, 240-45 (Mar. 1971).

525.   Heat and Mass Transfer Between Gas and Granular Material--2.

Chukhanov, Z.F.

Int. J. Heat Mass Transfer, V.13, N.12, 1805-17 (Dec. 1970).

526.   The Hydrodynamics of and Heat Exchange in Fluidized Beds of
Fine-Grained Material with a Local Spouting Zone.

Pomortseva, A.A.; Baskakov, A.P.

Khim. Tekhnol. Topl. Masel, V.15, N.12, 34-37 (1970).

527.   Gas-Particle Heat Transfer in Fixed and Fluidized Beds.

Kato, K.; Wen, C.Y.

64th AIChE Nat. Meet. (New Orleans 3/16-20/69), Che. Eng.
Progr. Symp. Ser. V.66, N.105, 100-108 (1970).

528.   Heat Transfer from an Internal Surface to a Pulsed Bed.

Brazelton, W.T.; Kobayashi, M.; Ramaswami, D.

62nd AIChE Annu. Meet. (Washington, DC 11/16-20/69), Chem.
Eng. Progr. Symp. Ser., V.66, N. 105, 58-67 (1970).

529.   Wall-to-Bed Heat Transfer in Fluidized and Packed Beds.

Gabor, J.D.

62nd AIChE Annu. Meet. (Washington, DC 11/16-20/69), Chem.
Eng. Progr. Symp. Ser., V.66, N.105, 76-86 (1970).

530.   Hydrodynamics of Cocurrent Countergravity Solids Transport
for Liquid-Fluidized Heat Exchangers.

Kopko, R.J.

PA State Univ. Diss. (1969), 273p; Diss. Abstract INT B V.31, N.4, 1925B-1926B (Oct. 1970).

531.   Heat Transfer Characteristics in Air Fluidized Up to 900°F.

Callahan, J.T.

Amer. Soc. Mech. Eng. Winter Ann. Mtg. (NY 11/29-12/3/70), Paper N. 70-WA/TEMP3, 14p.

532.   Two Heat Transfer Coefficients Were Defined For Heat Transfer From a Horizontal Discontinuous Finned Tube in a Fluidized Bed.

Bartel, W.J.; Genetti, W.E.; Grimmett, E.S.

63rd AIChE Ann. Mtg. (Chicago 11/29-12/3/70), Preprint N.151, 14p.

533.   The Effect of Tube Orientation on Heat Transfer with Bare and Finned Tubes in a Fluidized Bed.

Schmall, R.A.; Genetti, W.E.; Grimmett, E.S.

63rd AIChE Ann. Mtg. (Chicago 11/29-12/3/70), Preprint N. 15H, 25p.

534.   The Concentration of (Inert Heat Carrier) Particles Settling Out of a Fluidized Bed of Finely Dispersed Catalyst.

Brun-Tsekhovoi, A.R.; Katsobashvili, Ya R.; Khotomlyanskii, L. N.; Petrov, V.N.; Skoblo, A.I.

Khim I Tekhnol Topl. I Masel, V.15, N.7, 15-18 (1970).

535.   Heat Transfer Around a Horizontal Tube in a Fluidized Bed.

Keairns, D.L.

Res. Results Serv. MS (Manuscript) Ind. Eng. Chem., V.62, N.8, 77-79, N.70-147, 25p. (Aug. 1970).

536. Heat Transfer in a Mechanically Stirred, Gas-Solid Fluidized System.

Williams, J. A.; Smith, V.C.

61st AIChE Ann. Mtg. (Los Angeles 12/1-5/68), Chem. Eng. Progr. Symp. Ser., V.66, N.101, 70-74 (1970).

537. The Flow of Fluidized Solids Past Arrays of Tubes-Heat Transfer and Pressure Loss Studies.

Van der Kolk, M.; Botterill, J.S.M.; Cahndrasekhar, R.

61st AIChE Ann. Mtg. (Los Angeles 12/1-5/68), Chem. Eng. Progr. Symp. Ser., V.66, N.101, 61-69 (1970).

538. (A Model for Predicting) Heat Transfer (From a Wall) to Particle Beds with Gas Flows Less Than or Equal to That Required for Incipient Fluidization.

Gabor, J.D.

Chem. Eng. Sci., V.25, N.6, 979-84 (June 1970).

539. Heat Transfer and Pressure Loss for the Flow of Fluidized Solid Across Banks of Tubes.

Botterill, J.S.M.; Chandrasekhar, R.; Van Der Kolk, M.

Brit. Chem. Eng., V.15, N.6, 769-72 (June 1970).

540. Surface to Fluidized Bed Heat Transfer.

Ahluwalia, M.S.; Botterill, J.S.M.; Desai, M.; Wasan, D.T.

Chem. Eng. Sci., V.25, N.4, 749 (Apr. 1970).

541. British Chemical Engineering Nomogram No. 143. Heat Transfer Coefficients for Non-Finned Heat Exchangers Inside Fluidized Beds.

British Chemical Engineering; Balakrishna-Rao, K.; Rao, K.B.

Brit. Chem. Eng., V.15, N.4, 541 (Apr. 1970).

542. Statistical Models for Surface Renewal in Heat and Mass Transfer -- 3. Residence Times and Age Distributions at Wall Surface of a Fluidized Bed, Application of Spectral Density.

Koppel, L.B.; Patel, R.D.; Holmes, J.T.

AIChE (Amer. Inst. Chem. Engrs), J. V.16, N3, 456-64, 464-71 (May 1970).

543. Heat Transfer Between Fluidized Beds and Heated Surfaces -- Effect of Particle Size.

Yamazaki, R.; Jimbo, G.

34th Soc. Chem. Eng. Jap. Ann. Mtge. (Tokyo 4/2/69), J. Chem. Eng. Jap., V.3, N.1, 44-49 (Jan. 1970).

544. A (Colburn J-Factor Type) Correlation for Heat Transfer in Liquid Fluidized Beds.

Hamilton, W.

Can. J. Chem. Eng., V.48, N.1, 52-55 (Feb. 1970).

545. Local Heat Transfer at Horizontal Tubes in Fluidized Beds.

Noack, R.

Ver Deut. Chem. Eng. Ann. Mtg. (Bayreuth 9/30-10/2/69), Chem. Ing. Tech., V.42, N.6, 371-76 (Mar. 1970).

546.   (Measurements of the) Surface-to-Bed Heat Transfer in a

Liquid-Fluidized Bed.

      Uppala, S.R.; Genetti, W.E.

      Res. Results Serv. Ms. (Manuscript) Ind. Eng. Chem., V.62,

N.3, 82-83,(Mar. 1970)

547.   Consecutive Film and Surface Renewal Mechanism for Heat or

Mass Transfer from a Wall.

      Wasan, D.T.; Ahluwalia, M.S.

      Chem. Eng. Sci., V.24, N.10, 1535-42 (Oct. 1969).

Appendix B

Notes on Notation and Unit Factors

CONTENTS

I. Units of Measure, 805
II. Use of Tables, 808

LIST OF TABLES

Table B-1 SI Base Units and Their Definitions, 808
Table B-2 Examples of SI-Derived Units, 810
Table B-3 List of SI Prefixes for Forming Decimal
Multiples and Submultiples, 810
Table B-4 Commonly Used Symbols and Definitions, 811
Table B-5 Recommended SI Units and Conversion Factors, 816

I. UNITS OF MEASURE

Historically, units of measure are arbitrary, whereby different investigators working in a particular field elected to devise convenient definitions. To standardize definitions of measure, the scientific and engineering communities have formulated a policy of an International System of Units (SI) through the International Organization of Standardization (ISO).

Transition to SI has advanced considerably over the past decade. The Metric Conversion Act of 1975 (PL 94-168) was enacted, declaring the coordination and planning of increasing use of the metric system (SI) in the United States to the government policy. A memorandum by the Assistant Secretary of Commerce for Science and Technology in the Federal Register of October 26, 1977 (pp. 56513 and 56514, V. 42, N. 206) interprets and modifies SI for the United States. In addition, the Act also provides for the establishment of the U.S. Metric Board to coordinate voluntary conversion. Despite this increased activity, the complete changeover to SI has not materialized. Consequently, in this transition phase, practicing engineers, scientists, and students must be familiar with several systems of units: English-British Units, cgs, and SI.

SI is the abbreviation for the International System of Units (Le Systeme International d'Unites). The prelude to SI was the cgs (centimeter-gram-second) system of metric units. In contrast, SI is based on the meter, kilogram, and second as the fundamental units.

The SI system utilizes three classes of units. The first is referred to as *base units*. By convention, these are dimensionally independent. The second are *supplementary units,* which are used to measure plane and solid angles. *Derived units* are those formed by algebraic combinations of base units, supplementary units and other derived units. Specific names and symbols are assigned to the units in each class.

The advantage of SI over English units is the elimination of conversion factors within the system. That is, all derived combinations are in terms of unity. For example, the derived unit of power is the *watt,* which in base units is defined as 1 joule of work completed in 1 second of time.

There are seven *base units,* each considered to be dimensionally independent with specific definitions. These are:

- meter (m) for length
- kilogram (kg) for mass
- second (s) for time
- ampere (A) for electric current
- kelvin (K) for temperature
- mole (mol) for the amount of a substance
- candela (cd) for luminous intensity

Table B-1 provides the definitions of each of these units.

At present, there are only two *supplementary units* in the SI system. Both of these are purely geometric:

- radian (rad)—for the unit of plane angle
- steradian (sr)—for the unit of solid angle

The radian is the plane angle between two radii of a circle that cut off, on the circumference, an arc equal in length to the radius. The steradian is the solid angle that, having its apex in the center of a sphere, cuts out an area of the surface of the sphere that equals that of a square with sides of length equal to the radius of the sphere.

Derived units are expressed algebraically in terms of base units having mathematical symbols for multiplication and division. A number of derived units have been given special names and assigned symbols. Examples of derived units and those given special names are noted in Table B-2.

There are several other units that are widely used but are not part of SI. These include the minute, hour, day and year as units of time; degree, minute and second of arc (in addition to the radian); the metric ton (1,000 kg); the liter (1 cubic decimeter); the nautical mile; and the knot. These may be used along with SI units.

Prefixes for decimal multiples and submultiples of SI units are listed in Table B-3. The symbol of a prefix is combined with the unit to which it is directly attached, thus forming a new unit symbol that can be raised to a positive or negative power and can be combined with other unit symbols to form compound units.

Distinction between upper case and lower case symbols is important as shown by the following examples:

- M = mega = 10^6
- m = milli = 10^{-3} (where m is a prefix)
- N = newton
- n = nano = 10^{-9}

Care should be exercised when a compound unit includes a unit symbol that is also a symbol for a prefix. As an example, the Newton-meter should be written as $N \cdot m$ to avoid confusion with mN (millinewton).

Symbols can be used together with modifying subscripts and/or superscripts. Subscripts are often used to designate a place in space or time, or a constant or reference point. Superscripts can be used to designate a dimensionless form, a reference or equilibrium value, or mathematical identification such as an average value, derivative, tensor index, etc.

Table B-4 provides a partial list of commonly used symbols and their definitions.

The remainder of this appendix provides tables of units and conversion factors between SI, cgs and English units prepared by the American Petroleum Institute (API), Washington, DC. Tables and conversion factors have been grouped into the following categories.

1. Space, Time
2. Mass, Amount of Substance
3. Heating Value, Entropy, Heat Capacity
4. Temperature, Pressure, Vacuum
5. Density, Specific Volume, Concentration, Dosage
6. Facility Throughput, Capacity
7. Flow rate
8. Energy, Work, Quantity of Heat, Power
9. Mechanics
10. Transport Properties

Metric units recommended for general use are shown under the heading "API preferred metric unit."

II. USE OF TABLES

The following tables were reprinted from API Publication 2564—Manual of Petroleum Measurement Standards: Chapter 15, "Guidelines for the Use of the International System of Units (SI) in the Petroleum and Allied Industries, "2nd edition (December 1980) pp. 2–31, courtesy of the American Petroleum Institute, 2101 L Street, Northwest, Washington, D.C.

Those metric units recommended for general use appear under the heading "API Preferred Metric Unit." Other units are given under the heading "Other Allowable." Preferred units do not preclude the use of other multiples or submultiples, as the choice of such a unit-multiple is established by the magnitude of the numerical value.

Notation used conforms to SI practice, that is—groups of three digits to the left or right of the decimal marker are separated by spaces. No commas or triad spacers are used. E-notation is employed for convenience. Asterisks (*) denote that all succeeding digits are zeroes. If a conversion factor ends in zero but does not have an asterisk, then any subsequent digits would not necessarily be zeroes. For example:

$$3.077E + 00 = 3.077 \times 10^0 = 3.077$$

$$10.273\ 304E + 2 = 10.273\ 304 \times 10^2 = 1\ 027.330\ 4$$

Table B-1. SI Base Units and Their Definitions
(courtesy of the American Petroleum Institute—API Pub. 2564)

Quantity	Name	Symbol	Definition
Length	Meter (or metre)	m	The meter is the length equal to 1 650 763.73 wavelengths in vacuum of the radiation corresponding to the transition between the levels $2p_{10}$ and $5d_5$ of the krypton-86 atom. (Eleventh CGPM, 1960, Resolution 6)
Mass	Kilogram	kg	The kilogram is the unit of mass (not force); it is equal to the mass of the international prototype of the kilogram. (Third CGPM, 1901, Resolution 3) This international prototype, made of platinum-iridium, is kept at the International Bureau of Weights and Measures. A copy of the international prototype is maintained by the national standards agency of each major country. The kilogram is the only base unit defined by an artifact and is the only base unit having a prefix.

Table B-1. continued

Quantity	Name	Symbol	Definition
Time	Second	s	The second is the duration of 9 192 631 770 periods of the radiation corresponding to the transition between the two hyperfine levels of the ground state of the cesium-133 atom. (Thirteenth CGPM, 1967, Resolution 1)
Electric Current	Ampere	A	The ampere is that constant current which, if maintained in two straight parallel conductors of infinite length, of negligible circular cross section, and placed 1 meter apart in vacuum, would produce between these conductors a force equal to 2×10^{-7} newton per meter of length. (CIPM, 1946, Resolution 2 approved by the Ninth CGPM, 1948)
Temperature	Kelvin	K	The kelvin, unit of thermodynamic temperature, is the fraction 1/273.16 of the thermodynamic temperature of the triple point of water. (Thirteenth CGPM, 1967, Resolution 4) The unit kelvin and its symbol K are used to express an interval or difference of temperature. (Thirteenth CGPM, 1967, Resolution 3) In addition to the thermodynamic temperature, Celsius temperature (formerly called Centigrade) is widely used. The degree Celsius (°C), a derived unit, is the unit for expressing Celsius temperatures and temperature intervals. Celsius temperature, t, is related to thermodynamic temperature, T, by the following equation: $$t = T - T_0$$ Where: $T_0 = 273.15$ by definition. The temperature interval 1 C equals 1 K exactly.
Amount of Substance	Mole	mol	The mole is the amount of substance of a system that contains as many elementary entities as there are atoms in 0.012 kilogram of carbon-12. When the mole is used, the elementary entities must be specified and may be atoms, molecules, ions, electrons, other particles or specified groups of such particles. (Fourteenth CGPM, 1971, Resolution 3)
Luminous Intensity	Candela	cd	The candela is the luminous intensity, in a given direction, of a source that emits monochromatic radiation of frequency 540×10^{12} hertz and that has a radian intensity in that direction of 1/683 watt per steradian. (Sixteenth CGPM, 1979)

Table B-2
Examples of SI Derived Units With Special Names

Quantity	Name	SI Unit Symbol	SI Unit Expression in Terms of Other Units	SI Unit Expression in Terms of SI Base Units
Frequency	hertz	Hz		s^{-1}
Force	newton	N		$m \cdot kg \cdot s^{-2}$
Pressure	pascal	Pa	N/m^2	$m^{-1} \cdot kg \cdot s^{-2}$
Energy, work, quantity of heat	joule	J	$N \cdot m$	$m^2 \cdot kg \cdot s^{-2}$
Power, radiant flux	watt.	W	J/s	$m^2 \cdot kg \cdot s^{-3}$
Electric potential, potential differences, electromotive force	volt	V	W/A	$m^2 \cdot kg \cdot s^{-3} \cdot A^{-1}$
		Ω	V/A	$m^2 \cdot kg \cdot s^{-3} \cdot A^{-2}$
Electric resistance	ohm	S	A/V	$m^{-2} \cdot kg^{-1} \cdot s^3 \cdot A^2$
Conductance	siemens	m^2		
Area	square metre	m^3		
Volume	cubic metre	m/s		
Speed, velocity	metre per second	m/s^2		
Acceleration	metre per second squared	kg/m^3		
Density	kilogram per cubic metre			
Concentration (of amount of substance)	mole per cubic metre	mol/m^3		
Specific volume	cubic metre per kilogram	m^3/kg		
Luminance	candela per square metre	cd/m^2		

Table B-3
SI Prefixes For Forming
Decimal Multiples and
Sub Multiples

Factor	Prefix	Symbol
10^{18}	exa	E
10^{15}	peta	P
10^{12}	tera	T
10^9	giga	G
10^6	mega	M
10^3	kilo	k
10^2	hecto	h
10^1	deka	da
10^{-1}	deci	d
10^{-2}	centi	c
10^{-3}	milli	m
10^{-6}	micro	μ
10^{-9}	nano	n
10^{-12}	pico	p
10^{-15}	femto	f
10^{-18}	atto	a

Table B-4
Commonly Used Symbols and Definitions

	Symbol	Unit or Definition
General Symbols		
Acceleration	a	m/s^2
of gravity	g	m/s^2
Base of natural logarithms	e	
Coefficient	C	
Difference, finite	Δ	
Differential operator	d	
partial	δ	
Efficiency	η	
Energy, dimension of	E	$J, N \cdot m$
Enthalpy	H	J
Entropy	S	J/K
Force	F	N
Function	ϕ, ψ, χ	
Gas constant, universal	R	To distinguish, use R_o
Gibbs free energy	G, F	$G = H - TS, J$
Heat	Q	J
Helmholtz free energy	A	$A = U - TS, J$
Internal energy	U	J
Mass, dimension of	m	kg
Mechanical equivalent of heat	J	Unity, dimensionless
Moment of inertia	I	$(m)^4$
Newton law of motion, conversion factor in	g_c	Unity, dimensionless
Number		
In general	N	
Of moles	n	
Pressure	p	Pa,bar
Quantity, in general	Q	
Ratio, in general	R	
Resistance	R	
Shear stress	τ	Pa
Temperature		
Dimension of	θ	
Absolute	T	K (Kelvin)
In general	T, t	°C
Temperature difference, logarithmic mean	$\bar{\theta}$	°C
Time		
Dimension of	T	s
In general	t, τ	s, hr
Work	W	J

Table B-4 continued

	Symbol	Unit or Definition
Geometrical Symbols		
Linear dimension		
Breadth	b	m
Diameter	D	m
Distance along path	s, x	m
Height above datum plane	Z	m
Height equivalent	H	m
Hydraulic radius	r_H, R_H	m, m^2/m
Lateral distance from datum plane	Y	m
Length, distance or dimension of	L	m
Longitudinal distance from		
datum place	X	m
Mean free path	λ	m
Radius	r, R	m
Thickness		
In general	B	m
Of file	B_f	m
Wavelength	λ	m
Area		
In general	A	m^2
Cross section	S	m^2
Fraction free cross section	σ	
Projected	A_p	m^2
Surface		
Per unit mass	A_w, s	m^2/kg
Per unit volume	A_s, a	m^2/m^3
Volume		
In general	V	m^3
Fraction voids	ϵ	
Humid volume	ν_H	m^3/kg dry air
Angle	α, θ, ϕ	
In x, y plane	α	
In y, z plane	ϕ	
In z, x plane	θ	
Solid angle	ω	
Other		
Particle-shape factor	ϕ_s	

Intensive Properties Symbols

Absorptivity for radiation	α	
Activity	a	
Activity coefficient, molal basis	γ	

Table B-4 continued

	Symbol	Unit or Definition
Intensive Properties Symbols (continued)		
Coefficient of expansion		
Linear	α	$m/(m \cdot K)$
Volumetric	β	$m^3/(m^3 \cdot K)$
Compressibility factor	z	$z = pV/RT$
Density	ϱ	kg/m^3
Diffusivity		
Molecular, volumetric	D_v, δ	$m^3/(s\ m), Mm^2/s$
Thermal	α	$\alpha = k/C_p m^2/s$
Emissivity ratio for radiation	e	
Enthalpy, per mole	H	$J/kmol$
Entropy, per mole	S	$J/(kmol \cdot K)$
Fugacity	f	Pa, bar
Gibbs, free energy, per mole	G, F	$J/kmol$
Helmholtz free energy, per mole	A	$J/kmol$
Humid heat	c_s	$J/(kg\ dry\ air \cdot K)$
Internal energy, per mole	U	$J/kmol$
Latent heat, phase change	λ	J/kg
Molecular weight	M	kg
Reflectivity for radiation	ϱ	
Specific heat	c	$J/(kg \cdot K)$
At constant pressure	c_p	$J/(kg \cdot K)$
At constant volume	c_v	$J/(kg \cdot K)$
Specific heats, ratio of	γ	
Surface tension	σ	N/m
Thermal conductivity	k	$(J \cdot m)/(s \cdot m^2 \cdot K)$
Transmissivity of radiation	τ	
Vapor pressure	p*	Pa, bar
Viscosity		
Absolute or coefficient of	μ	$Pa \cdot s$
Kinematic	ν	m^2/s
Volume, per mole	V	$m^3/kmol$

Symbols for Concentrations

Absorption factor	A	$A = L/K*V$
Concentration, mass or moles		
per unit volume	c	$kb/m^3, kmol/m^3$
Fraction		
Cumulative beyond a given size	ϕ	
By volume	χ_v	
By weight	χ_μ	

Table B-4 continued

	Symbol	Unit or Definition
Symbols for Concentrations (continued)		
Humidity	H, Y_H	kg/kg dry air
At saturation	H_s, Y^*	kg/kg dry air
At wet-bulb temperature	H_w, Y_w	kg/kg dry air
At adiabatic saturation temperature	H_a, Y_a	kg/kg dry air
Mass concentration of particles	c_p	kg/m^3
Moisture content		
Total water to bone-dry stock	X_ϕ^*	kg/kg dry stock
Equilibrium water to bone-dry stock	X^*	kg/kg dry stock
Free water to bone-dry stock	X	kg/kg dry stock
Mole or mass fraction		
In heavy or extract phase	x	
In light or raffinate phase	y	
Mole or mass ratio		
In heavy or extract phase	X	
In light or raffinate phase	Y	
Number concentration of particles	n_p	$number/m^3$
Phase equilibrium ratio	K^*	$K^* = y^*/x$
Relative distribution of two components		
Between two phases in equilibrium	α	$\alpha = K_i^*/K_j^*$
Between successive stages	β	$\beta = (y_i/\nu_i)_x/(x_i/x_i)_{n+1}$
Relative humidity	H_R, R_H	
Slope of equilibrium curve	m	$m = dy^*/dx$
Stripping factor	S	$S = K^*V/L$

Rate Symbols

Quantity per unit time, in general	q	
Angular velocity	ω	
Feedrate	F	kg/s, kmol/s
Frequency	f, N_f	
Friction velocity	u^*	$u^* = (\tau_w\varrho)^{1/2}$, m/s
Heat transfer rate	q	J/s
Heavy or extract phase rate	L	kg/s, kmol/s
Heavy or extract product rate	B	kg/s, kmol/s

Table B-4 continued

	Symbol	Unit or Definition
Rate Symbols (continued)		
Light or raffinate phase rate	V	kg/s, kmol/s
Light or raffinate product rate	D	kg/s, kmol/s
Mass rate of flow	w	kg/s, kg/hr
Molal rate of transfer	N	kmol/s
Power	P	W
Velocity, in general	n	m/s
Revolutions per unit time	u	m/s
Longitudinal (x) component of	u	m/s
Lateral (y) component of	v	m/s
Normal (z) component of	w	m/s
Volumetric rate of flow	q	m^3/s, m^3/hr
Quantity per unit time, unit area		
Emissive power, total	W	W/m^2
Mass velocity, average	G	$G = w/S$, $kg/(s \cdot m^2)$
Vapor or light phase	$G, \bar{G}$	$kg/(s \cdot m^2)$
Liquid or heavy phase	$L, \bar{L}$	$kg/(s \cdot m^2)$
Radiation, intensity of	I	W/m^2
Velocity		
Nominal, basis total cross		
section of packed vessel	v_s	m/s
Volumetric average	$V, \bar{V}$	$m^3/(s \cdot m^2)$, m/s
Quantity per unit time, unit volume		
Quantity reacted per unit time,		
reactor volume	N_R	$kmol/(s \cdot m^2)$
Space velocity, volumetric	Λ	$m^3/(s \cdot m^3)$
Quantity per unit time, unit area,		
unit driving force, in general	k	
Eddy diffusivity	δ_E	m^2/s
Eddy viscosity	ν_E	m^2/s
Eddy thermal diffusivity	α_E	m^2/s
Heat transfer coefficient		
Individual	h	$W/(m^2 \cdot K)$
Overall	U	$W/(m^2 \cdot K)$
Mass transfer coefficient		
Individual	k	$kmol/(s \cdot m^2)$(driving force)
Gas film	k_G	To define driving force use
		subscript:
Liquid film	k_L	c for $kmol/m^3$
Overall	K	p for bar
Gas film basis	K_G	x for mole fraction
Liquid film basis	K_L	
Stefan-Boltzmann constant	σ	$5.6703 \times 10^{-8} W/(m^2 \cdot K^4)$

Table B-5
Recommended SI Units and Conversion Factors

Quantity	SI Unit	Customary Unit	Metric Unit — API Preferred	Metric Unit — Other Allowable	Conversion Factor (Multiply Quantity Expressed in Customary Units by Factor to Get Metric Equivalent)	Notes See Pg. 850
SPACE, TIME						
Length	m					
		naut. mi	km		1.852* E+00	
				naut. mi	1	
		mi	km		1.609 344* E+00	1
		mi (U.S. statute)	km		1.609 347 E+00	1
		chain	m		2.011 684 E+01	1
		rod	m		5.029 210 E+00	1
		fathom	m		1.828 804 E+00	1
		m	m		1 E+00	
		yard	m		9.144* E-01	
		ft	m		3.048* E-01	
		ft (U.S. survey)	m		3.048 006 E-01	1
		link	m		2.011 684 E-01	1
		in	mm		2.54* E+01	
				cm	2.54* E+00	

Table B-5 (continued)
Recommended SI Units and Conversion Factors

Quantity	To convert from	to		Multiply by	
	cm	mm		1.0* E+01	
	mm	mm		1	
			cm	1	
Surface Texture m	mil	μm		2.54* E+01	
	micron (μ)	μm		1	
	μin	μm		2.54* E-02	
	nm	μm		1.0* E-03	
Length/Length m/m	ft/mi	m/km		1.893 939 E-01	
Length/Volume m/m³	ft/U.S. gal	m/m³		8.051 964 E+01	
	ft/ft³	m/m³		1.076 391 E+01	
	ft/bbl	m/m³		1.917 134 E+00	
Length/Temperature m/K	See "Temperature, Pressure, Vacuum"				
Area m²	mi²	km²		2.589 988 E+00	1
	mi² (U.S. statute)	km²		2.589 998 E+00	
	ha	m²		1.0* E+04	1
	acre	ha	m²	4.046 873 E-01	1
		m²		4.046 873 E+03	1
	sq chain	m²		4.046 873 E+02	1
	sq rod	m²		2.529 295 E+01	1

Table B-5 (continued)
Recommended SI Units and Conversion Factors

Quantity	SI Unit	Customary Unit	Metric Unit API Preferred	Metric Unit Other Allowable	Conversion Factor (Multiply Quantity Expressed in Customary Units by Factor to Get Metric Equivalent)	Notes See Pg. 850
SPACE, TIME (CONTINUED)						
Area (continued)		yd^2	m^2		8.361 274 E−01	
		ft^2	m^2		9.290 304* E−02	1
		ft^2 (U.S. survey)	m^2		9.290 341 E−02	1
		in^2	mm^2	cm^2	6.451 6* E+02 6.451 6* E+00	
		cm^2	mm^2	cm^2	1.0* E+02 1	
		mm^2	mm^2		1	
Area/Volume	m^2/m^3	ft^2/in^3	m^2/cm^3		5.669 291 E−03	
Area/Mass	m^2/kg	cm^2/g	m^2/kg		1.0* E−01	
Volume, Capacity	m^3	cubem	km^3		4.168 182 E+00	2
		acre·ft	m^3	ha·m	1.233 489 E+03 1.233 489 E−01	1 1

Table B-5 (continued)
Recommended SI Units and Conversion Factors

	m³	m³		1
	yd³	m³		7.645 549 E−01
	bbl (42 U.S. gal)	m³		1.589 873 E−01
	ft³	m³		2.831 685 E−02
		dm³	L	2.831 685 E+01
Volume, Capacity m³	Can. gal	m³		4.546 09* E−03
		dm³	L	4.546 09* E+00
	U.K. gal	m³		4.546 092 E−03
		dm³	L	4.546 092 E+00
	U.S. gal	m³		3.785 412 E−03
		dm³	L	3.785 412 E+00
	L	dm³	L	1
	U.K. qt	dm³	L	1.136 523 E+00
	U.S. qt	dm³	L	9.463 529 E−01
	U.K. pt	dm³	L	5.682 615 E−01
	U.S. pt	dm³	L	4.731 765 E−01
	U.K. fl oz	cm³		2.841 308 E+01
	U.S. fl oz	cm³		2.957 353 E+01
	in³	cm³		1.638 706 E+01
	mL	cm³		1

Table B-5 (continued)
Recommended SI Units and Conversion Factors

Quantity	SI Unit	Customary Unit	Metric Unit— API Preferred	Metric Unit— Other Allowable	Conversion Factor (Multiply Quantity Expressed in Customary Units by Factor to Get Metric Equivalent)	Notes See Pg. 850
SPACE, TIME (CONTINUED)						
Volume/Length (Linear Displacement)	m^3/m	bbl/in	m^3/m		6.259 342 E+00	
		bbl/ft	m^3/m		5.216 119 E−01	
		ft^3/ft	m^3/m		9.290 304* E−02	
		U.S. gal/ft	dm^3/m	L/m	1.241 933 E+01	
Volume/Mass	m^3/kg	See "Density, Specific Volume, Concentration, Dosage"				
Plane Angle	rad	rad	rad		1	
		deg (°)	rad	°	1.745 329 E−02	3
					1	3
		min (′)	rad	′	2.908 882 E−04	3
					1	3
		sec(″)	rad	″	4.848 137 E−06	3
					1	3

Table B-5 (continued)
Recommended SI Units and Conversion Factors

Solid Angle	sr		sr			1	
Time	s	million years (MY)	Ma			1	4
		yr	a			1	5
		wk	d			7.0*	E+00
		d	d			1	
		h	h			1	
				min		6.0*	E+01
		min	s			6.0*	E+01
				h		1.666 667	E−02
				min		1	
		s	s			1	
		millimicrosecond	ns			1	

Table B-5 (continued)
Recommended SI Units and Conversion Factors

Quantity	SI Unit	Customary Unit	Metric Unit API Preferred	Metric Unit Other Allowable	Conversion Factor (Multiply Quantity Expressed in Customary Units by Factor to Get Metric Equivalent)	Notes See Pg. 850
MASS, AMOUNT OF SUBSTANCE						
Mass	kg	U.K. ton (long ton)	Mg	t	1.016 047 E+00	
		U.S. ton (short ton)	Mg	t	9.071 847 E−01	
		U.K. cwt	kg		5.080 235 E+01	
		U.S. cwt	kg		4.535 924 E+01	
		kg	kg		1	
		lb	kg		4.535 924 E−01	
		oz (troy)	g		3.110 348 E+01	
		oz (avdp)	g		2.834 952 E+01	
		g	g		1	
		grain	mg		6.479 891 E+01	
		mg	mg		1	
		μg	μg		1	

Table B-5 (continued)
Recommended SI Units and Conversion Factors

Mass/Length	kg/m	See "Mechanics"			
Mass/Area	kg/m²	See "Mechanics"			
Mass/Volume	kg/m³	See "Density, Specific Volume, Concentration, Dosage"			
Mass/Mass	kg/kg	See "Density, Specific Volume, Concentration, Dosage"			
Amount of Substance	mol	ft³ (60°F, 1 atm)	kmol	1.195 29	E−03	6
		ft³ (60°F, 14.73 lbf/in²)	kmol	1.198 06	E−03	6
		m³ (0°C, 1 atm)	kmol	4.461 53	E−02	6
		m³ (15°C, 1 atm)	kmol	4.229 28	E−02	6
		m³ (20°C, 1 atm)	kmol	4.157 15	E−02	6
		m³ (25°C, 1 atm)	kmol	4.087 43	E−02	6

Table B-5 (continued)
Recommended SI Units and Conversion Factors

Quantity	SI Unit	Customary Unit	Metric Unit — API Preferred	Metric Unit — Other Allowable	Conversion Factor (Multiply Quantity Expressed in Customary Units by Factor to Get Metric Equivalent)	Notes See Pg. 850
HEATING VALUE, ENTROPY, HEAT CAPACITY						
Heating Value (Mass Basis)	J/kg	Btu/lb	MJ/kg kJ/kg	J/g kW·h/kg	2.326 000 E−03 2.326 000 E+00 6.461 112 E−04	
		cal/g cal/lb	kJ/kg J/kg	J/g	4.184* E+00 9.224 141 E+00	
Heating Value (Mole Basis)	J/mol	kcal/g mol Btu/lb mol	kJ/kmol MJ/kmol kJ/kmol		4.184* E+03 2.326 000 E−03 2.326 000 E+00	
Heating Value (Volume Basis—Solids and Liquids)	J/m³	therm/U.S. gal	MJ/m³ kJ/m³	kJ/dm³ kW·h/dm³	2.787 163 E+04 2.787 163 E+07 7.742 119 E+00	7, 12 7
		therm/U.K. gal	MJ/m³ kJ/m³	kJ/dm³ kW·h/dm³	2.320 798 E+04 2.320 798 E+07 6.446 660 E+00	7, 12 7

Table B-5 (continued)
Recommended SI Units and Conversion Factors

To convert from	To	To	Multiply by		Reference
therm/Can. gal	MJ/m³	kJ/dm³	2.320 799	E+04	7, 12
	kJ/m³		2.320 799	E+07	7
		kW·h/dm³	6.446 663	E+00	
Btu/U.S. gal	MJ/m³	kJ/dm³	2.787 163	E−01	7
	kJ/m³		2.787 163	E+02	
		kW·h/m³	7.742 119	E−02	
Btu/U.K. gal	MJ/m³	kJ/dm³	2.320 800	E−01	7
	kJ/m³		2.320 800	E+02	
		kW·h/m³	6.446 660	E−02	
Btu/Can. gal	MJ/m³	kJ/dm³	2.320 799	E−01	7
	kJ/m³		2.320 799	E+02	
		kW·h/m³	6.446 663	E−02	
Btu/ft³	MJ/m³	kJ/dm³	3.725 895	E−02	7
	kJ/m³		3.725 895	E+01	
		kW·h/m³	1.034 971	E−02	
kcal/m³	MJ/m³	kJ/dm³	4.184*	E−03	7
	kJ/m³		4.184*	E+00	
cal/mL	MJ/m³		4.184*	E+00	
ft·lbf/U.S. gal	kJ/m³		3.581 692	E−01	

Table B-5 (continued)
Recommended SI Units and Conversion Factors

Quantity	SI Unit	Customary Unit	Metric Unit API Preferred	Metric Unit Other Allowable	Conversion Factor (Multiply Quantity Expressed in Customary Units by Factor to Get Metric Equivalent)		Notes See Pg. 850
HEATING VALUE, ENTROPY, HEAT CAPACITY (CONTINUED)							
Heating Value (Volume Basis—Gases)	J/m^3	cal/mL	kJ/m^3	J/dm^3	4.184*	E+03	7
		$kcal/m^3$	kJ/m^3	J/dm^3	4.184*	E+00	7
		Btu/ft^3	kJ/m^3	J/dm^3	3.725 895	E+01	7
Specific Entropy	$J/(kg \cdot K)$	$Btu/(lb \cdot °R)$	$kJ/(kg \cdot K)$	$J/(g \cdot K)$	4.186 8*	E+00	
		$cal/(g \cdot K)$	$kJ/(kg \cdot K)$	$J/(g \cdot K)$	4.184*	E+00	
		$kcal/(kg \cdot °C)$	$kJ/(kg \cdot K)$	$J/(g \cdot K)$	4.184*	E+00	
Specific Heat Capacity (Mass Basis)	$J/(kg \cdot K)$	$kW \cdot h/(kg \cdot °C)$	$kJ/(kg \cdot K)$	$J/(g \cdot °C)$	3.6*	E+03	
		$Btu/(lb \cdot °F)$	$kJ/(kg \cdot K)$	$J/(g \cdot °C)$	4.186 8*	E+00	
		$kcal/(kg \cdot °C)$	$kJ/(kg \cdot K)$	$J/(g \cdot °C)$	4.184*	E+00	
Molar Heat Capacity	$J/(mol \cdot K)$	$Btu/(lb\ mol \cdot °F)$	$kJ/(kmol \cdot K)$	$J/(g \cdot °C)$	4.186 8*	E+00	
		$cal/(g\ mol \cdot °C)$	$kJ/(kmol \cdot K)$	$J/(g \cdot °C)$	4.184*	E+00	

Table B-5 (continued)
Recommended SI Units and Conversion Factors

TEMPERATURE, PRESSURE, VACUUM

Quantity	SI Unit	Customary Unit	Metric Unit API Preferred	Metric Unit Other Allowable	Conversion Factor (Multiply Quantity Expressed in Customary Units by Factor to Get Metric Equivalent)	Notes See Pg. 850
Temperature (Absolute)	K	°R K	K K		5/9 1	
Temperature (Traditional)	K	°F °C	°C °C		(°F−32)/1.8 1	
Temperature (Difference)	K	°F °C	K K	°C °C	5/9 1	
Temperature/Length (Geothermal Gradient)	K/m	°F/100 ft	mK/m		1.822 689 E+01	
Length/Temperature (Geothermal Step)	m/K	ft/°F	m/K		5.486 4* E−01	
Pressure	Pa	atm (14.696 lbf/in² or 760 mmHg at 0°C)	MPa kPa	bar	1.013 250* E−01 1.013 250* E+02 1.013 250* E+00	

Table B-5 (continued)
Recommended SI Units and Conversion Factors

TEMPERATURE, PRESSURE, VACUUM (CONTINUED)

Quantity	SI Unit	Customary Unit	Metric Unit API Preferred	Metric Unit Other Allowable	Conversion Factor (Multiply Quantity Expressed in Customary Units by Factor to Get Metric Equivalent)	Notes See Pg. 850
		bar	MPa kPa	bar	1.0* E−01 1.0* E+02 1	8
		at (kgf/cm²) (technical atmosphere)	MPa kPa	bar	9.806 650* E−02 9.806 650* E+01 9.806 650* E−01	
		lbf/in² (psi)	MPa kPa	bar	6.894 757 E−03 6.894 757 E+00 6.894 757 E−02	
		inHg at 60°F inHg at 32°F inH₂0 at 39.2°F inH₂0 at 60°F	kPa kPa kPa kPa		3.376 85 E+00 3.386 38 E+00 2.490 82 E−01 2.488 4 E−01	
		mmHg at 0°C (torr) cmH₂0 at 4°C	kPa kPa		1.333 22 E−01 9.806 38 E−02	

Table B-5 (continued)
Recommended SI Units and Conversion Factors

	lbf/ft²(psf)	kPa	4.788 026	E−02	
	μmHg at 0°C	Pa	1.333 22	E−01	
	μbar	Pa	1.0*	E−01	
	dyn/cm²	Pa	1.0*	E−01	
Vacuum, Draft Pa	inHg at 60°F	kPa	3.376 85	E+00	
	inH$_2$0 at 39.2°F	kPa	2.490 82	E−01	
	inH$_2$0 at 60°F	kPa	2.488 4	E−01	
	mmHg at 0°C (torr)	kPa	1.333 22	E−01	
	cmH$_2$0 at 4°C	kPa	9.806 38	E−02	
Liquid Head m	ft	m	3.048*	E−01	
	in	mm	2.54*	E+01	
Pressure Drop/Length Pa/m	psi/ft	kPa/m	2.262 059	E+01	9
	psi/100 ft	kPa/m	2.262 059	E−01	
	psi/mi	kPa/km	4.284 203	E+00	

Table B-5 (continued)
Recommended SI Units and Conversion Factors

Quantity	SI Unit	Customary Unit	Metric Unit API Preferred	Metric Unit Other Allowable	Conversion Factor (Multiply Quantity Expressed in Customary Units by Factor to Get Metric Equivalent)	Notes See Pg. 850
DENSITY, SPECIFIC VOLUME, CONCENTRATION, DOSAGE						
Density (Gases)	kg/m³	lb/ft³	kg/m³		1.601 846 E+01	
Density (Liquids)	kg/m³	lb/U.S. gal	kg/m³	kg/dm³	1.198 264 E+02 ; 1.198 264 E−01	7
		lb/U.K. gal	kg/m³	kg/dm³	9.977 633 E+01 ; 9.977 633 E−02	7
		lb/ft³	kg/m³	kg/dm³	1.601 846 E+01 ; 1.601 846 E−02	7
		g/cm³	kg/m³	kg/dm³	1.0* E+03 ; 1	7
		kg/L	kg/m³	kg/dm³	1.0* E+03 ; 1.0*	7
		°API	kg/m³		Use tables	10
Density (Solids)	kg/m³	lb/ft³	kg/m³	kg/dm³	1.601 846 E+01 ; 1.601 846 E−02	
Specific Volume (Gases)	m³/kg	ft³/lb	m³/kg	dm³/kg	6.242 796 E−02 ; 6.242 796 E+01	7

Table B-5 (continued)
Recommended SI Units and Conversion Factors

Quantity	SI Unit	Customary Unit	Metric Unit	Metric Unit	Factor		Note
Specific Volume (Liquids)	m³/kg	ft³/lb	m³/kg	dm³/kg	6.242 796	E−02	7
					6.242 796	E+01	7
		U.K. gal/lb	m³/kg	dm³/kg	1.022 242	E−02	7
					1.022 242	E+01	7
		U.S. gal/lb	m³/kg	dm³/kg	8.345 404	E−03	7
					8.345 404	E+00	7
Molar Volume	m³/mol	L/g mol	m³/kmol		1		
		ft³/lb mol	m³/kmol		6.242 796	E−02	
Specific Volume (Clay Yield)	m³/kg	bbl/U.S. ton	m³/Mg	m³/t	1.752 535	E−01	
		bbl/U.K. ton	m³/Mg	m³/t	1.564 763	E−01	
Yield (Shale Distillation)	m³/kg	bbl/U.S. ton	dm³/Mg	dm³/t	1.752 535	E+02	7
		bbl/U.K. ton	dm³/Mg	dm³/t	1.564 763	E+02	7
		U.S. gal/U.S. ton	dm³/Mg	dm³/t	4.172 702	E+00	7
		U.S. gal/U.K. ton	dm³/Mg	dm³/t	3.725 627	E+00	7
Concentration (Mass/Mass)	kg/kg	wt %	kg/kg		1.0*	E−02	
			g/kg		1.0*	E+01	
		wt ppm	mg/kg		1		
Concentration (Mass/Volume)	kg/m³	lb/bbl	kg/m³	g/dm³	2.853 010	E+00	7
		g/U.S. gal	kg/m³		2.641 720	E−01	
		g/U.K. gal	kg/m³		2.199 692	E−01	

Table B-5 (continued)
Recommended SI Units and Conversion Factors

Quantity	SI Unit	Customary Unit	Metric Unit — API Preferred	Metric Unit — Other Allowable	Conversion Factor (Multiply Quantity Expressed in Customary Units by Factor to Get Metric Equivalent)	Notes See Pg. 850
DENSITY, SPECIFIC GRAVITY, VOLUME, CONCENTRATION, DOSAGE (CONTINUED)						
Concentration (continued) (Mass/Volume)		lb/1000 U.S. gal	g/m^3	mg/dm^3	1.198 264 E+02	7
		lb/1000 U.K. gal	g/m^3	mg/dm^3	9.977 633 E+01	7
		grains/U.S. gal	g/m^3	mg/dm^3	1.711 806 E+01	7
		lb/1000 bbl	g/m^3	mg/dm^3	2.853 010 E+00	7
		mg/U.S. gal	g/m^3	mg/dm^3	2.641 720 E-01	7
		grains/100 ft^3	mg/m^3		2.288 352 E+01	
		grains/ft^3	mg/m^3		2.288 352 E+03	
Concentration (Volume/Volume)	m^3/m^3	bbl/bbl	m^3/m^3		1	
		ft^3/ft^3	m^3/m^3		1	
		bbl/(acre·ft)	dm^3/m^3	L/m^3	1.288 923 E-01	1
		U.K. gal/ft^3	dm^3/m^3	L/m^3	1.605 437 E+02	
		U.S. gal/ft^3	dm^3/m^3	L/m^3	1.336 806 E+02	
		mL/U.S. gal	dm^3/m^3	L/m^3	2.641 720 E-01	
		mL/U.K. gal	dm^3/m^3	L/m^3	2.199 692 E-01	

Table B-5 (continued)
Recommended SI Units and Conversion Factors

Quantity	Customary unit	SI unit		Conversion factor		
	Vol %	m³/m³		1.0*	E−02	
		cm³/m³		1		
	Vol ppm	dm³/m³	L/m³	1.0*	E−03	
	U.K. gal/1000 bbl	cm³/m³		2.859 406	E+01	
	U.S. gal/1000 bbl	cm³/m³		2.380 952	E+01	
Concentration (Mole/Volume) mol/m³	lb mol/U.S. gal	kmol/m³		1.198 264	E+02	
	lb mol/U.K. gal	kmol/m³		9.977 633	E+01	
	lb mol/ft³	kmol/m³		1.601 846	E+01	
	std ft³(60°F, 1 atm)/bbl	kmol/m³		7.518 18	E−03	6
Concentration (Volume/Mole) m³/mol	U.S. gal/1000 std ft³ (60°F/60°F)	dm³/kmol	L/kmol	3.166 93	E+00	6
	bbl/million std ft³ (60°F/60°F)	dm³/kmol	L/kmol	1.330 11	E−01	6

Table B-5 (continued)
Recommended SI Units and Conversion Factors

Quantity	SI Unit	Customary Unit	Metric Unit API Preferred	Metric Unit Other Allowable	Conversion Factor (Multiply Quantity Expressed in Customary Units by Factor to Get Metric Equivalent)	Notes See Pg. 850
FACILITY THROUGHPUT, CAPACITY						
Throughput (Mass Basis)	kg/s	million lb/yr	Mg/a	t/a	4.535 924 E+02	
		U.K. ton/yr	Mg/a	t/a	1.016 047 E+00	
		U.S. ton/yr	Mg/a	t/a	9.071 847 E−01	
		U.K. ton/d	Mg/d	t/d, Mg/h	1.016 047 E+00 / 4.233 529 E−02	
		U.S. ton/d	Mg/d	t/d, Mg/h	9.071 847 E−01 / 3.779 936 E−02	
		U.K. ton/h	Mg/h	t/h	1.016 047 E+00	
		U.S. ton/h	Mg/h	t/h	9.071 847 E−01	
		lb/h	kg/h		4.535 924 E−01	
Throughput (Volume Basis)	m³/s	bbl/d	m³/a, m³/d, m³/h		5.803 036 E+01 / 1.589 873 E−01 / 6.624 471 E−03	

Table B-5 (continued)
Recommended SI Units and Conversion Factors

Quantity	From	To	To (alt)	Conversion Factor
	ft³/d	m³/h		1.179 869 E−03
	ft³/d	m³/d		2.831 685 E−02
	bbl/h	m³/h		1.589 873 E−01
	ft³/h	m³/h		2.831 685 E−02
	U.K. gal/h	m³/h		4.546 092 E−03
	U.K. gal/h		L/h	4.546 092 E+00
	U.S. gal/h	m³/h		3.785 412 E−03
	U.S. gal/h		L/h	3.785 412 E+00
	U.K. gal/min	m³/h		2.727 655 E−01
	U.K. gal/min		L/min	4.546 092 E+00
	U.S. gal/min	m³/h		2.271 247 E−01
	U.S. gal/min		L/min	3.785 412 E+00
Throughput (Mole Basis) mol/s	lb mol/h	kmol/h		4.535 924 E−01
	lb mol/h		kmol/s	1.259 979 E−04
Pipeline Capacity m³/m	bbl/mi	m³/km		9.879 013 E−02

Table B-5 (continued)
Recommended SI Units and Conversion Factors

Quantity	SI Unit	Customary Unit	Metric Unit		Conversion Factor (Multiply Quantity Expressed in Customary Units by Factor to Get Metric Equivalent)	Notes See Pg. 850
			API Preferred	Other Allowable		
FLOW RATE						
Flow Rate (Mass Basis)	kg/s	U.K. ton/min	kg/s		1.693 412 E+01	
		U.S. ton/min	kg/s		1.511 975 E+01	
		U.K. ton/h	kg/s		2.822 353 E−01	
		U.S. ton/h	kg/s		2.519 958 E−01	
		million lb/d	kg/s		5.249 912 E+00	
		U.K. ton/d	kg/s		1.175 980 E−02	
		U.S. ton/d	kg/s		1.049 982 E−02	
		million lb/yr	kg/s		1.438 332 E−02	
		U.K. ton/yr	kg/s		3.221 864 E−05	
		U.S. ton/yr	kg/s		2.876 664 E−05	
		lb/s	kg/s		4.535 924 E−01	
		lb/min	kg/s		7.559 873 E−03	
		lb/h	kg/s		1.259 979 E−04	

Table B-5 (continued)
Recommended SI Units and Conversion Factors

Property	SI Unit	From	To	Factor	
Flow Rate (Volume Basis)	m³/s	bbl/d	dm³/s	1.840 131	E−03
		ft³/d	dm³/s	3.277 413	E−04
		bbl/h	dm³/s	4.416 314	E−02
		ft³/h	dm³/s	7.865 791	E−03
		U.K. gal/h	dm³/s	1.262 803	E−03
		U.S. gal/h	dm³/s	1.051 503	E−03
		U.K. gal/min	dm³/s	7.576 820	E−02
		U.S. gal/min	dm³/s	6.309 020	E−02
		ft³/min	dm³/s	4.719 474	E−01
		ft³/s	dm³/s	2.831 685	E+01
Flow Rate (Mole Basis)	mol/s	lb mol/s	kmol/s	4.535 924	E−01
		lb mol/h	kmol/s	1.259 979	E−04
		million SCF/SD	kmol/s	1.383 449	E−02
Flow Rate/Length (Mass Basis)	kg/(s·m)	lb/(s·ft)	kg/(s·m)	1.488 164	E+00
		lb/(h·ft)	kg/(s·m)	4.133 789	E−04
Flow Rate/Length (Volume Basis)	m²/s	U.K. gal/(min·ft)	m³/(s·m)	2.485 833	E−04
		U.S. gal/(min·ft)	m³/(s·m)	2.069 888	E−04
		U.K. gal/(h·in)	m³/(s·m)	4.971 667	E−05
		U.S. gal/(h·in)	m³/(s·m)	4.139 776	E−05
		U.K. gal/(h·ft)	m³/(s·m)	4.143 055	E−06
		U.S. gal/(h·ft)	m³/(s·m)	3.449 814	E−06

Table B-5 (continued)
Recommended SI Units and Conversion Factors

Quantity	SI Unit	Customary Unit	Metric Unit API Preferred	Metric Unit Other Allowable	Conversion Factor (Multiply Quantity Expressed in Customary Units by Factor to Get Metric Equivalent)	Notes See Pg. 850
FLOW RATE (CONTINUED)						
Flow Rate/Area (Mass Basis)	kg/(s·m²)	lb/(s·ft²) lb/(h·ft²)	kg/(s·m²) kg/(s·m²)		4.882 428 E+00 1.356 230 E-03	
Flow Rate/Area (Volume Basis)	m/s	ft³/(s·ft²) ft³/(min·ft²)	m/s m/s		3.048* E-01 5.08* E-03	
		U.K. gal/(h·in²) U.S. gal/(h·in²)	m/s m/s		1.957 349 E-03 1.629 833 E-03	
		U.K. gal/(min·ft²) U.S. gal/(min·ft²)	m/s m/s		8.155 621 E-04 6.790 972 E-04	
		U.K. gal/(h·ft²) U.S. gal/(h·ft²)	m/s m/s		1.359 270 E-05 1.131 829 E-05	
Flow Rate/Pressure Drop (Productivity Index)	m³/(s·Pa)	bbl/(d·psi)	m³/(d·kPa)		2.305 916 E-02	

Table B-5 (continued)
Recommended SI Units and Conversion Factors

Quantity	SI Unit	Customary Unit	Metric Unit API Preferred	Metric Unit Other Allowable	Conversion Factor (Multiply Quantity Expressed in Customary Units by Factor to Get Metric Equivalent)		Notes See Pg. 850
ENERGY, WORK, QUANTITY OF HEAT, POWER							
Energy, Work, Quantity of Heat	J						
		quad	EJ TW·h		1.055 056 2.930 711	E+00 E+02	
		therm	MJ kJ	kW·h	1.055 056 1.055 056 2.930 711	E+02 E+05 E+01	12
		U.S. tonf·mi	MJ		1.431 744	E+01	
		hp·h	MJ kJ	kW·h	2.684 520 2.684 520 7.456 999	E+00 E+03 E−01	13
		ch·h or CV·h	MJ kJ	kW·h	2.647 796 2.647 796 7.354 99	E+00 E+03 E−01	14
		kW·h	MJ kJ		3.6* 3.6*	E+00 E+03	

Table B-5 (continued)
Recommended SI Units and Conversion Factors

Quantity	SI Unit	Customary Unit	Metric Unit — API Preferred	Metric Unit — Other Allowable	Conversion Factor (Multiply Quantity Expressed in Customary Units by Factor to Get Metric Equivalent)		Notes See Pg. 850
ENERGY, WORK, QUANTITY OF HEAT, POWER (CONTINUED)							
		Chu	kJ	kW·h	1.899 101	E+00	15
					5.275 280	E−04	
		Btu	kJ	kW·h	1.055 056	E+00	
					2.930 711	E−04	
		kcal	kJ		4.184*	E+00	
		cal	kJ		4.184*	E−03	
		ft·lbf	kJ		1.355 818	E−03	
		J	kJ		1.0*	E−03	
		lb·ft²/s² (ft·pdl)	kJ		4.214 011	E−05	
		erg	J		1.0*	E−07	
Impact Energy	J	kgf·m	J		9.806 650*	E+00	
		ft·lbf	J		1.355 818	E+00	
Work/Length	J/m	U.S. tonf·mi/ft	MJ/m		4.697 322	E+01	
Surface Energy	J/m²	erg/cm²	mJ/m²		1.0*	E+00	

Table B-5 (continued)
Recommended SI Units and Conversion Factors

Quantity	SI unit	From	To	Factor	Exponent	Note
Power	W	quad/yr	EJ/a	1.055 056	E+00	
		quad/yr	GW	3.345 561	E+01	
		erg/a	TW	3.170 979	E−27	
		erg/a	GW	3.170 979	E−24	
		million Btu/h	MW	2.930 711	E−01	
		ton of refrigeration	kW	3.516 853	E+00	
		Btu/s	kW	1.055 056	E+00	
		kW	kW	1		
		hydraulic horsepower—hhp	kW	7.460 43	E−01	
		hp (electric)	kW	7.46*	E−01	
		hp (550 ft·lbf/s)	kW	7.456 999	E−01	
		ch or CV	kW	7.354 99	E−01	16
		Btu/min	kW	1.758 427	E−02	
		ft·lbf/s	kW	1.355 818	E−03	
		kcal/h	W	1.162 222	E+00	
		Btu/h	W	2.930 711	E−01	
		ft·lbf/min	W	2.259 697	E−02	
Power/Area	W/m³	Btu/(s·ft²)	kW/m²	1.135 653	E+01	
		cal/(h·cm²)	kW/m²	1.162 222	E−02	
		Btu/(h·ft²)	kW/m³	3.154 591	E−03	

Table B-5 (continued)
Recommended SI Units and Conversion Factors

ENERGY, WORK, QUANTITY OF HEAT, POWER (CONTINUED)

Quantity	SI Unit	Customary Unit	Metric Unit API Preferred	Metric Unit Other Allowable	Conversion Factor (Multiply Quantity Expressed in Customary Units by Factor to Get Metric Equivalent)		Notes See Pg. 850
Heat Flow Unit — hfu (Geothermics)		μcal/(s·cm^2)	mW/m^2		4.184*	E+01	
Heat Release Rate, Mixing Power	W/m^3	hp/ft^3	kW/m^3		2.633 414	E+01	13
		cal/(h·cm^3)	kW/m^3		1.162 222	E+00	
		Btu/(s·ft^3)	kW/m^3		3.725 895	E+01	
		Btu/(h·ft^3)	kW/m^3		1.034 971	E-02	
Heat Generation Unit — hgu (Radioactive Rocks)		cal/(s·cm^3)	μW/m^3		4.184*	E+12	
Cooling Duty (Machinery)	W/W	Btu/(bhp·h)	W/kW		3.930 148	E-01	13
Mass Fuel Consumption	kg/J	lb/(hp·h)	kg/MJ		1.689 659	E-01	13
			kg/(kW·h)		6.082 774	E-01	

Table B-5 (continued)
Recommended SI Units and Conversion Factors

Quantity	From			Value		Ref
Volume Fuel Consumption m³/J	m³/(kW·h)	dm³/MJ	mm³/J	2.777 778	E+02	7
			dm³/(kW·h)	1.0*	E+03	7
	U.S. gal/(hp·h)	dm³/MJ	mm³/J	1.410 089	E+00	7, 13
			dm³/(kW·h)	5.076 321	E+00	7
	U.K. pt/(hp·h)	dm³/MJ	mm³/J	2.116 809	E−01	7, 13
			dm³/(kW·h)	7.620 512	E−01	7
Fuel Consumption m³/m (Automotive)	U.K. gal/mi	dm³/100 km	L/100 km	2.824 811	E+02	7
	U.S. gal/mi	dm³/100 km	L/100 km	2.352 146	E+02	
	mi/U.S. gal	km/dm³	km/L	4.251 437	E−01	
	mi/U.K. gal	km/dm³	km/L	3.540 060	E−01	

Table B-5 (continued)
Recommended SI Units and Conversion Factors

Quantity / SI Unit	Customary Unit	Metric Unit API Preferred	Metric Unit Other Allowable	Conversion Factor (Multiply Quantity Expressed in Customary Units by Factor to Get Metric Equivalent)	Notes See Pg. 850
MECHANICS					
Velocity (Linear), Speed, m/s	knot	km/h	knot	1.852* E+00 / 1	
	mi/h	km/h		1.609 344* E+00	
	m/s	m/s		1	
	ft/s	m/s	cm/s / m/ms	3.048* E−01 / 3.048* E+01 / 3.048* E−04	17
	ft/min	m/s	cm/s	5.08* E−03 / 5.08* E−01	
	ft/h	mm/s	cm/s	8.466 667 E−02 / 8.466 667 E−03	
	ft/d	mm/s	m/d	3.527 778 E−03 / 3.048* E−01	

Table B-5 (continued)
Recommended SI Units and Conversion Factors

Quantity (SI unit)	Convert from	To	To (alt)	Multiply by	Multiply by (alt)	Note
	in/s	mm/s	cm/s	2.54* E+01	2.54* E+00	
	in/min	mm/s	cm/s	4.233 333 E−01	4.233 333 E−02	
Velocity (Angular) rad/s	r/min	rad/s	r/min	1.047 198 E−01	1	
	r/s	rad/s	r/s	6.283 185 E+00	1	
	deg/min	rad/s		2.908 882 E−04		
	deg/s	rad/s		1.745 329 E−02		
Reciprocal Velocity s/m	μs/ft	μs/m		3.280 840 E+00		18
Acceleration (Linear) m/s²	ft/s²	m/s²		3.048* E−01		
	gal (cm/s²)	m/s²		1.0* E−02		
Acceleration (Angular) rad/s²	rad/s²	rad/s²		1		
	rpm/s	rad/s²		1.047 198 E−01		
Corrosion Rate mm/a	in/yr (ipy)	mm/a		2.54* E+01		
Momentum kg·m/s	lb·ft/s	kg·m/s		1.382 550 E−01		
Force N	U.K. tonf	kN		9.964 016 E+00		
	U.S. tonf	kN		8.896 443 E+00		

Table B-5 (continued)
Recommended SI Units and Conversion Factors

Quantity	SI Unit	Customary Unit	Metric Unit — API Preferred	Metric Unit — Other Allowable	Conversion Factor (Multiply Quantity Expressed in Customary Units by Factor to Get Metric Equivalent)	Notes See Pg. 850
MECHANICS (CONTINUED)						
Force (continued)		kgf (kp)	N		9.806 650* E+00	
		lbf	N		4.448 222 E+00	
		N	N		1	
		pdl	mN		1.382 550 E+02	
		dyn	mN		1.0* E−02	
Bending Moment, Torque	N·m	U.S. tonf·ft	kN·m		2.711 636 E+00	
		kgf·m	N·m		9.806 650* E+00	
		lbf·ft	N·m		1.355 818 E+00	
		lbf·in	N·m		1.129 848 E−01	
		pdl·ft	N·m		4.214 011 E−02	
Bending Moment, Length	N·m/m	lbf·ft/in	N·m/m		5.337 866 E+01	
		kgf·m/m	N·m/m		9.806 650* E+00	
		lbf·in/in	N·m/m		4.448 222 E+00	
Moment of Inertia	kg·m²	lb·ft²	kg·m²		4.214 011 E−02	
		in⁴	cm⁴		4.162 314 E+01	

Table B-5 (continued)
Recommended SI Units and Conversion Factors

Quantity	SI Unit	Customary Unit	SI Unit	Factor	Exponent
Stress	Pa	U.S. tonf/in²	N/mm²	1.378 951	E+01
		kgf/mm²	N/mm²	9.806 650*	E+00
		U.S. tonf/ft²	N/mm²	9.576 052	E-02
		lbf/in² (psi)	N/mm²	6.894 757	E-03
		lbf/ft² (psf)	kPa	4.788 026	E-02
		dyn/cm²	Pa	1.0*	E-01
Yield Point, Gel Strength (Drilling Fluid)		lbf/100 ft²	Pa	4.788 026	E+01
Mass/Length	kg/m	lb/ft	kg/m	1.488 164	E+00
Mass/Area Structural Loading, Bearing Capacity (Mass Basis)	kg/m²	U.S. ton/ft²	Mg/m²	9.764 855	E+00
		lb/ft²	kg/m²	4.882 428	E+00
Modulus of Elasticity	Pa	lbf/in² (psi)	MPa	6.894 757	E-03
Section Modulus	m³	in³	cm³	1.638 706	E+01
Coefficient of Thermal Expansion	m/(m·K)	in/(in·°F)	mm/(mm·K), mm/(mm·°C)	5.555 556	E-01

Table B-5 (continued)
Recommended SI Units and Conversion Factors

Quantity	SI Unit	Customary Unit	Metric Unit		Conversion Factor (Multiply Quantity Expressed in Customary Units by Factor to Get Metric Equivalent)		Notes See Pg. 850
			API Preferred	Other Allowable			
TRANSPORT PROPERTIES							
Diffusivity	m^2/s	ft^2/s	mm^2/s		9.290 304*	E+04	
		cm^2/s	mm^2/s		1.0*	E+02	
		ft^2/h	mm^2/s		2.580 64*	E+01	
Thermal Resistance	$K \cdot m^2/W$	$°C \cdot m^2 \cdot h/kcal$	$K \cdot m^2/kW$		8.604 208	E+02	
		$°F \cdot ft^2 \cdot h/Btu$	$K \cdot m^2/kW$		1.761 102	E+02	
Heat Flux	W/m^2	$Btu/(h \cdot ft^2)$	kW/m^2		3.154 591	E−03	
Thermal Conductivity	$W/(m \cdot K)$	$cal/(s \cdot cm^2 \cdot °C/cm)$	$W/m \cdot K$	$W/(m^2 \cdot °C/m)$	4.184*	E+02	
		$Btu/(h \cdot ft^2 \cdot °F/ft)$	$W/(m \cdot K)$	$W/(m^2 \cdot °C/m)$	1.730 735	E+00	
		$kcal/(h \cdot m^2 \cdot °C/m)$	$W/(m \cdot K)$	$W/(m^2 \cdot °C/m)$	1.162 222	E+00	
		$Btu/(h \cdot ft^2 \cdot °F/in)$	$W/(m \cdot K)$	$W/(m^2 \cdot °C/m)$	1.442 279	E−01	
		$cal/(h \cdot cm^2 \cdot °C/cm)$	$W/(m \cdot K)$	$W/(m^2 \cdot °C/m)$	1.162 222	E−01	
Heat Transfer Coefficient	$W/(m^2 \cdot K)$	$cal/(s \cdot cm^2 \cdot °C)$	$kW/(m^2 \cdot K)$		4.184*	E+01	
		$Btu/(s \cdot ft^2 \cdot °F)$	$kW/(m^2 \cdot K)$		2.044 175	E+01	
		$cal/(h \cdot cm^2 \cdot °C)$	$kW/(m^2 \cdot K)$		1.162 222	E−02	
		$Btu/(h \cdot ft^2 \cdot °F)$	$kW/(m^2 \cdot K)$		5.678 263	E−03	

Table B-5 (continued)
Recommended SI Units and Conversion Factors

Quantity	SI Unit	From	To	Alt.	Factor	Exp	Ref
		Btu/(h·ft²·°R)	kW/(m²·K)		5.678 263	E−03	19
		kcal/(h·m²·°C)	kW/(m²·K)		1.162 222	E−03	19
Volumetric Heat Transfer Coefficient	W/(m³·K)	Btu/(s·ft³·°F)	kW/(m³·K)		6.706 611	E+01	
		Btu/(h·ft³·°F)	kW/(m³·K)		1.862 947	E−02	
Surface Tension	N/m	dyn/cm	mN/m		1.0*	E+00	
Viscosity (Dynamic)	Pa·s	lbf·s/in²	mPa·s	cP	6.894 757	E+06	19
		lbf·s/ft²	mPa·s	cP	4.788 026	E+04	19
		kgf·s/m²	mPa·s	cP	9.806 650*	E+03	19
		dyn·s/cm²	Pa·s		1.0*	E−01	19
			mPa·s	cP	1.0*	E+02	19
		P	Pa·s		1.0*	E−01	19
			mPa·s	cP	1.0*	E+02	19
		cP	mPa·s	cP	1.0*	E+00	19
Viscosity (Kinematic)	m²/s	ft²/s	mm²/s	cSt	9.290 304*	E+04	19
		in²/s	mm²/s	cSt	6.451 6*	E+02	19
		ft²/h	mm²/s	cSt	2.580 64*	E+01	19
		m²/h	mm²/s	cSt	2.777 778	E+02	19
		cm²/s	mm²/s	cSt	1.0*	E+02	19
		St	mm²/s	cSt	1.0*	E+02	19
		cSt	mm²/s	cSt	1.0*	E+00	19
Permeability	m²	D	μm²	D	1.0*	E+00	20
		mD	μm²	D	1.0*	E−03	20

Notes

1. Based on U.S. survey foot rather than the international foot.

$$1 \text{ U.S. survey foot} = \frac{1200}{3937} \text{ metre (exactly)}$$

1 international foot = 0.3048 metre (exactly)
1 U.S. statute mile = 5280 U.S. survey feet

2. The cubem (cubic mile) is used in the measurement of very large volumes, such as the content of a sedimentary basin.

3. In surveying, navigation, and so forth, angles will, no doubt, continue to be measured with instruments that read in degrees, minutes, and seconds and need not be converted into radians; for calculations involving rotational energy, radians are preferred.

4. The unit of a million years is used in geochronology. At the present time, abbreviations such as MY or mmy are used. The mega-annum is the preferred unit, but many simply prefer to use mathematical notation (that is, $\times 10^6$).

5. The year as defined in these tables is the calendar year, equivalent to exactly 365 mean solar days. For some purposes, the use of other years such as the sidereal year or the tropical year may be more appropriate. The conversion factors for years to seconds are as follows:

Calendar year 3.153 600* E+07
Sidereal year 3.155 815 E+07
Tropical year 3.155 693 E+07

6. The conversion factor is for an ideal gas, calculated by using a value of 8.314 41 J/(mol·K), which has a standard deviation of 0.000 26 J/(mol·K), for the molar gas constant [13]. The converted quantity, therefore, should be rounded to an appropriate number of significant digits commensurate with the precision of the original measurement, but in no case to more than five.

7. The special name litre (symbol L) has been approved for the cubic decimetre (symbol dm³) but use of this unit is restricted to the measurement of liquids and gases.

8. The use of the bar should be limited to physical measurement (for example, pressure gages); however, the kilopascal is preferred. It is recommended that only the pascal or standard multiples (kPa, MPa) be used in calculations.

9. Subsurface pressures can be measured in megapascals or as freshwater heads in metres. If the latter approach is adopted, the hydrostatic gradient becomes dimensionless.

10. See Table 3 of the ASTM-IP Petroleum Measurement Tables (ASTM D 1250, IP 200, API Standard 2540, ANSI Z11.83, ISO R91). The 1952 edition of the ASTM-IP tables converts API gravity at 60°F to density (kg/L) at 15°C, and an additional conversion from kg/L to kg/m³ is necessary. The 1980 edition of the ASTM-IP tables uses density in kg/m^3.

11. Quantities listed under "Facility Throughput, Capacity" are to be used only for characterizing the size or capacity of a plant or piece of equipment. Quantities listed under "Flow Rate" are for use in design calculations.

12. 1 therm = 100 000 Btu (IT). However, consumption of natural gas in the United States normally is expressed in therms based on the value of the Btu (59°F) (*Federal Register*, Vol. 33, No. 146, July 27, 1968). In this case, the conversion factor from therm to megajoule is 1.054 804 E+02.

13. Based on 550 ft·lbf/s horsepower.

14. ch·h or CV·h = cheval vapeur-hour ("metric" horsepower-hour).

15. Chu (Centigrade heat unit) is the quantity of heat required to raise 1 pound of water 1 degree Celsius.

16. ch or CV = cheval vapeur or "metric" horsepower; 1 ch = 1 CV = 75 kgf·m/s.

17. Seismic velocities will be expressed in m/ms (which has the same value as km/s) because the records are calibrated in milliseconds.

18. The reciprocal velocity unit is used in sonic logging work.

19. The centipoise (cP) is an acceptable name for the millipascal second (mPa·s), and

$$1 \text{ cP} = 1 \text{mPa·s}$$

The centistokes (cSt) is an acceptable name for the square millimetre per second (mm²/s), and

$$1 \text{ cSt} = 1 \text{ mm}^2/\text{s}$$

The following special names for non-SI viscosity units are not acceptable SI practice.

poise (P), where $1 \text{ P} = 1 \text{ dyn·s/cm}^2$
stokes (St), where $1 \text{ St} = 1 \text{ cm}^2/\text{s}$
reyn, where $1 \text{ reyn} = 1 \text{ lbf·s/in}^2$

20. The SI unit for intrinsic permeability (of porous media to fluids) is the m². In practice, the μm^2 is a more convenient unit. This working unit is called the darcy (D). In 1978, the API redefined the darcy as being exactly equal to $1 \mu\text{m}^2$. Previously, it had the value of $0.986\ 923 \times 10^{-12} \text{ m}^2$. The full definition of the darcy is as follows:

The darcy is a unit of permeability in fluid flow through a porous medium, having the dimensions of dynamic viscosity multiplied by volume flow rate per unit area and divided by pressure gradient, which simplifies to a dimension of area. A darcy is defined as being exactly equal to $1 \mu\text{m}^2$.

A permeability of one darcy will permit a flow of $1 \text{ m}^3/\text{s}$ of fluid of 1 Pa·s viscosity through an area of 1 m^2 under a pressure gradient of 10^{12} Pa/m:

$$
\begin{aligned}
1 \text{ D} &= 10^{-12} \text{ Pa·s} \left[\text{m}^3/ (\text{s·m}^2) \right] (\text{m/Pa}) \\
&= 10^{-12} \text{ Pa·s} (\text{m/s}) (\text{m/Pa}) \\
&= 10^{-12} \text{ m}^2 = 1 \mu\text{m}^2
\end{aligned}
$$

Appendix C

List of Cyclone Suppliers/Manufacturers

Advanced Ind. Technology Corp.
P.O. Box 555
Lodi, NJ 07644
(201) 546-5852

Alpine American Corp.
5 Michigan Drive
P.O. Box 389
Natick, MA 01760
(617) 655-1123

Bemis Co., Inc., Packaging Services
Div.
31527 Ave., NE
Minneapolis, MN 55418
(612) 340-6000

Black Clawson Co., Shartle Pandia
Div.
605 Clark Street
Middletown, OH 45042
(513) 424-7400

C-E Raymond Combustion Engineering, Inc.
200 W. Monroe Street

Chicago, IL 60606
(312) 236-4044

Combustion Engineering, Inc.
1000 Prospect Hill Road
Windsor, CT 06095
(203) 688-1911

Demco, Inc
P. O. Box 94700
829 SE 29, Oklahoma City
OK 73109
(405) 631-1321

Dorr-Oliver, Inc.
77 Hovemeyer Lane
Stamford, CT 06904
(203) 348-5871

Eagle Iron Works
P. O. Box 934
Des Moines, IA 50304
(515) 243-1123

Fisher Klosterman, Inc.
P. O. Box 11190 St. H
Louisville, KY 40211
(502) 776-1505

Gruendler Crusher & Pulverizer Company
2915 N. Market Street
St. Louis, MO 63106
(314) 531-1220

Heany Industries
Fairview Drive
Box 38
Scottsville, NY 14546
(716) 889-2700

Heyl & Patterson, Inc.
7 Pkwy. Ctr.
Pittsburgh, PA 15220
(412) 922-3300

Kennedy Van Saun Corp.
Beaver Street
Danville, PA 17821
(717) 275-3050

Krebs Engineers
1205 Chrysler Drive
Menlo Park, CA 94025
(415) 325-0751

Laval Separator Corp.
P. O. Box 6119
1911 N. Helm
Fresno, CA 93727
(209) 255-1601

McNally Pittsburg Mfg. Corp.
207 West Third Street

Pittsburg, KS 66762
(316) 231-3000

Polutrol, Inc.
14350 Chrisman Road
Houston, TX 77039

Prater Baumeister, Inc.
1515 S. 55 Ct.
Chicago, IL 60650
(312) 656-8500

Sprout Waldron Div.
Koppers Co., Inc.
Muncy, PA 17756
(717) 546-8211

Sweco, Inc.
6033 E. Bandins Blvd.
P. O. Box 4151
Los Angeles, CA 90051

Universal Road Machinery Co.
Emerick & Sphafeldt Sts.
Kingston, NY 12401
(914) 331-8248

Wemco Div. of Envirotech
Box 15619, 1796 Tribute Road
Sacramento, CA 95813
(916) 929–9363

Wilco Machinery Corp.
65 Mid Country Drive
Orchard Park, NY 14127
(716) 662-2100

Index

A

Abrasion, 635
  resistance, 633
Absorption, 365, 677–678, 706
Acoustic techniques, 413
Activation energy, 298, 301, 306,
  347, 349, 356, 361, 367
Adhesion, 8–11
  forces, 10
  number, 10
Adiabatic saturation temperature,
  676
Adipic acid, 75
Adsorption, 349, 480, 646
  capacity, 707
  coefficient, 356
Aeration, 62, 73, 122, 495, 498, 500
  gas, 495
  point, 500
  rate, 496
Aerodynamic properties, 19
Aerosols, 599, 662, 667
Age distributions, 720
Agglomeration, 20, 25
Agglutination, 8, 11
Aggregative fluidization, 146
Air classification, 594
Air-cloth ratio, 628
Air filtration, 630
Air gravity conveying, 93
Air jets, 97

Air lock feeder, 96
Air permeability, 555, 567
Air pollution control, 624, 646
Air retention, 558
Air separation, 276
Air slide, 92
Air-to-cloth ratio, 627
Airlock, 559, 624
Airy function, 440–441
Alkylated aromatics, 240, 242
Alkylation, 239
Allen's equation, 155, 596
Allyl chloride, 572
Aluminum halides, 246
Ammonium hydroxide, 73
Ammonium nitrate, 11
American Petroleum Institute, 807
American Society of Testing
  Materials, 633
Anemometry, 442, 458
  techniques, 428
Angle
  of difference, 44
  of fall, 44
  of internal friction, 5–7, 48, 59,
    82–83, 116
  of repose, 5–6, 14, 44, 53, 58,
    64, 66, 72
  of slide, 5, 7
Annular flow, 527, 530, 547, 554
Annular ring detectors, 441
Annular shear cells, 47

Apparent density, 3, 66
Archability, 44
Archimedes number, 32, 34, 151,
    523, 621
Arching, 51, 69
Aromatics, 239, 334
Aromatic compounds, 323
Aromatization, 239, 243
Arrhenius relationship, 371
Atomization, 648–649, 651, 655
Atomizer, 654
Atomizing scrubber, 677
Attrition, 2, 20, 27, 50
Austenitic steels, 80
Autocatalytic reaction, 347, 370, 372
Autocorrelation function, 420
Aviline production, 138
Axial dispersion, 382, 724
Axial mixing, 721, 742–743, 747,
    752
  coefficients, 751
Axial solids mixing, 753

B

Back illumination, 435
Backmixing, 385, 403, 744
  model, 697
Backscattering, 441
Baffled mixer, 589
Baghouse, 624–625, 630
Bauxite, 93
Beam expander, 447
Bed
  expansion, 76, 161–162, 164–165,
      173, 175–177, 183, 195, 315,
      432, 461, 689, 517, 723
  permeability of, 50
  porosity of, 187, 418–419, 776
  viscosity of, 420
  voidage of, 51, 145, 164, 353, 742
Behavior index, 45
Benzene, 236, 312
Bergius process, 326
Bernoulli's equation, 614
Bessel function, 440

Bifurcation-type instability, 501, 508
Bin activators, 72
Bingham fluid, 65–66
Biological wastes, 265
Bituminous coal, 19, 323, 330
Black liquor furnaces, 646
Blockage point, 513
Boiler tubes, 505
Boundary layer, 26–27, 594–595
Bragg cell, 447
Bridge circuit, 421
Bridge imbalance techniques, 416
Bridging, 51, 630
  phenomenon of, 496
British Gas Corporation, 273, 276,
    279
Brownian motion, 624, 630
Bubble
  assemblage model, 380, 383–385,
      699, 703, 718–720
  break-up, 710
  caps, 177, 178
  chains, 726
  characteristics, 406
  coalescence, 183, 717, 722, 727,
      729
  collapse rates, 718
  column, 428, 724
  detection, 713
  diameter, 702
  dynamics, 183, 373, 448
  flow, 312, 313, 547
  formation, 693, 701, 709, 721,
      733, 736, 738
  frequency, 405, 409, 411, 421,
      430, 724
  growth, 317, 687, 717, 719, 726
    theory, 689
  holdup, 163, 426
  motion, 188
  pattern, 697
  phase, 380, 383–384, 423, 428,
      456, 461
  point, 163
  populations, 696
  properties, 317, 402
  shape, 188, 736

size, 222, 224–225, 404, 409,
   417, 422–423, 432, 687, 702,
   704, 720
  distribution, 709
  splitting, 317, 403
  velocity, 194, 373, 503
Bubbling bed, 148, 222, 227
  models, 385, 387
Bubbling behavior, 727
Bubbling flow, 502
Bubbling fluidization, 163
Bubbling regime, 160, 163
Bubbling zone, 207, 373, 380, 383
Bubbly flow, 148, 163, 484, 490,
   503, 773
Buckingham π theorem, 104, 106,
   108
Bulk deformability, 122
Bulk densities, 2–3, 4, 11, 530
Bureau of Mines, 78
Bypassing, 146
  effects of, 161

C

Cake resistance, 627–628, 635
Caking, 4
Calcining, 138, 255, 260
Calcium chloride, 7
Calculus of variation, 169
Capacitance, 416
  effect of, 710
  probes, 184, 416–417, 421–423,
   691
Capillary forces, 9
Capture efficiencies, 646
Carbon black production, 633
Carbon monoxide, 688
Carbonium ion, 241–242
  mechanism, 239
  theory, 240
Carman-Kozeny equation, 141
Carman-Kozeny models, 162
Carrying capacity, 547

Carryover, 231
Cascade impactors, 20, 24
Cascade samplers, 437
Cat crackers, 138
Cat-to-oil coke, 242–243
Catalytic activity, 244
Catalytic coke, 242
Catalytic cracker regenerator, 499
Catalytic cracking, 236, 239, 242,
   247, 423, 472, 495
Catalytic decomposition, 689
Catalytic hydrocracking, 336
Catalytic hydrogenation, 326
Catalytic hydroliquefaction, 326
Catalytic reactors, 718
Catalytic synthesis, 333
Catalyst
  activity, 278, 320
  attrition, 239
  porosity, 243
  preparation operations, 44
Cavitation research, 413
Cell models, 390
Centrifugal force, 594, 606, 609
Centrifugation, 20
  classification, 24
Chain combustion, 370
Chain ignition, 348
Channeling, 161, 164, 198–199
  beds, 198
Char gasification, 286
Char separator, 284
Chemical attack, 635
Chemical drying, 255
Chemical reaction, 224
Chemical resistance, 633
Chemisorption, 349
Choked flow, 547
Choking, 511–512, 514–515, 517,
   519, 521, 548, 617
  point, 513
  system, 519
  transition, 512–513, 517
  velocity, 513, 519–522
  voidage, 520–521
Cinegraphic methods, 433
Clinkering point, 273, 275

Cloud penetration, 190
Clump size, 530
Cluster
  diameter, 548
  formation, 209
Constrained packed-bed flow, 479
Coal, 19, 528
  agglomeration, 291
  ashes, 273
  carbonization, 138
  drying, 255
  gasification, 231, 271–272, 333,
    339–341, 354, 388, 474, 688
  gasifier, 760
  liquefaction bottoms, 323
  naphtha, 323
  processing, 318
  tar, 332
Cobalt-molybdenum catalyst, 278,
  327
Cocurrent, 495
  downflow, 486, 488
Coefficient of internal friction, 8,
  10, 13
Coflowing jet, 580–581
COGAS process, 272–273, 286
Cohesion, 44, 81, 83
Cohesive forces, 47, 61
Cohesive materials, 83
Cohesive powders, 73–74, 76
Cohesive properties, 48 , 72, 75,
  149
Cohesive solids, 81
Coke, 236, 239, 242, 244, 246, 254,
  340, 341, 697
  formation, 243, 255
Coking, 138
Collection efficiency, 595, 602,
  608–610, 615, 618, 628, 632,
  661–662, 666, 673, 676, 679
Colloidal silica seeding, 122
Combustion, 260, 341, 346, 361,
  366, 370, 686
  efficiency, 208
  engineering 272–273, 284
  reactions, 760
Complete fluidization, 149
  velocity, 181

Complete reflux, 218
Complex number, 106
Compressibility, 44
Compression, 11
Concentrate feeding, 70
Condensation, 243, 676
Conductivity, 355, 416, 423, 426
Cone angle correction factor, 57
Conical flow, 70
Conradson carbon, 242–243
Consistency index, 65, 115, 125–126
Consolidating stress, 62
Constrained packed-bed flow, 477
Contact time, 667, 759
Contacting power concept, 667, 669
Continuity equation, 491, 496, 619,
  622–623
Continuity wave, 476, 478, 493,
  504, 516
  velocity, 505
Convection, 350–351, 352
Convective cooling, 458
Convective diffusion, 351, 353, 370
  equation, 389
Convective heat transfer, 784–785
Conversion inefficiencies, 199
Conveying systems, 559
Corona, 600
Core flow, 49
Coriolis forces, 686
Correlation techniques, 419, 432,
  449
Corrosion resistance, 320
Cotton bags, 633
Coulombic forces, 9
Coulombic solid, 489
Coulter counter, 25
Countercurrent flows, 487
  trickle flow, 312
Cracked oil, 249
Cracking, 327
  catalyst, 148, 160–163, 243–244,
    612, 690, 710, 717
Creep, 50
Critical aeration rate, 500
Critical Archimedes number, 32
Critical arching dimension, 72
Critical Froude number, 162

Critical height, 380
Critical Weber number, 653–655
Cross-correlation, 406, 420
Cross-flow jets, 581–583, 589
Crystallization, 256
Cumulative density function, 405
Cumulative distribution, 16
Cut size, 611
Cyclic olefins, 239–241
Cyclization, 242–243
Cyclohexane, 423
Cyclone, 20, 231, 249, 251, 255,
    259, 264, 532, 638
  dipleg, 496
  performance, 609
  separators, 593–594, 602–603,
    679

D

Darcy equation, 114, 140, 614, 627
Darcy friction factor, 550
Darcy-Weisbach equation, 28
Decomposition test, 78
Dedusting agent, 77
Deformation, 64, 66
Dehydrogenation, 242–243
Dense phase, 492, 688, 698
  conveying, 511, 522, 547, 564
  expansion, 163
  flow, 510, 512, 517, 523–524,
    526, 530, 532
  fluidized flow, 498
  slugging, 523
  transport, 555
  voidage, 195
Depth of field, 435–436
Devolatilization, 272, 298, 307
  reactions, 294
Diakon powder, 162
Diatomaceous earth, 72
Dielectric constants, 414–415, 427
Dielectric particles, 423
Diffraction, 444
Diffusion, 346, 349, 351–356, 358,
    365, 367–368, 573, 623–624,
    647, 732

coefficient, 350, 352, 354–355,
    363, 389, 749
Diffusional combustion, 370
Diffusional deposition, 595
Diffusional equation, 352, 359
Dilute phase, 492
  conveying, 529, 566
  flow, 510, 532, 548
  powder transport, 78
  regime, 517
  transport, 145, 547
  vertical transport, 545
Dimensional analysis, 58–59, 61,
    100, 104, 106, 108, 610,
    627–628
Dipleg, 603
Discrete model, 741
Discriminator, 420
  circuit, 419
Dispersed phase density, 217
Dispersibility, 44
Dissipative energy, 166
Dissipative forces, 172
Dissolution, 346
Distillation, 328–329, 337
Distribution constant, 18
Distribution laws, 14
Distributor, 380
Domestic sewage, 266
Donor solvent process, 318, 324
Doppler burst, 442-443, 445
Doppler flowmeters, 411
Doppler modulation, 447
Doppler system, 412
Doppler velocimeter, 413
Double flash exposures, 435
Downflow, 485
Drag
  coefficient, 28, 30, 154, 171, 190,
    544, 658, 662
  effects, 209
  forces, 26–27, 145, 166, 168,
    515, 648, 686
  resistance, 37
  theory, 527
Drained angle, 5
Drift flux, 486, 488, 491
  model, 485

plot, 502, 508
velocity, 612–613
Drop weight test, 122
Droplet
  breakup, 670
  dynamics, 647
  formation, 649
  Reynolds number, 658
  sprays, 435, 449
Dry dust filters, 624
Drying, 78, 255
  efficiency, 257
Dust
  collectors, 623
  constant, 78
  explosion, 78–80
  removal, 312
Dustpot, 613

E

Ebullating bed, 319, 326–327
Eddy currents, 609, 613
Effective bubble diameter, 516
Effective diameter, 552
Effective film, 351
Effective interfacial area, 677
Effective roughness, 528
Effective size, 25
Effective viscosity, 128, 166, 461
Efficiency, 24
  curves, 612
Ejector venturi scrubber, 677
Elasticity coefficient, 165
Elastomers, 340
Electrical conductivity, 20, 25
Electrical forces, 9
Electroconductivity technique, 315
Electromagnetic field, 702
Electromagnetic theory, 438
Electroresistivity probe
  measurements, 697, 717, 719
Electroresistivity techniques, 416,
  425
Electrostatic attraction, 623
Electrostatic deposition, 595
Electrostatic forces, 25, 624

Electrostatic precipitation, 599, 638
Electrostatic precipitators, 249, 599,
  601
Elutriation, 25, 215, 226, 228, 686
  data, 224
  rate, 219, 225
    constant, 222, 225
Emulsion phase, 183, 380, 383, 385,
  423, 425, 428, 456, 457, 698
  viscosity, 705
Energy balance, 659, 672
  method, 165
  model, 175, 177
Energy dissipation, 166–167
Entrained bed, 271, 284, 286, 294
  reactor, 332
Entrainment, 207–208, 226, 228,
  320, 506
  model, 226
  predictions, 231
  rate, 208, 216, 219, 224–225,
    231, 499–500
Eötvos numbers, 129
Equation of continuity, 64
Equation of motion, 64, 677
Equivalent diameter, 139
Ergun equation, 150, 152, 488, 498,
  506
Erosion, 544, 551
Ethylene glycols, 334
Euler equation, 170
Euler number, 28, 106
Evaporation, 671, 676
  condensation, 670
Exchange coefficients, 349–350,
  371, 402, 456
Exothermic gas-solid reactions, 782
Exothermic reactions, 702
Expanded flow bin, 82
Expansion coefficient, 128, 150
Expansion equation, 484, 515
Explosion flaps, 79
Explosion hazards, 78
Explosion properties, 77
Explosion test, 78
Extrusion flow, 122
Exxon Donor Solvent, 318–319

F

Fabric filters, 623, 628
  filtration, 624
Failure zone, 46
Falling sphere viscometer, 122
Falling weight, 78
Fanning friction factor, 124,
  527-528, 550
Faraday's cave, 428
Farmer's relationship, 442
Fast fluidization, 388, 525, 530
Fast fluidized bed, 373, 387-388
Fatigue, 50
Fatty acids, 334
Faujasite, 244, 246-247
Feed chutes, 64
Feeding nozzles, 5
Felt fabric, 633
Felt filters, 628
Fermentation, 724
Ferromagnetic properties, 426
Fiber optics, 404, 406, 432, 442
Fiberglass, 633
  filters, 629
Fibrous filters, 627
Fick's law, 352, 354, 357, 365
Field intensity, 599
Film penetration model, 790
Filter
  cake washing, 332
  efficiency, 627
  fabrics, 623
  porosity, 627
Filtration, 328-330, 593
Fin effectiveness, 770
Fines disposal, 555
Finned heat exchange, 770
Fischer-Tropsch, 337, 474
  method, 340
  plant, 336
  synthesis, 138, 332, 334-335
Fixed bed, 138, 140, 142-143, 154,
  161, 198, 236, 271, 334, 353
  catalytic cracker, 236
  gasifier, 272
  pilot, 341

  pressure drop, 145
  reactors, 278-279, 334, 340,
    389-390
Flat-bottomed bins, 57, 59
Flexicokers, 603
Flexicoking, 319-320, 324-325
Flooded disk scrubber, 677
Flooding, 70, 313, 501-502, 761
  instability, 502-503
Flotation, 256
Flow
  agents, 76-77
  behavior index, 125-126
  factor, 67
  function, 69
  instability, 500, 533
  modes, 475, 495
  pattern, 532, 725
  regime, 48, 487, 491
    diagram, 483
  resistance, 630
    coefficient, 726
  stability, 476, 491, 505
  flowability, 110
  flue gas desulfurization, 276
Fluid bed
  boiler, 775
  combustion, 209, 231
  contactors, 796
  reactors, 334
  viscosities, 130
  voidage, 183
Fluid catalytic cracking, 122,
  243-244, 778
Fluid cooking, 123
Fluid drag, 477
Fluid hydroforming, 123
Fluid mixing, 572, 747
Fluidity, 8
  coefficient, 8
Fluidization chart, 488
Fluidization number, 165
Fluidized-bed combustor, 337
Fluidized-bed dryer, 742
Fluidized-bed heat exchangers, 780
Fluidized-bed hydrogasifier, 699
Fluidized-bed operations, 44

Fluidized-bed reactors, 165
Fluidized-bed technology, 138
Fluidized cat crackers, 249
Fluidized flow, 489, 492
Fluidizing velocity, 697
Focal length, 435, 440
Form factor, 353
Fourier's law, 352, 354
Fourier's transform, 407
   lens, 440–441
Fourier's transformer, 440
Fractional efficiency curve, 610
Fractionation, 320
Francis equation, 116
Fraunhofer diffraction, 435
Free bubbling beds, 198, 215
Free-fall velocity, 154, 531, 649
Freeboard, 217, 223–225, 227, 383,
   402, 433–434, 438, 458, 461,
   686
   height, 215, 218, 225, 226
   region, 214, 432, 437,763
   zone, 208, 378
Frequency, 694
   response techniques, 755
   spectrum, 409
Freundlich isotherm, 349
Friction coefficient, 223
Friction drag, 594
Friction factor, 123–125, 140, 143,
   490, 520–521, 528–529, 531,
   550, 552
   correlations, 122
Friction loss, 124, 550
Frictional drag, 27
Frictional effects, 544
Frictional losses, 554, 667
Frictional pressure drop, 529, 545,
   550
Frictional pressure loss, 140
Frictional resistance, 351
Fringe spacing, 442
Froude number, 106, 146, 162–163,
   172–173, 175, 181, 515, 548
Fuel oil, 323
Fugitive dust, 72
Fully developed flow, 528

Funnel flow, 81–83
   bins, 80
Funnel-type flows, 51

G

Galileo number, 151, 163, 765
Gamma-ray transmission, 410–411
Gas
   absorber, 284
   absorption, 312, 676–677,
     679–680
   backmixing, 697
   channeling, 216
   cleaning, 624
   compression, 495, 498, 500
   distributors, 720
   exchange, 720
   holdup, 426, 726
   interchange, 723
   mixing, 572, 589
   oils, 236, 243, 249
   pycnometers, 3
Gas-gas mixing, 590
Gas-liquid flows, 439
Gas-liquid fluidization, 318
Gas-solid catalyzed reactions, 735
Gas-solid reactions, 761
Gasification, 138, 224, 271, 276,
   279, 282, 284, 333, 688
   reactor, 323
Gasoline, 236, 239, 246, 312,
   332–333, 336, 340–341
   blending, 323
   production, 236, 242
Gaussian distribution, 17–18
Geldart's classification diagram, 149
Geometric optics, 438, 442–443
Grade efficiency curve, 610
Granulated plastics, 555
Granulation, 11
Granulometric composition, 15
Gravity-assisted flows, 44, 59
Gravity
   flow, 62
   forces, 173
   settling, 595, 623

Gravitational acceleration, 28
Gravitational separation, 595
Grid design, 380
Grinding, 2, 78
  operations, 18, 77
Gulf streaming, 727
Gypsum, 72, 93

H

H-coal process, 326–328
Hagen-Poiseuille method, 128
Hartmann tube, 77
Heat
  capacity, 456, 707
  of combustion, 239, 281
  condition, 389
  conductance, 368
  conduction, 351–352
  conductivity, 349
  exchange, 671
    coefficient, 350, 759
  exchanger, 334, 759
  flow, 369
  interchange, 760
  of reaction, 341
  transfer, 318, 320, 346, 349,
      350–351, 355, 367, 416, 456,
      533, 647–648, 674, 701, 719,
      756–757, 762, 764, 767, 773,
      776, 780, 790
    coefficient, 318, 402, 428–429,
      456–457, 671, 699
    models, 760
    resistance, 670
Heating oil, 323
Heavy distillate oils, 318
Heavy fuel oils, 323
Heavy oil, 123
Henry's law, 255
Heterogeneous fluidization, 175
High pressure fluidization, 160
High pressure transfer, 555
High sulfur coal, 326
Hindered settling, 144
Hinze number, 654
Holdup, 316–317, 527, 695, 712

Holography, 411, 416, 436
Hooding, 476
Hopper flow factor, 62
Houdriflow catalytic cracking, 237
Houdry process, 236, 238
Humidity control, 11
Hvorslev failure surface, 46–47
Hydraulic diameter, 117
Hydrocarbon emissions, 208
Hydrocarbon research, 326
Hydrocarbons, 301
Hydroclones, 328, 602
Hydrocracking, 320, 330, 336
Hydrodynamic stability, 501
Hydrogasification, 295
Hydrogen donor solvent, 324
Hydrogen fluoride, 246
Hydrogen production, 312
Hydrogen sulfide, 279
Hydrogenation, 298, 301–302,
      319–320, 324, 327, 333, 336
Hydrotreater, 337, 341
Hydrotreatment processes, 319, 323,
      334
Hygroscopicity, 44

I

Ideal gas law, 173
Ignition test, 78
Image analysis, 20, 26, 404, 437
Impact method, 437
Impaction, 666
  mechanism, 676
  method, 20, 24
  parameter, 24
Impedance, 24, 416
  devices, 425
  probe, 317, 426
Impingement, 623–624
Incineration, 138, 255, 260
Incipient bubbling, 148
  velocity, 147
Incipient buoyancy, 148
Incipient fluidization, 93, 145, 187,
      192, 384
  velocity, 158

Incompressible flow, 655
Index of refraction, 444
Indirect-fired process heaters, 767
Inductance, 416, 425
  probe, 713
Industrial mixers, 587
Inertia forces, 173, 599
Inertial deposition, 595
Inertial impaction, 24, 647
Initial resistance to shear, 14
Insecticide manufacturing, 638
Instability, 503
Institute of Gas Technology, 173
Interception, 623, 666-676
  parameters, 673
Interfacial contact area, 680
Interferometric techniques, 443
Interlocking, 51
Intermediate law, 544
Intermediate range, 33
Internal friction, 57, 351
International Standards Organization,
  20
Interparticle forces, 160
Interparticle percolation, 50
Interparticle void fraction, 3
Intermediate channeling, 198
Inverse three-phase fluidization, 313
Ionization, 411, 600-601
Iron, 242-243
Iron catalyst, 19
Isokinetic conditions, 24
Isokinetic sampling, 432, 437
Isolation values, 559, 562
Isomerization, 239, 337
Isoparaffins, 242
Isotope tracer techniques, 743

J

Jenike design procedure, 69-70
Jet boundary layer, 581
Jet break-up, 651
Jet fuel, 323
Jet mixing, 572, 577-578, 580, 587,
  590

Jet penetration, 177-178
  length, 181
Jet Reynolds number, 581

K

Kanthol alloy, 425
Kinetic energy, 599, 674
Kinetic gas theory, 367
Kinetic theory, 350
Kinetics, 294
Knudsen diffusion, 355
Knudsen mechanism, 354
Kozeny's constant, 153
Kwauk's model, 487

L

Laminar flow, 26, 111, 114, 127,
  161-162
Laminar regime, 29
Laminar region, 125
Laminar settling regime, 32
Langmuir's isotherm, 349
Laser
  anemometer, 449
  anemometry, 411, 443
Laser-Doppler anemometry, 442
Laser-Doppler scheme, 443
Lateral mixing, 743
  rate, 755
Leaching, 256
Lean phase, 493
  conveying, 512, 519
  flow, 522-523, 526, 531
  reactions, 208, 432
  transport, 507
Light
  obscuration, 441-442
  scattering, 20, 25, 404
  techniques, 439
  transmission, 404
Lignites, 320, 323
Lime mud reburning, 235
Limestone, 72, 277
Limiting stress, 13

Liquefaction
  bottoms, 325
  yields, 324
Liquefied petroleum gas, 326, 341
Liquid atomization, 657
Liquid fluidized beds, 148, 157,
  315, 701, 780, 797–798
Liquid fluidized heat exchangers,
  799
Liquid fluidization, 162
Liquid pycnometer, 4
Liquid-solid fluidization, 162
Live-bottom feeder, 74
Loading ratio, 523
Lock hoppers, 277
Log-normal probability, 16
  distribution, 16
Loose bulk density, 3
Low-velocity conveying, 565, 567
Lurgi dry-ash process, 279
Lurgi gasifiers, 333
Lurgi methanation process, 334
Lurgi process, 341

M

Mach number, 654
Macroscopic instability, 501
Magnesium oxide, 7
Magnetic tracer techniques, 432
Main planes, 11
Main stresses, 11–12
Margoulis criterion, 369
Mass-bubbling, 167, 177, 194
Mass flow, 67, 73, 85, 508
  bins, 70
  vessels, 52
Mass flux data, 441
Mass transfer, 318, 346, 350–351,
  353, 355–356, 456, 658,
  670–671, 674, 677, 687–688,
  696, 698, 701, 706, 720, 724,
  745, 759
  coefficients, 229, 318, 353, 359, 362,
    383, 402, 456, 677–678, 694
  columns, 724
  rates, 358

Maximum principle, 65
Maxwell-Boltzmann statistics, 404
Maxwell distribution, 428
Mean free path, 31, 146
Mechanical attrition, 199
Mechanical conveying equipment,
  95, 97
Mechanical energy, 667
  balance, 659, 677
Mechanical interlocking, 51–52
Median diameter, 19

Melamine production, 138
Mercury intrusion techniques, 4
Metallurgical processes, 638
Methane, 271–272, 294, 338, 341
  formation, 307
Methanation, 276, 334
Methanol, 340
  synthesis, 339–340
Microdensitometer, 440
Microscopy, 26
Microwaves, 411, 413–414, 415
Middle distillate, 323
Minimum bubbling conditions, 92,
  158–159, 161, 181, 195
Minimum fluidization, 144–145,
  403, 502
  velocity, 93, 144, 146, 149,
    150–152, 154, 474
Minimum gas voidage, 145
Minimum transport velocity, 522
Mining industry, 624
Mixing, 44, 581
  axial, 721, 742–743, 747,
    752–753
  efficiency, 433, 574, 579
  length, 368
  models, 724
  patterns, 434
  processes, 756
Mobile gasoline synthesis, 337
Modified Froude number, 194–195
Modified Reynolds number, 151
Moisture, 4
  content, 4–5, 8
Molecular diffusion, 355, 390

Molecular forces, 9
Momentum, 490
    equation, 193
    exchange, 659, 674
    transfer, 349–351
    transport, 373
Monocyclic aromatics, 242
Moore's circle, 11–13, 48
Morphology, 26
Motor fuel, 312, 332–333, 337
Moving bed, 92, 532
    catalytic crackers, 237–238
    flow, 475
    gasification, 325
    heat exchangers, 44
Moving fluidized beds, 100
Multiclones, 616, 622
Multifilament fabrics, 632
Multiorifice, 199
Multiphase flow, 753

N

Naphtha, 246, 318, 323, 326–328,
    332, 336, 340
    octanes, 246
Napthalene, 7, 240, 242, 341
Natural gas, 271
Newton's equation, 155
Newton's law, 350, 544
    range, 29, 31, 33
Nickel, 242–243
    ore, 72
Noble gases, 79
Nonbubbling beds, 148
Nonfluidized flow, 486, 488–489,
    479–480, 492, 498, 500
Nonfluidized upflow, 477
Non-Newtonian fluids, 115
Normal distributions, 19
Normal probability, 18
Normal stresses, 12, 14, 66, 489
Number density, 443
    distribution, 421
Number of transfer units, 660, 663,
    665, 676
Nussel numbers, 354, 762, 765, 776
Nylon, 633

O

Octane number, 246, 340
Ohm's law, 600
Oil burners, 654
Olefins, 242
Onset of choking, 223
Onset of slugging, 199
Open-hearth furnaces, 646
Optical fiber probe, 64
Optical pyrometry, 456
Optical techniques, 438, 448
Ore-roasting, 44
Osterwald-de Waale model, 65
Oxidation reactions, 425
Ozone, 689

P

Pacflo, 477, 485
Packed bed, 145, 150, 474–475,
    485, 547, 799
    conveying, 522
    flow, 477, 479, 489, 499, 522,
    525, 554
Packed bulk density, 3, 44
Packet theory, 770, 783
Paint pigments, 567
Paraffins, 242, 334
Parametric dimensionless number,
    106
Partial oxidation, 319, 325, 328
    processes, 324
Particle
    agglomeration, 610, 624
    attrition, 512, 519
    behavior, 432
    bridging, 4
    circulation, 785
    collection, 673
        efficiency, 660, 664–665
    density, 3, 4
    inception, 623
    motion, 188
    Reynolds number, 142, 528, 544,
    554
    segregation, 198, 530, 741
    settling, 609

shape, 2
  factor, 142, 146
  size determination, 439
  distribution, 16, 439
slip velocity, 209
sphericity, 19
Particulate
  fluidization, 146, 148, 159,
    161–162
  removal, 646
Pebble heaters, 49
Peclet number, 382, 390
Pedestal components, 445, 447
Percolation coefficient, 192
Perfect mix reactors, 391
Perfect mixing, 391
Perforated plate distributors, 380
Permeability, 62, 197, 558, 632
  coefficient, 628
Perturbation analysis, 507
Perturbation technique, 501
Petroleum
  feedstocks, 123
  industry, 122, 138, 237
  products, 239
  refining, 235
Pharmaceutical industry, 76
Phase angle, 445
Phase difference, 443
Phase holdups, 313
Phosphoric acids, 246
Photodetector, 441
Photographic techniques, 404, 434,
  729
Photography, 403
Phototransducer technique, 429
Physical absorption, 677
Pickup velocity, 545
Piezoelectric detection, 705
Pipe erosion, 519
Pipeline mixing, 572–574, 577–578,
  581, 587
Platinum catalysts, 336
Plug flow, 126, 318, 380, 382, 689,
  724
  models, 388
  reactors, 391
Pneumatic blasting, 75–76

Pneumatic conveying, 7, 9, 92, 224,
  509–510, 512, 515, 519, 523,
  525, 532–533, 555, 557
Pneumatic nozzle, 648
Pneumatic spray nozzles, 656
Pneumatic transport, 77, 95, 215,
  222–223
Pneumatic type spraying, 657
Poisons, 247
Polycyclic aromatics, 240, 243
Polyethylene manufacturing, 138
Polymerization, 239, 242–243, 336,
  340, 346
Polynuclear aromatics, 243
Population balance model, 789
Pore volume, 4
Porosity, 150, 162, 186–187, 191,
  193, 364, 366, 418, 726
  fluctuation, 419–420
  wave, 475, 504, 515
Porous plastic distributor, 403
Porous plate distributors, 380
Potential energy, 95, 116, 166
Potential flow, 188, 662, 679, 690
  theory, 690
Potash, 72
  production, 255
Potassium chloride, 11
Poured angle of repose, 5
Powder flow properties, 62
Powdered chemicals, 555
Powdered coal, 122
Power law, 347
  fluid, 115, 120, 125
Power spectrum, 407–408
Prandtl number, 354, 369, 672, 765,
  776
Precondition, 79
Prefeeder arrangement, 73
Pressure drag, 27, 594
Pressure drop, 143, 161, 313, 548,
  551
Pressure forces, 594
Pressure leaf filter, 330
Pressure proof construction, 80
Pressure sensors, 80
Pressure swing process, 334
Pressure transducer, 407

Pressurized constructions, 79
Principal stress, 61
Probability, 696
Probability density distribution, 422
Probability function, 404
Pseudobridge, 495, 500
Pseudoplaticity, 115
Pthalic anhydride production, 138, 177
Pulse jet, 630
  cleaning, 632–633
Pulse phase conveying, 563
Pyrite roasting, 263
Pyrolytic devolatilization, 760

R

Radiation, 351
Radiative heat transfer, 781
Radio transmitter, 433
Radioactive tracer, 432
Random walk model, 741
Rate constant, 298, 348, 353, 367
Rathole, 44, 81
  flow analysis, 83
Ratholing, 51–52, 73
Reaction rates, 346
Reaction yields, 224
Reactivity, 273
Refraction, 444
Refractive index, 438
Reforming naphtha, 123
Reforming unit, 778
Regeneration, 341
Regenerator, 249, 472
Reiner-Philipoff model, 65
Relative bed expansion, 173, 175
Relative humidity, 674
Residence time, 318, 323, 325, 327, 329, 330, 448–449, 596, 606, 607, 620, 802
Residual fuel oil, 654
Residuum cracking, 254
Resistance coefficient, 155, 351, 369, 615
Resistance force, 30, 155
Resistance probe, 421, 423

Reverse airflow cleaning, 631
Reynolds number, 28, 32, 106, 125, 151, 353, 671
Rheological measurements, 127
Richardson-Zaki equation, 162, 486, 488, 502, 517
Richardson-Zaki expansion equation, 487
Richardson-Zaki relation, 549
Rise velocity, 129, 190, 402, 406, 409, 417, 419–420, 425, 430, 448, 461, 503, 516, 554, 691, 739
  equation, 691
Riser, 472, 483, 487, 547
  cracking, 250
  flow, 489, 509
  regeneration, 251
Roasting, 255, 260
  operations, 235
Roscoe surface, 46
Rosin-Rammler distribution, 18
Rosin-Rammler mean, 18
Rosin-Rammler photo, 16
Rotating cylindrical viscometer, 130
Rotating fluidized beds, 686
Rotational cells, 47
Ruby lasers, 437

S

Safety discs, 79
Salicylic acid, 7
Saltation limits, 35
Saltation velocity, 519, 544, 547, 551–552
Sand cracking, 123
Sasol plant, 332
Saturation, 224
Sauter mean diameter, 434, 439, 658, 661, 663, 680
Scale factors, 100
Scaling laws, 581
Scattered light, 443–444
  distribution, 439
Scattering coefficient, 439
Scattering functions, 438

Schmidt number, 353
Screen-packed bed, 797
Screw conveyor, 624
Screw feeders, 70
Scrubber, 638
  models, 660
  performance, 663, 667
Secondary atomization, 654
Sedimentation, 20, 25, 593, 742
Segregation, 531, 565, 740, 742
Selectivity, 243, 246
Sensible heat, 266, 278
Separation criterion, 621
Settling chamber, 595, 597
Settling equipment, 595
Settling formulas, 34
Settling number, 621
Settling regimes, 33
Settling times, 599, 620-621
Settling velocity, 24, 32-33, 224,
    553, 549, 595-596, 607, 618
Sewage sludge, 265
Shape factor, 143, 154
Shear cell tester, 47, 67
Shear resistance coefficient, 14
Shear stress, 11, 489, 690
Shear zone, 48
Shell-Koppers Process, 286-287
Sherwood number, 353, 671
Shift conversion, 276, 278-279
Shock pressure proof, 79
Sieve size standards, 21, 23
Sieving, 20, 623
Silica-alumina catalyst, 236, 244,
    246
Similarity theory, 100
Similarity transformation, 102
Simplex number, 106
Simplexes, 106
Single bubble models, 193
Single particle behavior, 545
Size distribution, 2, 16, 19, 22, 491,
    551
Skeletal density, 3-4
Slagging Lurgi, 272-273, 277, 279
Slide valve, 249, 251, 472, 491
Slip factor, 117

Slip stick, 80
  flows, 81, 475, 501, 508
Slip velocity, 24, 126, 209,
    474-475, 477, 480-481,
    483-485, 487-489, 493, 495,
    500, 502, 506, 517, 529, 531,
    554
Slip zone, 46, 50
Slope angle, 44
Slow reactions, 382
Sludge incineration, 264
Slug flows, 93
Slug phase conveying, 563
Slug velocity, 515
Slugging, 146, 164, 198-199, 224,
    387, 409, 525, 529, 547, 691
Slugging bed, 129, 222, 387, 554,
    741
  flow, 554
Slugging conveying, 515, 529, 530
Slugging flow, 512, 551
Slugging phenomenon, 122
Slump velocity, 239
Socony Vacuum Oil Co., 236
  process of, 238
Soda ash, 93
Sodium chloride, 7
Solid-catalyzed chemical reactions,
    183
Solids
  arching, 52
  attrition, 208, 551
  deposition, 547, 551
  downflow, 490
  feeders, 44
  flows, 64
  holdup, 526
  mixing, 432, 696, 712, 740, 742,
    747, 750, 754
  transport, 799
  upflow, 490
  waste handling, 99
Solvent-Refined Coal Process (SRC
    process), 328-329
Sonic agglomeration, 595
Sonic sifters, 20
Sour water stripping, 326

Space velocity, 325
Specific surface, 142
Spectral analysis, 408
Spectral density functions, 409
Spherical cap bubbles, 129
Spherical compartment model,
    167–168
Splitting, 733
Spouted beds, 149, 312
Spray breakup processes, 658
Spray density distribution, 655
Spray nozzles, 651, 655
Spray patterns, 680
SRC process, 328–329
SRC II process, 331
Stability, 500
    analysis, 501
Stack sampling, 24
Stack testing, 437
Stagnation point, 27
Standard definition, 17
Standard deviation, 16, 18
Standpipe, 44, 249, 472, 474–475,
    477–478, 483, 485, 487, 490,
    492, 498, 547
    design, 509
    flow, 480, 488, 490, 500,
        505–506, 509
    operation, 495
    performance, 497
Static forces, 10
Stationary fluidization, 485
Stationary mixers, 589
Steam boiler, 285
Steam conditioning, 674
Steam gasification, 782
Steam generation, 328
Steam reforming, 319
Stephan flow, 357–358
Stereoscopy, 436
Stick-slip downflow, 53
Stirling engine, 782
Stokes approximation, 781
Stokes-Cunningham correction factor,
    31
Stokes equation, 155

Stokes law, 31, 36, 128, 544, 595,
    597–598, 602, 606, 624
    range, 29
Stokes number, 662–664, 666, 673
Stokes region, 649
Storage bunkers, 49
Storage vessels, 80–81
Stream stripping, 243
Streaming flow, 484
Streamline motion, 594
Stress deformation, 65
Stretford process, 284–285
Subbituminous coals, 319–320
Sulfide ores, 263
Sulfide roasting, 260–261, 263
Sulfur, 323, 326, 328
Sulfur dioxide, 677
Sulfur recovery, 276, 279
Sulfuric acid, 263
Superficial velocity, 487, 495
Supply Demand Analysis, 505
Surface roughness, 160
Surface tension energy, 166, 169
Surface tension forces, 129, 177, 649
Surge vessels, 44
Suspension downflow, 485
Suspension flow, 501, 545
Suspension upflow, 485
Swirling flows, 589
Synthesis gas, 272, 278, 333, 334
Synthetic crude oil, 326
Synthetic fibers, 632
Synthetic natural gas, 286

T

T-junction, 581
T-mixers, 578
Tangential stress, 351, 369
Tar, 272
    sands, 326
Target efficiency, 24, 658, 663, 666,
    673, 676
Tensile strength, 48, 633
Terminal settling velocity, 30, 548

Terminal velocity, 30, 95, 162, 209, 224, 520, 531, 544, 549, 695
Texaco process, 272
Theoretical cut, 609
Thermal conductivity, 369
Thermal cracking, 123, 236, 239, 423
Thermal diffusion, 367
Thermal diffusivities, 771
Thermal efficiency, 266, 330, 333, 339, 341
Thermal ignition, 370
Thermal instabilities, 698
Thermal oxidation, 264
Thermal precipitation, 595
Thermal techniques, 428
Thermoanemometer, 429
Thermography, 456
Thermoplastic flow, 247
Thread count, 632
Three-phase fluidization, 138, 312–313, 315–316, 724, 745
Three-phase fluidized systems, 426
Time-independent fluid, 125
Titration methods, 433
Toxic dusts, 638
Tranpacflow, 477, 480, 485, 493, 495
Transfer coefficients, 350, 358, 699, 708
Transfer line, 543
    contacting, 250
Transfer units, 677
Transient heat transfer, 457
Transit times, 448
Transition flow regime, 142
Transition range, 29
Transport disengaging height, 208–209, 215
True density, 3
Tubular plug flow, 319
Turbine fuel, 336
Turbulent bed contactor, 312
Turbulent contact absorber, 11, 312
Turbulent exchange coefficient, 368
Turbulent flow, 27, 111, 773

Turbulent fluid bed, 388
Turbulent regime, 525
Two-phase flow, 406, 456, 485, 646, 722, 773
Two-phase models, 709
Two-phase theory, 196, 729, 736, 760
Tyler series, 20

U

Ultrasonic probes, 411
Ultrasonic techniques, 411
Unconstrained packed-bed flow, 477
Ultraviolet detector, 459
U.S. sieve series, 20
Utility boiler, 273, 284

V

Vacuum bottoms, 318, 325–326
Vacuum distillation, 319, 328, 332
Vacuum filter, 285
Vacuum flash-drying, 330
Vanadium, 242–243
Van der Waal's forces, 9, 623
Varsol, 3
Venturi atomizers, 658
Venturi scrubber, 260, 265, 644–645
Vertical conveying, 519
Vertical downflow, 490
Vertical pneumatic conveying, 516, 522, 524, 528
Vertical pneumatic transport, 530
Vessel vibrations, 80
Vibrators, 74
Vibrofluidized beds, 797
Vinyl chloride production, 138
Viscosity, 127, 164
Viscous dissipation, 65
Viscous drag coefficient, 128
Viscous flow, 680
Viscous forces, 609
Visibility, 442, 445, 447
Visual techniques, 403

Void fraction, 122, 139, 166, 168,
   175, 176, 209, 698
Voidage, 49, 50, 197, 223, 480–481,
   484, 488, 490–492, 495, 504,
   506, 517, 528, 554
Volume surface mean, 18
Volumetric feeding, 69
Volumetric flux, 485

W

Wall friction, 59, 69, 496, 531
Waste gasification, 123
Waste heat exchanger, 278
Waste incineration, 235
Wastewater treatment, 724
Wave impedance, 445
Wave number, 652, 653–655
Wave velocity, 504
Weber number, 317, 653
Wheatstone bridge, 459
Wool bags, 633
Working bulk density, 44

X

X-ray, 404, 687, 713
   adsorption, 728
   photography, 183, 728
   techniques, 129, 403
Xylene, 312

Y

Yarn size, 632
Yield locus, 46, 48
Yield stress, 61, 66

Z

Zeolite, 243, 244, 246
   catalyst, 244, 247, 340
   cracking catalysts, 245
Ziegler particle theory, 770
Zinc chloride catalyst, 336